A. Y. Goor studied forestry at the University of California, Yale University (Ph.D.), and the University of Oxford. He was a member of the Forest Service of Palestine and later of Israel, and is Arid Zone Advisor to the Forestry Division of the United Nations' Food and Agriculture Organization. His UN work has taken him on missions to the arid zones of India, South America, Turkey, Greece, Africa, the Middle East, the U.S.S.R., Japan, and the South Pacific. Dr. Goor has served as chairman of several international forestry conferences, and his writings in the field have appeared in many languages.

C. W. Barney received his training at the State University of New York College of Forestry at Syracuse University, the University of Vermont, and Duke University (D.F.). He is Professor of Silviculture at Colorado State University, where he served as Head of the Department of Forest Management and Wood Utilization for many years. He was formerly a Technical Aide with the Soil Conservation Service, United States Department of Agriculture. Dr. Barney has also been Chairman of the Division of Silviculture of the Society of American Foresters.

FOREST TREE PLANTING IN ARID ZONES

A. Y. GOOR

Forestry Consultant
Food and Agriculture Organization
of the United Nations

C. W. BARNEY

Colorado State University

SECOND EDITION

THE RONALD PRESS COMPANY • NEW YORK

To the late Tom Gill
a truly international forester

Library of Congress Catalog Card Number: 76–22314
PRINTED IN THE UNITED STATES OF AMERICA

Preface

Faced with the problem of an ever-increasing population, the nations of the world have become more and more concerned with shortages of food and essential raw materials, including timber and other forest products. These shortages and the desire to improve living standards have led to increasing efforts to improve agriculture and forestry in semiarid and arid areas of the world where production is below its potential and where consumption is considerably less than adequate for the health and well-being of the people.

In recent years a great deal of vital information on afforestation methods for arid zones has become available. Large-scale afforestation programs are now carried out on a scientific basis in many of the semiarid countries. It is estimated that between 300 and 400 million forest tree seedlings are planted every year in the low-rainfall zones of the world with varying degrees of success. To help reduce failures, by describing techniques and species used in afforestation under differing conditions of aridity and soil and as they are influenced by the purpose of the plantation, is the prime purpose of this book. A more general purpose is to serve as an overall guide for the increasing number of foresters practicing or intending to practice in arid and semiarid zones.

The authors have attempted to reflect recent and substantial advances in a number of forestry concepts. Among the most important of these are: (1) the ecological effects of forests on the environment; (2) an understanding of the problems raised by the pollution of the environment by faulty use of chemicals; (3) the multiple use of forest crops, including plantations, for the benefit of the community; and (4) the development of productive plantations based on intensive cultivation and the use of quick-growing species and improved seed sources. These concepts are not new, but the swiftness and intensity of the changes in policies and technology created by them are so great that little of comparable impact occurred in forestry science and practice in the whole of the last century.

The book is based on the theoretical and practical results obtained by the combined efforts of many foresters, ecologists, soil scientists, plant physiologists, and specialists in other allied sciences. It owes much to a prior publication, *Tree Planting Practices for Arid Zones* by A. Y. Goor, which was commissioned by the Food and Agriculture Organization of the United Nations. That volume was originally published in 1955, and revised in 1963.

Special acknowledgment is due to the Food and Agriculture Organization for its financial support of this Second Edition and to Mr. H. Steinlin, Director of the Forest Resources Division, who permitted us to use material and photographs from the original publication and other sources. Thanks are also due to others in many countries whose knowledge, assistance, and cooperation have helped to make our book possible.

A. Y. GOOR
C. W. BARNEY

Tel Aviv, Israel
Fort Collins, Colorado
September, 1976

Contents

1 Arid Zones   **3**

General, 3 · Climate, 9 · Soil, 25 · Ecology of Arid-Zone Vegetation, 31 · Forests in Arid Zones, 45

2 Collecting and Handling Tree Seed   **53**

The Seed, 53 · Genetic Considerations in Forest Planting, 54 · Collecting Seed, 63 · Transport of Seed, 70 · Extraction of Seed, 71 · Seed Quality, 77 · Dormancy and Pretreatment, 86 · Germination, 91 · Sanitation, 92 · Storage, 93 · Distribution, 97

3 Forestry-Tree Nurseries   **100**

Nurseries in Arid Zones, 100 · Development of the Nursery Area, 108 · Plant Production, 113 · Care of Nursery Stock, 150 · Costs, 198 · Nursery Records, 198

4 Afforestation   **202**

Forest Planting in Low Rainfall Zones, 202 · Selecting the Site, 204 · Preparing the Site, 204 · Water Harvesting, 217 · Spacing, 225 · Season for Planting, 227 · Seeding, 229 · Field Planting, 233 · Care of Plantations After Planting, 244 · Protection from Grazing and Fire, 248 · Protection from Insects and Disease, 250 · Tools, 254 · Construction of Roads and Paths, 256 · Stores and Sheds, 256 · Cost of Afforestation, 257

5 Special Plantations 264

Major Types of Plantations, 264 · Production Plantations, 266 · Plantations to Improve the Environment, 299 · Soil Stabilization Plantations, 314 · Amenity Plantations, 331 · Air Pollution and Selection of Tree Species, 338

6 Species for Arid-Zone Afforestation 345

Choice of Species, 345 · Trials for Introduction of Exotics, 352 · Silvics of Arid-Zone Tree Species, 353

Appendixes 461

A. Conversion Factors, 463
B. Summary of Seed Handling Practices by Species, 464
C. Summary of Nursery Practices by Species, 472
D. Site Requirements of Trees Suitable for Arid Zones, 476

Botanical Index 479

Subject Index 487

FOREST TREE PLANTING IN ARID ZONES

1

Arid Zones

GENERAL

It is estimated that over thirty-five percent of the earth's land surface is situated in arid zones. The term "arid zone" as used here includes not only the arid but also the semiarid regions. In general regions that receive less than 300 mm (12 inches)* of precipitation a year are considered arid. These include all the deserts of the world; the most important of which are: the Sahara and Kalahari deserts in Africa; the Arabian, Syrian, Turkestan, Gobi, Iranian, and Indian or Thar deserts in Asia; the deserts of Australia; the North American deserts of Mexico and western United States; and in South America the Chaco and the Patagonia cold desert of Argentina, and the Atacama desert of Chile and Peru.

Semiarid regions receive an annual precipitation of over 300 mm (12 inches) and up to 600 mm (24 inches); usually concentrated in one or two relatively short periods of the year. Many of the semiarid regions border the deserts and include large tracts of steppe, savanna, chaparral, garigue, and similar vegetation formations. Vegetation in these areas consists of grass, grass with scattered trees, scrub trees, or open forests of low trees. The Mediterranean basin and regions with similar climate in other continents are classed as semiarid. One silvicultural criterion for distinguishing arid from semiarid regions is that irrigation is required for establishing a plantation in arid regions and not required in semiarid.

Regions in which water is scarce are usually sparsely populated. In fact, less than 1 percent of the world's population resides in arid zones despite the fact that many parts of the humid regions are less desirable for habitation.

Human Environment in Arid Zones

In arid zones living conditions are often harsh. The most obvious hardship in such areas is the perpetual shortage of water. But many

* For conversion factors of weights, measures, and temperatures see Appendix A.

3

other factors make living difficult; among these are: lack of transportation in the vast uninhabited areas, problems of producing food, shortage of fuel for heating and cooking, little or no natural shade for relief from a hot sun under cloudless skies, and no relief from the incessant drying winds and blowing dust that can penetrate even the best shelter. The barren landscape of these regions is monotonous and uninspiring to many people, and a few may even find it hostile. These and other adverse elements of the environment that are found to a greater or lesser extent in the different arid zones of the world, make living conditions difficult. But some people like and enjoy life in arid zones and try wherever possible to change the environment so that it can better fulfill their needs and increase their enjoyment of life. Others who cannot or do not wish to adjust to such an environment usually emigrate to other regions in search of more comfortable surroundings. A growing concern of every society that must deal with arid regions is to try, not only to satisfy the material needs of the people, but also to enhance their comfort by developing a more enjoyable place to live.

Most people who inhabit arid zones have become acclimated to the prevailing environment and to frugal use of water for all needs. Their per capita use of water is minimal; they drink little, wash little, and they practice a type of agriculture and industry that does not require much water.

The arid zone environment, which people wish to change, is a complex of interrelated and variable factors of climate, soil, and vegetation. Altering any one factor in the environment affects the action of the other factors producing changes that continue until the whole environmental complex develops a new balance. No factor is completely divorced from this interwoven complex of which human activities are a part. If the vegetation of an area is destroyed by overgrazing, faulty cultivation, overcutting of the woods, frequent fires, or trampling of the soil, the bare surface soil will be subject to wind and water erosion. Excessive runoff carries away the soil forming gullies which, if they are left unchecked, will in time become deeper and more numerous and change the entire configuration of the area. The sparser the vegetation and thus the fewer the roots and stems left to bind and shield the surface soil, the faster the upper soil will be eroded away. Without the top soil only the more xeric vegetation can grow because water is not readily absorbed by the subsoil. If this vegetation is removed, more soil will be eroded and even less water will be absorbed by the subsoil causing a still further degradation of the vegetation. In most arid zones of the world the environment has deteriorated due to interference by man and his animals in the normal development of vegetation. Many of these areas resemble deserts and have desert conditions. However, a more favorable environment may be restored when harmony is reestablished between nature and human activities.

Yet with all the advanced knowledge and new techniques known to improve desert conditions, and with all the international, national, and private efforts in all the arid zones of the world devoted to the improvement of the environment, only a small part of the man-made deserts can be healed and only a small fraction of the natural deserts can be salvaged from perpetual barrenness. Climate and soils make redemption of deserts difficult. Yet such portions that have been developed, or could be made habitable, in the aggregate cover an area large enough to support a population of several million. Some of these areas which have been irrigated are now among the most fertile lands in the world. Examples are to be found in many arid zones of the world such as: Rajasthan, India; Kazakstan, U.S.S.R.; the Nile Valley in Egypt; the Negev of Israel; the Colorado River project area in western United States; and the Casa Blanca in Peru.

Other projects aim toward improving the microclimate of the desert areas by planting trees. These are costly ventures and can usually be afforded only by mining companies, oil well operations, or similar well-financed enterprises. Here good soil and valuable water are dedicated to man's comfort rather than to agriculture.

The use of developed lands in arid zones ranges over a wide spectrum and depends on the suitability of the site and the ability and incentive of the people to attain the desired goal.

Tracts of land occur in the arid zones that are sterile and whose environment cannot be improved without undue difficulty and expense. Such areas are not considered in this book, rather only those lands that can be reclaimed with reasonable effort and cost.

The first step in improvement of an area is to identify all the factors that oppose or hinder its development. The effect of these factors must be reduced or, if possible, eliminated before they can cause further deterioration in the habitability of the area. Overgrazing, indiscriminate destruction of the woody vegetation, faulty methods of cultivation resulting in soil erosion by wind and water, and use of saline water in irrigating agricultural crops are the main causes for the reduction of large areas of forest and agricultural land to near desert conditions. If destruction has not been complete one can, by utilizing advanced techniques, restore the environmental conditions to nearly the same level they had before the disturbance. Under certain conditions, it is even possible to achieve greater material and recreational benefits than were obtainable under the older methods. For example, if these areas are planted with forest trees, properly cared for, and then replanted after harvest, they can produce a continuous flow of products and benefits.

Usually where degraded forests are growing, the natural forest can be improved or a better one established by planting.

In arid zones water is the critical resource and particular emphasis must be placed on its efficient use. Normal daily life of the people and growth and development of vegetation in arid zones are limited by the amount and quality of the available water supply. Consequently, the first consideration of any undertaking to enhance living conditions in arid zones is water development. This includes harvesting and conserving available water, importing additional usable water from outside the area, and digging wells in favorable sites. All available water must then be apportioned for its best use. One must remember that different vegetation types vary greatly in potential evapotranspiration. If grassland or an open savanna is converted by planting to a dense forest, the evapotranspiration for that area may be significantly increased. It is extremely important, when planning forest plantations that will cover large areas in arid zones, to compare the probable value of the forest crops and the amenities with the benefits that might be derived if the ground water consumed by the trees were used for other purposes. Allocation of this water must, therefore, be a compromise between the need of water for personal use, improving comfort of the inhabitants, the production of crops, and the manufacture of goods by industry.

Other environmental factors that should be studied and, if possible, improved, are: soil, vegetation, temperature, and wind. With proper techniques these can be regulated or changed to make the region more habitable and productive.

In any regional development plan, the human and natural resources and the available money must be carefully appraised. These must then be apportioned in such a manner that they will maintain a balanced environment, improve the well-being of society, and increase the production of economic crops.

Forest Tree Planting in Arid Zones and Its Importance

The open forest vegetation within the arid zones is continually being cut or burned to clear land for the production of food. In addition, the ever-increasing demand by people for greater harvests of forest products hastens the drain on these sparse forest resources. If unrestrained, the axe, fire, and cultivation can destroy in a relatively short time the forest that took centuries to develop. The practice of clearing forests in order to obtain cultivable land is as old as civilization and is exhorted in Scripture: "But the mountain shall be thine; for it is a wood, and thou shalt cut it down: and the outgoings of it shall be thine . . " (Joshua 17:18). The practice of thousands of years ago is still the practice in many countries today. The newly cleared lands when brought under cultivation rapidly lose their fertility by excessive and continued exploitation and the soil itself by erosion. Once the soil is impoverished to a degree that it can not support the people cultivating it, they are forced to shift to a new area of forest and clear the land of trees in order to grow their crops. Thus the cycle of forest clearing, cultivation, impoverishment, and eventual abandonment of land is continued.

This procedure commonly called "shifting cultivation" is an onslaught on the vegetation and soil. It is carried out over large areas in the arid zones, usually with complete disregard by the people for the enormous damage it causes by robbing them of their one vital source of livelihood—the productive soils. Destruction of the productive capacity of an area may be rapid, taking only a few years; or it may be quite slow, requiring a century or more.

Agricultural lands can, however, be saved from destruction if proper precautions are taken in time. If fields are protected from drying and eroding winds by planting trees as wind barriers, and if correct agricultural practices are followed when cultivating the fields, it should be possible to maintain the productivity of the land forever.

Forest trees play an important role among the people's needs in arid zones. Foresters have planted trees in arid zones for nearly a century, but unfortunately results have usually been disappointing. The loss of ninety percent or more of the planted trees was so common that even fifty percent survival was considered an outstanding success. Probably one reason for the high losses of planted trees is that most foresters engaged in these undertakings were trained either in the wet, tropical or the humid, temperate forest regions. Consequently, they tried to apply techniques that were successful in these regions to the arid zones; and some even tried to establish plantings of wet zone species. Another reason for failure was that sites used for afforestation were usually those found unfit for agricultural production and consisted of overexploited, shallow soils, on steep, rocky slopes. If any arable land remained, it was thought to be essential for the production of food crops. Utilization of poor land by foresters became a tradition and even something of a virtue. Perhaps, it is for these reasons that many people believe that afforestation in arid zones is not expected to yield economic returns nor bring social benefits.

A new era started about three decades ago, when it was suggested that foresters need not feel guilty when forest trees are planted on fertile lands because by using improved techniques, suitable species, and better seedlings, forests can produce in some places equal and often higher annual returns per hectar than many food crops could, if grown on the same site.

During these last three decades great progress has been made in the development of the techniques for growing and caring for forest tree plantations in arid zones. Most of the attention was devoted to the production of economic forest crops, but in the late 1960's a new concept in forest planting gained popularity. This was to establish plantings not only for the production of forest crops, but also to improve environmental conditions. Although forest tree plantings for environmental improvement certainly was not new, it has gained impetus as part of the general public concern for protecting and improving environmental values.

In the more arid zones, forest trees are usually planted to mitigate the effects of low rainfall, strong persistent dry winds, and poor soil. If judiciously selected and spaced, forest trees can provide many benefits to society. They can protect homesteads from winds, sift dust, arrest the flow of sand, help reduce heat-loads by their shade, and generally make the surrounding area more pleasing and more habitable. They also help to protect fields and conserve soil moisture, resulting in better crops. Trees in such areas are planted and cared for mainly with the object of improving the microclimate.

In more favorable areas of arid zones where rainfall is more plentiful, wind more moderate, and soil more fertile, forest trees are usually planted to provide products for economic returns. The products may be timber, fuelwood, posts, honey, fruit, fodder, et cetera. Generally the trees give both protection and economic returns, some to a greater, others to a lesser degree.

Forest establishment in low-rainfall zones has proved to be effective in making these regions more comfortable to live in and raising the level of the local economy. Tree planting is by no means restricted to areas that formerly bore forest growth; trees can be successfully planted in some regions that apparently have "always" been devoid of trees.

It is the responsibility of forest planners to develop forestry in arid zones for its maximum contribution to the overall effort for social advancement and economic return. To achieve these objectives the forest planner must decide what type of forest tree plantation is most likely to satisfy the major needs of society.

Four main types of plantations are recognized that may be established to fill man's needs and comfort. These are plantations for environmental improvement, protection plantations, production plantations, and amenity plantations. Combinations of two or more of these types are common.

The decision as to the type of forest plantation to establish will depend on the benefits sought by its establishment and the environmental conditions prevailing in the area. The various types of plantations are described in detail in Chapter Five.

Cost and Benefits

It is impossible fully to assess the monetary value of the improvement in the microclimate afforded by trees and the aesthetic enjoyment derived from plantations. The economic doctrine of supply and demand, if tenable, is so illusive that it is difficult for planners to decide what portion of the resources at their disposal should be allotted to the different types of plantations in their overall regional development plan. It is certain, however, that if environmental values are to be preserved when considering afforestation of an area, economic sacrifices will be required.

The techniques used and the species selected in planting forest trees for different purposes vary with the types of plantations desired, and the intensity of cultivation is dictated by the expected returns in social benefits and value of crops.

Many plantations—ranging in size from only a few trees up to long stretches of shelterbelts—have been established throughout the arid zones of the world for the benefit of the inhabitants and their fields and livestock. But if we consider the vast area of the world's arid zones, the total area of the few widely-separated plantations that have so far been established is small indeed. The need for more plantations is great and the importance of shelter is increasingly felt in many parts of the arid zones.

Plantations in arid zones are costly and difficult to execute. Untold millions of seedlings have died soon after planting and whole plantations perished in arid zones because not enough importance was given to knowledge of the climate, soil, and vegetation of the area to be planted.

CLIMATE

Climate is the average weather conditions of a place over a period of years in relation to various atmospheric phenomena such as precipitation, temperature, and wind. The essential characteristic of an arid climate is that during all or part of the year potential water loss through evaporation and transpiration exceeds precipitation. In most arid regions humid periods occasionally occur in which precipitation exceeds evapotranspiration. Such periods can vary in length from a few days to several months, depending on the locality. The absolute amount of precipitation does not in itself define aridity. The rate of evaporative loss, which is governed by temperature, relative humidity, and duration and velocity of the wind, plays a major role in evapotranspiration and aridity.

It has long been the general belief that the influence of forests on the amount of precipitation in a region is considerable. However, present knowledge indicates that vegetative cover has little influence on the amount and distribution of precipitation over large areas, although vegetative cover does affect the amount and pattern of the moisture reaching the ground in and near the forest. The question of the influence of forests on total water yield is still quite controversial.

Precipitation

Precipitation is, perforce, the principal statistic and starting point necessary for defining arid climate, but by itself it is not an adequate index of aridity. Its effectiveness is controlled not only by its amount and distribution but also by losses through runoff and evapotranspiration. The amount of water available to the roots determines to a great extent the type of vegetation that can grow in an area.

It is, of course, well known that annual precipitation varies from one locality to another within a region, and from one year to the next in the same area. Furthermore, the magnitude of such variations is related to the general climatic type in different parts of the world. As a rule, arid zones have relatively large variations in total, maximum, mean, and minimum annual rainfall. Jodhpur, India, for example, has an average annual rainfall of about 367 mm (14 inches), but the recorded maximum is 1178 mm (46 inches) and the minimum is 25 mm (1 inch). In regions where the average annual rainfall is about 400 mm (16 inches), a year with a deficit of 100 mm (4 inches) is considered a drought year during which damage to the vegetation may be great. In areas where the annual rainfall is extremely low, i.e., where the quantity of rainwater reaching the root zone is barely sufficient for the existence of xeric types of vegetation, even a shortage of 50 mm (2 inches) in one year becomes a decisive factor in the survival of certain species of plants. In some areas of Spain with an annual precipitation of 350-550 mm (14-22 inches), moisture deficiency in any year is a direct factor in growth reduction of trees. The minimum annual rainfall in an arid area is critical and must be carefully studied and evaluated as an ecological factor before planting. In contrast, in regions with high annual rainfall, a shortage of 200 mm (8 inches) in one year may have little or no adverse effect on the vegetation.

Some regions have one or two rainy seasons each year during which showers may be of long or short duration. Usually a climate with one annual peak rainfall period is effectively wetter and supports a better forest than a climate with two annual peaks and the same total rainfall. In a few arid regions the total annual rainfall may occur in 10 to 20 rainy days and in some places all the precipitation may come within a single month. Storms may vary in intensities from heavy downpours to drizzles. When heavy showers occur, especially on clay soils, most of the rainwater is not absorbed by the soil but flows over the surface to streams. During drizzles and light, brief showers most of the water may evaporate before it can infiltrate into the soil, especially if the soil is hot. If the dry periods are long and the temperatures high, much of the rainwater that was absorbed by the soil is brought back to the surface by capillarity and evaporates. In some regions the rains occur mainly during the hot summer; in other regions the rain falls principally during the cold winter season. Summer rains seldom penetrate deeply into the soil due to evaporation from the soil surface, absorption and transpiration by plants, and rapid surface runoff on slopes. In dry regions virtually all of the available soil moisture is used or evaporates before winter begins. In contrast, winter rains normally penetrate deeply into the soil and may contribute a proportion of the rain water to underground flow or storage. Most of the available winter moisture in the top layer of the soil is removed by evaporation before the summer growing season begins.

The difference in vegetation caused by differences in seasonal distribution of rain can be seen by comparing two regions with equal average annual rainfall of about 600 mm (24 inches). The first region lies north of the Sahara in southern Algeria and the other region south of the Sahara in northern Nigeria. In the Algerian area the rains come during the cool winter months, November to April, and much of it in showers of over 10 mm (0.4 inches) per day. If the soil is not hard and the slopes not excessive, most of the rainwater penetrates the soil as rapidly as it falls and is available for use by vegetation. In the northern Nigerian region the rains occur during the hot period from June through September. Many of the showers are so light that most of the water evaporates soon after falling on the hot soil and only a small fraction of the rain penetrates the soil and is available to plants. As an ecological factor for the growth of vegetation the 600 mm (24 inches) of rain in the Algerian area is two or three times more effective than the same amount in northern Nigeria. The vegetation of the Algerian area is an open forest of evergreen oaks and that of northern Nigeria is a bush savanna.

In the summer-rainfall areas of the Republic of South Africa a mean annual precipitation of 850 mm (34 inches) is the minimum required for successful commercial plantations, but in the cooler winter-rainfall areas 700 mm (28 inches) is considered adequate.

Mist and Dew

The occurrence of mist and dew is a critical factor in the survival of plants in many arid areas. Mist is a suspension of microscopic water droplets (0.1 mm [0.04 inches] or less in diameter) in the air near the earth's surface. Dew is a deposit of water formed at night by condensation of water vapor from the air onto the surface of exposed objects. The frequency of occurrence of mist and dew and the amount deposited on plants vary greatly among the different regions of the arid and semiarid zones. Some of this moisture deposited on the leaves is imbibed by plants through open stomata. It appears that in some of the arid zones xerophytes depend for their survival on mist and dew absorbed in this manner during periods in which no precipitation occurs. Some of the water deposited on the leaves may collect into larger drops and fall to the ground, thus adding some moisture to the soil. In addition the higher humidity associated with mists reduces evapotranspiration, thus conserving soil moisture.

Classification of Arid Climates

General. Within the arid zones of the world there are many degrees of dryness. Such terms as "desert," "subdesert," and "Mediterranean" have been used to designate the principal climatic variations that support different vegetative growth forms. Arid zones are typified by a number of ecological features such as widely spaced plants, highly specialized plant structures, and characteristic, often alkaline, soils. In essence, however, these are merely the results of the controlling factor, i.e., the inadequate precipitation often associated with excessive heat. In general the arid zone climates are defined as follows:

1. *Desert*—twelve dry months in the year, where vegetation can grow only if the water table is high or irrigation is applied.
2. *Subdesert*—nine to eleven dry months in the year.
3. *Mediterranean*—usually one or two but occasionally up to seven dry months during the summer or the warm seasons of the year.

A month is considered dry when its total precipitation in millimeters is equal to or less than twice its mean temperature in degrees Centigrade. This may be written in equation form as:

$$P_m \leqq 2T_m$$
$$P_m = \text{Total monthly precipitation in mm.}$$
$$T_m = \text{Mean monthly temperature in } °C.$$

Most deserts are situated above or below latitude 25° to the north or south of the Equator, and they are usually flanked by sub-deserts, which are surrounded by semiarid (Mediterranean) belts, which in turn border tropical or temperate zones to the north or south of them.

Arid zones, as we have said, are often associated with excessive heat, but cold arid zones can also exist according to the criteria given above. In fact, some cold arid zones are quite extensive.

Meigs' Classification. Meigs classified dry climates into semiarid, arid, and extremely arid. The extremely arid classification is based on records that show at least one year without rain. The semiarid and arid classifications are based upon Thornthwaite's moisture index. This index shows that any effective system of defining climate in forestry must include the major active processes which control the complex interaction of vegetation and atmosphere especially as expressed in the availability of moisture to the plants. The principle involved in this classification is that precipitation represents the main transfer of moisture from the water vapor of the air (e.g. rain from the clouds) to the ground. The completion of this hydrologic cycle is through evaporation. Heat energy especially solar energy is required to change the water in soil and plants from liquid to vapor. Thus, evaporation and transpiration transfer back to the atmosphere not only water but also energy. Thornthwaite's classification of climates is based mainly on humidity, as computed from the durations and intensities of rains, minus the amount and duration of evaporation from the soil and transpiration by plants. Negative values of Thornthwaite's index indicate dry climate. Regions with moisture indices equal to, or less than, 40 percent belong to absolutely arid climate.

The intensity of transpiration in an area depends mainly on the amount of moisture in the soil and vegetation, the intensity and duration of solar radiation, and the density and type of the vegetation in the area. Vegetation types vary in the external surface area of leaves and stems and the number and distribution of exposed stomatal cavities. Furthermore, soils differ in the amounts of solar radiation they absorb. These differences result in differences in potential evapotranspiration from an area. In arid zones soil temperature may be extremely high during the day. Maximum soil temperatures occur at the surface and temperatures decrease with depth below the surface. High soil temperatures especially in the surface layers are primarily responsible for the rapid loss of moisture from arid zone soils. In addition, the intensity and duration of the winds, especially dry winds, must be considered. Winds remove the moist air from around the plants and above the soil and thus maintain or accelerate the rate of evapotranspiration.

If a forest is destroyed by clearing or fire, and herbaceous vegetation replaces the forest in that area, there may be a reduction in the plant surfaces exposed to radiation. Under such conditions Thornthwaite's classification of that area will change due to diminished evapotranspiration. Altering a dense chaparral or maquis formation to a savanna type of vegetation may reduce evapotranspiration in an area by 80 percent or more. Evapotranspiration is the principal component of the hydrologic cycle that can be modified by land management to effect an increased water yield. It is therefore important when contemplating planting forest trees over large areas in the arid zones to consider not only the returns from such plantations in forest crops and amenities, but also the drain on the available ground water by the planted trees as compared to the value that could be derived from this water if it were used to produce other crops and benefits.

Measurements of evapotranspiration are difficult and none of the many types of instruments devised for this purpose give accurate or comparative results for different ecological conditions. The soil-filled tank or the "evapotranspirometer" which has been installed in many parts of the world for measuring evapotranspiration is one of the most acceptable instruments. Unfortunately, however, the "evapotranspirometer" has not been used extensively enough in arid zone stations to be of practical use when classifying or comparing climates of different regions.

Where data on precipitation and evapotranspiration are available for given regions, the water balance as proposed by Thornthwaite may be shown graphically and used for comparisons.

Meigs' classification of the dry homoclimates of the world based on Thornthwaite's moisture index is shown in Figures 1–1 and 1–2.

Major Types of Climate. Obviously, the length of the season (or seasons) with adequate precipitation, taking into account the seasonal temperature, is of major importance to classification. The effectiveness of rainfall is also greatly influenced by the amount and intensity of each storm, the number of rainy days, their distribution throughout the year, the temperature, and the evaporation during and between the rainy seasons. If these factors are considered, three major types of arid zone climates can be recognized: Mediterranean, tropical, and continental.

Mediterranean. The rainy season starts in the autumn and continues through the winter. It usually lasts three to five months a year but is frequently interrupted by dry, sunny periods lasting from a few days to four or five weeks. The summers are hot, sunny, and almost completely rainless. Winter temperatures are mild, rarely dropping to freezing. Despite its name, this climate is by no means limited to the Mediterranean countries. It occurs in North America in California, in South America in Chile, in South Africa, and in western Australia.

Tropical. The rainy season occurs in summer, although near the equator there may be two rainfall maxima in the year. Near the northern and southern limits of the tropics, the rainy seasons coalesce into a single maximum in the summer. The greater the distance from the equator, the shorter the rainy season. In the monsoon region, the contrast between the wet summer and the long, dry winter is most pronounced.

Continental. Although there is usually a tendency toward summer precipitation, often no distinct season of maximum precipitation is evident.

Rainfall is fairly evenly distributed throughout the year, and the period of maximum rainfall varies with the locality.

Temperature Belts

In nature, growth of any particular plant occurs only between certain limits of maximum and minimum temperatures, and for long exposures, a characteristic temperature or temperature range (the optimum) exists that promotes the most active growth. The minimum temperatures are seldom lower than about 2° C (36° F), and the maximum temperatures are generally below 45° C (113° F). When temperatures are below minimum, dormant plants remain inactive and actively growing plants are usually damaged or killed. Thus it is not the severity of cold, but when it occurs that matters.

Cold temperatures are most damaging when plants are budding and growing in the spring. When the plant is dormant in winter, or when the branches and leaves have become hardy, severe cold rarely causes serious damage. Thus trees that are undamaged while dormant by temperatures as low as −45° C (−49° F) may be completely or partially killed by light frosts that occur just after growth resumes in the spring. Damage is indicated by browning or "burning" of the foliage. In southern France, millions of olive trees (*Olea europaea* L.) and Aleppo pines (*Pinus halepensis* Mill.), both native to the area, died when a cold wave followed an early warm spell in the spring of 1956.

Leaves of pines and other evergreen conifers may be killed back from the tip by desiccation when the soil is frozen and the transpiration loss is high. Such damage, known as "winter kill," usually occurs on only the windward side of the crown. Winter kill is a serious problem in attempts to establish evergreens in a cold, dry region where a protective ground cover is absent. This damage can be prevented, or at least mitigated, by mulching.

Arid climates can be defined only by including the temperature element. A simple method of expressing the aridity of a region by showing the relationship of temperature to rainfall was used by Bagnouls and Gaussen. This method is demonstrated in the pluviothermic graphs in Fig. 1–3.

The months of the year are shown by capital letters on the horizontal axis of the graph. Temperatures (C and F) and monthly rainfall (mm and inches) are shown on the vertical axis. The scale of the temperature axis is double that of the precipitation axis. Such graphs make it easy to distinguish the dry months, defined at the beginning of this chapter.

The shaded area between the rainfall curves (solid) and the temperature curves (dashes) are the dry months. The more widely this shaded

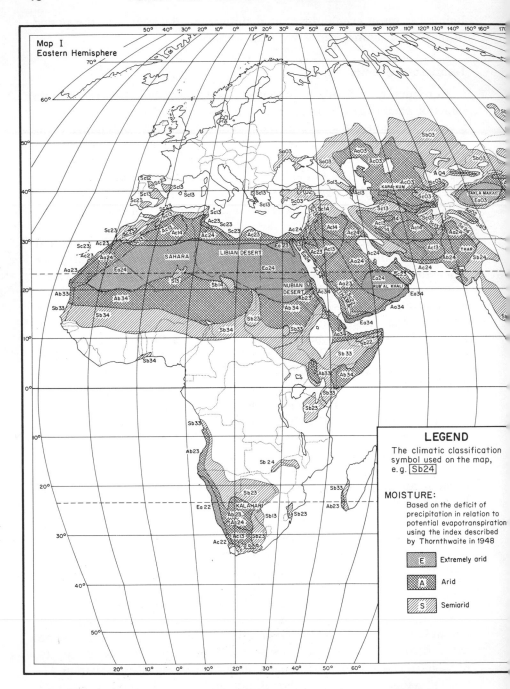

Fig. 1–1. Distribution of arid homoclimates, Eastern Hemisphere.

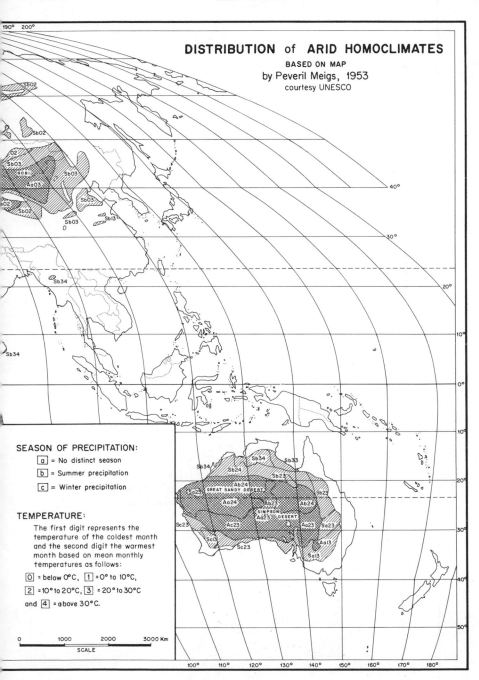

Fig. 1–1. *Continued.*

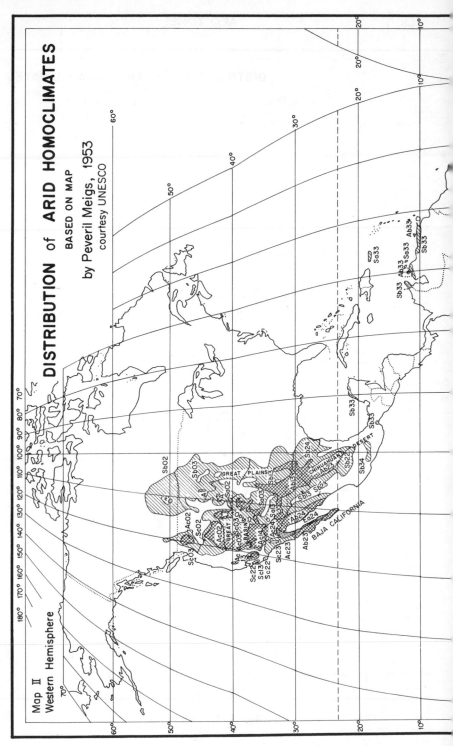

Map II
Western Hemisphere

DISTRIBUTION of ARID HOMOCLIMATES
BASED ON MAP
by Peveril Meigs, 1953
courtesy UNESCO

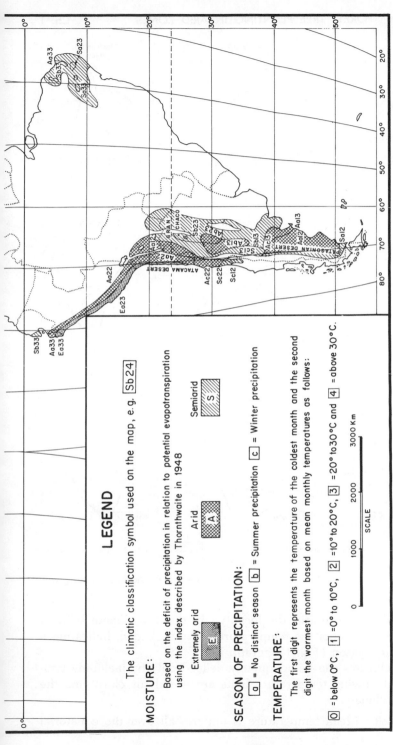

Fig. 1–2. Distribution of arid homoclimates, Western Hemisphere.

LEGEND

MOISTURE:

The climatic classification symbol used on the map, e.g. Sb 24

Based on the deficit of precipitation in relation to potential evapotranspiration using the index described by Thornthwaite in 1948

Extremely arid — E

Arid — A

Semiarid — S

SEASON OF PRECIPITATION:

a = No distinct season   b = Summer precipitation   c = Winter precipitation

TEMPERATURE:

The first digit represents the temperature of the coldest month and the second digit the warmest month based on mean monthly temperatures as follows:

0 = below 0°C, 1 = 0° to 10°C, 2 = 10° to 20°C, 3 = 20° to 30°C and 4 = above 30°C.

SCALE

0   1000   2000   3000 Km

19

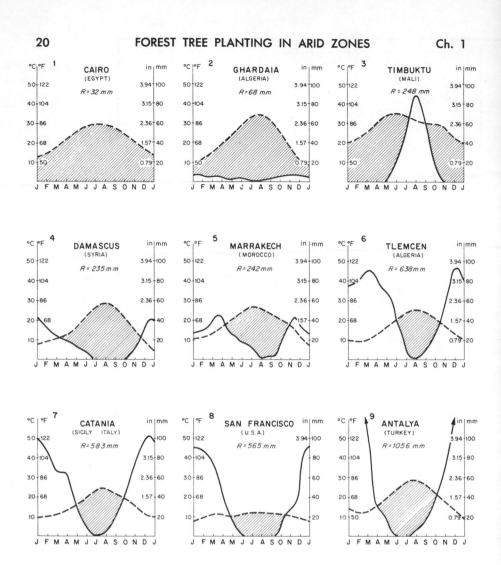

R   Mean monthly rainfall ——— Temperature °C or °F – – Dry season [////]   J F M   The months of the year

Fig. 1–3.   Pluviothermic diagrams

area is spread, the more arid the locality. In desertic climate without rain the entire area under the temperature curve is shaded, indicating a permanently dry season (Fig. 1–3, graph 1).

Since arid climates can be adequately defined only by including temperature, the following temperature belts are useful for classifying the aridity of the climate.

Equatorial Belt.   Mean temperature is uniform all over the equatorial

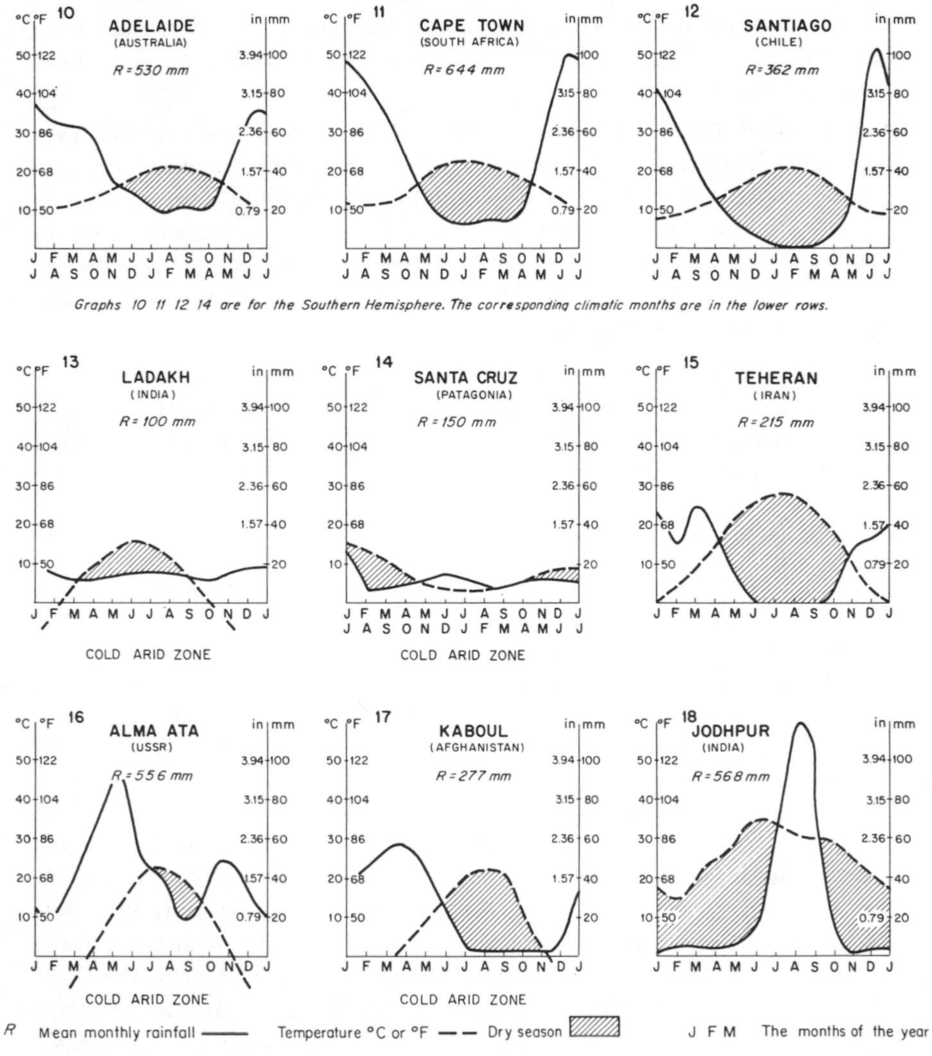

Graphs 10 11 12 14 are for the Southern Hemisphere. The corresponding climatic months are in the lower rows.

COLD ARID ZONE

COLD ARID ZONE

COLD ARID ZONE

COLD ARID ZONE

COLD ARID ZONE

R Mean monthly rainfall ———   Temperature °C or °F — — Dry season   J F M   The months of the year

of different parts of the arid zones.

belt. Everywhere the monotony of the temperature is an outstanding feature; only small differences will be found between the means of the
coldest and warmest months. The mean diurnal range is greater than the
mean annual range.

Tropical Belt. With increasing distance from the equator, the mean
annual temperature becomes lower and the winters cooler, but the summers are warmer because of a decrease in cloudiness. The seasonal

change in temperature is more pronounced. The range in annual temperature increases, and winter is distinctly a cool season. Summer heat is rarely interrupted.

Subtropical Belt. Hot summers and cool or cold winters are the predominant features of the yearly rhythm. Summer temperatures are generally hotter than those on the equator. Spring and autumn are important divisions of the year. The weather is variable, especially in winter. Although the annual range of temperature increases with increased latitude, it is also greatly influenced by the distance from the ocean, i.e., the continentality.

Continental Belt. The temperature ranges from hot in summer to very cold in winter. The yearly range increases with continentality. The mean diurnal temperature range is less than the mean annual range. Arid areas within this belt belong to the cold-type dry zones.

Cold Arid Zones

In cold arid zones, the temperatures are too low for plant growth during a great part of the year. The beginning of the short period in which temperatures are high enough for plant growth is usually the period of melting snow with some occasional rain. The moisture favors growth in the beginning of the growing season, but at the end of the growing season these areas are dry and growth ceases. (Fig. 1–3, graphs 13, 14, 16, 17.)

The woody vegetation of cold arid zones is limited to only a few species of hardy low trees and shrubs. Willows, poplars, and low shrubs grow in small isolated pockets and along river beds near Kargil and on the cold arid Ladakh Plateau in the western Himalayas of India. Willows and poplars are also found where the water table is near the surface in the Tsaidam region and the Takla Makan of western China, the Gobi of Mongolia, and the Karakum desert in the U.S.S.R. Species of *Polylepis, Buddleia,* and *Laretia* occur in the dry cold regions of northeastern Chile, western Bolivia, the Atacama tableland, and the mountains of eastern Peru. Cold arid regions with sparse, low, woody plants also occur in Patagonia, in portions of the Great Basin of western United States, and in the arctic regions.

Wind

Although rainfall and temperature are the main factors on which aridity is based, other factors also have a bearing. Thus, loss of water by evaporation from the soil is no less important than rainfall. Evaporation increases rapidly in high temperatures, strong winds, and decreases in humidity. High temperatures in hot areas and wind in cold ones are the principal factors responsible for reduction of the soil moisture available for plant growth. Transpiration by plants accounts for great losses of moisture from the soil. Transpiration not only depends on wind, temperature, and humidity, but also on plant anatomy, morphology, and physiology.

Arid regions tend to be windy because there is little vegetation to slow air movement, and strong convectional currents develop because of daytime heating.

The effect of winds on rainfall is considerable. Winds from the sea may carry rain-bearing clouds to an area, or the wind may blow steadily for weeks or months from a dry region and bring only dry weather. The maritime trade winds and the monsoons are the source of rains for some dry regions of India and Africa. Heavy mists carried by winds from the Pacific are the only source of moisture available to the vegetation in parts of the Atacama Desert, one of the driest areas in the world. In this area slopes that are sheltered from the mist-laden wind are completely devoid of vegetation. In the Great Plains of North America persistent winds increase evapotranspiration and make the area dry despite moderate annual precipitation. In Rajasthan, India the dry monsoon that blows from the northwest during the dry season dissipates the few clouds that may form and thereby makes the region the driest in India.

In the Mediterranean area, the hot, dusty, and dry winds, which are known by the local names of sirocco, harmattan, and khamsin, originate deep in the desert regions of North Africa and South Arabia where winters are hot. They blow unceasingly for hours or days and cause extreme desiccation. Similar hot winds are known in California, Chile, Argentina, Australia, and many other arid zones, where they blow from the hot deserts. Warm, dry chinook winds of high velocity may cause extreme drought during the winter on the high plains east of the Rocky Mountains in North America. Such winds can overnight completely absorb by sublimation 150 mm (6 in) of snow. Just as effective are the winds that desiccate the arid zones of Patagonia and parts of Asian USSR. Therefore, the importance of wind in producing arid conditions must not be overlooked. The complete drying of shallow pools of water and the surface soil in a little over an hour following a veritable deluge has been observed in Patagonia where the velocity of the dry wind was over 150 km/hr (93 mi/hr).

Altitudinal Climates

Altitudinal climates on mountains or high plateaus are a local modification of the lowland climate of the region. Consequently, because ele-

vation strongly affects the climate within arid areas, it is also a major
determinant of natural plant growth, and it strongly influences the possibilities for afforestation and choice of species. Temperatures may vary
not only with altitude but also with the location of the plateau in reference to chains of mountains or large bodies of water.

Mountains exert a powerful influence on wind direction, temperature,
cloudiness, and precipitation. The intensity of the insolation reaches its
maximum at high altitudes. Most of the heat received by the soil and vegetation is by direct insolation rather than by warm air currents. Hence, a
marked contrast is found between the vegetation of north and south aspects in the same altitudinal zone on high mountains outside the tropics.

In semiarid zones, altitude may markedly affect the character of both
climate and vegetation. Despite the more intense insolation, the higher
altitudes are colder than the lowlands because of greater re-radiation of
heat into space. The difference of temperatures between high and low
altitudes is greater in summer than in winter. Evaporation diminishes
somewhat with increased altitude because of cooler temperatures,
whereas rainfall generally rises with altitude. Mountains within hot,
arid zones may have snowfields because of both altitude and aspect.
Mountains deflect the general direction of prevailing winds. Thus, local
winds are controlled by topography. Hot dry winds, such as the berg of
South Africa and the chinook east of the Rocky Mountains, are actually
produced by and are associated with mountain ranges.

Plateau climate prevails in some arid areas. A plateau is an extensive
area of high and fairly uniform elevation that often has a continental
climate. The larger and higher the plateau, the stronger its influence on
climate. Near the equator, the mean monthly temperatures on plateaus
are naturally lower than those at sea level. In the subtropics, high plateaus have a daily temperature range equal to, or greater than, those
situated at sea level. Their monthly mean temperatures show a definite
seasonal trend. Annual precipitation on these plateaus tends to be low.
Typically it occurs in a few brief, heavy showers. Evaporation is generally much higher on subtropical plateaus than on the neighboring lowlands. Evaporation also varies with the location of the plateau with
reference to chains of mountains or large bodies of water.

Light

Although light provides the energy for photosynthesis, the severest
competition among arid zone plants appears to be for soil moisture and
minerals rather than for light. Moisture is usually not sufficient to support a dense population of plants so the majority of plants that start to
grow are soon eliminated by competition for soil moisture. The few
that do survive are normally so widely spaced that they do not shade

each other. The open vegetation of most arid zones is exposed to the full intensity of the sun and is said to be "light saturated."

Some tree species are known to be more tolerant to shade than others, but suppression of plants due to competition for light, even of tree species with lower ability to utilize light, has not been observed in arid zone vegetation. Consequently, minimum light requirements of various species are not major considerations in planning and management of plantations in arid zones.

SOIL

Soil formation results from the integrated effects of vegetation and the climate, conditioned by time, that act upon the parent rock material. Local soil differences are usually related to parent rock. The amount and duration of moisture in the soil are major factors in its development. For practical purposes, arid-zone soils are those containing too little water for growth of crops without irrigation, except during and for a brief period after the rainy season. Such soils. however, may, and usually do, support vegetation with a low water requirement or with root systems that reach the water deep in the soil.

Soil Orders

Soils are classed in three orders: zonal, azonal, and intrazonal.

Zonal Soils. Zonal soils are those in equilibrium with the environment and the characteristics of which fully express the effect of climate and local vegetation. A pit or ditch dug in a zonal soil will reveal several distinct layers or strata of varying thicknesses. These strata are technically termed horizons and are referred to collectively as the profile. The upper horizon in which leaching of soluble minerals occurs is termed the "A" horizon. The "B" horizon immediately below receives and accumulates the leached material. The "C" horizon just below the "B" is the more or less decomposed parent material. Desert, Prairie, and Chernozem soils belong to this order.

Azonal Soils. Azonal soils are without the well-developed profile characteristics of zonal soils because their youth or conditions of relief or parent material have prevented such development. Alluvial soils and sands are azonal.

Intrazonal Soils. Intrazonal soils have more or less well-developed profile characteristics, but some local factor has overwhelmed, or at least significantly modified, the normal effect of climate and vegetation in their formation, thus producing soils that differ distinctly from zonal soils. Swamp soils and saline soils belong to this category.

Effect of Arid Climate on Soils

The scanty vegetation that develops on arid soils cannot protect them during infrequent, but intense, brief showers. Consequently erosion is common and very apparent in arid zones. As a general rule, the lower the rainfall, the greater the proportion of the land area that is being actively eroded or receiving the products of erosion. Therefore, arid zones have fewer zonal soils, more intrazonal soils, and many more young azonal soils (i.e., constantly rejuvenated soils) than the more humid zones.

Breaking down of the parent material, or rock weathering, is the result of both physical disintegration and chemical decomposition. In arid areas, physical weathering predominates, mainly because of great fluctuations in temperature. During comparatively short periods of time for soil development, coarse soil material with low clay content develops in arid regions from parent rocks that weather to clay soils in humid regions.

Sandy soils develop in arid regions from the weathering of sand-stones and other rocks. Scanty vegetation and lack of soil moisture make it possible for the sand to move with the wind, building up shifting dunes and sandfields. Blowing sand plays an important part in eroding even the hardest rocks.

Soil-forming processes leading to the formation of normal soil depend on the interaction of vegetation with the weathering mineral particles and require many decades without interruption for completion. In the arid environment, scantiness of the vegetation impedes the soil-forming processes since few root channels are present to promote infiltration of rain water, and the surface is not protected from water and wind erosion.

Leaching, or the downward movement of water soluble chemicals, is slow and seldom completely removes all the solutes in arid soils. The more soluble salts, such as sodium chloride and sodium sulphate, are the first to be leached, then gypsum (calcium sulphate) and calcium carbonate. The leached material may accumulate in layers. In the Prairie-Plains of the United States, calcium is leached completely from the soil when the annual rainfall exceeds 500 mm (20 in), but accumulates in layers near the surface when the rainfall is less than 500 mm. The accumulation of calcium carbonate by leaching is often combined with lime from ground water brought near the surface of the soil by evaporation of capillary columns and surface films. This forms thick layers of calcium carbonate which are exposed as a massive surface of hard crusts when surface soil is eroded away.

In many desert areas, or in regions surrounding such areas to a distance of several hundred kilometers, the formation of the upper crust of the soil may differ from the soil formation that would have developed as a result of normal weathering of the parent rock material in the area. This is due to the fact that in most deserts the upper crust of the parent rock material has been continually subjected to great fluctuations of temperatures, especially between day and night, causing the crust to crack into smaller and smaller particles and in time to form soil with little or no vegetable matter. The fine dust particles from the upper surface of the soil are then picked up and carried away by the wind. This process is repeated, wind after wind, year after year. This dust, at times of almost pure fine clay, may be transported by the wind for hundreds of kilometers and then deposited when the wind dies down or as rain washes it from the air. As the dry top layers are removed, the lower moist layers are exposed to the sun and hot winds. These in turn dry quickly and are picked up by the wind. Dust from the Sahara carried by the high velocity ghebli wind is deposited in North Africa or carried as far as Italy across the Mediterranean Sea. Dust picked up by the wind over the Syrian or Sinai deserts settles in the Middle East, and storms that originate in the Sind desert in India and Pakistan may deposit the dust in New Delhi over 500 kilometers to the northeast. Deposits of windborne soil are known as "loess" and may be very deep. However, the properties of this loess are not identical with those of the loess of the humid regions. Similar dust storms are known in southwestern United States, Argentina, Australia, and other areas where deserts exist. The heavier particles formed by the weathering of sandstones, when propelled by the wind, skip and roll along the surface for varying distances within the desert and even to the fringes of the desert. Sooner or later, these coarser particles pile up into shifting dunes that move in the direction of the prevailing wind. These dunes are not only unstable, but are also extremely low in fertility. Due to differences in the rate of weathering of different minerals, the mineral composition of dunes differs from that of the parent rock material.

The Major Soil Groups

The major soil groups in arid areas include Desert soils, Brown and Gray soils, Chestnut soils, Chernozem soils, and their azonal and intrazonal subtypes.

Desert Soil (Red Desert soils and Sierozems). Desert soils form a poorly defined zonal group which has not yet been sufficiently studied. They have a light-colored surface layer with low organic content, a transitional subsoil similar to or darker and with more clay than the surface, and an accumulation of calcium carbonate about 30–90 cm (1–3 ft) below the surface. Red Desert soils are formed in hot climates and are similar to

Desert soils except for their redder color. Rock weathering in the desert is mostly physical, and surface textures tend to be sandy although silt loams do occur. Intermittent flooding from adjacent upland regions may provide seasonal moisture. Evidence of water action is often spectacular, although rainfall is less than 100 mm (4 in) per year. Rainfall often is intense and extensive alluvial fans of gravel are common.

Sierozems are similar to the Desert soils, but usually their soil layers are slightly thicker and the depth to the calcium carbonate layer slightly greater. They receive a little more rainfall than the Desert soils.

Desert vegetation is sparse, often consisting only of isolated highly specialized shrubs, small trees, and bunchgrasses. Wind erosion is extremely active in the desert, leaving the surface soil in many places covered by the "desert pavement." This consists of coarse stones or rock fragments that remain after the original accompanying fine material has been blown away. Beneath the scanty vegetative cover that provides some protection, fine soil material may be found (Fig. 1–4).

Brown Soils (Gray soils, Reddish-Brown soils, and Calcisols). These soils occur in semidesert areas where annual rainfall is between 100 and 200 mm (4 to 8 in). They occasionally develop on loess. The Brown soils have a brown surface horizon that grades below into lighter colored soil and finally into a layer of calcium carbonate accumulation. The Reddish-Brown soils, which are formed in warmer climates, are redder but otherwise similar. The Calcisols resemble the Brown and Reddish-Brown soils, but usually have a pale grayish surface layer. They contain only small amounts of organic matter (1–2 per cent) resulting from the decomposition of plants. Calcisols contain calcium carbonate throughout and have one layer of especially high accumulation at or near the depth of rainfall penetration. This layer is often less than 30 cm (12 in) below the surface, whereas in the Brown and Reddish-Brown soils its depth is from 30 to 90 cm (12–36 in). Incomplete leaching due to scanty rainfall results in sodium salts generally remaining in all these soils, their concentration is greater in the more arid regions. Where the water table is near the surface, saline or alkaline soils may develop. Usually the plant cover over these soils is sparse, consisting mainly of small, usually thorny, bushes. Despite the meager natural vegetation, trees may be grown successfully with the proper cultivation techniques.

Chestnut Soils (Reddish Chestnut soils). The Chestnut and Reddish Chestnut soils are found in many parts of the world under somewhat less arid conditions—i.e., 250–300 mm (10–12 in) annual rainfall—than the soils just described. The proportion of organic matter in their upper horizon is only 2–3 per cent. The depth of the layer of lime or gypsum accumulation is generally from 45 to 135 cm (1.5–4.5 ft) below the surface. The

Fig. 1–4. "Desert pavement" in Tamanrasset, central Sahara.

upper horizon is dark brown because of the organic matter, and the subsoil is chestnut-colored. The Reddish Chestnut soils are similar to these but they are redder because they are formed in a warmer climate. The natural vegetation of these soils in cool temperate climates is mixed tall- and short-grass steppe, and in warm climates mixed grasses and shrubs.

Chernozem. This great soil group is one of the most important in dry climates. These soils are usually formed under a continental climate with 300–450 mm (12–18 in) mean annual rainfall. Because of their high organic content (from 5 to 12 per cent) the surface horizons are nearly black. Although their organic matter has been derived from plant fragments, these have, through complex chemical and microbiological processes, lost all identity with the original structures. Where environmental conditions are most favorable for the development of Chernozems, notably the Ukraine, they are a deep black. However, their color ranges from gray in the more humid areas to dark brown in the more arid. Chernozem generally develops on loess, and the thickness of the dark-colored layers varies from 40 to 150 cm (1.3–4.9 ft). The sharpness of the transition from the organic layer to the underlying light-colored parent material varies locally. In the Chernozem, leaching of soluble sodium salts is complete, but that of calcium carbonate and calcium sulphate is not. Thus, although there is no accumulation of sodium salts, a layer of lime sometimes accompanied by gypsum is present. The more calcareous the parent material and the more arid the climate, the nearer the layer of accumulation is to the surface. Vegetative cover is a savanna with widely scattered trees, or a steppe with luxuriant grass in spring and early summer.

In India a soil known locally as regur, or black cotton soil, is found typically on the dark-colored Deccan trap rock and basalt. This soil occupies a large area in the southern half of the subcontinent and is covered with vegetation of the grass-steppe type. The depth and development of the calcium carbonate layer vary greatly for such non-typical Chernozem. Rainfall and temperature under which these soils develop are much higher than for a typical Chernozem. These soils have often been called "tropical Chernozems," but this terminology should be avoided because their dark color is due, not to high humus content, but to the dark minerals of the parent material. Similar soils occur in eastern Australia, Rhodesia, Morocco, Java, Argentina, and Uganda. Of these tropical soils, those of the first two localities most closely resemble the true Chernozems.

Rendzina and Terra Rossa. The soil types described above belong to normal or zonal soils. The intrazonal soils, associated with calcareous parent material, are also important in arid areas. They belong to two groups; one is brown- and gray-black, including gray or white chalk soils, and the other is predominantly red or reddish-brown. The first group is known as the Rendzina, the second as the Terra Rossa soils.

A Rendzina soil typically has a brown or black surface horizon underlain by light gray or pale yellow, soft calcareous material. The dark color is not necessarily correlated with the organic content but it may result from dark minerals. Rendzinas are generally formed on soft limestone but may also be found on chalk or marl. These soils contain free calcium carbonate, which is often in nodules or concretions. They generally support grass or grass-and-forest vegetation.

The name Terra Rossa has been given to the red soil formed on hard limestone or marble under a Mediterranean climate. These soils have a weakly developed surface horizon with incorporated humus and a striking red, fine-textured subsoil that passes directly to the parent rock at a depth varying from a few centimeters to more than a meter. Calcium carbonate is generally leached away but, if present, is mostly in the form of iron-coated fragments of lime. These fragments by reason of their size are chemically inactive until broken by cultivation.

Saline and Alkaline Soils. In arid zones, saline and alkaline soils occupy a major place among the intrazonal soils. They owe their distinctive characteristics either to the presence of an excess of sodium salts or to the predominance of sodium among the exchangeable bases.

Saline soils, also called white alkali soils, contain an excess of sodium salts, generally sodium chloride and sodium sulphate. They usually occur in depressions. During dry seasons, they show white efflorescences of salts, hence the name "white alkali." During rains, the salts are dissolved and washed down. The soil properties depend on the height of the water table, the amount and distribution of rainfall, the concentration and composition of soluble salts, and the general characteristics of the soil of the region. Saline soils occur frequently in arid zones and may represent modified Calcisols, Chestnut soil, or Chernozems. Although they are generally devoid of vegetation, they may support a few scattered halophytes that have become adapted to such an environment. Most halophytes are herbaceous, but shrubs can be found in some localities and in a few rare places a scattering of widely spaced trees.

Alkaline soils are characterized by the presence of sodium carbonate. In an area of saline soils, alkalinity may develop in depressions. During rain, sodium and potassium carbonate solutions dissolve and disperse the organic matter which diffuses through the soil, coloring it dark brown or black. These soils are, therefore, known also as "black alkali." Sodium carbonate solution also strongly tends to disperse inorganic colloids, which dry to a gel and finally to a structureless, impervious mass.

No sharp line of division exists between saline and alkaline soil. Different stages of transition may occur, depending on the position of the water table, the composition of ground-water, the nature of the soil minerals, and the degree of leaching by rainfall or by irrigation. An excess of sodium salts in saline soils results in the partial or complete replacement of the exchangeable calcium by exchangeable sodium.

Alluvial Soils (Lithosols). Probably the most important azonal soils in arid regions are the Alluvial soils, which are derived from material recently transported by streams and deposited on floodplains or deltas. Alluvial soils may be found in all stages of development, depending on their age. However, the term, Alluvial, should be used to designate only young soils in which the soil characteristics are still dominated by the parent material. Some Alluvial soils are extremely fertile and are among the most valuable agricultural soils.

Lithosols are shallow, stony soils over bedrock. They occur extensively on steep mountain slopes and steep parts of dissected plains and plateaus, especially in arid and semiarid regions.

ECOLOGY OF ARID-ZONE VEGETATION [2]

The study of the complex interrelationships between organisms, communities of organisms, and their environment, including changes in the communities due to changes in the environment, is known as ecology. The environment includes biotic as well as abiotic factors. The ecologist

[2] The term "arid zone" is used here and throughout the book in the generic sense to include not only arid, but also semiarid and extremely arid zones. It is believed that specific use of the term will be evident from the text.

often refers to environment as "habitat," whereas the forester may use the term "site."

The interacting ecological system that includes all organisms of a community, their abiotic environment, and the flow of energy in the community is known as an ecosystem. An ecosystem consists of the following described four components involved in the conversion and flow of energy. (1). Abiotic. Non-living materials such as water, carbon dioxide, oxygen, soil, and minerals. (2). Producers. Green plants of all kinds such as trees, bushes, grass, and algae. (3). Consumers. Large and small animals of all kinds. (4). Decomposers. Fungi and bacteria which break down plant and animal material so that it can be recycled and used again by the plants. The extent and rate of exchange of material, therefore energy, depends greatly on climate, especially temperature and moisture.

Composition of major plant communities in arid zones reflects the great climatic and soil variations of these zones. But because the common characteristics of arid zones everywhere are low rainfall and a deficiency of soil moisture during at least part of the year, many of the adaptations of both individual plants and plant groups are similar despite great geographical separation.

The vegetation of arid regions is the result of long evolutionary development during which individual plants became adapted to the low, erratic rainfall of the arid environment. Arid-zone plants are also subjected to extreme temperatures, frequent fires, and damage by biotic agents, such as mammals, birds, insects, and disease. They are able to survive only because they have evolved great resistance to the damaging physical and biological factors of their environment.

The harshness of the physical environment is mitigated by the presence of such vegetation, and as a result the modified environment can support a greater amount of less highly specialized vegetation. The most important environmental changes are those affecting soil moisture relationships. Plants improve the soil by the addition of humus which tends to decrease runoff and increase infiltration. Infiltration may also be increased because water can enter the soil via the channels formed by decaying roots.

The vegetation in each arid zone is clearly the product of the environment. Nevertheless, different types of vegetation may be found in similar environments, depending on the stage of development of the flora and the plant species available in the region. Such differences are the result of the geographical changes of the earth's surface during its long geological history. Thus, the Cactaceae of Mexico and the mallee scrub of Australia, with their special physiognomic and floristic characteristics, are confined to those two areas. In other regions of the world with a similar climate, the vegetation and flora are quite different, but similar climates as a rule give the vegetation a similar physiognomy and morphology.

Within a given geographical unit, geology has a strong bearing on plant development. Soil conditions in dry climates, and therefore the vegetation, are closely related to the geology of the underlying rock. Where soils are derived from dissimilar materials, differences in vegetation will occur. Boundaries between plant communities often will be found to follow closely the line of contact between two geological formations.

Although over a large area climate is the dominant factor affecting plants, soil and exposure locally determine the composition of the plant community. Cultural improvement of the soil makes possible the improvement of the vegetation cover. Altitude also plays an important part in the structure and distribution of plant communities. In a given locality, mountain ranges of similar geological structure have essentially the same vegetation. The differences in mountain vegetation are associated with altitude and exposure.

In arid zones, any factor that influences the water balance is decisive for the survival and growth of every plant. The valleys and flats subject to runoff from higher areas may receive water equal to several times the actual amount of rainfall on the area itself. Such areas frequently develop a savanna in the midst of almost rainless, barren desert.

The species comprising the vegetation of arid zones are determined not only by physical factors, but also by competition among the plants and the plant communities. In arid and semiarid areas, where water is the critical factor for the survival and growth of plants, there is great competition for the little water available. In general only species or types of vegetation that have root systems which penetrate quickly to layers of soil where water is available can survive. Sparseness of the vegetation is the inevitable result of drought and competition. Whenever the land in arid climates is impoverished by excessive grazing, water loss by surface runoff increases, and competition for the small amount of moisture that infiltrates the soil becomes extremely keen.

The vegetation of every area is continually changing. As soil conditions improve and become less harsh, more advanced plants invade the area. This progressive replacement of one plant community by another plant community is known as succession. Ultimately, the area will be occupied by a plant community that is in equilibrium with the environment. This community is known as the climax and is composed of the "most mesic" plants that can be supported by the prevailing climate. Mesic may be defined as an average moisture condition between xeric (dry) and hydric (wet).

In arid and semiarid zones, one seldom encounters the true "climax" of succession because the progressive development of the vegetation is usually modified by man's agriculture and husbandry, and by fire and pests. Often these agents produce an apparent reversal of natural succession with a reversion to some earlier and more primitive stage of vegetation. This retrogression is always abnormal and is produced by some disturbance that outweighs the influence of climate. Because the disturbance, if continuously applied, may hold the vegetation in the more primitive stage, it causes a false climax. Recognition of man-caused false or disturbance climaxes is often difficult, but it is essential for proper selection of species in afforestation.

Many arid zones have experienced climatic changes during their existence. These climatic changes, at least within human history, appear to be mainly sporadic or cyclic increases or reductions in precipitation. Because the changes have been relatively small, both positive and negative, and of short duration they have, in the long run, had little permanent effect on the vegetation of the area.

Historical records of gradual and continuous increased desiccation or of ecological retrogression ascribable to climatic change do not exist. Furthermore, no conclusive evidence has been found to support the belief that deserts are extending to neighboring territories due to climatic changes. However, ample evidence exists that throughout many arid areas the vegetation has all but disappeared as a result of physical destruction of the vegetation and soil by man and his livestock. Many of these areas resemble deserts and desert conditions prevail in them. It is by no means uncommon to find small relics of the original climax vegetation that escaped destruction within these artificial deserts. Examples of such relic vegetation can be seen in the Thar Desert and the Moab and Ahaggar (Hoggar) Mountains. In the Thar Desert, a grove of a few hundred *Tecoma undulata* G. Don trees has escaped destruction and stands alone in an otherwise treeless landscape. All of the trees are quite old and no regeneration can be found among the trees. This particular grove has been protected by religious beliefs and no one in the area will destroy or use the wood of these trees, not even the dead branches that have fallen from them. A grove of old *Cupressus sempervirens* L. is found on a cliff in the Moab Mountains of southern Jordan and it constitutes the only remaining vestige of this species in the whole region. This grove was saved from destruction by its inaccessibility. Very old, isolated cypress trees are scattered over a large area of the Ahaggar Mountains in the central Sahara. Here again no young trees or seedlings can be seen. Some of these trees are more than a thousand years old; they are still vigorous and produce viable seeds. The slow disappearance of this woodland is due to its destruction by continuous and excessive grazing of sheep and goats. The presence of these relic groves appears to indicate that no significant climate change has taken place in the regions concerned for a great many years.

Classification of Arid-Zone Vegetation

Because the arid areas of the world are so extensive, the diversity of their vegetation is not surprising. Several systems for classifying arid-zone vegetation have been proposed. None of the systems is entirely satisfactory or applicable to all zones so that the limits of the different zones vary with the criteria applied to the regions. The classification for arid-zone vegetation suggested by Beard and Pichi-Sermolli, which is based chiefly on the ecological conditions of the habitat and the physiognomy or the general appearance of the vegetation, has been adopted here.

Beginning with the driest types, the vegetation groups of arid zones may be subdivided as follows.

Desert. Although extensive areas completely devoid of any vegetation, i.e., absolute deserts, are not often encountered, vast tracts with such sparse vegetation that they may quite appropriately be called deserts do exist. Desert vegetation consists of widely scattered patches of herbs, shrublets, dwarf shrubs, and occasionally a solitary tree. Between these individuals or patches, the soil is apparently devoid of life; but when rain falls, the seeds of ephemerals, or short-lived plants, germinate, complete their life cycle in a few days, and then again disappear. Such areas usually receive less than 100 mm (4 in) of rain per year.

Subdesert Shrub and Grass. This type includes all those plant communities consisting of herbs, grasses, shrublets, and low shrubs that are scattered, either individually or in small colonies, on land that is more than half bare of vegetation. Single, stunted, or dwarf trees are occasionally present. On some sites, the plant communities are a mixture of all these vegetative types, whereas in other places the community is dominated by one type and the other types are widely scattered.

Subdesert Shrub and Scattered Trees. This type consists of a very open grouping of shrubs or shrublets with scattered trees. The shrubs, usually solitary or in small groups, are 1–2 m (3–6.5 ft) high. The shrublets are solitary or associated with shrubs in small colonies. Succulents are common components of this vegetation, and some perennial grasses and herbs may be found. These plants are irregularly scattered over the soil surface and are separated by large spaces bare of vegetation where, after rain, a few ephemerals spring up. The trees are deciduous or succulent, have a single main stem, and are rarely more than 6–7 m (20–23 ft) high. They are always solitary and scattered but frequent enough to be the most notable physiognomic feature of this vegetation.

Subdesert Grassless Scrub.   This division consists of an open grouping of dwarf trees, usually not exceeding 3 m (10 ft) in height. Stunted shrubs are intermixed with low shrubs, shrublets, succulent bushes, and bulbous and tuberous plants. Individual plants are irregularly scattered and relatively far apart. Although ephemeral grasses and herbs may occur after rains, the absence of perennial grasses, and the fact that the tallest trees are very widely scattered or virtually absent, are two important characteristics of this vegetation type.

Subdesert Grassy Scrub.   This type consists of an open community of woody plants, with ground vegetation of grasses and other herbs. The dominant woody plants are deciduous shrubs or short-boled trees less than 4 m (13 ft) in height. The taller shrubs are solitary, or a few are grouped in the center of a thicket that is surrounded by small shrubs, shrublets, and herbs. Taller trees, if present, are scattered at wide intervals. Scattered tufts of perennial grasses and shrublets make up the ground vegetation. Among the shrubs, as well as among the ground vegetation, wide bare areas normally occur. These areas are quickly occupied by ephemerals after every rainfall.

Succulent Scrub.   This type consists of open plant communities dominated by succulent plants. In America it consists chiefly of spreading or tree-like prickly pear cactus (*Opuntia* spp.) with scattered, often thorny shrubs. In some areas, tall column-cacti are visually dominant. The ground is grassless, and frequently the bare soil is exposed. In the Old World, the succulent shrub type consists of cactus-like plants which dominate the physiognomy of the plant communities. These plants are accompanied by more or less succulent shrubs. Grass may or may not be present. The main characteristics of this vegetation type are the abundance of plants which show extreme reduction of leaves (microphyllous), the development of storage tissues to form succulent stems, and the presence of thorns and spines.

Xerophilous Open Woodland.   This type includes open communities of woody plants, grasses, and herbs, among which large shrubs, shrublets, and perennial grasses are dominant. The large shrubs are usually from 3 to 5 m (10–16 ft) in height, mostly deciduous and thorny. Trees are scattered among the large shrubs and are characteristic of the physiognomy. Climbers may be present. The trees and large shrubs frequently have flat, umbrella-like crowns. Their crowns do not form a continuous canopy, thus leaving large openings where low shrubs, shrublets, tuft or perennial grasses, and herbs form a discontinuous ground vegetation that leaves part of the soil surface bare. These bare areas may be partially covered by ephemerals after rains.

Open and Wooded Grassland. In the grassland vegetation type of the semiarid zone, grasses and herbs are dominant, whereas trees and big bushes are virtually absent or widely scattered, covering on the whole less than 50 per cent of the ground. Although grasses dominate the landscape, the woody plants are the conspicuous physiognomic feature. The grasses may be procumbent and matted, in patches or in clumps, and normally are less than 2 m (6.5 ft) tall. Two principal types of grassland may be recognized: the open grassland or steppe, typically treeless, and the wooded grassland. The wooded grassland may be subdivided into scattered-bush grassland, scattered-tree grassland, and palm-stand grassland.

Evergreen Scrub. This type grows near the upper limit of the semiarid zone and consists of a closed scrub of evergreen or semi-evergreen shrubs, large bushes, small trees, climbers, and an occasional large tree. A few deciduous plants are intermixed. The shrubs are 2–3 m (6.5–10 ft) tall and are either thornless with leathery, glossy leaves or thorny and succulent. Climbers, especially succulent ones, are common. Although shrublets, herbs, and grasses are everywhere, they do not constitute a regular ground cover. The larger trees are widely scattered and in some communities are tall, candelabra-like euphorbias.

Other Subdivisions. In regions where this broad classification lacks the desired precision for a particular purpose, each vegetation type may be subdivided according to ecological, edaphic, climatic, physiognomic, and floristic criteria. For example, the vegetation of the extremely arid Rajasthan desert in India can be subdivided into the following major units:

1. Vegetation of shifting sand dunes.
2. Vegetation of stabilized sand dunes.
3. Xerophytic vegetation on sandstone rocks.
4. Halophytic vegetation.
5. Sandy loam vegetation.

Each division requires an intensive study, and each may be further subdivided into many well-defined communities.

The foregoing classification does not include all the vegetation types of the semiarid regions of the world. It does not include the regions having subtropical or continental climates. The classification of semiarid vegetation of such areas therefore should be further extended to include among others the thorn woodlands known as monte-type of South America, where hard-leaved, microphyllous, evergreen spiny trees 3–10 m (10–33 ft) tall, mostly of the Mimosaceae or Caesalpiniaceae, form an open to fairly closed stand community; the woodlands of the Saharo-Sindian and Irano-Turanian plant communities of the Near East; the xerophytic and degraded woodlands of the Mediterranean region; the woodlands of

North America; and the mallee and savanna woodlands of Australia.

Under certain conditions—especially where better soils are found—a dense tree cover can exist, forming a forest with high trees and straight trunks. The roots usually penetrate deep into the soil, frequently more than 25 m (80 ft). Long superficial roots that can quickly absorb much of the rainwater are also characteristic of these trees. They are slow growing and usually reproduce from seed or coppice from root or stump.

Thus, notwithstanding their distribution over large areas of the world and the heterogeneity of the types of vegetation, the common character-istics of arid zones do permit a study of their features as a whole and a classification of their respective groups of vegetation.

When plants are classified into large groups based on water relation-ship, the three major categories commonly recognized are: hydrophytes, mesophytes, and xerophytes. These refer to plants of wet, moist, and dry areas, respectively. This book is concerned mainly with xerophytes.

Xerophytes

Xerophytes may be defined as plants of dry habitats. By ecological definition they are plants growing on soils that ordinarily become de-pleted of water during at least part of the year. In arid regions, all plants not confined to the margins of streams or lakes or to similar moist soils are considered xerophytes. They must either evade or endure re-current drought. Plants have evolved many different adaptations that permit them to survive xeric conditions.

Succulence is perhaps the most spectacular mechanism of xerophyt-ism. In fact, succulent vegetation as previously described is one of the major types of vegetation in the earth's arid areas. Succulence is a dis-proportionate multiplication of cells of parenchymatous elements in re-lation to the more rigid tissues. These cells remain distended and turgid enabling succulents to accumulate quantities of water during brief rains. The cell sap often contains much dissolved material: pentosans and mucilages. Water storage, accompanied by low transpiration rates dur-ing the dry season, enables succulents to resist prolonged drought. Succu-lence in various species occurs in stems, leaves, or roots.

Non-succulent, perennial plants also have morphological and physio-logical adaptations enabling them to withstand drought. The principal adaptations are described in the following paragraphs.

Rapid elongation of taproots is common in some species adapted to arid lands (Fig. 1–5). Excluding ephemerals, non-succulent plants, the seedlings of which have a rate of taproot penetration sufficiently rapid to keep ahead of progressive drying of the soil from the surface downward and are thus not subjected to surface drought, are potentially capable of growing in such habitat. Absence of this characteristic must exclude numerous species from arid areas. The importance of rapid elongation of the taproot is well illustrated by *Haloxylon ammodendron* Bunge, the seeds of which germinate soon after the snow melts. As the snow melts and the moisture penetrates the soil, rapid root elongation keeps pace with the penetration although the surface soil may dry completely.

Six to eight weeks after the germination of the seed, *Aspidosperma quebracho-blanco* Schlecht. has a taproot about 1 m (3 ft) long but the aerial part is only 6–10 cm (2.4–4 in) high. In large trees, the taproot has the same diameter as the trunk at the root collar and tapers down very slowly—a taproot 30 cm (12 in) in diameter at the top is likely to be 15 cm (6 in) in diameter, 8 m (26 ft) deep in the soil. The taproots of *A. quebracho-blanco* trees not more than 12 m (40 ft) high have been excavated and followed to a depth of 16 m (53 ft). The superficial lateral roots are also long, occupying an approximately circular area that extends 10–15 m (33–50 ft) from the tree. A few of these superficial roots bend abruptly downward and grow to a great depth. A thick layer of soil devoid of water occurs in some areas. The roots of this species can penetrate the dry layer reaching deep sources of underground moisture.

Fig. 1–5. The roots of this shrub, which have been exposed by erosion, penetrated over 12 m (40 ft) in reaching moisture in the subsoil. (Photo A. J. Urbanovski)

These adaptations enable this magnificent tree to grow in areas with less than 300 mm (12 in) annual rainfall and concomitant low atmospheric moisture.

In the same area of Argentina where the *Aspidosperma* grows, *Acacia farnesiana* (L.) Willd., *Acacia macracantha* Humb. & Bonpl., *Prosopis nigra* Hieron., *Caesalpinia paraguaiensis* (Parodi) Burkart, and *Zizyphus mistol* Griseb. can be found, all with roots much longer than 8 m (26 ft).

An extensive, much branched, superficial root system is another important ecological adaptation of arid-zone vegetation. When the soil is so dry that roots cannot absorb water as rapidly as it is lost by transpiration, the plant wilts. Most plants have approximately equal ability to absorb moisture from the soil which is in actual contact with their rootlets. However, the extent of branching and the number and length of rootlets and presence or absence of root hairs differ markedly among plants. These variations have an important bearing on the relative efficiency of the root system of different species. A large volume of soil containing a small amount of moisture can yield as much water for plant growth as a large amount of moisture contained in a small volume. A great total length of root system relative to the aerial part of the plant is, therefore, an important adaptation in some desert plants. An extensive root system is important both because it increases the moisture-absorbing area, giving each plant a larger catchment area, and because only a relatively small portion of the plant is exposed to the dry atmosphere. Because of the great spread of roots, wide spacing of vegetation in arid zones may, in fact, be the result of root closure, thus the site is actually fully occupied. Although only a small part of the ground may be covered by vegetation, it has frequently been found that most of the soil is occupied by root systems competing for soil moisture.

In addition to the great horizontal extent of the root system, many desert trees and shrubs have roots so deep that they reach the permanently moist subsoil.

The depth of penetration of such trees as *Acacia tortilis* Hayne, *Haloxylon ammodendron* Bunge, and *Prosopis juliflora* (Swartz) DC is exceptionally great. *Prosopis* roots have been found more than 35 m (115 ft) below the surface. Although the moisture supply at such depth may be too small to maintain active growth except when supplemented by surface moisture during and immediately after the rainy season, it prevents —or at least shortens—the period of complete drought in the root zone.

Xerophytes can usually survive drought and considerable loss of water from their leaves and green surfaces. This distinguishes them sharply from mesophytes, whose leaves can tolerate relatively little dehydration without injury.

Another important feature of arid-zone plants is their greatly reduced transpiration during drought. Although some desert plants have relatively low transpiration rates, it has been established that this is by no means a characteristic feature of all xerophytes. In fact, most of the non-succulent xerophytes transpire water as freely as the mesophytes when an adequate water supply is available. However, their special adaptation, which mesophytes lack, is the drastic curtailing of water loss during periods of drought.

Other morphological and physiological adaptations can be noted whereby transpiration of arid-zone plants is reduced. Important among these are seasonal changes in size and presence of organs that affect water economy. For example, many species, chiefly in the tropics, shed their leaves during extremely dry periods, thus greatly reducing their transpiring surface.

Although many species retain their leaves, they have evolved special structural adaptations that apparently lessen transpiration. These adaptations reach their maximum efficiency during the peak of the dry season. Plants with evergreen leaves which are tough, leathery, and often heavily wax-coated, have a high resistance to desiccation. Plants of this type are referred to as sclerophylls, or hard-leaved plants. The thickness of the wax coating is frequently directly related to relative humidity. For example, *Bulnesia retamo* Griseb., which grows in areas with about 100–600 mm (4–24 in) annual rainfall, has a higher vegetable wax coating when growing in the areas with less rainfall. Eucalypts, especially mallee, and most of the maquis vegetation are outstanding examples of sclerophylls.

Mallee is a scrub forest dominated by eucalypt shrubs and small trees that covers hundreds of square kilometers on the edge of the Australian desert. Mallee embraces several species of eucalypts plus representatives of a dozen other families. *Eucalyptus oleosa* F. Muell., *E. oleosa* var. *glauca* Maiden, *E. dumosa* A. Cunn., *E. uncinata* Turcz., and *E. largiflorens* F. Muell. are some of the better known mallees. Leaves of the xeric scrub are monotonously grayish-green. These bushes are usually less than 3 m (10 ft) tall, although in a few places they reach a maximum of 10 m (33 ft). However, mallee of nearly uniform height, not exceeding 1 m (3 ft), covers immense tracts. Stems of the mallee grow from a large lignotuber that is connected to an enormous root system. Because the lignotubers are buried in the sandy soil they are protected from fire. During drought years many of the branches growing from the lignotuber die, but in rainy years new shoots quickly sprout again. If a specimen of the mallee is grown in a site somewhat more moist than its native habitat, only one, two, or three branches will grow out of the lignotuber, but these may attain a height of 10 m (33 ft) and resemble a normal tree forking at ground level.

The reduction of size of leaf blades—microphylls—is another important adaptation feature of dry-zone vegetation that mitigates the effect of drought. It has been shown that the smaller the leaf blade the less likely it is to be overheated when exposed to strong solar radiation. The tendency to develop small leaf blades is very evident in such trees as African acacias. In some species, this tendency has progressed so far that the leaves have become needle-like as in *Casuarina* and *Tamarix*. In still other plants, such as the Australian wattles (*Acacia* spp.), the leaf blades have been completely lost. The function of the leaves in these plants is then carried out entirely by the petioles or the stems, which contain the chlorophyll. A reduction in cell size is also found in dry-zone species; in fact, it has been found that drought-resistant strains can be selected on the basis of their cell sizes.

These adaptations enable xerophytes to grow in dry areas. Although they are the characteristic plants of deserts, xerophytes are by no means confined to arid lands; nor are all desert plants xerophytes. The structural and physiological modifications of xerophytes have evolved under different intensities and kinds of drought, producing characteristic responses to the peak of the dry season. On the basis of their reaction to drought, xerophytes may be classified as follows.

Drought-Escaping. Plants of this group, known as ephemerals, are annuals adapted to a short growing season of about 4 to 6 weeks. They are able to complete their life cycle from germination to seed maturation during the brief period after rains while the upper layers of the soil are moist.

Drought-Evading. Plants of this type require only a scanty rainfall because they conserve moisture as a result of their small size, restricted growth, low water requirements, and wide spacing.

Drought-Enduring. These are principally small, widely spaced shrubs and trees. They make very little growth in a single season. When the soil moisture drops below the permanent wilting point, the leaves wilt, dry, or may drop off completely. The plants remain alive, enduring the drought, but make no growth until water is again available to the roots. Most of these plants can endure several months with no available water and quickly resume growth when rains once again replenish the soil moisture. The woody vegetation of most semiarid and arid areas belongs to the drought-enduring type.

Drought-Resisting. Plants of this group resist drought by accumulating a supply of water that is used when none can be absorbed from the soil. Thus they may continue to grow for long periods, even extending their roots through dry soil. Succulents, such as the cacti and *Agave*, belong to this group. A few drought-resisting species are non-succulent but have stumps or underground parts with large cavities in which water is

Fig. 1–6. *Allenrolfea occidentalis* (S. Wats.) Kuntze, an extreme halophyte growing in highly saline substratum near the eastern edge of the Bonneville Salt Flats, Utah. This species tolerates more alkali than any other North American desert shrub.

accumulated. Trees such as *Adansonia digitata* L. of the African grasslands are thus enabled to bloom before the rains actually break the long drought.

Halophytes

Halophytes grow on saline soils and are especially adapted to withstand salinity (Fig. 1–6). They include both the succulent and nonsucculent plants. Halophytes are important in arid and semiarid zones because of the frequent occurrence there of saline soils. As a group their ecology is characterized by the ability not only to endure a high concentration of certain salts, but also to absorb water under these conditions. That halophytes can absorb large amounts of water from highly concentrated soil solutions is shown by their high transpiration rates. However, in a few places, such as in the dry saline hammadas of the Near East, even halophytes have difficulty in growing.

Plants on saline soil grow chiefly during the rainy season after the soil solution has been diluted and part of the salt has moved below the root zone. The characteristic shallow rooting of many halophytes is, therefore, a distinct advantage in their survival. In contrast to these are a few highly specialized plants with deep root systems. For example, *Prosopis tamarugo* F. Phil. grows in salt basins at high altitudes in northern Chile. Its roots penetrate the upper salt crust, which is often 30–50 cm (12–20 in) thick, and utilize the slightly less salty water found in the deeper soil.

Phreatophytes

Phreatophytes are plants that draw their main water supply from the permanent ground water, or from the capillary fringe just above it, and are more or less independent of precipitation. Many of the tree species in arid zones, such as poplars, willows, mesquite, and tamarisk, are phreatophytes. Some non-phreatophytes, such as acacias and eucalypts, when planted in arid zones produce deep roots and in effect become phreatophytes.

Because of their high transpiration rate, phreatophytes extract much more water from the ground than is necessary for normal growth. They thrive in wide, shallow river basins where water tables are high. Such riverine vegetation composed of economically low-valued trees and shrubs, may invade bottom land areas and cause a great loss of water which could be used for other purposes. Removing phreatophytes along streams might eliminate most of the transpiration loss, but removal of shade and wind protection would increase the direct evaporation loss. The water temperature of unshaded streams may rise above the physiological limit for some game fish and other aquatic animals. Streamside and lakeside trees are extremely important for their recreational and aesthetic values and for wildlife habitat. Removal of phreatophytes over large areas is not always sound management and is unlikely to gain public support. However, in some places poplar and willow trees of great economic value may be grown where low-valued phreatophytes have been removed.

Lomas

The vegetation formation of shrubs and low trees known as "lomas" is found in southern Peru and northern Chile in areas with little or no rainfall. Lomas occupy the foothill slopes facing the Pacific Ocean at an elevation of 300 to 800 mm (1,000 − 2,600 ft) a.s.l. This vegetation depends for its moisture supply entirely on the water of the ocean mists and fogs that collects on the aerial parts of the plants and subsequently drips to the ground. In some places the moisture deposited by this so-called "fog drip" is equivalent to 450 mm (17 in) of rainfall per year. Trees of the lomas are chiefly species of *Caesalpinia* and *Acacia*. Due to the excessive atmospheric moisture, the trunks and branches of the trees are solidly covered with lichens. Above and below the narrow mist belt the land is completely dry and barren. Similar vegetation moistened only by mists is found in the coastal deserts of Baja California (Mexico) and in the Namib of South-West Africa.

FORESTS IN ARID ZONES

The arid and semiarid regions were never completely covered with forests, but there is little doubt that at one time most of them bore trees, or maquis, or one of the different types of vegetation described above.

The history of virtually all of these regions shows how the clearing of forests or other native vegetation for cultivation, timber, fuel, and grazing, as successions of people, armies, and livestock swept over them, destroyed all but the vestiges of the original vegetation. This destruction has been so great in most places that the only remnants extant of some tree species and vegetative types (as they were developed under natural conditions over many centuries) are found in isolated pockets.

These remaining groups of vegetation are either thorny, unpalatable to grazing animals, or composed of wood not used as fuel. In some places several species of trees and grasses that grow among them have been protected and saved from annihilation because the animals dislike reaching through the thorns.

Destruction of vegetation has also resulted in soil erosion. Deep layers of topsoil have been washed down to the flood plains below and out to sea. In many places erosion has left only a thin layer of subsoil capable of supporting only poor vegetation. In other places erosion has exposed the bare rock. Loss of vegetation causes a change in the microclimate and is conducive to still greater desiccation.

Restoration to the original forest types may require a succession through intermediate stages. This may be accomplished by the use of pioneer or nurse crops. On the most seriously eroded soils, the nurse crop must be selected from xerophilous brush species, but in more favorable areas, species of moderate economic and aesthetic value may be used.

The natural forests of the arid zones range from high forests to open forests, with a large number of types between these extremes.

High Forests

Only relatively few islands of high forests can be found in the arid zones, and these are usually located in the transition between the semiarid and the humid temperate or the humid tropical regions. They have been zealously guarded and preserved by foresters wherever they are not protected by their inaccessibility. Their annual productivity is small, seldom more than 2 cubic meters per hectare (29 cubic feet [or 145 board feet] per acre). They may contain a few fast-growing trees, but usually their growth is slow. Even when they are properly managed, they may not be harvested in a rotation of less than 80 years. With better roads for easy accessibility and intensive silvicultural treatment they will, at best, produce only slightly more than they do now—an amount that would barely satisfy present demands.

Many of these remnants have, however, been depleted of their best timber, so that they cannot be harvested economically, and some of the products that formerly were important have decreased in value. For example, in some localities the demand for fuelwood and charcoal has diminished drastically. Another management problem is the unavailability of labor for these forests, which often grow a great distance from settlements. The cost of transporting labor to the forested areas makes silviculture and harvesting uneconomic.

Open Forests

Within the arid zones there are immense areas of scattered trees and herbaceous vegetation. Often the trees are scrubby, low-growing, and poorly formed. Vegetation of this type is known by various names in different countries; a few of the more common names are: savanna, campos cerrados, chaco, chaparral, maquis, garigue, and veldt.

Savanna. The term savanna is applied to a grassland which covers large areas in the tropic and subtropical arid zones. Savannas are generally characterized by two strata of vegetation: an open forest stratum 8 − 15 m (26-50′) high, rarely higher and often lower, and a stratum of herbaceous species predominantly grasses. The woody cover is invariably irregular in its growth, and never has the characteristics of woodland that produce an impression of a true forest. Grasses and other plants of the herbaceous layer may be dense and quite tall, but in the more arid areas they are likely to be sparse and low.

Savannas are found on a variety of soils, but in the less arid regions they are generally on permeable sandy soils that may be almost sterile. Most savannas have been repeatedly subjected to fires most of which were started by man as part of his cultivation practices. Fires have been used to clear the land for easy cultivation and as a means of regenerating pastures by removing the old dry grass to favor new growth. Usually the best trees for timber, poles, and posts were cut leaving only the poorest trees most of which are not worth conserving as a forest.

Long ago repeated burning by farmers and hunters destroyed the original forest formations and these were replaced by the open tree, brush, and grass formations which characterize the savanna. Thus man must be considered one of the most important environmental factors in maintaining the savanna formation.

The burning of the vegetation has often been followed by the deterioration of the soils due to poor cultivation methods. When the productive capacity of the soils has been exhausted, the population simply abandons the land, moves to a new area, and repeats the process.

Where only the vegetation has deteriorated and the soil still maintains part if its fertility, application of silvicultural measures may bring back or establish an improved forest.

Campos cerrados, chaco, et cetera. Although savanna formations are best known over large areas in Africa, similar formations exist in other continents. The "campos cerrados" and "catinga" in Brazil, the "chaparioles" of north-west South America, the "chaco" of Argentina, Paraguay, and Bolivia and the sub-desert vegetation types of the Pacific coast of South America are ecological equivalents of the African savanna. Savanna vegetation types are also found in Asia and Australia.

Chaparral, maquis, garigue. The "chaparral" type of vegetation in Mexico and the southewestern United States is a formation of small trees, chiefly *Quercus* spp., and dense shrubby vegetation. In the Mediterranean basin the open forest shrub formations are known as "maquis" and "garigue." The "maquis" are evergreen sclerophyllous low trees up to 8 m (25') high—but usually lower—which form the top layer of the formation that usually includes 2 to 3 lower layers of brush, creepers, and grass. The "garigue" represents the remains of a maquis and is a low generally open sclerophyllous scrub about 1.5 m (5') high with scattered low trees. The grass cover in these formations is never as extensive as in savannas.

Veldt. The "veldt" is an open grassland of South Africa generally similar to the savanna but with only a few bushes and almost no trees.

The sites on which the different types of open forest formation exist, including the savanna, steppe or open grassland formation, and the shrub and low tree formations such as chaco, chaparral, maquis, garigue, and veldt are in general areas of great potential for planting forest trees. Although trees grow slowly in most such areas and yields from existing native woodlands are very low and poor in quality, the production of many sites when planted with selected species, including exotics, may be high. The condition and appearance of the native trees in such areas often give an entirely erroneous concept of the potential productivity of many sites. The principal problems in such areas are to find useful, high-yielding species and to develop economical methods of clearing and preparing the sites for establishing plantations.

Forestry Programs and Policies

Adverse climatic and edaphic conditions for tree growth impede forest establishment in arid zones. In addition, any forestry program has to be considered within the framework of a general land-use policy. The relationship of forestry to agriculture and animal husbandry must always be kept in mind. Consequently, a forest policy must be conceived and realized as part of a more general policy for the development and rational utilization of land resources.

Forests cannot be expected to alter the general climate of a region or to increase rainfall, but trees and shrubs are known to have a beneficial effect on microclimate. The influence of any woodlot or row of trees is very marked in its vicinity. By reducing wind velocity, trees reduce moisture losses caused by evaporation from the soil and transpiration by vegetation. Furthermore, when wind velocity is reduced, wind erosion is significantly decreased. Wind erosion always causes great economic loss wherever it occurs, but in arid and semiarid land wind erosion is a major calamity. Trees planted as windbreaks, shelterbelts, or woodlots have a pronounced beneficial effect on agricultural yields by protecting orchards, fields, and pastures against damaging winds. Over and above its role in protecting the soil against wind erosion, a vegetative cover, including trees, shrubs, and grasses, may be established to stop moving sand and to prevent gully and sheet erosion.

Forests regulate stream flow, hold the soil, and protect reservoirs against silting. At the same time, they may supply the wood needs of the local population in the form of firewood, charcoal, posts, poles, wood for agricultural implements and farm buildings, and raw materials for industries. Often in semiarid and arid environments special heed is given to minor products, such as bark for tannin, fruit, seed and foliage for animal fodder, gums, resins, and oils. Trees may also be grown for the nectar gathered from their flowers by honey bees. The "greening" effect of trees in otherwise desolate country is certainly important, and aesthetic and recreational considerations in themselves frequently justify the establishment of forest plantations.

Part or all of these objectives can be attained either by conservation, by improvement, by conversion of existing forest areas, or by the creation of new forest stands. The establishment of forest plantations often calls for changes in the current land-use practice and requires the development of more intensive agriculture and a revision of grazing practices. If alternative areas for grazing cannot be found, it will be necessary through range improvement to increase the grazing capacity of the land. New legislation aimed at better protection of trees may be necessary to implement a forest policy. Excessive demands for forest products that result in overcutting should be mitigated by developing substitutes. Generally, the pressure of the population on the forest should be reduced.

Pilot projects and thorough research are prerequisites to the implementation of a new forest policy. In areas selected as representative of the natural economic and demographic conditions of larger regions, these pilot projects would show, at least on a small scale, how a part of the social and economic hardships usually affecting the population of semiarid and arid lands can be alleviated. These would also allow an appraisal of techniques used to implement land-use policies. If they are needed, widespread educational programs should inform the populace of the benefits of trees and forests. Qualified technicians, acquainted with both dry-zone forestry and with general land-use and improvement, are required for such work.

Once it has been decided to propagate a certain tree species on a given site by artificial reproduction—either by planting or by seeding—the first step is to obtain seed or cuttings of that species.

BIBLIOGRAPHY *

AUBREVILLE, A. Climats, fôrets et désertification de l'Afrique tropicale. Soc. d'Édi-
1949   tions Géographiques, Maritimes et Coloniales, Paris. 351 p.
BAGNOULS, F., and H. GAUSSEN.   Saison sèche et indice xérothermique. Bull. Soc.
1953   Hist. Nat. Toulouse 88:193–239.
BEARD, J. S. Climax vegetation in tropical America. Ecology 25:127–158.
1944
———. The savanna vegetation of northern tropical America. Ecol. Monogr.
1953   23:149–215.
BÉGUÉ, L. Ecology. FAO Spec. Program Educ. Train. in Afr., Train. Cent. Savanna
1963   Afforestation Tech. Sudan, 9 Nov.–19 Dec. 1963. FAO/SAVAFTECH-
ECO/1. Food Agric. Organ. U. N., Rome. 76 p.
BELTRÁN, E. (editor). Las zonas áridas del centro y noreste de México y el apro-
1964   vechamiento de sus recursos. Inst. Mex. Recur. Nat. Renov., Mexico, D.F.
186 p.
BERG, L. S. Natural regions of the U.S.S.R. (Translated from the Russian by O. A.
1950   Titelbaum.) Macmillan, New York.   436 p.
BEUZEVILLE, W. A. W. DE. The climatological basis of forestry, New South Wales.
1946   Pt. 1. N.S.W. For. Comm. (Commonw. Rural Reconstr. Comm.), Sydney.
62 p.

* Periodical and serial title abbreviations according to: Word-abbreviation list. National Clearinghouse for Periodical Title Word Abbreviations. Am. Natl. Stand. Inst., Columbus, Ohio.

BOBEK, H. Die natürlichen Wälder und Geholzfluren Irans. Bonn Geogr. Abh. 8.
1951 Bonn. 62 p.
BROOKS, C. E. P. Climate through the ages. rev. ed. McGraw-Hill, New York.
1949 395 p.
CABLE, D. R. Soil temperature variations on a semidesert habitat in southern
1969 Arizona. USDA For. Serv. Res. Note RM–128. Rocky Mount. For. Range
      Exp. Stn., Ft. Collins, Colo. 4 p.
———. Competition in the semidesert grass-shrub type as influenced by root systems,
1969 growth habits, and soil moisture extraction. Ecology 50:27–38.
CAIN, S. A. Foundations of plant geography. Harper, New York. 556 p.
1944
CATINOT, R. Sylviculture tropicale dans les zones sèches de l'Afrique. Rev. Bois
1967 For. Trop. No. 111:19–32; No. 112:3–29.
CLEMENTS, F. E. Plant succession. Carnegie Inst. Washington, Publ. 242. Washing-
1916 ton, D. C. 512 p.
———. Plant succession and indicators. H. W. Wilson, New York. 453 p.
1928
CLEMENTS, F. E., E. V. MARTIN, and F. L. LONG. Adaptation and origin in the plant
1950 world: the role of environment in evolution. Chronica Botanica, Waltham,
      Mass. 340 p.
COZZO, D. Bosques en las lomas de Lachay inducidos exclusivamente por neblinas.
1971 Rev. For. Argent. 15:63.
CROCKER, W. Growth of plants: twenty years' research at Boyce Thompson Institute.
1948 Reinhold, New York. p. 28–138.
CZECZOTTOWA, H. A contribution to the knowledge of the flora and vegetation of
1938– Turkey. Verlag des Repertoriums, Berlin-Dahlem.
1939
DAN, J., and D. H. YAALON. The application of the catena concept in studies of
1966 pedogenesis in Mediterranean and desert fringe regions. Trans. Int. Congr.
      Soil Sci. (8th Bucharest 1964) 8(5):751–758.
DAUBENMIRE, R. F. Plants and environment: a textbook of plant autecology. 3rd ed.
1974 John Wiley & Sons, New York. 422 p.
DREGNE, H. E. (editor). Arid lands in transition. Am. Assoc. Adv. Sci., Publ. 90.
1970 Washington, D. C. 524 p.
DUVDEVANI, S. Dew in Israel and its effect on plants. Soil Sci. 98:14–21.
1964
EYRE, S. R. Vegetation and soils: a world picture. 2nd ed. Aldine, Chicago, 328 p.
1968
FAO. Forest influences. FAO For. Prod. Stud. 15. Rome. 307 p.
1962
———. Proceedings of the joint FAO/U.S.S.R. international symposium on forest
[1972] influences and watershed management, Moscow 17 Aug-6 Sep. 1970. Food
       Agric. Organ. U. N., Rome. 452 p.
GAUSSEN, H. Délimitation des aires de végétation selon le climat. Int. Union For.
1958 Res. Organ., 12th Congr., Oxford, 1956. Papers v.1:134–137.
GINDEL, I. Attraction of atmospheric moisture by woody xerophytes in arid climates.
1966 Commonw. For. Rev. 45:297–321.
GOOD, R. D'O. The geography of flowering plants. 4th ed. Longman, London.
1974 557 p.
GOODELL, B. C. Watershed treatment effects on evapotranspiration. Pages 477–482
1967 in W. E. Sopper and H. W. Lull (editors). Forest Hydrology. [Int. Symp.
      For. Hydrol., Univ. Park, Pa., Aug.-Sept. 1965.] Pergamon Press, New York.
      813 p.
HADEN-GUEST, S., J. K. WRIGHT, and E. M. TECLAFF (editors). A world geography
1956 of forest resources. Am. Geogr. Soc. Ronald Press, New York. 736 p.
HILLS, E. S. (editor). Arid lands: a geographical appraisal. Methuen, London and
1966 UNESCO, Paris. 461 p.

HORTON, J. S., and C. J. CAMPBELL. Management of phreatophyte and riparian vege-
1971 tation for maximum multiple use values. USDA For. Serv. Res. Pap. RM-
117. Rocky Mount. For. Range Exp. Stn., Ft. Collins, Colo. 23 p.
HUECK, K. Las regiones forestales de Sur America. Inst. For. Latinoam. Invest.
1957 Capacitación, Bol. 2. Merida, Venezuela. 40 p.
KAUL, R. N. Afforestation in the cold desert of India. Indian For. 91:2–9.
1965
KITTREDGE, J. Forest influences. McGraw-Hill, New York. 394 p.
1948.
KOZLOWSKI, T. T. Tree growth, action and interaction of soil and other factors.
1955 J. For. 53:508–512.
KRAMER, P. J., and T. T. KOZLOWSKI. Physiology of trees. McGraw-Hill, New York.
1960 642 p.
LARSON, M. M., and G. H. SCHUBERT. Root competition between ponderosa pine
1969 seedlings and grass. USDA For. Serv. Res. Pap. RM-54. Rocky Mount. For.
Range Exp. Stn., Ft. Collins, Colo. 12 p.
LAURIE, M. V. Tree planting practices in African savannas. FAO For. Dev. Pap. 19.
1974 Rome. 185 p.
LEACH, W. Plant ecology. 4th ed. Methuen, London and John Wiley & Sons, New
1956 York. 106 p.
LOGAN, F. L. Geography of the central Namib Desert. Pages 127–143 in W. G.
1969 McGinnies and B. J. Goldman (editors). Arid lands in perspective. Am.
Assoc. Adv. Sci., Washington, D. C. 421 p.
MEHER-HOMJI, V. M. Les bioclimats du sub-continent indien et leurs types ana-
1963 logues dans le monde. Impr. L. Jean, Gap. 386 p.
MOOR, H. W. Vegetation and climate. Emp. For. J. 16:200–214.
1937
MOUTERDE, P. La végétation arborescente des pays du Levant. École. Fr. Ingén.
1947 Beyrouth, Publ. Tech. Sci. 13. Beirut, Lebanon. 48 p.
PASE, C. P., and M. M. FOGEL. Increasing water yield from forest, chaparral, and
1967 desert shrub in Arizona. International Conference on Water for Peace
(Washington, D. C. May, 1967) vol. 2, p. 753–764.
PHILIPPIS, A. DE. Classification and indices of climate with reference to the forest
1939 vegetation of Italy. (Transl. from Nuovo G. Bot. Ital. 44:1–169, 1937.)
U. S. Soil Conserv. Serv., Handbook for Climatologists, Part VI. Washing-
ton, D. C. 181 p.
RAEDER-ROITZSCH, J. E. Watershed management. FAO Lectures. Peshawar, Pakis-
1968 tan.
RAIKES, R. L. Formation of deserts of the Near East and North Africa: climatic, tec-
1969 tonic, biotic, and human factors. Pages 145–154 in W. G. McGinnies and
B. J. Goldman (editors). Arid lands in perspective. Am. Assoc. Adv. Sci.,
Washington, D. C. 421 p.
RIKLI, M. Das Pflanzenkleid der Mittelmeerländer. 3 vols. Huber, Bern. 1418 p.
1943–1948
ROLLEY, J. Forest conditions in Syria and Lebanon. Unasylva 2:77–80.
1948
SCHULMAN, E. Dendroclimatic changes in semiarid America. Univ. Ariz. Press,
1956 Tucson. 142 p.
THIMANN, K. V. (editor). The physiology of forest trees. Ronald Press, New York.
[1958] 678 p.
THORNTHWAITE, C. W. Introduction to arid zone climatology. Pages 15–22 in
1958 UNESCO, Arid Zone Research XI. Climatology and microclimatology.
Proc. Canberra Symp. Paris.
THORNTHWAITE, C. W., and F. K. HARE. Climatic classification in forestry. Unasylva
1955 9:51–59.
TORTORELLI, L. A. Maderas y bosques Argentinos. Editorial Acme S.A., Buenos
1956 Aires. 910 p.

TSCHERMAK, L.   Waldbau auf pflanzengeographisch-ökologischer Grundlage. Springer
    1950   Verlag, Vienna. 722 p.
UNESCO. Arid Zone Programme I. Reviews of research on arid zone hydrology.
    1953   Paris. 212 p.
———.   Arid Zone Research V. Plant ecology: proceedings of the Montpellier
    1955   symposium. Paris. 124 p.
———.   Arid Zone Research VI. Plant ecology: reviews of research. Paris. 377 p.
    1955
U. S. DEPARTMENT OF AGRICULTURE.   Soil: the yearbook of agriculture 1957. U. S.
    1957   Dep. Agric., Yearb. Agric. 1957. Washington, D. C. 784 p.
WEAVER, J. E., and F. E. CLEMENTS. Plant ecology. 2nd ed. McGraw-Hill, New
    1938   York. 601 p.
WHITE, G. F. (editor). The future of arid lands: papers and recommendations from
    1956   the International Arid Lands Meetings. Am. Assoc. Adv. Sci. Publ. 43.
           Washington, D. C. 453 p.
WILDE, S. A.   Forest soils: their properties and relation to silviculture. Ronald Press,
    1958   New York. 537 p.
WULFF, E. V.   An introduction to historical plant geography. (Transl. by E. Brissen-
    1943   den from Russian edition of 1933, revised 1939.) Chronica Botanica, Wal-
           tham, Mass. 223 p.
ZOHARY, M. The flora of Iraq and its phytogeographical subdivision. Iraq Dep.
    1950   Agric. Bull. 30. Baghdad. 201 p.
———.   The arboreal flora of Israel and Transjordan and its ecological and phyto-
    1951   geographical significance. Oxford Univ. Imp. For. Inst., Inst. Pap. 26.
           Oxford. 59 p.
———.   Ecological studies in the vegetation of the Near Eastern deserts. I. En-
    1952   vironment and vegetation classes. Israel Explor. J. 2:201–215.
———.   Plant life of Palestine: Israel and Jordan. Ronald Press, New York. 262 p.
    1962

2

Collecting and Handling Tree Seed

THE SEED

In most spermatophytes seeds are formed in the ovary or female cone only after fertilization of the ovule (egg) by the sperm nuclei from the pollen of the male. In the angiosperms, the ovary develops into a fruit containing the seed, but in the gymnosperms there are no ovaries and the seeds are borne "naked," i.e. not enclosed in a fruit. Although gymnosperm seeds are "naked," they are nearly always protected by cone scales or other structures.

sperms—e.g., eucalypt or acacia. In other angiosperms and in the gymnosperms, male and female organs are in separate flowers or cones. Male and female flowers or cones may be borne on the same tree, as in oak or pine; or each may be borne separately on a different individual, as in juniper, pistachio, and carob (*Ceratonia siliqua* L.).

The mature seed contains an embryo. The embryo has a meristematic tip (radicle), which ultimately develops into the root; a central part (hypocotyl), which develops into the stem of the seedling; and a second meristematic tip (epicotyl), in which new stem growth originates and which, until secondary growth occurs, is called the plumule. Attached to the upper end of the hypocotyl are the seedling leaves or cotyledons. The number of cotyledons may be one, as in the palms; two, as in hardwoods; or a few to many, as in pines. The cotyledons either contain the stored food or absorb it from specialized food storage tissues surrounding the embryo. This food storage tissue is commonly called the "endosperm." However, the term "endosperm" should be applied only to such storage tissues as occur in the seeds of angiosperms; the equivalent structure in the gymnosperm seed is actually the female gametophyte. In most species of conifers and small-seeded angiosperms, after completing their role as absorbing organs, the cotyledons function as ordinary leaves for several weeks until the primary leaves are produced on the new stem growth.

The embryo and endosperm are enclosed in a seed coat, or testa, that varies among tree species from a thin membrane to a stone-like shell. The seed coat protects the embryo from desiccation, physical damage, and insect or fungal attack. The seed coat may be permeable to water, as in conifers, eucalypts, and oaks, or impermeable, as in most legumes, for example, carob, *Prosopis,* and acacia.

Seeds may or may not have appendages that facilitate dispersal. Such appendages to seeds or fruits are characteristic of some genera and certain groups. In conifers, such as cedar, cypress, and most pines, the seeds are winged. In broad-leaved species such as ash and maple the fruit is winged, and in poplar and willow the seeds are supported in their flight by tufts of cottony hair.

When placed in suitable conditions of moisture and subjected to the proper temperature, a mature, non-dormant seed will germinate and develop into an independent plant. This plant, when grown under ecological conditions similar to those that favored its parents, will normally be similar to them.

GENETIC CONSIDERATIONS IN FOREST PLANTING

General

Most tree regeneration in arid zones is artificial and perforce expensive. Therefore, every effort should be made to ensure that each seedling planted yields the maximum return or advantage expected from it. This can be assured in part by proper selection of the seed and of the stock to be planted, and further by taking proper care of the growing stand.

Among the characteristics desired for trees in arid-zone forestry are drought resistance, resistance to destructive insects and diseases, straightness of bole, production of fodder-leaves, and durable wood. All such traits are seldom found in nature in one tree. In collecting seeds for artificial reproduction, special effort should be made to gather them from trees that have one or more desired characteristics superior to the average specimen of the same species growing on similar sites. Such trees are called "plus" trees. From the genetic standpoint, a plus tree (or any tree) in a natural forest is the product of the interaction of the genetic constitution of the particular specimen (i.e., the "genotype") with the environment. The resulting individuals, described on the basis of their demonstrable characteristics, are called "phenotypes." A stand of superior phenotypes constitutes a "plus stand."

Trees transmit their genetic characteristics to their progeny either vegetatively or by seed. However, similar phenotypes do not necessarily reproduce offspring with similar traits. Trees grown from the seed of superior phenotypes under environmental conditions different from (or even similar to) those of the parents may not possess all the desired characteristics of the parent tree. Parent trees that have been verified by testing as superior or desirable under a specific propagation system are called "elite" trees. Forests containing a majority of elite trees are known as "elite stands." Stands of superior phenotypes reproduced vegetatively from rooted cuttings or by grafting, and preserved for the collecting of seeds, are called "seed orchards." To establish clones in seed orchards cuttings are taken from superior trees and rooted or grafted to vigorous seedling stock. These are then planted in the seed orchard using wide spacing, usually about 9×9 m (30×30 ft), so that each tree will have ample space for full crown development. After a few years it will be possible to obtain cuttings from these clones which in turn can be rooted or grafted to produce stock at reasonable cost for field planting.

Seed should be collected from plus trees or stands, preferably from elite trees; or still better, from seed orchards composed of trees that exhibit many of the desired characteristics expected of the trees to be planted. Cones and fruit gathered indiscriminately from low-branched or stunted trees, because they are accessible and easy to collect, may not yield seed that will produce trees with desirable traits. Such seed may be cheap to collect and suitable for developing plantations whose chief purpose is soil conservation or dune fixation, since in these plantations the major concern is usually covering the soil as quickly as possible with vegetation. If, however, the purpose of forestry is to produce timber, the desirable characteristics are fast growth; tall, straight, little-tapered boles; few or short, thin branches; and, depending on the locality, ability to withstand drought, wind, unfavorable soil, frost, disease, and insect attack. However, if the plantation is to shelter fields, sparcity or poor development of branches is not a "plus" quality. On the contrary, the trees selected should have live branches nearly the full length of the bole. Similarly, trees will not be suitable for sheltering cattle from the sun if shade-producing branches are short or lacking. The cost of producing seed by controlled cross-pollination in seed orchards or of collecting seed from elite trees constitutes only a small fraction, usually less than two percent, of the cost of an afforestation program. It has been estimated that a pine seed orchard of one hectare can produce enough seed to plant from 250 to 500 hectares per year and that many times this area could be planted using the seed from one hectare of eucalypts.

Research to develop improved strains of trees is necessary to help advance arid-zone afforestation; yet little has been done in this field. A program to produce superior genotypes by cross-pollination of trees with desirable characteristics should be initiated. Such an undertaking is expensive and difficult, but it is one that will in time repay its cost by increasing the number of genetic strains with valuable attributes. These strains may then be used in developing seed orchards.

It takes a long time to prove that a tree is an elite tree and that its progeny will have desirable characteristics. But no matter how difficult and costly, it is of the greatest importance in establishing plantations. The added expense of selecting and protecting elite stands and collecting seed from them is more than compensated for by the high quality of the stands that can be grown from their seed. For example, the risk that a stand might be damaged by disease or insects may be greatly reduced by planting trees produced from seed collected from a parent tree that is resistant to such attacks. In selecting trees for disease or insect resistance, one usually looks for genotypes with high resin or gum flow which might suffocate the adults or larvae of invading insects, or for those with apparent immunity to the disease. Another important reason for seeking trees with heritable resistance to disease and insect damage is to make the use of persistent, non-selective, toxic chemicals to control these parasites unnecessary. Furthermore, although environmentally acceptable chemical and biological controls have been found for some pests, similar controls are not available to combat other pests including some of the most serious. Sufficient information now exists to identify the objectives and to specify the procedures to be used in breeding resistant varieties, but progress towards developing such varieties will depend to a considerable extent upon the demand for them and the resources available for research. The time required to develop and test new varieties may be no more than a few years or as long as several decades. Although the latter may appear to be too long a time to be justifiable, it is actually a relatively short time in the life of a major afforestation program.

All newly developed resistant varieties should be tested empirically before being used on a large scale. To be acceptable resistant strains should be free from the damaging agent for at least two or three short rotations. One should avoid varieties that are resistant to one pest and susceptible to another in the same area. Finally the resistant strain should be capable of producing products of acceptable quality and in economic amounts.

The canopy of the stand should be opened by thinning to promote better seed production. Experiments have shown that seed production in certain species can be significantly increased by fertilizing the trees. Consequently it may be advisable to fertilize selected seed trees using ammonium phosphate, ammonium nitrate, superphosphate, or other fertilizers. The seed orchard should be cared for in much the same way as a fruit orchard, including regular cultivation and irrigation when necessary.

Plus or elite trees or stands and seed orchards should be protected and carefully tended. Dead or dying trees and trees with poor form should be removed from elite stands. These stands must be preserved for the production and collection of seed; no other use can be permitted. Collecting must be done carefully, with the minimum damage to the tree; cutting branches for collections of fruits or cones should be avoided.

Seed and cone insects may be so destructive that they prevent the trees from attaining high seed production. The principal method for controlling these insects is by use of insecticides approved for horticulture. It may be necessary to spray the trees one or more times each year depending on the species of insect and the size of the actual or anticipated invasion. Proper sanitary practices are also extremely important; branches, cones, fruit, and large seeds (such as acorns) if left on the ground may harbor broods of insects which will emerge and infest the new seed crop. This material as well as egg masses should be removed and destroyed. Fortunately, due to the dryness of the arid zones there is little risk of damage to seeds by fungi.

Provenance

Collecting seed for afforestation from trees having the desired gentic characteristics is only part of the task. Usually the seed trees should grow in an environment which is similar, as nearly as possible, to that of the area in which the seedlings are to be planted. Obviously, exact matching of environments in arid-zone afforestation will be difficult, if not impossible, but one should strive for as close a correspondence as feasible. Small-tract adaptability trials covering a wide range of species and parent-tree environments should be a continuing part of the planting program. These trials should include several provenances preferably representing the environmental extremes within the range of the species. Seed trees should also be selected in the country or area where a species has been introduced as an exotic since the response to the new environment may be quite remarkable.

The locality in which there is a population of trees of a given species, possessing distinct genetic characteristics and evolved under the local environment, or the site or origin of the seed from trees with such characteristics, is known as "provenance" (or "provenience").

Provenance does not refer to the country of origin with its present political boundaries, or even to an administrative or geographical district within a country. Use of the term in a regional sense is also improper. Provenance refers to an area, small or large, in which a tree, or more commonly a group of trees of a certain species, possesses distinct characteristics that have evolved as a result of the environment of that area. These characteristics are so distinct that the trees can be classed as an ecotype, or race, within the species. To aid in the choice of such ecotypes or races for introduction into new regions some general, simple environmental comparisons of the tree's native habitat with the proposed habitat are most helpful. These comparisons should include such critical factors as: minimum temperature, annual precipitation and its seasonal distribution, and edaphic conditions.

Prior to about 1940, when large-scale afforestation was carried out in most countries, the only considerations for collecting forest tree seed were the species and the ease of collection. Locality of collection or origin of the seed were rarely thought to be important. Yet as early as 1864 De Vilmorin stated that "by using one or another race of pine one could create on the same soil a forest of little or of great value." It is only since 1940 that the importance of using seed of a desired provenance has become evident and that the practice of selecting exact provenances is being universally accepted.

In arid or semiarid zones, provenance is of utmost importance. Besides the improved technical characteristics, such as straightness of the bole, that are expected in trees grown from the seed of a given provenance, the success or failure of a whole plantation will depend on the provenance's ability to withstand drought. In areas where moisture is the limiting factor of tree distribution, even a small deficit of precipitation may rule out the use of certain provenances of a species.

Maritime pine (*Pinus pinaster* Ait.), for example, has a wide natural distribution. Its natural range stretches from Morocco and Portugal in the west to the south of Italy in the east. In Spain alone, it grows on a great variety of soils from sea level to 1,500 m (4,900 ft) above. It is found in regions with from less than 400 mm to over 1,500 mm (16–60 in) of annual precipitation and in areas where temperatures of −10° C to over 40° C (14°–104° F) have been registered. Such a wide range of habitat indicates its great ecological adaptability. It is not surprising, therefore, that over forty races of maritime pine have been distinguished in Spain, each growing in a small localized ecologic area. Depending on localities compared, the trees vary from tall to short, from straight to crooked, from fast to slow growth, from a few small branches to many large ones, and with great variation in the wood texture.

Disregarding the races of maritime pine that grow in the temperate humid Atlantic climate or in the continental sub-humid climate of the northwest of Spain, and examining some of the various races that grow in the center and the southeast of the peninsula where the climate is "Mediterranean," arid, or semiarid with three to five "dry" months a year, we find the following races:

1. The races of the plains of Castile, "Olmedo," "Coca," and "Almazan" (Fig. 2–1, graph 1 and Fig. 2–2, A), are drought-resistant

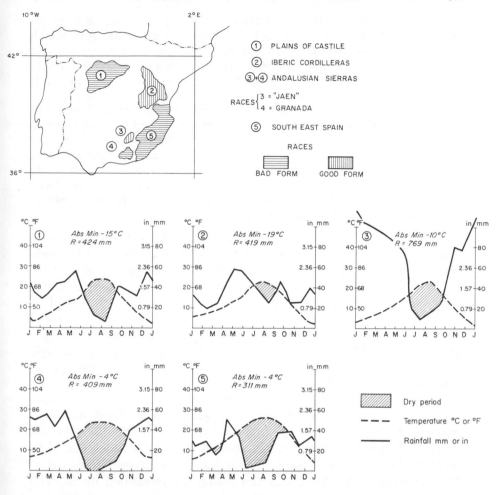

Fig. 2—1. Pluviothermic diagrams of areas of different provenance of *Pinus pinaster* Ait. in Spain.

races that grow on poor sandy soils. The production of resin is high (from 3 to 5 kg [6.6–11 lbs] per tree per year). The trunks are stunted and twisted. These races are not recommended for timber-producing plantations.

2. The races of the Iberic Cordilleras, "Teruel" and "Cuenca" (Fig. 2–1, graph 2; and Fig. 2–2, B), grow mainly on Triassic red sands. They are trees with good form, trunks straight and slender, crown small. Increment is rapid, though not as rapid as that of the Atlantic races. These are the best races for timber production in the "Mediterranean" regions.

3. Of the races of the Andalusian Sierras, "Jaen" (Fig. 2–1, graph 3; Fig. 2–2, C, and Fig. 2–2, D) grows on dolomitic soils which are usually occupied by garigue vegetation. The trees have straight trunks; the increment is slower than that of the Iberic Cordilleras race, yet satisfactory. The race "Granada" (Fig. 2–1, graph 4; and Fig. 2–2, E), however, which is geographically a neighbor and grows under similar climatic conditions, has a bad form and slow increment; it is not recommended for afforestation.

4. The races of southeast Spain in the provinces of Castellon, Valencia, and Murcia (Fig. 2–1, graph 5) are very drought resistant, and resemble some of the races of Corsica. They grow on sandy or calcareous dolomitic soils. The trees are of very poor form. They are planted in areas of low rainfall. No economic returns are expected from such plantations.

From the pluviothermic graphs representing the different regions in which the above races grow, it is clear that, even if the climatic conditions appear to be similar, the races that have developed in them have different shapes and uses. This shows the necessity for a serious examination of the origin of the seed selected for afforestation. It should be possible to find within this species a type that will grow in many semiarid afforestation projects. Consequently, when ordering seed of maritime pine from Spain, it is not sufficient merely to specify the phenotypic characteristic desired; the provenance of the seed and its ecological requirements must also be specified.

Efforts should be made to obtain seed from trees of native stock growing as close as possible to the proposed planting site. Seed should be collected within a distance of from 100 to 200 km (62–124 mi) and within 500 meters (1,600 ft) in elevation of the area in which it is to be planted. Preferably, seed used in arid zones should come from parent trees growing in the driest localities within the prescribed limits. This holds true for native or for exotic species.

Eighty-five seed collection zones have been established in California, U.S.A. based on physiographic and climatic regions. Zones are limited to about 80 km (50 mi) in latitude and up to 300 m (1,000 ft) in altitude. Where possible boundaries of the zones follow natural features, such as crests of mountain ranges, ridge tops, and rivers. Zones are numbered so that seed collection information may be handled by electronic data processing. Seedlings of *Pinus ponderosa* Laws. grown from seed collected in five different seed zones differed noticeably in size. Seeds from zones in the higher altitudes produced smaller seedlings than did seed from the lower zones.

There may, of course, be unobserved or unpredicted conditions of environment in the locality of the new plantation. These may lead to grave errors in the choice of provenance. Poor yield or even complete

Fig. 2–2A. A natural stand of *Pinus pinaster* Ait. of the race "Olmedo" growing in Vallandolis, Spain. (Photo R. Cayuela; courtesy Jesús Tornero)

Fig. 2–2B. A natural stand of *Pinus pinaster* Ait. of the race "Cuenca" growing near Cañeto, Spain. (Photo R. Cayuela; courtesy Jesús Tornero)

Fig. 2–2C. A natural stand of *Pinus pinaster* Ait. of the race "Jaen" growing in the Andalusian Sierras. (Photo R. Cayuela; courtesy Jesús Tornero)

Fig. 2–2D. A four-year-old plantation of the race "Jaen" of *Pinus pinaster* Ait. El Santo y Cañada Bellosa, Spain. (Photo Ortego; courtesy Jesús Tornero)

Fig. 2–2E. A natural stand of *Pinus pinaster* Ait. of the race "Granada." Due to its bad form it is not recommended for afforestation. (Photo R. Cayuela; courtesy Jesús Tornero)

failure of a plantation has occurred because the wrong race was used. Moreover, some races react to the new environment differently from what is expected. A few may develop better than in their original habitat; others may produce poorer trees and decline.

Mistakes in the choice of seed of a given provenance can be averted, or at least minimized, by planting small trial plots in the new localities before embarking on a large-scale plantation. Clearly, with species that have wide natural or artificial distribution, such as *Pinus halepensis* Mill., *P. nigra* Arnold, *P. radiata* D. Don, and *Eucalyptus camaldulensis* Dehnh., one must consider many ecotypes. From these, the races most likely to succeed should be selected and tested in sample plots.

COLLECTING SEED

High quality seed is necessary to start a successful afforestation program. The seed should come from healthy parent trees which have the desired characteristics and which are growing in the proper ecological environments. Furthermore, the parent trees should not be growing in the vicinity of trees of the same species that possess undesirable characteristics because pollen from these trees may fertilize the flowers of the parent trees and thus adversely affect the seed. Seed collected from single isolated trees may not produce good progeny even though the parent tree may be of good growth and form. For economic reasons, only seed of the species that are likely to be used and in the quantities required for use, sale, and storage for future use should be collected. The amount to be placed in storage will be determined by the expected longevity of the seed under the proposed storage method.

Age of Parent Trees

The parent trees selected for production of the seed should be of the optimum age for producing sound seed. This age varies with species and site. Although some hardwoods occasionally produce viable seed in their fourth year (e.g., acacia) and some pines in their fifth, many of these seeds are not viable. The pines usually produce seed with a higher germination percentage after their eighth or ninth year.

Some species produce sound seed until the overmature parent trees eventually succumb to time and the elements, whereas others produce only a few seeds in old age, and they are generally poor and of low viability.

Season of Seed Maturity

In a new site, exotic species may produce more or less seed than they normally do in their native habitat. The month of seed maturity in the new site may also differ markedly if a great latitudinal change has been made. Trees from the Southern Hemisphere transplanted to the Northern will flower and produce fruit in accordance with local seasons and not in the same calendar month as in their native home. *Eucalyptus camaldulensis* Dehnh. flowers in Australia between November and February, but when grown in the Middle East it flowers mainly in March and April and again in September and October. Changes in altitude, precipitation, length of day, and many other site factors will also have an effect on the month of seed maturity.

Some trees of a species produce seed in larger amounts and more regularly than others. Although flowering and fruiting of most species are restricted to definite seasons, a few have prolonged fruiting periods. Eucalypt seed may be gathered during almost the entire year, with peak ripening periods in the spring and autumn. White quebracho (*Aspidosperma quebracho-blanco* Schlecht.) has an extended fruiting and seeding period. Its seeds are usually collected between March and June. Pine and cypress seeds can be collected in the late summer before the cones open. One of the main difficulties encountered in seed collection is that all cones or fruits do not ripen at the same time. Maturation date of cones and fruits has been observed to vary not only from stand to stand but also among cones and fruits on the same tree. The degree of cone or fruit maturity is very important because as they mature seed viability and vigor increases, usually reaching a maximum just before the cones or fruit release their seed or drop to the ground. Seeds of most broad-leaved trees mature in the autumn or beginning of winter. Seeds of soft maples, *Populus, Salix,* and *Ulmus* (except *U. parvifolia* Jacq.) mature in the spring or early summer. The seeds of white broom (*Genista raetam* Forsk.) and acacia ripen in summer. The period of ripening varies somewhat from year to year according to the weather and the locality.

Identification of Parent Trees

Before seeds are harvested, the parent trees must be correctly identified. In some places, identification is easy, but where species of certain genera that do not differ much in appearance grow together, such as many pines, eucalypts, and acacias, errors of identification are likely to be made unless great care is taken. If incorrectly labelled seed is sown, the error may not be detected until many years later, or the reason for early failure of a plantation may never be known.

It is, therefore, absolutely necessary to have trained crews to identify the seed bearers, and to avoid blunders, especially in closely related species; it is also advisable to form a reference collection of fruits, cones, and seeds (Fig. 2–3). The collection may be kept in small glass vials or bottles, and these should also contain a few leaves or needles and, if possible, flowers and bark of the species. Often the services of a trained forest botanist are needed to identify the species. A detailed record should be kept of the exact locality of collection, and, if possible, each parent tree should be permanently tagged.

Statement of Origin

Every seed lot which is sent out by a station or by an individual should be accompanied by a statement showing the species, variety, and race of the parent tree or trees; date of collection, and the provenance including climatic conditions, altitude, and soil conditions. The statement should also indicate whether the seed came from normal, plus, or elite trees. Such statements are needed in addition to health certificates.

Harvest Forecast

After it has been decided what seed to collect and the amount required in a given year for seeding or storing, an estimate of the potential crop should be made. A month or two before harvest, cones or fruits are counted on a number of sample trees. To gain the most information

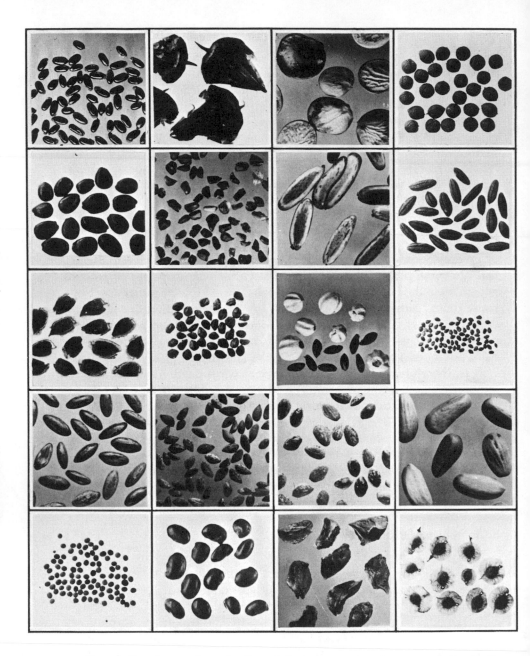

Fig. 2–3. Types of seed. From left, top row: *Acacia cyanophylla* Lindl., *Araucaria heterophylla* (Salisb.) Franco, *Bauhinia purpurea* L., *Celtis occidentalis* L., second row: *Ceratonia siliqua* L., *Cupressus* spp., *Delonix regia* (Bojer) Raf., *Elaeagnus angustifolia* L., third row: *Grevillea robusta* A. Cunn., *Juniperus scopulorum* Sarg., *Melia azedarach* L. (pits and seeds), *Morus alba* L.; fourth row: *Parkinsonia aculeata* L., *Pinus halepensis* Mill., *Pinus pinaster* Ait., *Pinus pinea* L.; bottom row: *Rhus* spp., *Sophora japonica* L., *Taxodium distichum* (L.) Rich., *Ulmus pumila* L. (*Araucaria* and *Ulmus* 35% actual size; others 70%.)

from the estimate, one should sample the crop in several locations within a seed collection zone. The results are applied to the seed bearers, and the trees from which seed is to be collected are marked. The harvester should collect seed from marked trees only. In years of bumper crops, more seed is collected than is required for sowing during the next seeding period; excess should be stored for use in poor years.

Seed Years

Many species produce good seed crops only at intervals of two, three, four, five, or more years. A year in which the seed production is abundant for a particular species in a particular locality is known as a "seed year." A "seed year" for one species in a given locality may be a poor year for other species in the same locality. Furthermore, a "seed year" is rarely a regional occurrence for a species but is usually limited to a few localities within the region.

Many species do not bear a full seed crop every year. It is, therefore, necessary to harvest and process a supply of seed for the two, three, or more years in which the crop is scanty. All arrangements for collection, transport, extraction, and storing of the seed of a good seed year must, accordingly, be adequate, and operations should follow a certain sequence to facilitate the work. Not only is it more economical to collect during a seed year, but the seeds will be of higher quality and retain their viability in storage longer than seeds produced in off years.

Ripeness of Seed

Seed of most species should be harvested when the fruit or cones reach maturity and before dispersal. Except for the few species whose seeds have immature embryos, viability is maximum at maturity of the fruit or cones and diminishes thereafter. Seedlings produced by fresh, fully mature seeds have the highest vigor. Although immature seeds of some species may germinate, the seedlings are usually weak or abnormal and therefore worthless for use in field planting.

The degree of ripeness of seeds or cones can often be judged by the color. Pine and cypress cones, as well as acorns, lose their green color and change to a gray-brown when ripe. However, cones and fruits of other species often mature on the trees without an appreciable change in color, and insect infested cones or fruit may change from green to the mature color without actually ripening. One-year-old unripe fruit of cypress is reddish violet. The fruit of the strawberry tree (*Arbutus andrachne* L.) turns from yellow to reddish violet when ripe. Fleshy and pulpy fruit, such as that of hawthorn (*Crataegus* spp.), commonly loses its hardness and becomes soft at maturity.

One of the best ways to determine whether a seed or fruit is ripe is to cut a few seeds or cones in cross-section with a sharp knife. By experience, one can usually appraise the texture or hardness of the embryo and endosperm. These should not be milky and the seed coat should not collapse but snap apart when cut.

Seed ripeness is also judged by the specific gravity of the fruit, which decreases as maturity approaches. Several liquids, depending on the species to be tested, may be selected in which ripe cones or fruit will barely float. Liquids commonly employed are SAE 30 motor oil, linseed oil, and kerosene (paraffin oil). Seeds and cones on all trees within a stand do not mature at quite the same time, but when tests show that nearly all seeds from a few sample trees in the stand are mature, collection of seeds from the stand may begin.

Harvesting Seed

Seeds or fruit of some species mature and fall to the ground under the tree on which they grow, e.g., nuts, acorns, and fleshy fruits such as those of the strawberry tree and the hawthorns. Other seeds or fruits either remain attached to the tree or are dispersed by the wind or eaten by birds or animals soon after maturity. Frequently, the time between seed maturity and dispersal is extremely short. In fact, seeds of white oaks (e.g., *Quercus macrocarpa* Michx.) often germinate on the tree and must be harvested carefully to prevent damage; they should be planted or placed in moist cold storage immediately.

Heavy seeds and fruits that drop to the ground under the parent tree must be picked up as soon as possible to avoid loss from, or damage by, fungi, rodents, or insects. A cloth or plastic sheet should be spread on the ground under the tree before the fruits or cones mature. If this is not possible, the ground should be cleaned of leaves, branches, and undergrowth to make collecting easy and to minimize impurities in the seed collected.

Most seeds for afforestation are collected from standing trees. Dissemination in most species occurs soon after maturity, and the harvest must be well-organized to avoid loss of the crop. In arid zones, and especially in hot arid zones, the cones and fruit mature quickly and often open up, releasing their seeds in a matter of a few days or even hours. Many workers are required for this operation during a relatively short period; for some species it may be only a day or two, in others a week or two. Cones or fruits of some species mature and remain attached to the branches of the tree for months or even years. It is advisable, however, to collect such seeds as soon after maturity as possible. If they are left too long on the tree, they are likely to be eaten by rodents or birds, or they may be infested by insects.

If the trees and their branches are low, fruits remaining attached to the branches can be picked manually by collectors standing on the ground. For medium-sized trees, sticks are often used for beating the branches to shake down the seed or dislodge the fruit. Poles with shears, saws, or hooks of various designs attached at one end are commonly employed for detaching tips of fruit or cone-bearing branches (Fig. 2–4). Poles vary in length and weight. Light rigid bamboo, aluminum, or plastic poles 4–6 meters (13–20 ft) long are favored. Using such poles the seed harvester, standing on the ground, can bring down fruit or cones from branches 7–8 meters (23–26 ft) overhead.

Trees that are too tall for the seed to be harvested by using poles must be climbed. Trained men may climb certain tall trees without equipment, but not all trees can be easily or safely worked that way. Thus, there is a tendency to skip the difficult ones, although they may have been marked as good seed bearers.

It is always dangerous to climb tall trees and reach out for the side branches without the aid of equipment, but with suitable equipment— ladders, climbing irons, and safety belts—even tall trees can be mounted without excessive risk. Ladders should be light and made up of short sections that can be fitted securely together, and chained to the trunk of the tree. Seed harvesters wearing safety belts and climbing irons, like those of telephone linemen, can usually climb tall trees of narrow

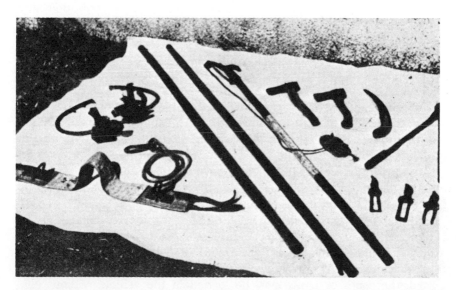

Fig. 2–4. Equipment for seed collection: climbing irons and security belt, shears with long handles, axes, pruning saws, and different types of pruning shears. Scale 1:25. (Courtesy FAO)

diameter. Scaffolding set on the ground or mounted on a truck is often used and on flat ground, mainly in seed orchards, special truck-mounted ladders or hydraulic lifts may be employed. Mechanical tree shakers are occasionally used to shake cones or fruit from trees, but their high cost and the difficulty of moving the equipment about the forest restricts their use. In addition, there is the danger that too vigorous action of the machine will break the stem and branches of the tree.

Collecting seed from tall trees is difficult and expensive as a rule, but to ensure that the seed comes from superior trees, the additional difficulty and expense are fully justified. Repeated trials have shown that the progeny of selected, quick-growing trees give the most valuable crop. Seed from small, low-branching, and crooked trees should never be accepted, even though it is easier and cheaper to collect. Defects in trees grown from seed from genetically inferior parents will be revealed only many years after planting. Bole form is not the only characteristic to consider; for some uses, it is of little concern. In species, such as the acacias, planted for soil conservation, sand-dune fixation, or fuel, it is only necessary for the seed bearer to have strong and sturdy growth.

TRANSPORT OF SEED

Fruits or seeds when harvested are put into buckets or into sacks hanging from the harvesters' shoulders, or dropped onto tarpaulins on the ground. Then, as soon as is convenient, they are emptied into bags, usually of paper, burlap, or cloth like those used for cement or sand, and are transported to the depot. The capsules of eucalypts and the cones of pines should be placed in tight cloth sacks or other receptacles as soon as harvested, because they may open during transport and the seed be lost.

For easy handling in transport, it is advisable to put only from 10 to 20 kg (22–44 lbs) of fruits, seeds, or cones in each sack. Sacks containing seed should be labelled to show the collection number, the name of the species, the locality, and the date of collection. Complete and detailed information should be recorded in a notebook under the collection number. A duplicate label should be placed inside the sack to assure positive identification if the outside label is lost.

The sacks are transported to the storage site on pack animals or by vehicle. If the distance is considerable, the sacks should be carefully arranged in the vehicle to ensure air circulation among them. If the distance is short, and if only one species and provenance are to be transported, the cones or fruits may be loaded in the vehicle without containers. The vehicle must be cleaned of all seed carried on previous trips before a new lot is loaded. Tarpaulins spread on the floor of the vehicle will permit recovery of any seeds released during the trip.

EXTRACTION OF SEED

The seed processing and storage depot should be centrally located, and all its facilities for extraction, cleaning, drying, and storing should be concentrated to permit proper supervision. If large quantities of seed are collected, provisional extraction and storage places may be installed in the field near the collection site. There, most of the chaff can be removed, and the fruits or seeds dried and temporarily stored in huts before being taken to the permanent store.

When consignments of fruits, cones, or seeds arrive at the storage depot, they must be sorted and distributed to the places where they will be treated.

Seed brought to the storage area must be extracted and cleaned. This entails separation of the seed from all or some parts of the fruits, leaves, branches, cones, pods, capsules, soil, pebbles, and other impurities brought in with it without reducing its viability. Extraction in the broad sense includes drying of fruit, separation of seed from the fruit, dewinging, de-pulping, and cleaning.

Extraction techniques vary greatly according to species. Some are as simple as picking up the desired seed by hand and leaving the impurities on the floor—a method suitable for large seed. Conversely, the impurities may be picked out by hand, leaving the seeds in the receptacle—a technique often used to extract small seed mixed with few impurities. Simple, uncomplicated apparatus, such as sieves, flotation tanks, and winnowing machines, are commonly used.

Air Drying

Nearly all newly harvested seed must be dried before it is sown or stored. Fruits and cones have a variable moisture content when ripe. Moisture content of most pine cones varies between 35 and 65 per cent. In nature, fruits dry by exposure to the wind and the heat of the sun. The rate of drying depends on the climatic conditions. If left too long on the tree, the cones of some pines and cypresses will open, and the seeds will be lost. Cones of these species must be collected just before ripening, quickly transported to the storage depot, and spread out to dry.

Cones, fleshy fruits, and seeds with high moisture content should not be left in the containers more than 24 hours. Most should pass quickly to the drying floors or screens allotted to them. Drying floors are usually hard platforms that are smooth, tight, and cleaned of all impurities. At times, tarpaulins are spread on the ground for drying cones. At some processing plants, brick platforms are built for this purpose because they are cheap to construct and maintain. The platform may be divided into compartments to allow different seed lots to be dried simultaneously.

The size of the compartment may be standardized. Cones are then placed on standard racks of wire screen with a mesh size that allows the seed to drop through onto a canvas or tray. A standard cover of wire netting or glass can be used to protect the seed from birds or to raise the temperature and hasten the drying process (Figs. 2–5, 2–6). Care must be taken to protect cones under glass from overheating.

Non-pulpy fruits or seeds of broad-leaved species are spread on the drying floor in layers of not more than 2–5 cm (0.8–2 in). The depth of cones should not exceed 10–15 cm (4–6 in), and they must be stirred frequently until they open. As they open, they should be collected periodically from the top layer and tumbled to shake out any seed left in them.

Cones of pines (e.g., *P. halepensis* Mill., *P. brutia* Ten., *P. pinaster* Ait.) collected in the rainless season may be exposed to the sun and wind until they open. This may take from three to ten days, depending on the drying conditions. Once open, they release their seeds when shaken or stirred. When cones or seeds are dried in the open, tarpaulins or plastic sheets should be available to shield them from rains.

Acorns should be dried only superficially if collected in rainy weather; at other times, they need not be dried and should be stored in dry sand or by moist stratification.

Seeds of only a few species are dry enough to be stored or sown soon after harvesting. The hardcoated seeds, such as those of acacia, carob, and white broom, if ripe when collected, can be stored as soon as they are extracted from the pods or husks.

It is better to extract seeds from fleshy or pulpy fruits as soon as possible, rather than to dry them. Not only is it easier to remove the seeds from fleshy fruit, but seeds covered with pulp will be damaged if the pulp ferments. But where fleshy fruits, such as those of *Crataegus* spp. or *Arbutus andrachne* L., must be dried, they should be spread in thin layers on the drying floors. Free air circulation about them is necessary; otherwise they will become moldy and ferment. The length of time required for the pulpy cover of the seed to dry depends on the species, the degree of moisture in the pulp, and the climatic conditions. When the fruits are sufficiently dry, they can be stored pending extraction of the seeds.

Seeds are extracted from fleshy or pulpy fruit by maceration. The fruits are placed in water in a warm place to soften the pulp, which is then broken down by vigorous stirring or by rubbing against wire screening. Hydrochloric acid will aid in softening pulp. Sodium hydroxide helps cut resin when juniper "berries" are being treated. The seeds of most species will sink, and the floating pulp can be skimmed from the surface without difficulty. The seeds should be washed with

Fig. 2–5. Cone-drying rack with wire mesh bottom. Note seed drawers. (Courtesy FAO)

Fig. 2–6. Concrete platform for drying seed. Note wire netting and glass frames of standard size. Left, cones of *Pinus halepensis* Mill.; right, pods of *Prosopis juliflora* (Swartz) DC. (Courtesy FAO)

fresh water after the flesh has been removed and, if they are to be stored, must be thoroughly dried after separation from the pulp.

Kiln Drying

In more humid areas, and for refractory species, artificially heated and ventilated kilns are used to dry cones and, though rarely, the fruits of a few angiosperms. Kiln drying is especially advantageous where large quantities of seeds are required. Kilns may be of different forms and sizes, but all are based on the same principle: hot air is circulated between racks in a room or cabinet in which cones or seeds are spread. Heating must be even, because fluctuation in temperature may cause "casehardening" of moist cones. Casehardened cones dry only on their surface and will not open. The air in the kiln should be relatively cool, usually not above 40°–60° C (104°–140° F), to assure uniform drying. The wet-bulb temperature must never exceed 50° C (122° F); if it exceeds 50° C for more than 30 minutes, most or all of the seeds will be killed. The moving air must, of course, be drier than the fruit, and the moisture-laden air must be quickly withdrawn from the kiln.

Cones should always be precured and air dried before being kiln dried. Not all cones and seeds are fully ripe when harvested. Pre-curing ensures complete ripening of all seeds; it may take from two to six weeks, depending on the species. Preliminary air drying reduces casehardening and prevents damage to seeds by high temperature. Furthermore, it reduces the amount of fuel required in kiln drying and so saves expense.

Separation

In the processing of many genera there is no actual removal of the true seed from the fruit, for example, in *Acer, Betula, Fraxinus, Platanus, Quercus,* and *Ulmus.* The whole fruit of species of these genera is universally accepted and planted as the seed, and extraction procedures consist merely of removing bracts, cups, and other inert matter and, occasionally, of partial dewinging. In a few species of legumes, pieces of the pods containing one or two seeds may be planted because of the expense of complete extraction. Seeds of most legumes can, however, be separated from the pod by threshing in standard or modified agricultural machines.

Seeds may be effectively separated from cones or chaff by tumbling in a revolving drum of wire mesh (Fig. 2-7). The chaff or cones remain in the drum and the seeds pass through the mesh and are collected in trays.

Cedar (*Cedrus*) seeds should not be extracted from the cones before storage because they lose their viability quickly after extraction. When seeds are needed for sowing, the cones are opened by hand to extract them; unlike pine or cypress cones that open when dried, cedar cones harden after collection, and must be soaked in water to facilitate extraction. After treatment the cones can be easily broken apart.

Eucalyptus seeds are easily extracted by drying the capsules in the sun and by shaking or tumbling them to dislodge the seeds. Where the sun is hot and the capsules are green, the capsules may harden on the outside (casehardened) and the seed remain enclosed. Spreading the seed in a shed with hot-air circulation permits easy opening of the capsules.

Dewinging

It is advisable to dewing the winged seeds of pines, spruces, and some hardwood species before they are sown or stored. Small quantities can be rubbed lightly over a screen or between the hands; seeds in sacks can be lightly beaten with sticks. Machines (modified popcorn polishers) in which stiff brushes or rubber squeegees that rub the seeds against sponge or corrugated rubber are used in southeastern United States where large quantities of pine seed have to be dewinged (Fig. 2–8).

Cleaning

Seeds that have been separated from their wings, hair, or pulp should be cleaned of impurities. Passing the seed through a series of screens of different mesh, vibrated by hand or mechanically, not only separates it from impurities but also separates large from small seeds. Wings and

Fig. 2–7. Cleaning eucalypt seed with a revolving drum. (Courtesy FAO)

Fig. 2–8. Interior view of dewinging machine for pine seeds. Revolving brushes loosen the wings by rubbing the seeds over the ribbed rubber lining. (Courtesy Tennessee Valley Authority)

light impurities can be removed by winnowing or fanning. Complete cleaning is not always possible or even desirable. Seeds of many species should not be cleaned to a purity higher than a given percentage; beyond that, an increasing amount of good seed is separated out with the impurities. Besides, the added effort of extra cleaning is time-consuming and expensive.

When put into water, filled seeds of some species sink; light and empty seeds, wings, and twigs float on the surface. The sunken seeds are retrieved and dried. This is the process of separation by flotation. It is an effective way of separating filled from empty seed of many species of conifers and hardwoods which have 100,000 or fewer seeds per kg (45,000/lb).

For some species, special methods of extraction and separation are necessary. For example, balsa (*Ochroma* spp.) seeds are successfully cleared of their floss by placing the uncleaned mass on a wire sieve of 0.3 mm (0.012 in) mesh and setting fire to the floss. The fire flashes across and the seeds drop through the mesh. The process not only does not damage the seed but it apparently hastens germination and raises the germination percentage. Good results are obtained when the seeds are allowed to drop through the sieve into a pan of water below the screen. This method may also be used to clean cottonwood (*Populus* spp.) seed. However, damage to the seeds may exceed 50 per cent.

SEED QUALITY

The elements of seed quality which are of universal interest, and for which tests are usually made to determine value for sowing, are genuineness, purity, viability, and weight.

Sampling

Most quality tests are made by using small samples drawn from the entire lot of seed. The samples must be drawn in such a way that they will fairly represent the lot under test. Extremely large lots may be reduced to bulk samples by means of probes, sampling tubes, or sampling cups.

The bulk sample is subsequently reduced to the working sample by either successive halving by hand or by mechanical seed dividers. The mechanical divider separates the seeds into 16–36 different streams, half of which are retained for the working sample, or passed through the divider one or more times, until a suitable small amount remains as the working sample (Fig. 2–9).

Fig. 2–9. Electric seed-sample divider. (Courtesy National Seed Laboratory, Fort Collins, Colo.)

At least two samples must be used in each purity and germination test, so that the results can be analyzed, compared, and evaluated.

Genuineness

The species of the seeds can be determined in three basic ways:

1. Identification of parent tree and certification of seed lot.
2. Identification of seed by use of an analytic key and comparison of seed with seed display set.
3. Identification of seedling.

Each seed-testing laboratory should develop correctly labelled collections of seed and seedling herbariums, containing the full range of sizes, colors, and morphological differences that are known for each species.

Genuineness of variety, race, strain, and form must usually be determined by extended growing tests because they are characteristics that can seldom be determined by inspection of the seed or seedlings.

Purity

Purity is the percentage by weight of the clean, whole seed of the desired species (i.e., the "pure" seed) in a given lot. Purity of seeds is determined by inspection and by weighing the seeds and impurities carefully in samples from each lot. The working sample containing all the impurities is weighed to the nearest milligram and then the pure seed is removed and weighed separately. Pure seed of the species under consideration include:

1. Mature, undamaged seeds.
2. Immature, undersized, shrivelled, and germinated seeds, if they can be definitely identified as the subject species.
3. Pieces of seeds more than one-half their original size.
4. Seeds without damage to the testa, regardless of whether empty or full.
5. "Seeds" (botanically fruit, for example, those of *Betula* and *Ulmus*) regardless of whether they contain a true seed, unless it is readily apparent by unaided visual examination that they do not.
6. Diseased seeds.
7. Seed or fruit with attached wings of *Acer, Betula, Catalpa, Chamaecyparis, Cupressus, Fraxinus, Liquidambar, Liriodendron, Platanus, Thuja,* and *Ulmus.*

Impurities include:

1. Seed of species other than the one under consideration.
2. Pieces of broken or damaged seeds one-half the original size or less.
3. Seeds of Leguminosae and Coniferae with seed coats entirely removed.

4. Broken and detached wings.
5. Attached wings of *Cedrus, Picea, Tsuga,* and *Pinus.* Except for the pine species noted below, the entire wing should be removed as an impurity.
6. Attached wings of *Abies, Larix, Libocedrus, Pseudotsuga, Pinus echinata* Mill., *P. elliottii* Engelm., *P. palustris* Mill., *P. rigida* Mill., and *P. taeda* L. should be removed except for the part enclosing the seed that is difficult to remove in seed processing without damaging the seed.
7. Other matter such as: soil, sand, stones, stems, leaves, cone scales, pieces of bark, pieces of fruit, and all other matter not seeds.

Purity percentage is calculated as follows:

$$\text{Purity } \% = \frac{\text{Weight of ``pure'' seed}}{\text{Total weight of original sample}} \times 100.$$

The accepted allowance of impurities in forest-tree seeds varies from 10 to 40 percent according to species. In general, a higher purity percentage is expected in large-seeded species, such as oak and some conifers, than in the smaller seeds of eucalypts or casuarina. Homogeneity of purity and germination tests should be determined by standard statistical procedures, such as the chi-square test.

Number of Seeds Per Unit Weight

It is important to know the number of seeds per unit of weight in each lot to be stored because this number and the germination energy percentage can be used to calculate the approximate weight of seed required to produce a given number of seedlings. Seeds of the same species from different localities, or even from the same tree in different years, vary in size and weight. Therefore, the number of seeds per unit of weight of a given lot is also a good expression of the quality of the seeds because, obviously, large or full seeds are heavier than small or empty ones. Seedlings produced by the larger seeds in a new seed lot are larger and more vigorous than seedlings from the smaller seeds. Although the difference in germination percentage between large sound seeds and small sound seeds of the same species is usually not significant, exceptions do occur. For example, it has been observed that the large seeds of *Eucalyptus citriodora* Hook. germinate quicker and have a higher germination percentage than medium-sized seeds from the same seed lot, and the medium-sized seeds were better than the smaller seeds.

To determine the number of seeds per unit of weight, two or three random samples of, say, 100 gr are taken from the lot. The size of the sample will be governed by the size of the seed; for extremely small seeds such as eucalypts, 0.1 gram will suffice. The number and weight of whole seeds are then determined. Just as in the purity test, broken and foreign seeds are rejected and all others retained. The number of pure seeds per kilogram can be easily calculated as follows:

Number of pure seeds per kilogram =

$$\frac{\text{Number of "pure" seeds in sample} \times 1,000}{\text{Grams of "pure" seed in sample}}.$$

The approximate number of seeds per kilogram for several arid-zone species is given in Chapter 6 and Appendix B.

Germinability Tests

Every lot of seeds that has been dried and cleaned must be tested for germinability before being sent to its destination, whether that be direct sowing in the field, sowing in the nursery, or storage.

Cutting Test. Empty seeds in a consignment may be due to excessive drying, insect infestation, or lack of fertilization. The methods used to determine the percentage of empty seed in a given lot depend on the species. Cutting tests afford a quick means of determining the number of filled seeds. If one cuts the seed and inspects the embryo, the soundness of the seed can easily be established. The test is suitable for large seeds, such as acorns, as well as for small ones, such as *Platanus* spp. When small seeds are to be cut, they may be kept from slipping by placing them on the sticky side of drafting tape or similar pressure-sensitive tape.

Oil-Spot Test. If the seeds of pines and some legumes are crushed on glazed paper a translucent oil spot will be left. It is claimed by some that the oil spot will be large for fresh, viable seed and small for old, weak seed. This is based on the belief that food reserves, consisting of fats and oils, will be consumed as the seed ages, or that the fats will be converted to fatty acids in dead seeds. However, the results of the oil spot test are so variable that its value in indicating viable seeds is questionable.

Flotation Test. In some large-seeded species of conifers and in pistachios, the soundness of the seed may be judged by the number that will float in water. Nearly all empty seeds of *Pinus brutia* Ten., *P. pinea* L., and *Pistacia* spp. will float, whereas the filled ones sink. This method is not suitable for small seeds, because many filled small seeds may be buoyed up by tiny bubbles clinging to their coats.

Color. The color of some species is often a means of distinguishing empty from sound seed. Empty seeds frequently are lighter in color than filled ones. This is true in *Pinus halepensis* Mill., but in *P. sabiniana*

Dougl. and *P. pinea* L. the black outer cell layer of the seed coat is loosened and lost during processing. Color of the seed coat does not appear to be significant in germination of *Pinus ponderosa* Laws. Tests have shown no difference in viability among seeds with light-colored, mottled, or dark coats. Colors may be distinctly different, as in *Pistacia atlantica* Desf. where red seeds are empty, and dark green or blue ones are filled.

Transparency. Viewing the seeds of some species of *Ulmus* and *Betula* over a strong light source makes it possible to distinguish filled from empty seeds.

X-Rays. Seed analysts in some laboratories have successfully employed X-ray photography not only to distinguish filled from empty seeds but also to determine the extent of embryo development (Fig. 2–10).

Chemical Stains. A number of chemicals have been used with some success to distinguish living from dead seeds. The degree to which the embryo of the sample becomes stained after immersion for a short time in a solution of the chemicals indicates the viability and vigor of the seed lot. Because embryos are studied, these tests are a refinement and

Fig. 2–10. X-ray photography reveals various conditions of seed development in pine (a) normal, (b) empty, (c) partially filled, and (d) malformed embryo. (Photo R. W. Stark)

elaboration of the cutting test. The characteristic color reaction of a few of the more common chemical stains are: iodide-potassium-iodide stains living tissue blue (actually a starch test); indigo-carmine (½–1 part per thousand) stains dead tissue blue; sodium selenite stains live tissue red; and sodium tellurate stains live embryos black. The last two chemicals are highly poisonous and dangerous to handle.

The chemical most commonly used is tetrazolium chloride (TZC).[1]

Enzyme activity of the living embryo releases hydrogen, which changes TZC to formazan, producing a red stain. Seeds are prepared by first soaking them in cold water for 12 hours; they are then cut longitudinally to expose their embryo or germ. The part without the embryo, or with the smaller segment of it, is discarded. The embryo is then immersed in 1 per cent TZC at 20° C (68° F) and left for 24 hours in total darkness. At the end of the period, the seeds are examined under magnification. Deep staining indicates live seeds; pale or mottled staining indicates weak ones incapable of normal germination; and absence of staining indicates dead ones. Examination must be done rapidly, because formazan is broken down by light. TZC tests are not infallible and should supplement rather than replace actual germination tests.

Germination Tests. Often filled seeds that are apparently sound may not germinate because they are too old, have rudimentary embryos, or were not fertilized. To determine the germination percentage of a seed lot, representative random samples are taken and are tested by subjecting them to favorable germination conditions. The tests may be made in containers, such as pots or tins used in nurseries, or in a simple covered dish such as a Petri dish, which is ideal for testing a few samples or small seeds such as those of *Eucalyptus* and *Cupressus*. The seeds are spread on a water-holding substratum, usually blotting paper or cloth. Adequate, not excessive, moisture is achieved by using only enough water barely to moisten the substratum. Petri dishes are easy to keep sterile and are convenient when only a small number of samples are to be tested. They permit no more than minimum control of temperature, light, aeration, and moisture. These environmental factors can be adequately controlled in the more elaborate germinators, such as the Copenhagen and the Rodewald, in which a dozen or more samples can be tested simultaneously.

Although a variety of germination media are acceptable for tests, the one used must provide proper aeration and sufficient but not excessive moisture to each seed. It is important that the medium be sterile to prevent damage to the seeds by fungi and other biotic agents. The

[1] 2,3,5-triphenyltetrazolium chloride or 2,3-diphenyl-5-methyltetrazolium chloride.

International Rules for Seed Testing prescribe a temperature of 30° C (86° F) for 16 hours (day) and 20° C (68° F) for 8 hours (night) during tests of most tree species. The rules also prescribe exposure of the seeds to light during the tests of most species that they list which are used in arid zone planting.

Many laboratories prefer making the germination tests in sand or vermiculite in a box or flat placed in the greenhouse. This method usually lacks close environmental control, but it is better suited to testing large seeds with hypogeous germination (such as *Quercus* and *Juglans*) than the other germinators described.

Samples should be large enough to ensure that at least a few seeds germinate. For seeds known to have characteristically high germination, 25 or 50 seeds will be sufficient, but for those of difficult germination 200, 500, or 1,000 may be needed. Because it is tedious and takes a lot of time to count hundreds of samples by hand, most large seed-testing laboratories employ vacuum-box seed counters (Fig. 2–11).

Seeds of some species will not germinate unless their dormancy is overcome by special pretreatment. Most seed that is not dormant, or that has been properly pretreated to break dormancy, starts germinating 7 to 14 days after the beginning of the test when placed in a germinator under optimum conditions. The period of active germination is usually

Fig. 2–11. Vacuum seed counters simplify counting samples for germination tests. (Photo L. Bass; courtesy National Seed Laboratory, Fort Collins, Colo.)

less than 30 days. Seeds germinating after that period are unlikely to produce vigorous seedlings. For a genus with rapid germination, such as *Populus,* the test may be completed in 24 hours.

At regular intervals until the end of the active germination period, the number of seeds that have normal germination should be recorded. Albino (lacking chlorophyll) seedlings and those with abnormal growth should not be counted. Once a seed has germinated and been counted, it should be removed from the germinator to avoid any possible chance of its being counted twice.

Test Results and Calculations

The results of the germination tests can be expressed in several ways. The most common are germination percentage, germinative energy, and germination capacity.

Germination Percentage. The actual percentage of the total number in the sample that has germinated up to the termination of the test, whether this is a one-day or a one-year period, is termed germination percentage; it is useful in research and in testing agricultural seeds.

Germinative Energy. A more valuable statistic is the percentage of seeds that germinate within some specified period. This is known as the germinative energy. The period may be arbitrarily set at 1 week, 10 days, or 2 weeks, or it may terminate when the highest mean daily germination is reached. Germinative energy is expressed as 90 per cent in 7 days, 31 per cent in 14 days, and so on. Germinative energy includes only the most vigorous seedlings, i.e., those most likely to develop into useful trees.

When the germination test is finished, a final cutting test should be made to determine the condition of the ungerminated seeds. Often, several sound seeds are found that have not germinated. In the legumes, such seeds are called "hard seeds." A large number of ungerminated, sound seeds may indicate that the test period was too short or that embryo dormancy was not broken. Some seeds may be found that are empty or "blind." In studies of pregermination treatments, the empty seeds should be subtracted from the sample size before calculating percentages. A few seeds may be covered with fungus or may be rancid. This condition commonly indicates that the seeds were dead when the test started; they may have been too old, improperly handled, or killed by too severe a pregermination treatment. The percentage of sound, empty, and decayed seeds should be recorded for each sample.

Germination Capacity. Germination capacity can now be calculated. It is the percentage that germinated plus the percentage of sound seeds remaining. This statistic is of limited value because, almost invariably, it is considerably higher than the actual tree percentage. It may also be calculated directly from the cutting test, without actually germinating the seeds. In that case, germination capacity will obviously be the same, whether the filled seeds are alive or dead.

The results of the germination tests are used to calculate the quantity of seed that must be sown in the field or the nursery to obtain a given number of seedlings. It must be remembered, however, that in the nursery, and especially in direct sowing in the field, the number of surviving seedlings is likely to be much smaller than indicated by the tests because of seedling losses caused by unfavorable climate, rodents, birds, insects, and disease, particularly damping-off. In anitcipation of these losses, nurserymen usually sow more seed than germination tests indicate will be required to get the necessary number of seedlings. In each nursery, in each region, and for each species, the requisite excess quantity of seed is established by practice based on past losses.

Seed testing is not a matter for the research station alone. Before seeding or storing the seed, every seed store should make its own tests. Only a little basic equipment is required to conduct such tests.

Weight of Seed Required.   The weight of a particular seed lot required to produce a given number of seedlings depends on its effective germination, which, in turn, is based on its utilization value.

The utilization value is calculated from the percentages of purity and germinative energy as follows:

$$\text{Utilization value} = \frac{\text{Purity \% } \times \text{ germinative energy \%}}{100}.$$

Utilization value multiplied by the average number of "pure" seeds per kilogram (or pound) of the seed lot equals its *effective germination* per kilogram (or pound).

The number of seedlings required, divided by the effective germination, equals the number of kilograms of the seed lot that must be planted to produce the desired number of seedlings.

Sample Calculations.

Purity: If there are 100 gm of impurities in 1 kg, the purity is 90 per cent.

Germinative Energy: If 80 out of 100 seeds germinate within the prescribed period, germinative energy is 80 per cent.

Utilization Value = (90 per cent × 80 per cent) ÷ 100
    = 72 per cent.

Effective Germination: If there are 5,000 seeds per kilogram of "pure" seed in the seed lot, each kilogram should produce 5,000 × 72 per cent, or 3,600 useful seedlings.

Weight of Seed Required: If 1,000,000 seedlings are needed, 1,000,000 ÷ 3,600 = 278 kg.

Actually, in nursery practice and direct seeding, this amount would be doubled or tripled to compensate for seedling losses during the first few years.

DORMANCY AND PRETREATMENT

Seeds of most tree species germinate readily when subjected to favorable conditions of moisture and temperature. However, even if conditions for germination are apparently ideal, viable seeds of some species cannot be induced to germinate until they undergo some physical or physiological change. Such seeds are said to be dormant.

Normally dormancy persists for less than six months and usually presents no problem in artificial reproduction, although lack of dormancy may necessitate special procedures. For example, since white oak seeds germinate immediately upon maturity, they cannot be easily stored and should be sown as soon as collected. In some species, including many used in arid-zone afforestation, dormancy persists for many months or even for years. In nature, overcoming prolonged dormancy may span several years with only a small percentage of the seeds germinating in any one year. Because it is highly desirable in artificial regeneration to have germination occur quickly and uniformly, seed pretreatments are required for these species. Dormancy in seeds of most refractory species can be broken by the proper chemical or physical pretreatments.

Six distinct types of dormancy may be recognized:

1. Embryo dormancy.
2. Seed-coat dormancy.
3. Induced or secondary dormancy.
4. Immature embryo.
5. Mechanical resistance of the seed coat.
6. Double dormancy combining two or more of the other types.

Dormancy of the seeds, which probably evolved millions of years ago, allows a species to survive temporarily unfavorable environmental conditions. By the timing of the natural processes whereby dormancy is broken, germination of some, if not all, seeds occurs during a period when growing conditions generally are favorable. For example, seeds of some species will not germinate unless subjected to temperatures below freezing, and others will not survive unless germination occurs early in the rainy season. Seeds of the latter species are unaffected by brief showers or by minor changes in the weather that precede the rainy season. Should germination occur, the seedlings would be killed by the subsequent drought. These seeds must pass through the distinct change in the weather that precedes the advent of the rainy season before they will germinate.

Through different methods of pretreatment dormancy may be broken, the time required for germination shortened significantly, and the number of useful seedlings increased. From a practical standpoint germination of pretreated seed leads to more uniformity in the seedbeds, making it easier to handle the seedlings. The pretreatment of seeds should be so timed that the seed will germinate at a time which is climatically the most favorable.

Embryo Dormancy

Embryo dormancy is said to exist when the germination of fully developed seeds appears to be blocked by internal factors. This type of dormancy is found in the seeds of several tree species, and its cause is only partially understood. In some species, embryo dormancy is apparently due to growth-inhibiting chemicals in some part of the seed—not necessarily in the embryo or germule itself. A large number of growth-inhibiting chemicals are known to occur in seeds of many species. A few of the more common of these chemicals are coumarin, phthalides, phenols, caffeine, and cocaine. In nature these substances are removed or neutralized by a process known as "after-ripening." After-ripening may require only a few days or weeks, but in some species it may take more than a year.

The artificial conditions used to promote after-ripening are usually simulations of the conditions thought to be required for the process in nature. Physiological changes that occur in the seeds during after-ripening depend chiefly on moisture and temperature. In some species after-ripening may be brought about by subjecting the dry seeds to low temperatures, often several degrees below freezing. In other species, after-ripening is promoted by cold stratification. Cold stratification is accomplished by placing the seeds between layers of moist sand, peat, vermiculite, or similar water-absorbent material and keeping them at a temperature just above freezing for 30 to 120 days. Cold stratification may be done in loosely constructed, shallow, wooden boxes, or in polyethylene bags that are placed in a coldroom, or in some countries, notably the USSR, in well-insulated outdoor pits. The exact temperature and length of time that the seed must be cold stratified to overcome dormancy have not been determined for many species. For species that have been studied, one or two months at 4° C (39° F) is usually sufficient.

If the seeds are tiny, they should be put in cloth sacks before stratification to prevent them from becoming mixed with the stratifying medium and lost. However, naked stratification offers a much more convenient method of treating small seeds. In this method the seeds are soaked in cold water for about 24 hours, then are allowed to dry until their seed coats are just barely dry. They are then sealed, without moisture-retaining material, in polyethylene bags. Each bag should, of course, be properly labelled. Lightly dusting the seeds with a commercial seed-protectant fungicide before sealing the bags is recommended. The sealed bags may be placed on trays and kept in the refrigerator or cold room for the required length of time.

Embryo dormancy in a few species may be overcome by applications of certain chemicals. For example, a 3 per cent solution of thiourea has been found to be quite effective in breaking dormancy in seeds of bitter-brush (*Purshia tridentata* (Pursh) DC). Ethylene chlorhydrin has been used successfully to break dormancy in some species of *Quercus*, and a 2 per cent solution of potassium nitrate has been found to stimulate germination of some eucalypts.

Seed dormancy of a number of species (e.g., those of *Prunus*) is broken when the seeds are eaten by animals and they pass intact through the digestive tract. However, simulating the digestive processes in the laboratory usually fails to break dormancy in these species. A pregnancy test described in an ancient Egyptian papyrus suggests that certain female hormones (estrogens) present in the digestive tract of both sexes may actually be responsible for breaking dormancy rather than the digestive process itself.

The wavelength of radiation received by some seeds after they have imbibed water also affects their ability to germinate. Imbibed seeds of Douglas-fir, some eucalypts (e.g., *E. camaldulensis* Dehnh.), and some pines (e.g., *P. nigra* Arnold) will germinate only if they are exposed to light, especially to the red region of the visible spectrum. Imbibed seeds of these species that are deeply buried or kept in darkness during and after imbibition, and thus receive only infrared radiation (including the so-called "far red"), will not germinate. This phenomenon should be carefully considered for each species before planting in the nursery or field. Deep sowing of dry seed of light-requiring species may result in poor germination or in complete failure.

Seed-Coat Dormancy

Seeds of many species do not germinate because they have thick, hard, bony, or wax-covered seed coats that completely prevent the entrance of water and exchange of gases. Such seeds are said to have seed-coat dormancy. Seed-coat dormancy is found in *Juniperus, Ilex, Taxus* and in most legumes including *Acacia, Ceratonia, Cercis, Gleditsia, Gymnocladus,* and *Robinia*. There is at least one advantage in handling hard-coated seeds—they are easy to store. In fact, some legumes have retained their viability for over 50 years under ordinary room conditions.

To induce germination of these seeds the seed coat must be made permeable, either naturally or artificially. In nature a gradual increase in permeability often occurs as a result of the action of microorganisms and the chemicals released during the decay of the fruit. A more rapid increase in permeability occurs in some species whose seeds are eaten by birds and mammals and pass intact through the animals' digestive tracts. These seeds are subjected to the action of strong digestive chemicals which are quite effective in breaking seed-coat dormancy. Seeds of gum arabic and carob that have passed through the digestive tracts of goats germinate readily when placed in favorable conditions. In fact, feeding the pods of these species to goats and collecting the seeds from the droppings is considered to be a convenient pretreatment for these species.

Seed-coat dormancy may be overcome artificially by either mechanical or chemical scarification. One of the simplest and most direct methods of mechanical scarification is to cut, drill, or file a small hole in the coat of each seed before planting. This allows the seed to imbibe water, and as it does it will swell and rupture the seed coat permitting normal germination.

Large quantities of seed may be scarified quickly using simple mechanical equipment that abrades the seed coats by causing them to be rubbed against a coarse surface. One of the common scarifiers consists of a drum lined with sandpaper, cement, or crushed glass. The seeds to be treated are put in the drum, and it is rotated until the seed coats are thinned but not worn completely through. A somewhat similar device employs rotating abrasive disks. Another method suitable for small amounts of fairly large seeds is to mix them with dry, sharp sand and tumble them in a concrete mixer.

The most common method of chemical scarification is to soak the seeds in concentrated sulphuric acid for a prescribed period of time.[2] This method is commonly used for the hard seeds of many species of legumes. The length of the period for soaking in acid varies from a few minutes to three or four hours, depending on the species being treated. The optimum period of treatment for the species being planted should be determined locally.

After the seeds have soaked in the acid for the prescribed time, they should be removed and thoroughly washed in cold, running water to remove all traces of acid. Acid-treated seeds may be sown immediately or dried and stored until needed.

A hot-water treatment is effective for many legumes and a few other species with seed-coat dormancy. This treatment requires no special equipment and is convenient, easy to apply, and relatively safe. The

---

[2] CAUTION: Sulphuric acid must be handled with great care to avoid severe burns or damage to one's clothing. When handling acid always wear goggles and protective clothing.

seeds may be put in wire baskets or cloth sacks and dipped in boiling water for the requisite time, usually one to five minutes. However, a better procedure is to bring the required amount of water (usually two to three times the bulk volume of the seeds) to a boil; then remove it from the heat and pour the entire quantity of seeds to be treated into it. The seeds are allowed to soak as the water gradually cools to room temperature. The proper relationship between the weight of seeds and the volume of water can be determined by a few tests. The risk lies in using too much water and thereby cooking the seeds. When the hot-water treatment is effective, the seeds imbibe water and begin to swell as the water cools. When the treatment is properly applied, it will be found that some seeds have escaped the treatment and remain unswollen even after prolonged soaking. If there are many such seeds they may be separated from the swollen seeds and treated again. The swollen seeds, if viable, will germinate normally. Seeds that have been scarified by hot water cannot be dried and stored, but must be sown immediately.

Other chemicals such as hydrochloric acid, nitric acid, sodium hydroxide, and ethyl alcohol have been used with some success for breaking seed-coat dormancy in a small number of species. However, these chemicals are generally less effective than either the hot-water or sulphuric-acid treatments.

A short period of warm, moist stratification may increase the permeability of the seed coat in species that are stored or pretreated by cold stratification. The process depends on the action of microorganisms and decay of organic material and is similar to the natural process previously described. Warm stratification may be accomplished by merely interrupting the cold stratification period for two to four weeks and allowing the temperature to rise to ordinary room temperature (20° to 25° C [68° to 77° F]). The seeds are then returned to cold stratification for the remainder of the treatment period. This treatment is achieved in some nurseries, where the climate permits, by sowing the seedbeds in the autumn and lightly mulching so the soil will warm up when short periods of mild weather occur during the winter.

Induced or Secondary Dormancy

In a few species seeds which are capable of germination at maturity, or which have after-ripened, may become dormant if improperly stored or handled. This dormancy is referred to as induced or secondary. Dormancy in some species of ash (*Fraxinus*) is apparently induced by changes in the true seed coat that occur during dry storage. A period of cold stratification will usually break the secondary dormancy in ash seeds. Temperatures above 12° C (54° F) have been reported to induce dormancy in fully after-ripened juniper seeds, and in some herbaceous plants seed dormancy can be induced by chemical growth inhibitors or exposure to light. Although very little is known about secondary dormancy, it is clear that careful handling of tree seeds is required.

Mechanical Resistance of the Seed Coat

Mechanical resistance of the seed coat is thought to be a factor in the slow germination of the seeds of some acacias and some species that produce woody nuts or pits. It can be demonstrated in the laboratory that great hydrostatic pressures are required to burst the coats of these seeds. But whether or not such pressures exceed those developed by imbibition is not clear. However, a pretreatment is occasionally applied to the large bony pits of olive and species of *Prunus* to crack the seed coat before planting.

Immature Embryo

The embryos of the seeds of a few species are only partially developed when the fruit ripens and drops from the tree. During the after-ripening period, which may require several months, the embryo grows to full size, and the seed is then capable of germinating. Immature embryos are commonly found in ginkgo seeds and have been found in some species of *Fraxinus*. Warm stratification for a few weeks followed by a longer period of cold stratification is recommended for after-ripening *Fraxinus excelsior* L. and *F. anomala* Torr.

Double Dormancy

Seeds of some species apparently have two types of dormancy, both of which must be broken in the proper order and at the proper time to obtain full germination. The usual combination of double dormancy is impermeable seed coat and embryo dormancy. Such a combination is encountered in some seed lots of *Cercis* spp. It is probable that the seeds of some species of *Juniperus* have not only seed-coat dormancy, but also a complex embryo dormancy involving separate chilling requirements for radicle development and for top growth.

GERMINATION

Once dormancy is broken and the seeds are placed in the proper conditions of moisture, temperature, oxygen, and light, the growth of the embryo, or germination, commences. The initial step in germination of nearly all seeds is the imbibition of water, which is frequently accompanied by a marked increase in size or swelling of the seed. However, because water is also imbibed by dead seeds, swelling of the seeds is not a reliable indicator of their capacity to germinate. Soon after imbibition begins, there is an increase in enzyme activity and respiration rate. Food reserves are mobilized and move toward the radicle. The number of cell divisions in the radicle increases, and a rapid elongation of new and previously formed cells occurs.

The first physical evidence of germination is the breaking of the seed coat and the emergence of the radicle. The strong, positive geotropism of the radicle causes it to grow vertically into the soil. The radicle may obtain considerable length and develop many lateral branches before appreciable growth of the hypocotyl or plumule occurs.

Two types of germination have been recognized based on the normal position of the cotyledons during germination. If the cotyledons remain underground and enclosed in the buried seed, germination is said to be hypogeous. Hypogeous germination is commonly found in many species that produce large seeds, including many hardwoods, such as the oaks, and a few gymnosperms, such as araucaria and ginkgo. If the cotyledons are lifted above ground by the elongation of the hypocotyl, germination is said to be epigeous. Epigeous germination is typical of most small-seeded species including pines, spruces, acacias, and eucalypts.

In the pines, after the radicle has penetrated a few centimeters into the soil, the hypocotyl and cotyledons begin to elongate. As the hypocotyl increases in length, it straightens to a vertical position lifting the cotyledons above the ground. Initially, the cotyledons of the pines function as absorbing organs and remove the stored food from the cells of the female gametophyte. After they are lifted above ground and freed from the seed coat, they spread in a more or less horizontal plane and function as leaves.

The first phase of germination in the oaks is the emergence of the radicle, which soon develops into a large taproot with numerous lateral branches. Growth of the root may proceed for several weeks during the winter in unfrozen soil. The second phase begins with the advent of spring when the warming of the soil stimulates the growth of the epicotyl. It pushes up through the soil, the primary leaves of the plumule develop, and the seedling begins its existence—no longer dependent on the stored food of the seed.

SANITATION

Stored seed should be free of insects and fungi. Any insects or fungi in the seeds before storage should be destroyed completely, but if this is not possible, their development must be inhibited during storage.

Insects that are not controlled can seriously harm seed and reduce germination. Seeds extracted in a kiln where the temperature exceeds

50° C (122° F) are usually purged of insects. In sealed storage, insects and microorganisms use up the oxygen which is replaced by carbon dioxide and water. When the oxygen concentration drops to 2 per cent or less by volume, the insects, both adults and larvae, are killed.

Insecticidal dusts used for treating seeds may be active chemicals, or they may be inert chemicals, such as finely ground feldspar, alumina, silica, dolomite, and anhydrite. Stored seeds infested by insects should be removed from the storeroom before new, uninfested seeds are brought in for storage.

Most fungi develop and propagate under humid conditions. Consequently, they are not generally a great menace to seed stores in arid zones. If fungi attack seeds in humid stores, the seeds are almost certain to be severely damaged. Seeds that have been dried to a moisture content of 10 per cent or less and then sealed in air-tight containers are usually safe from further fungal attack.

The fungus flora of stored seed consists chiefly of species of *Penicillium, Aspergillus, Alternaria, Cladosporum, Fusarium,* and *Rhizopus.* Formaldehyde solutions and fumigants are successfully used to destroy fungi that have already attacked the seed.

Carbon bisulphide is the fumigant most commonly used to rid seeds of insects. Two other fumigants, methylbromide and paradichlorobenzene, also produce good results. In the process of fumigation, the seeds and the insecticide are placed together in tightly sealed boxes or cans for 24 hours. To reduce damage, seeds should be fumigated only when their moisture content is below 12 per cent and the temperature less than 29° C (84° F). The length of exposure should not exceed 24 hours and preferably should be 12 hours or less, and the seeds should be aerated immediately after fumigation. Most fumigants are dangerous to use; therefore, always follow carefully the directions given by the manufacturer.

Contaminated seeds of some moderate- to large-seeded species may be separated from the good by immersing the lot in water and retrieving the sound seeds that sink. The infected and hollow seeds which float are scooped up and destroyed. This method is employed for some pines and pistachios. The sound seeds should then be dried and fumigated.

STORAGE

Because not every species produces an abundant crop of seeds every year, and because a steady supply of seed is of great importance to the fulfillment of nursery and afforestation programs, proper storage is essential.

Large quantities of seeds of the more important species should always be available in stores because if seeds sown fail to produce seedlings owing to bad weather, disease, or animal damage, it will be necessary to resow. Seeds of superior genetic qualities, or of exotic species that are difficult to obtain, should also be stored in ample amounts. It is imperative, therefore, that storage conditions be such that the seeds maintain the highest germinability until they are sown. Depending on the species, and under good storage conditions, seeds will retain their ability to germinate for from 2 months to more than 50 years. In addition to storage conditions and species characteristics, viability of seed in storage also depends on the year the seeds matured and were collected. Seed collected in certain years from a particular tree may retain their viability much longer than seed from the same tree collected in other years. When properly stored saxaul (*Haloxylon ammodendron* Bunge) seed keeps from 6 to 8 weeks, quebracho from 6 to 12 months, some pines from 10 to 15 years, and several of the legumes retain their viability for over 50 years.

Enough seed of each species should be stored to meet nursery and planting needs between seed years. Stores should be large enough to hold sufficient quantities of all species collected in seed years. Seed that is not likely to be used because of a change in policy in afforestation or because of loss of viability should be taken out of the store each year and thrown away or destroyed before the new collection season begins.

It is advisable to have several small compartments in a store, rather than one large one. Small compartments are easy to fumigate. Thus, dimensions of 3 × 3 × 3 m (10 × 10 × 10 ft) are recommended. Racks should be arranged to make it easy to reach every container stacked on them. All labels should be visible (Fig. 2–12).

Containers

Containers in which seed is stored may be tin cans, glass jars, pots glazed on the inside, jerricans of metal or plastic, or drums. All receptacles should be airtight and lids must, therefore, fit tightly to prevent moisture and insects from entering. They should be of standard sizes and shapes so that when one is filled with seed of a given species with a known purity percentage, the approximate number of seeds it contains can be estimated. Containers of standard shape are also easier to stack and to handle when seeds are transported.

The essential requirement for success in storing seeds for long periods is the maintenance of proper moisture and a cool or cold temperature. With the exception of large-seeded species, such as oaks and walnuts, most seeds keep best in a low, constant humidity.

Temperature and Moisture

Cold temperatures favor storage of nearly all species. Low temperatures reduce the rate of respiration and other metabolic processes and, thus, the rate at which food is used. Cold also reduces insect damage since the optimum temperature for most seed insects is 28° to 35° C (82°–95° F). Seed removed from cold storage often deteriorates rapidly because of high moisture content, and it should be sown immediately or carefully dried before further short storage at a warm temperature. This difficulty may also be encountered when seeds are shipped from a cold climate to a warm and, perhaps, humid one.

The ideal conditions for storage of seed of most arid-zone species have not yet been determined, but the following suggestions will be useful:

1. If refrigeration is not available, seeds of some species, such as the eucalypts and legumes, may be stored for many years at ordinary room temperature with its normal daily and seasonal fluctuations. It is desirable to pack the seeds in airtight containers to maintain a nearly constant humidity and protect them from insects and rodents. Desiccating chemicals, such as calcium chloride, may be placed in cloth bags in the containers with the seeds to reduce the humidity and thus prolong their viability.

Fig. 2–12. Inside the seed store. Note door with heavy insulation. (Courtesy FAO)

2. A most effective method of storing seeds of conifers, and of many deciduous species, is in sealed containers at cool or cold temperatures. The moisture content of the seeds of most conifers and many of the small-seeded hardwood species should be between 5 and 10 percent. Seed are stored at constant temperature. The most common practice is to keep the temperature at or just below freezing. Under these conditions the seed will neither ferment nor sprout. This method of storage may be considered the "standard" one. Some pines, such as *Pinus radiata* D. Don and *P. ponderosa* Laws., stored in airtight containers at a constant temperature of 4° C, will retain their viability for over 15 years. Dry seed of many temperate zone species can be stored without injury at extremely low temperatures; some species as low as −195° C (−320°F), but such temperatures are not practical.

Seed moisture content for most species is determined by weighing a small sample of the seed lot, drying it in an oven, reweighing, and calculating the moisture content in percent by the following formula:

$$\frac{\text{Original weight} - \text{Oven-dry weight}}{\text{Oven-dry Weight}} \times 100 = \text{Percent Moisture Content}$$

The *International Rules for Seed Testing* prescribe oven-drying the seeds at 105° C (221° F) for 16 hours for all genera of tree and shrub seed except the following: *Abies, Cedrus, Fagus, Picea, Pinus,* and *Tsuga.* Seeds of these genera contain volatile oils and resins which will be driven off at 105° C, therefore the moisture content of these seeds must be determined by toluene distillation. In this method ground seed tissue is boiled in toluene to drive off the moisture which is condensed and its volume determined. Electronic moisture meters may also be used for the approximation of moisture content for routine seed handling.

The expense of constructing an insulated and ventilated room, cooled by refrigeration units, is normally justified where large quantities of seeds, seeds from a large territory, and seeds of various species, especially exotic species difficult to obtain, must be preserved.

If such an installation is not possible because of financial or other reasons, a well-insulated store should be built by using the best available insulating material, such as cork or wood planks with layers of straw between. The temperature in stores of this kind will fluctuate less than that outside, and they are inexpensive to build. Seeds kept in them will maintain their viability longer than seeds stored where the temperature fluctuates widely. They should be so planned that refrigeration units may be added later. A large household refrigerator can be used for small quantities of valuable seeds.

3. Moist cold storage is required for seeds, such as acorns and nuts of some broad-leaved species. These seeds cannot be dried with-

out loss of viability. They should be stratified by mixing them with one to three times their volume of moistened sand, vermiculite, charcoal powder, or a similar water-retaining material, and then placing them in a cold room. The container used should permit free drainage and aeration. It is desirable to dust the seeds with a commercial seed-protecting fungicide before stratification to prevent molding. Acorns may also be stored in this way or in dry sand.

In cold arid zones, where below-freezing temperatures and some snow regularly occur, seeds may be stored in the ground. The bags containing them are buried in holes under a mulch of straw and protected against rodents by wire netting. Outdoor storage should be used only if spring sowing is intended since the seed will lose its viability quickly after the first winter.

DISTRIBUTION

Seed distribution to nurseries, or for direct sowing in the field, should be made only shortly before the actual time of sowing because seeds of some species are likely to deteriorate once they are removed from storage. The seed should be protected from moisture during distribution by being kept in waterproof containers. The containers used for distribution should be strong enough to withstand any rough handling during transportation. For easy handling, they should not be too large or weigh more than 20 kg (45 lb).

Seed parcels should be properly labelled inside and outside, giving the species, origin, and date of collection. The addresses of the sender and of the consignee should be clearly written on each parcel. If seeds are to be shipped to another country, the sender should be careful to comply with the export laws of his own country and the import laws of the recipient's.

BIBLIOGRAPHY

BALDWIN, H. I. Forest tree seed of the north temperate regions with special refer-
1942   ence to North America. Chronica Botanica, Waltham, Mass. 240 p.
BALDWIN, H. I., and G. D. HOLMES. Handling forest tree seed. FAO For. Dev. Pap.
1955   4. Rome. 110 p.
BARON, F. J., and G. H. SCHUBERT. Seed origin and size of ponderosa pine planting
1963   stock grown at several California nurseries. U. S. For. Serv. Res. Note PSW-
         9. Pac. Southwest For. Range Exp. Stn., Berkeley, Calif. 11 p.
BUCK, J. M., et al. California tree seed zones. U. S. For. Serv. Calif. Reg., San Fran-
1970   cisco and Calif. Div. For., Sacramento. 5 p. plus map.
CALLAHAM, R. Z. Provenance research: investigation of genetic diversity associated
1964   with geography. Unasylva 18 (2/3):40–50.
CÂNDIDO, J. F. Effect of seed size and substrate on germination of Eucalyptus citri-
1970   odora Hook. Turrialba 20:255–257.

CHING, T. M., and M. C. PARKER. Hydrogen peroxide for rapid viability tests of
1958   some coniferous tree seeds. For. Sci. 4:128–134.
COOLING, E. N. Proposals for organization and functioning of seed unit. U. N. Dev.
1971   Programme: Spec. Fund Proj. UNSF/FAO GRE-20/230. [Food Agric.
        Organ. U. N.], Athens. [68] p.
CROCKER, W., and L. V. BARTON. Physiology of seeds: an introduction to the experi-
1953   mental study of seed and germination problems. Chronica Botanica, Wal-
        tham, Mass. 267 p.
CUNNINGHAM, R. A. Provisional tree and shrub seed zones for the Great Plains.
1975   USDA For. Serv. Res. Pap. RM-150. Rocky Mount. For. Range Exp. Stn.,
        Ft. Collins, Colo. 15 p.
EVENARI, M. Germination inhibitors. Bot. Rev. 15:153–194.
1949
FIELDING, J. M. The role of exotic species in forest tree improvement. Proc. World
[1962] For. Congr. (Seattle, 1960) 5(2):742–746.
FAO. Agricultural and horticultural seeds; their production, control and distribution.
1961   FAO Agric. Stud. 55. Rome. 531 p.
————. Forest seed directory 1975. Food Agric. Organ. U. N., Rome. 283 p.
1975
GRANO, C. X. Tetrazolium chloride to test loblolly pine seed viability. For Sci.
1958   4:50–53.
HARMOND, J. E., N. R. BRANDENBURG, and L. M. KLEIN. Mechanical seed cleaning
1968   and handling. U.S. Dep. Agric., Agric. Handb. 354. Washington, D. C.
        56 p.
HOEKSTRA, P. E., E. P. MERKEL, and H. R. POWERS, JR. Production of seeds of forest
1961   trees. U. S. Dep. Agric. Yearb. Agric. 1961: 227–232. Washington, D. C.
HOLMES, G. D. Methods of testing the germination quality of forest tree seeds and
1951   the interpretation of results. For. Abstr. 13:5–15.
HOLMES, G. D., and G. BUSZEWICZ. The storage of seeds of temperate forest tree
1958   species. For. Abstr. 19:313–322, 455–476.
HUSS, E. Methods used at the Swedish Forest Research Institute in seed investiga-
1951   tions, Medd. Statens Skogsforsknings Inst. 40(6). Stockholm. 82 p.
INTERNATIONAL SEED TESTING ASSOCIATION. International rules for seed testing 1966.
1966   Proc. Int. Seed Test. Assoc. 31:1–152.
————. Amendments to the international rules for seed testing 1966. Proc. Int. Seed
1972   Test. Assoc. 37:187–209.
JAMES, E. An annotated bibliography on seed storage deterioration. U. S. Dep.
1961   Agric., Agric. Res. Serv., Crops Res. ARS 34-15-1. Washington, D. C.
        81 p.
KMECZA, N. S. Using tree shakers for pine cone collection in Region 8. U. S. For.
1970   Serv., Tree Plant. Notes 21(1):9–11.
KOZLOWSKI, T. T. (editor). Seed biology. 3 vol. Academic Press, New York. 416,
1972   447, and 422 p.
LANQUIST, K. B. Portable automatic cone kiln. U. S. For. Serv., Tree Plant. Notes
1959   No. 35. p. 10–14.
MAGINI, E. Forest seed handling equipment and procedures. II. Seed treatments,
1962   storage, testing and transport. Unasylva 16:20–35.
MAGINI, E., and N. P. TULSTRUP. Tree seed notes. FAO For. Dev. Pap. 5. Rome.
1955   354 p.
MALAC, B. F. More on stratification of pine seed in polyethylene bags. U. S. For.
1960   Serv., Tree Plant. Notes No. 42. p. 7–9.
MARTIN, A. C., and W. D. BARKLEY. Seed identification manual. Univ. Calif. Press,
1973   Berkeley. 221 p.
MATUSZ, S. Collection of seeds from standing trees. United Nations Joint Commit-
1964   tee on Forest Working Techniques and Training of Forest Workers. FAO/
        ECE/LOG/144. Geneva. [72] p.

Mirov, N. T., and C. J. Kraebel. Collecting and handling seeds of wild plants.
1939   U.S. Civilian Conserv. Corps, For. Publ. 5. Washington, D.C. 42 p.
Morandini, R. Forest seed handling equipment and procedures. I. Seed production,
1961   collection and production [sic]. Unasylva 15:185–199.
Rietz, R. C. Kiln design and development of schedules for extracting seed from
1941   cones. U. S. Dep. Agric. Tech. Bull. 773. Washington, D. C. 69 p.
R[obertson], F. [C. F.]. The pretreatment of forest seed to hasten germination. For.
1948–   Abstr. 10:153–157, 281–285.
1949
Schubert, G. H., and R. S. Adams. Reforestation practices for conifers in California.
1971   Calif. Dep. Conserv. Div. For., Sacramento. 359 p.
Schubert, G. H., and J. A. Pitcher. A provisional tree seed-zone and cone-crop
1973   rating system for Arizona and New Mexico. USDA For. Serv. Res. Pap.
        RM-105. Rocky Mount. For. Range Exp. Stn., Ft. Collins, Colo. 8 p.
Shumilina, Z. K. Stratification of seeds of trees and shrubs (Stratifikatsiya semyan
1961   drevesnykh i kustarnikovykh porod. 1940). Transl. from Russian by Z.
        Shapira. Israel Program Sci. Transl., Jerusalem. OTS 60–51012. 64 p.
Stoeckeler, J. H., and P. E. Slabaugh. Conifer nursery practice in the Prairie-
1965   Plains. U. S. Dep. Agric., Agric. Handb. 279. Washington, D. C. 93 p.
Toole, E. H., S. B. Hendricks, H. A. Brothwick, and V. K. Toole. Physiology of
1956   seed germination. Annu. Rev. Plant Physiol. 7:299–324.
Tornero Gomez, J. Posibilidades y limitaciónes de las coniferas de crecimiento
1965   rápido en los programas de repoblación forestal. FAO Joint Sub-Commission
        on Mediterranean Forestry, 9th Sess., Athens 23–26 June 1965. FO-FAO/
        MSC/65/Q.G. CONF. Rome. 48 p.
U. S. Department of Agriculture. Seeds: the yearbook of agriculture 1961. U. S.
1961   Dep. Agric., Washington, D. C. 591 p.
U. S. Forest Service. Seeds of woody plants in the United States. Prepared by the
1974   Forest Service; C. S. Schopmeyer, technical coordinator. U. S. Dep. Agric.,
        Agric. Handb. 450. 883 p.
Wakeley, P. C. Planting the southern pines. U. S. Dep. Agric., Agric. Monogr. 18.
1954   Washington, D. C. 233 p.
Wang, B. S. P. Tree-seed storage. Canadian For. Serv. Publ. 1335. Ottawa. 32 p.
1974
Wright, J. W. Genetics of forest tree improvement. FAO For. For. Prod. Stud. 16.
1962   Rome. 399 p.
Zobel, B. J., J. Barber, C. L. Brown, and T. O. Perry. Seed orchards—their con-
1958   cept and management. J. For. 56:815–825.

3

Forest-Tree Nurseries

NURSERIES IN ARID ZONES

Most afforestation in arid zones is done by planting nursery-reared seedlings; only where the most favorable soil-moisture conditions exist can trees be established by seed sown directly in the field.

Nearly all nursery-reared plants are grown from seed. A few species such as *Plantanus orientalis* L. and species of *Populus, Salix, Ficus,* and *Tamarix* may be propagated by cuttings. However, rooted cuttings constitute only a small fraction of the nursery stock grown for arid-zone afforestation.

Afforestation in arid zones is unusually expensive, and the cost incurred in every operation must be kept as low as possible if the undertaking is to be economically sound. However, the success of a plantation should not be jeopardized by unwarranted frugality.

The cost of nursery stock is a major expense of afforestation. To keep the cost as low as possible, the nursery must be efficiently managed. Every effort should be made to produce suitable plants at a reasonable cost by use of sound business practices and careful administration. In a well administered nursery there should be no excuse for not delivering the full number of plants which were undertaken to produce at the time they are needed for outplanting.

Mechanical equipment for all types of nursery activities is undergoing intensive development with the objectives of increasing the number and quality of plants produced and reducing costs. A nurseryman should always be watching for inventions which might be used to improve nursery production. The use of machinery is especially important where labor is scarce or production is high. The nurseryman should also have some skill as a mechanic and be able to make emergency repairs, thus preventing serious loss or damage of stock.

Selection of the Nursery Site

The selection of a nursery site, its proper layout and management are essential for the economical production of high-quality nursery stock for afforestation. Location, topography, soil, water supply, and available labor must all be carefully considered because they affect not only the cost of production, but also the quality of the stock and hence the success of afforestation. The higher initial cost of a good site will be more economical in the long run than the subsequent expense of correcting unsuitable conditions at an inexpensive, poor site.

Results from recent experiments show that the nursery climate has a pronounced effect on the root regenerating capacity of bare-root seedlings after they are transplanted in the field. Nurseries where early fall freezing temperatures occur favor production of plants with high root regenerating capacity; seedlings grown in nurseries located in areas where late frosts occur have roots which start regenerating late in the season. Such root acitvity will have a bearing on the choice of the site for the nursery and of the season for planting the seedlings.

In cold climates, to reduce the possibility of having the nursery beds still frozen and snowbound when the soils of the planting sites are in the most favorable condition, the nursery should, ideally, be located somewhat south in the Northern Hemisphere and north in the Southern Hemisphere, and at a slightly lower altitude than the area to be served.

Forest nurseries may be either temporary or permanent. Whether a temporary or a permanent nursery is to be established depends on the size of the area to be planted, the time required to carry out the project, and the availability of suitable sites. In arid zones, due to the scarcity of satisfactory sites for temporary nurseries, usually only one permanent nursery is established in a region, rather than several temporary nurseries.

The Temporary Nursery

Temporary nurseries are planned to supply seedlings for only a few seasons, and thus they require only a small capital investment. The temporary nursery should be located on the planting site near the center of the area to be planted. The temporary nursery must be established on a proposed planting site a year or two before the site is scheduled to be planted.

Although elaborate site preparation is usually not required, and only small, temporary buildings are needed, an adequate supply of water is essential for a temporary nursery. If possible, the nursery should be so situated that the water can be distributed to the seedbeds by gravity.

When compared with the permanent nursery, the number of seedlings produced in any season in most temporary nurseries is small, usually only 50,000 to 100,000 (Fig. 3–1). If fewer than 25,000 seedlings are required for a particular planting site, it is normally easier to transport them to the site from permanent nurseries, unless the planting sites are too remote or the roads too difficult for transport during the planting season.

The temporary nursery does not need a large labor force, but even a small nursery requires some overhead staff, at least an overseer and a few semipermanent part-time workers.

Temporary nurseries are designed to produce only one-, two-, or, rarely, three-year-old seedlings. The older seedlings may be potted or balled, but "transplant stock" (as will be discussed later) is better produced in permanent nurseries.

A number of advantages of temporary nurseries are worth considering. Because they depend on the intrinsic fertility of the virgin soil, they do not require the application of fertilizers. The planting stock is preconditioned as a consequence of having been grown under the environmental conditions of the prospective planting site (Fig. 3–2). Transportation costs and time between lifting and field planting are minimal. In fact, the stock is lifted only as needed, thus eliminating any need for temporary storage on the planting site and reducing planting "shock."

The disadvantages of temporary nurseries are the poorer quality of the stock produced and, despite the lower capital investment, the higher cost per thousand of plantable seedlings. Thus, wherever millions of naked-rooted seedlings and transplants must be produced annually, permanent nurseries should be established. Furthermore, species that require special care must be grown in permanent nurseries. If flexible, lightweight receptacles are used, even balled stock can be produced more cheaply in the permanent nursery and can be economically transported to the planting site.

The Permanent Nursery

Permanent nurseries should be established wherever the nursery is to supply seedlings to a large area or district in which afforestation will be carried out over a period of many years. The permanent nursery may also supply other planting areas in the vicinity that local nurseries, if there are such, cannot supply in the required quantity.

A large capital investment is needed for the permanent nursery to assure a steady rate of production of high quality planting stock. An ample supply of water of an alkalinity as low as it is possible to find in the region must be secured. Permanent buildings and roads must be constructed and, wherever practicable, electric power should be installed. Large capital investments are justified only if there will be a continuous

Fig. 3–1. A temporary nursery in the mountains of Lebanon. Plastic bags are used in the transplant beds. (Photo V. U. Contino; courtesy FAO)

Fig. 3–2. A temporary nursery in the arid plains of the Negev. The plants are grown under the environmental conditions of the planting site. (Courtesy FAO)

afforestation program, because during the first few years the operation of a permanent nursery will not show a profit. The number of seedlings to be produced annually must be large—a minimum of approximately one million is necessary for successful operation. Although the design and layout of the nursery are based on the minimum production, the size and arrangement should provide for expansion and an increased output in the future, if necessary.

If possible, the nursery should be established near the center of the district to be served and on a road with good access to the main road network. The nursery site should be selected so that the distance to the main planting areas will be as short as possible. The nursery will be linked through a network of forest roads to the plantation roads, which will be extended to the planting sites during afforestation.

A centrally located nursery reduces the hazards as well as the cost of transportation. Only rarely is the use of naked-rooted stock advisable in arid-zone plantations; consequently, the transport of planting stock, consisting mainly of balled seedlings in pots or other containers, is quite expensive and an important factor in determining the planting budget. Furthermore, if the transport distance is great, the balled soil may be shaken from the roots and the trees desiccated during transportation.

Under favorable climatic conditions a nursery may be established in the transition area between two different phytoclimatic zones, thus making it possible to grow the species of both zones in one nursery. In arid zones, however, plants should be raised in the nursery under climatic and soil conditions as nearly similar to those of the area to be planted as is possible. Such preconditioning of the plants in the nursery to the environment of the planting site will help to improve survival of field-planted stock—even though it may do no more than eliminate the less hardy individuals.

Water Supply. The availability of water for irrigation is of utmost importance in selecting the nursery site and in determining the potential size of the nursery. In many nurseries, plants must be watered throughout most of the year. High-quality plants cannot be produced without proper and uniform watering. Even in humid regions, a short period of drought would be disastrous without supplemental watering.

The amount of water required daily will depend on the size of the nursery, method of irrigation, and porosity of the soil. This requirement should be computed accurately, and care be taken to ensure that an adequate amount will be available throughout the whole year. As a guide, where plants are grown in beds with sprinkler irrigation, an amount of water equivalent to 100 mm (4 in) of rain must be available for the growing season.

Pumping from shallow or superficial wells is expensive, and wherever possible the water source should be streams or springs that will facilitate distribution by gravity. Although water can sometimes be pumped economically from a permanent stream or spring, pumping, especially from deep wells, should be considered only where a permanent nursery is to be established. Deep-well pumping is extremely expensive and can be contemplated only where no other source of water exists.

Water Quality. In arid zones, the quality of water available for irrigation is as important in successful nursery operation as the amount. It is usually difficult to find irrigation water that does not contain some concentration of undesirable chemicals. It is most important to be certain that the water not contain appreciable concentrations of salt, alkali, or other toxic chemicals.

Before a nursery site is chosen, the properties of the water available for irrigation should be determined by laboratory analysis. When samples are taken, it should be remembered that the mineral content varies not only with the geologic formation bearing the water, but also with the season of the year. Where irrigation water is obtained from a public water system, an analysis is usually easily procured from the authorities in charge of the system.

Based on the analyses of the water used in a number of nurseries and observations of the effect of impurities on seedlings, it appears that water containing more than 500 ppm (parts per million) of dissolved solids is highly undesirable for irrigating forest nurseries. If the water contains more than 500 ppm, it will raise the pH of the nursery soil, which in turn will favor an increase in damping-off and root rots, inhibit iron metabolism, and cause chlorosis. If such water must be used, acidification or other expensive soil treatment will be required to reduce the pH to an acceptable level. Some chemicals are more harmful than others; e.g., water containing as few as 100 ppm calcium carbonate or 125 ppm calcium bicarbonate will produce harmful effects.

The species to be raised and the cultural practices will also have a bearing on the allowable concentration of salt or alkali. For conifer stock, which may remain in nursery beds two or three years, the concentration of dissolved solids should not exceed 200 ppm with much less than 100 ppm calcium carbonate and 125 ppm calcium bicarbonate permitted. Water having as many as 500 ppm dissolved solids can be safely used for container or balled stock of conifers during one season. After planting in the field the dissolved solids are washed away by rain.

Because of lack of subsurface drainage in most arid-zone soils, the harmful chemicals contained in the irrigation water are brought back toward the soil surface by evaporation and tend to accumulate in a layer a few centimeters below the surface. Concentration of harmful chemicals may also occur in containers or soil balls, if they do not receive enough water to wet the soil above field capacity and thus promote the drainage through the soil that will carry the chemicals away.

Soil. Although a large proportion of the planting stock in arid-zone nurseries is raised in containers, the quality of the soil is nevertheless important because some species, e.g., *Albizia lebbek* (L.) Benth., are raised only in beds and others are raised in beds before transplanting to the containers. The nursery soil should not be greatly different from the soil of the typical planting site. No attempt should be made, however, to match the poor soil of a planting site when selecting the location for the nursery.

In humid climates, a generally favorable nursery soil for production of naked-rooted stock is a sandy loam of light to medium texture having about 15 to 20 per cent silt-plus-clay. Such soil has good air–water relationships, is easily worked, and does not crust or crack on drying, thereby damaging the seedling roots. A deep soil (2–3 m [6.5–10 ft]) with moderately rapid internal drainage is desirable to prevent upward movement of alkalies by surface evaporation. Usually, rapid internal drainage associated with coarse sands or gravelly subsoils requires large amounts of water for adequate irrigation of seedlings. Such soils are thus somewhat less desirable in arid zones than finer-textured soils having up to 35 per cent silt-plus-clay. Furthermore, if balled stock is to be produced, a moderately heavy soil is often desirable to aid in forming a satisfactory ball. However, the soil must not be so heavy that it is difficult to work and has little or no interior drainage. If furrow irrigation is to be used, a fairly heavy subsoil will be needed to retain the moisture in the root zone.

The soil should be free of large stones and boulders, which make the soil extremely difficult to work, especially with machines, and which are expensive to remove. Unusually light, fine, sandy soil should be avoided because the surface sand, when blown by the wind, will cut off or damage newly germinated seedlings. Soils underlain by a hardpan close to the surface are generally unsatisfactory, but a deep hardpan may prevent water loss by preventing deep percolation.

A nursery soil should be moderately fertile, but physical qualities, such as texture and depth, are more important because fertility can be maintained by proper use of fertilizers. The soil must not contain harmful chemicals. Some chemicals, e.g., lime, are required in small amounts but are undesirable for most trees when present in large quantities. In general, soils that would produce moderately good yields of agricultural crops will be suitable for tree nurseries. However, abandoned farmland may lack the proper fungi for development of mycorrhizae. This deficiency can be remedied by inoculating the soil with the required fungi before sowing the tree seed.

The pH of the soils in arid zones is rarely below 6.0 and commonly is between 6.0 and 7.2. Soils with a pH of 7.5 or higher should be avoided as nursery sites because the excess carbonates and alkalies in these soils will create many difficulties in raising seedlings. A concentration of more than 500 ppm of soluble salts in the soil solution will produce unhealthy, poor planting stock due to chlorosis, damping-off, phosphate (and other nutritional) imbalance, and crusting by deposition of salts brought to the surface by evaporation. Although many species of hardwoods can endure higher concentrations and develop into plantable stock, it is better to avoid such soils. When the soil is too alkaline the pH may be lowered by applying the proper amount of phosphoric acid, ammonium sulphate, or powdered sulphur to the soil.

Topography. The ideal nursery site is a nearly level, plane surface without large boulders or rock outcrops. A slight slope, between 1 and 2 per cent, is advantageous because it prevents water from collecting and standing in pools. If water covers the beds for even a few days, the plants will be drowned or severely damaged. Areas where runoff from winter rains accumulates should be avoided unless an adequate drainage system can be installed. The runoff from irrigation and rain must be controlled by carefully planned and properly constructed waterways.

Knolly or rolling topography is undesirable. Leveling such sites is expensive and leaves only poor subsoil for seedling culture. In mountainous areas, where the slope exceeds 5 per cent, terraces will be needed. The first step in the construction of a terrace should be to remove the top soil and set it aside so that it can be spread back over the surface of the terrace after it is formed. Often the stones removed in preparing the soil can be used in building retaining walls for the terraces.

South, southwest, and west aspects in the Northern Hemisphere and north, northwest, and west aspects in the Southern Hemisphere tend to be abnormally hot and dry and should not be chosen if suitable sites on other aspects are available.

The site should be protected from the wind either by uncut forest, planted windbreaks, or topographic position. However, nurseries on the lee side of long ridges, especially near the foot of such ridges, often experience much greater wind damage than comparable areas elsewhere. Thus, where it is possible to choose another site, areas on or near the lee side of a ridge should be avoided.

The bottom of a narrow, deep valley is generally an undesirable site for a nursery for several reasons. Damaging winds frequently blow up and down such valleys. The danger of flooding is always present and although the alluvial soil of a valley bottom may make it quite attractive as a nursery site, it must be remembered that the soil was deposited there by floods. Cold-air drainage at night often produces unseasonable frosts in valley bottoms. If the valley is deep and narrow, the seedbeds may be excessively shaded by the valley walls. Nurseries that are located in narrow valleys are forced to adopt an inefficient, long, narrow ground plan.

Labor. A permanent nursery should never be established far from a good source of part-time labor because during the peak seasons of transplanting and lifting a large force of supplementary workers will be required. Women are especially effective in nursery work that does not require unusual physical strength. Frequently, women constitute more than 50 per cent of the total labor force. Generally women cause less damage to delicate planting stock than do men, and much nursery work, such as hand weeding, is extremely monotonous, and women apparently are psychologically better adapted to these tasks than are men.

The overseer, or superintendent, and mechanic should live on or near the nursery because they must be available constantly to supervise the work and keep the equipment in good repair.

DEVELOPMENT OF THE NURSERY AREA

Ground Plan

The ideal geometric plan for a nursery is a square, or a rectangle that is not more than twice as long as it is wide. The general layout is often dictated by the topography of the available land and by the necessities of access, irrigation, and drainage. The ground plan should be designed to eliminate wasteful travel by workers within the nursery, with buildings centrally located or placed near the area of their most frequent use.

The entire area should be divided into working compartments to facilitate management planning and record-keeping. A large scale map of the nursery should be prepared, and an adequate number of copies made for annual administrative planning. A detailed operating plan dividing the nursery grounds according to use must be prepared showing the projected use of each area for the following two or more years. Areas to be used for seedbeds and for transplant beds should be designated, and the species and age of stock indicated. Areas to be left fallow or to be sown with a cover crop should also be shown in a similar manner. The specific operations depend on the number of seedlings to be grown each year, cultural practices, and the extent and nature of the area available.

Annual production, tree species, age and type of planting stock, and cultural practices determine the size of the area required. A larger area is needed to produce deciduous trees in beds than is required to raise the same number of conifers, carobs, or eucalypts in containers. The length of time individual species must spend in the nursery is extremely important in determining the total area required. Most broad-leaved species remain in the nursery from seven to nine months, most pines some fifteen months, and cedar and spruce seedlings may require two years or longer. If trees are transplanted in the nursery, they will occupy several times more area in the transplant bed than they required in the seedbed. (See Table 3–1.)

Table 3–1. Net area required per million seedlings and transplants— excluding pathways, roads, and windbreaks. Based on 400 plantable seedlings and 50 plantable transplants per square meter (1.2 sq yd).

Age Class of Stock *	Hectares (*Acres*) Required					
	1st Year	2nd Year	3rd Year	4th Year	5th Year	Total
1 + 0	0.25					0.25 (0.62)
2 + 0	0.25	0.25				0.50 (1.24)
3 + 0	0.25	0.25	0.25			0.75 (1.85)
1 + 1	0.25	2.00				2.25 (5.56)
2 + 1	0.25	0.25	2.00 (4.94)			2.50 (6.18)
1 + 2	0.25	2.00	2.00			4.25 (10.50)
2 + 2	0.25	0.25	2.00	2.00		4.50 (11.12)
3 + 2	0.25	0.25	0.25	2.00	2.00	4.75 (11.74)
2 + 3	0.25	0.25	2.00	2.00	2.00	6.50 (16.06)

* For meaning of age class designations see "Transplanting," page 120.

Half a million potted plants, or about one million naked-rooted seedlings can be grown per hectare (202,000 potted or 405,000 naked-rooted seedlings per acre). But only about 250,000 naked-rooted plants can be raised on one hectare (101,000 per acre), if planted at the proper intervals in the row and with enough spacing between the rows to permit mechanical cultivation.

Leveling

The first operation in establishing a nursery will often be minor "leveling" of the ground, or terracing if slopes are steep. Absolutely level areas are undesirable and surface drainage must not be impaired by leveling. If natural surface drainage is slow, it should be corrected by sloping the surface and providing waterways. Stones should be removed, but boulders, if there are only a few, may remain in place. Where leveling is needed, it should be done with heavy machines, such as bulldozers and scrapers. On unusually steep slopes leveling must be done by hand. The topsoil should be removed when leveling starts and returned to the surface when the work is completed or used to fill containers for potted stock.

After leveling, the area is plowed to a depth of 40–50 cm (16–20 in), then disced and harrowed. All roots and rhizomes that are uncovered during these preparations must be removed and destroyed. The grounds then will be ready for road building and for laying out the irrigation system according to the prepared plan.

Roads

The nursery road system must permit access by trucks and tractors to every part of the nursery. A good road system is especially valuable in transporting heavy loads of soil, potted plants, or bundled seedlings. Wherever possible, the fields for growing naked-rooted plants or areas for placing the pots, cans, or boxes used for raising balled plants should be rectangular. Paved roads are costly to build and maintain; therefore, such roads should be kept as short as possible.

Seedbeds

Seedbeds may be prepared to grow seedlings in the natural soil, in artificially prepared "soil," or in pots. If seedlings are to be grown in the natural soil and the soil is uniform throughout the nursery, the seedlings are usually grown in rotation with the transplants. Where the soils are not uniform, the seedbeds should occupy the best soil, and the seedlings should be grown in rotation with a cover crop, or the seedbeds should lie fallow after each crop.

Seedbeds are laid out in straight, parallel lines with adjacent beds separated from each other by narrow pathways. The pathways should be wide enough to permit the workers to kneel comfortably and reach into the beds to work. The usual width of paths is approximately 60 cm (24 in). Seedbeds should be narrow enough to allow all plants in them to be reached easily by the workers when replacement or weeding is necessary. In India, for example, it has been found that the most practical width is 75 cm (30 in). In other countries, beds up to 1.2 m (4 ft) may be desired. If all work is done by hand, seedbeds should be fairly short, no longer than 4–6 m (13–20 ft), to allow easy movement of laborers among the beds. In some nurseries machines are used to prepare and form the beds. These machines are actually a complex of equipment drawn by a horse or tractor and consist of a plow or set of large discs to till the soil, smaller discs to heap up the soil, and levellers to even the beds and the paths between them. Two men with the proper combination of equipment can prepare an area of 2 hectares (5 acres) in an 8-hour day. Where either animal- or tractor-drawn machines are used the seedbeds should be long—50 m (164 ft) or more.

Pots used in the seedbeds should be embedded with their upper surface level with the paths. The spaces between the pots should be filled with sand to prevent evaporation from the sides of the pots and to maintain a lower temperature. Cans and other containers may be placed in the ground in the same way as the pots.

Where seedlings are grown in natural soil, the beds are usually made with their surface level with the bordering paths. Unless surface drainage is slow, there is no advantage in making the seedbeds higher than the paths. If the surface of the seedbed is below the level of the paths, the seedlings will almost certainly be killed or damaged by flooding and sedimentation.

Irrigation System

The distribution of irrigation water must be carefully planned to ensure that an adequate amount of water will be available in all parts of the nursery. The main distribution system in the nursery may be open ditches, surface pipes, or underground pipes. If possible, the flow of water in the pipes should be by gravity.

Open ditches are relatively inexpensive to construct, but they require annual maintenance to keep them from filling in with silt and vegetation. Ditches require much more land area than other systems. If they are not lined, much water may be lost by seepage. Ditches also impede travel and movement of machinery in the nursery.

Surface pipes can be moved from one part of the nursery to another readily, and the system can be expanded or reduced as needed. However, water standing in pipes, exposed to the direct rays of the sun, may be heated to scalding and will seriously damage seedlings if it is applied before it cools. In cold regions, the pipes must be drained or dismantled before winter to prevent trapping water that will freeze and burst the pipes. Surface pipes also obstruct travel in the nursery and are generally suitable only for small nurseries.

In large nurseries it is preferable to distribute the water under pressure in underground pipes with a complete network of main and secondary lines serving the whole nursery. The main pipes must be large enough to supply water to the sprinklers without a serious loss of pressure. Because the initial investment is large, an underground system is justified only in a permanent nursery. In cold regions the pipes must be laid below the frost line, or installed so they can be drained.

Fences and Windbreaks

The entire nursery should be well protected by a surrounding fence or hedge. If necessary, barbed wire can be used to keep out large animals and wire netting to protect the area from small mammals, especially rabbits. The fence should have one main entrance and, where needed, exit gates for equipment and workers. Turnstiles, rather than standard hinged gates, are usually more convenient for workers carrying heavy loads.

Protection from damaging winds is absolutely essential in arid zones. This is usually attained by planting windbreaks consisting of one or two rows of trees and shrubs completely around the nursery and, if necessary, within the nursery around each compartment. During the first few years after planting it is advisable to irrigate these windbreaks to obtain rapid height growth. In some new nurseries quick-growing windbreak plants, including grasses, such as *Arundo donax* L. and *Pennisetum purpureum* Schumach., have been planted for temporary protection until the trees grow high enough to be effective. Among the woody plants that may be utilized for windbreaks are species of *Cupressus, Casuarina, Juniperus, Populus, Elaeagnus, Ulmus,* and *Tamarix.* Hedges of shrubby species, such as *Prosopis juliflora* (Swartz) DC, *Parkinsonia aculeata* L., and *Dodonaea viscosa* Jacq. are useful around blocks of seedbeds (Fig. 3–3). In some nurseries too many windbreaks and hedges have been

Fig. 3–3. Seedbeds protected against the wind by a hedge of *Dodonaea viscosa* Jacq. The seedlings are protected from birds by wire frames. (Courtesy FAO)

planted. These not only occupy valuable soil but are expensive to maintain.

It is customary to have small flower gardens to beautify the nursery, or vegetable gardens and fruit trees for the staff. Such practices are advisable and appreciated, but this practice should not be overdone and the nursery superintendent should decide the amount that can be allowed. Gardens require labor, land, and water, and when provided in nurseries these amenities are usually at the expense of raising plants for afforestation.

Buildings and Storage Areas

The nursery buildings should include housing for the superintendent and a permanent staff, an office, a store or cellar for seeds, a tool shed, and a packing shed. A shower room and, depending on the customs of the country, a kitchen and dining room should be provided for the workers. A small workshop is needed to facilitate minor repairs to equipment. Sheds for tractors, trucks, and horses or mules may also have to be provided. The size of these buildings and the area they will occupy will vary with the size of the nursery and local conditions.

A large area must be reserved for storing stocks of pots, containers, pipe, lumber, fencing, and other material. A small area may be needed for preparing compost and another for drying fruit and extracting seeds.

PLANT PRODUCTION

Physiological Condition of Seedlings

Production of high quality seedlings requires a knowledge of the effects of nursery environment and cultural practices on the seedling's physiological condition. Occasionally the physiological condition of seedlings can be determined from their outward appearance, but often there is no visible indication of their condition. Although aerial portions of temperate zone trees go through seasonal periods of growth and rest, a few roots of some trees, particularly conifers, grow throughout the year, if soil temperature and moisture are favorable. Moisture and temperature, especially the relationship between night and day temperatures, have a strong influence on seedling development and the reactivation of root growth in the spring. Many temperate zone species require at least a few hours exposure to freezing temperatures before growth resumes. The ability of the seedling to produce new root growth is considered a good index of its physiological condition. However, experiments in Tunisia show that in spite of the many variations in climate and soil in plantation areas, little difference among seedlings can be detected after four years of growth of plants whose initial root regeneration potential differed.

Soil Preparation

Thorough preparation of the soil is the prime prerequisite for all nursery work; good tilth is especially important for seedling establishment. Deep plowing and harrowing improve aeration and drainage, and favor optimum root development. Soil preparation techniques vary according to the type of soil and local practice. Although the work may be done by hand or mechanically, machine methods are preferred, if not required, in large nurseries.

Plowing should be to a depth of 30–40 cm (12–16 in). Autumn or winter plowing is desirable, but if it must be delayed until spring it should not be done when the soil is too wet. Harrowing should immediately follow spring plowing; the disc or drag may be attached directly to the plow. If plowing has been done in autumn, harrowing should be done before sowing while moisture conditions are favorable. Cross-harrowing often helps to produce the desired tilth.

Sowing

Sowing is a painstaking nursery operation. Its object is to obtain, from the best seed available, the maximum number of healthy, sturdy seedlings for transplanting or field planting. Only seed of the tree species that are to be used in the plantation should be sown. Seeds of other species which happen to be in storage should not be used even though seeds of the desired species are not available, unless it is concluded that the substitute species will have all or nearly all the favorable properties of the desired species. The success of sowing will determine whether the nursery will be able to supply the required number of seedlings and whether the afforestation program can be carried out.

Seeds of all species are not sown at the same time in the nursery because the proper season for sowing varies with the seeding characteristics of the species, geographic location of the nursery, and cultural practices. Three major groups, each containing species that have similar characteristics, or that require similar cultural practices may be distinguished. These are slow-growing species, fast-growing species, and broad-leaved species grown to produce naked-root stock.

Time of Sowing. Seeds of species with slow seedling growth rate are sown early in the autumn. This group includes carob (*Ceratonia siliqua* L.) and many conifers. Seedlings of species in this group are transplanted during the winter, and the transplants should be ready for field planting in the next planting season.

Conifers should be sown in the autumn during the time when seeds are naturally shed from the trees. Experience has shown that plants from spring sowings grow slowly and are too small to be planted during the following winter. In certain slow-growing species, such as those of *Cedrus* and *Juniperus,* it may be necessary to keep the plants in the nursery for more than one year. Seeds of such species may be sown in the spring. Pretreatment of seeds to break dormancy, such as stratification, must be done at the proper time so that the required treatment period will be completed before the anticipated planting date.

Proper correlation of soil preparation with local climate is important in planting slow-growing species, particularly conifers. Heavy winter rains may cause severe damage to newly prepared seedbeds, and if rain should occur just as the germination of the seeds starts, complete failure may be the result. Warm temperatures accompanying the first rains may promote the growth of damping-off fungi, causing severe losses among newly germinated seedlings. To reduce such losses, seeds of most conifers should be sown during the first weeks of autumn so that the seedlings will be established by the time the rains come. Some conifers, however, may not germinate if they are sown too far in advance of the winter rains. *Pinus halepensis* Mill., *P. pinea* L., and *P. brutia* Ten. will not germinate at all if sown during the summer. For successful establishment, these species must germinate just before the first heavy rains.

Seeds of fast-growing species—those that do not need more than eight months in the nursery—should be sown during late spring. In this group are *Casuarina* spp., eucalypts, and acacias; these should be sown in the order given. Seedlings are transplanted when they are about one month old, and the transplants are ready for field planting early in the winter of the same year.

A too early sowing of fast-growing species often results in excessive top development; but a too late sowing, during the high temperatures of summer, will result in low germination and increase the likelihood of losses from damping-off. If eucalypts are sown too early, during cool spring weather, they either germinate slowly or fail completely.

All seeds of a given fast-growing species should not be sown at the same time; rather they should be divided into four or five equal lots and individual lots sown in sequence at intervals of about a week to ten days. This procedure not only will reduce losses from unexpected heavy rains, but also will ensure a steady supply of seedlings of the desired size for transplanting.

Seeds of most of the broad-leaved species to be grown as naked-rooted plants are generally sown at the end of winter or in early spring. This group includes *Robinia pseudoacacia* L., *Fraxinus* spp., *Acer* spp., *Melia azedarach* L., and *Ailanthus altissima* (Mill.) Swingle. Seedlings should be ready for field planting the following winter.

Labels. In nurseries growing many species and especially where the seedlings are of different provenances, it is of utmost importance to indicate the origin of the plants. Each lot of seed sown and of plants lined out must be labelled immediately after planting. The label should show the species and the identification number by which the origin of the seed or seedlings can be traced. It is also useful to add the date of sowing or transplanting. In addition, a map should be prepared of the nursery beds showing the position of each lot of seedlings or transplants so if the label is lost a reliable record of the origin of the plants will still be available.

All these efforts will be wasted if similar care is not exercised to maintain the identity of plants at all stages during handling and dispatch, and even until they are planted and labelled in the field.

Several types of labels including wood, plastic, and aluminum are available. More important than the type of label used is to have the writing on the label legible and not effaced by water or handling while they are in use in the nursery.

Seedbed-Sowing Techniques. Whenever it is possible, it is a good practice before sowing seeds to sort them into three size classes by sieving and to sow each size in separate beds. This should result in stands of seedlings that are nearly uniform in size in the seedbeds. Uniformity of seedlings will allow cultural practices to be based on seedling size and result in production of higher quality planting stock and a saving in time and money.

Seedbeds may be sown either broadcast or in lines. Broadcast sowing is done by scattering the seeds by hand, or by shaking them from cans that have perforations in the lid to allow the seeds to drop through. Extremely small seed should be mixed with some inert, granular, bulking material to facilitate even distribution. If beds are broadcast sown, hand weeding or chemical weeding must be used because the continuous carpet of seedlings will not permit the use of machines. In most nurseries hand weeding is more expensive than mechanical or chemical methods.

In arid-zone nurseries sowing in lines has generally been more successful than broadcast sowing. For sowing in lines, parallel drills (lines impressed into the seedbed) are made 20 cm (8 in)—or any desired distance—apart. The depth of the drill varies with the species to be sown. The drills are conveniently made by pressing the cleats of a "marking board" or "marking roller" into the soil.

A typical marking board consists of five to ten parallel wooden cleats, separated from each other by the desired spacing between lines of seedlings. They are secured to cross-bracing or fastened directly to a wide board or piece of plywood. The cleats are usually triangular or an inverted trapezoid in cross-section. The length of the cleats varies, but often it is made the same as the bed width so that the lines of seedlings will run across the bed, making hand weeding easier. Some nurseries use marking boards up to 3 m (10 ft) long and make the drills for seeding run the length of the bed. The "marking roller" is a weighted wooden or concrete cylinder with the cleats fastened to it parallel to its axis or with protruding bands, resembling tires, encircling it and separated from each other by the desired spacing between rows. The length of the roller is usually just slightly less than the width of the bed, and the drills, either transverse or longitudinal, are made by pulling the roller the length of the bed.

A seeding trough is an aid in obtaining even distribution of seeds throughout the length of the drill. A simple trough can be made by hinging two boards to each other in such a way that the hinged joint can be closed to form the trough and opened to release the seeds. The seeds can be easily distributed evenly along the bottom of the trough with the fingers.

After the seeds are sown, whether broadcast or in drills, they should be covered with sand, which should be gently pressed down to eliminate air spaces around the seeds and establish a good contact between the seeds and the soil. A light, smooth roller or a wide board placed over the row and pressed down with the feet will give the desired firmness without packing the soil. Sand is preferred for covering because it does not crust over and interfere with seedling emergence during germination.

Where machine cultivation is used, the distance between rows will depend on the size and type of equipment. If opening of the furrow, sowing, and covering are done manually, special care must be taken to keep the furrows parallel and straight to avoid destruction of seedlings by machine cultivators. When cultivation is done by a plow and disc pulled by a tractor, the distance between the rows may be 1.5 m (5 ft) or more. If a small plow, drawn by a horse or mule, is used, closer spacing is required. Where cultivation is by hand, 0.5–0.7 m (1.6–2.3 ft) between rows may suffice. Occasionally sowing is done in double rows about 20 cm (8 in) apart, and cultivation is then carried out only between the pairs of rows. Where furrow irrigation is used instead of sprinklers, the distance between rows may vary from 0.4 to 1.0 m (1.3–3.3 ft). Where machine cultivation is to be used, the length of the rows should be at least 50 m (164 ft).

Density in seedbeds is determined by the ratio between germination and ultimate survival. This ratio is not constant due to differences in seed quality, soil fertility, weather during germination, intensity and quality of nursery care, losses from pests, and competition. A calculated amount of over-sowing must be done to compensate for these and for other unexpected losses. Minimum distance between plants is usually at least 20 cm (8 in), but much denser sowing may be required for some species depending on their pattern and habit of growth. Between 500 and 700 seedlings per sq m (50–70 per sq ft) are expected in the seedbeds when broadcasting seeding is used.

Seed size is another factor in determining density of sowing because adequate space must be provided for the germination of each individual seed. The amount sown per unit of area or length of line depends upon the species, the cultural practices, and especially upon the germinative energy and purity of the seeds. A team of two men using a seeding trough can sow 30 m (100 ft) of seedbeds 1.2 m (4 ft) wide in an hour. In large nurseries, beds are sown using commercial agricultural seeders modified to handle forest tree seed.

Depth of sowing also depends on the size of the seed. The normal depth of sowing is from one to three times the diameter of the seed, but in many places it is desirable to sow slightly deeper to avoid the washing of seeds from the soil by irrigation and heavy rains.

Seedlings of most species of *Pinus, Eucalyptus, Casuarina,* and *Cupressus* are transplanted in the nursery before they are ready for field planting. Some fast-growing species can be field planted immediately after lifting them from the seedbeds. Seedlings which are not transplanted should be grown in lines or rows. When conifer seedlings are raised for subsequent transplanting, the seeds should be sown in beds in the same way as for seedlings that are planted directly in the field.

Container-Sowing Techniques. Most broad-leaved species are sown in beds, including *Ailanthus altissima* (Mill.) Swingle, *Dalbergia sissoo* Roxb., *Robinia pseudoacacia* L., *Acer* spp., *Fraxinus* spp. and the majority of the deciduous species of *Quercus.* However, species that produce long tap-roots, such as carob, *Ceratonia siliqua* L., are usually grown in containers.

In general, conifer seedlings grow more slowly than seedlings of broad-leaved species. Seeds of most conifers are usually sown in seedbeds and, if necessary, the seedlings may later be transplanted into containers. But several species of pine, e.g., *P. pinea* L., produce strong taproots and are sown directly in containers. Recent experiments in the Sudan show that even small seed such as those of *Eucalyptus microtheca* F. Muell. can conveniently be sown directly in polythene tubes. Four or five seeds are sown per pot, but only one seedling per pot is left to develop.

To reduce the incidence of damping-off, containers should be filled with a light soil which has not been previously used. When the soil is put into the container it should be pressed down to remove air pockets and then carefully levelled. It should then be thoroughly watered to ensure an even distribution of moisture throughout the container. After the excess moisture has drained from the container, the seeds may be sown and covered with clean sand to a depth equal to about twice the diameter of the seeds. Small seeds, such as those of the eucalypts or *Casuarina* spp., can be sown on the surface and then covered with sand. Larger seeds should be pressed lightly into the soil before being covered. The covering soil is gently firmed about the seeds, and the container again watered.

The maximum number of seedlings that can be grown per container will vary with species characteristics and size of container. From 300 to 500 seedlings of most species can be grown in cans 24 × 24 × 12 cm (9.5 × 9.5 × 4.7 in) high. However, only 100 to 200 carob (*Ceratonia siliqua* L.) seeds can be sown in cans of this size because the seedlings must remain in the cans longer than most other species.

Germination tests should be used to determine the amount of seed needed to yield at least 2 or 3 seedlings per pot. It is better to over-sow and have to thin out the unwanted seedlings than to have to resow because of poor germination or to replace seedlings that die.

Sowing in containers has several advantages. (1) The containers can be easily moved with the growing seedlings to the planting site. (2) The seedlings are kept fresh with a minimum of soil disturbance until they are planted. (3) If all seedlings in a container cannot be planted in one day, those left are protected from drying. (4) The danger of seedling loss because of spreading disease in the soil is much less for those grown in containers than for seedlings grown in beds.

Care During Germination

Seedbeds will require thinning to obtain uniform and proper distribution of plants. Where seedlings are too dense, the surplus must be removed to permit healthy development of the remainder. Although many seedlings may be raised in a single container, only one vigorous seedling should be left per pot after transplanting, if the intact soil ball containing the roots is to be field planted.

During and immediately after germination, artificial shading may be desirable although it is expensive especially if used on a large scale. The best height growth of seedlings occurs under about ⅓ to ½ shade, but growth is more uniform when seedlings are grown in the open. Standard frames with wire netting may be covered with sacking or with other material, such as bamboo sticks or leafy branches, to provide the desired amount of shading. Care must be taken to ensure good aeration through the seedbeds because the warm, moist atmosphere associated with poor ventilation is very favorable to the development of damping-off fungi. Furthermore, excessive shading may cause etiolation and delay hardening-off in the autumn.

During germination and the seedling stage, care, other than frequent and careful watering, is usually not required. Even if an overhead irrigation system is available, watering before and during germination should be done by hand using a watering can or fine spray from a hose. Several waterings daily may be necessary because the soil must be kept moist at all times. Watering must be done in such a way that the germinating seeds will not be disturbed nor the soil puddled. After the seedlings have passed through the germinating stage and have become established, less frequent watering will be required, and overhead irrigation may safely be used.

Depending on the species, seedlings will usually be ready for transplanting when they are from one to four months old. Care of seedlings that do not require transplanting is identical with that given the seedlings that do.

Transplanting

Any plant that is growing in or that has been lifted from the seedbed in which it was originally sown is technically a "seedling." If a seedling is lifted and replanted in the nursery in another bed or receptacle it is thereafter termed a "transplant." Seedlings and transplants are further classified by the length of time they were grown as seedlings and transplants in the nursery. The class of stock and its age is conventionally shown by two numbers separated by a plus (+) sign or hyphen (-). The first number indicates the number of years or fraction of a year that the plant was grown as a seedling, the second figure the number of years or fraction that the plant was grown in the nursery after transplanting. Thus planting stock designated as "1 + 1" is two growing seasons old. It was grown for one season in the seedbed and was then lifted, transplanted, and grown for another season in the transplant bed. Seedlings up to one year old that have not been transplanted are designated "1 + 0" stock. If the stock was transplanted twice, first after one year as a seedling and the second time after one year as a transplant, and if it subsequently remained in the transplanted bed two more years, it would be referred to as "1 + 1 + 2" stock. Transplants should be used in all unfavorable sites. A compact, fibrous root system and average or larger stem diameter are important characteristics of good planting stock for such areas. It is very important that the transplants are large enough so that their roots will not be wholly in the dry surface soil after field planting.

Most species grown for afforestation in arid zones are transplanted in the nursery at least once. This applies to those raised in containers as well as those grown in seedbeds. Transplanting is routine nursery practice for the most important species of conifers, eucalypts, and *Casuarina*.

Transplanting principles and techniques for each nursery need to be considered carefully because this is a critical factor in the successful operation of a nursery.

Transplanting of seedlings is done primarily to induce better development of the root system by increasing the number of fine, absorbing rootlets, which develop most profusely near the severed root ends. Top growth may be checked slightly by transplanting and, if the reduction of top growth is small, a more favorable top/root ratio is obtained. High-quality transplants essentially have a normal top and a compact root system with a large number of fine, absorbing rootlets. The presence of such absorbing roots increases the probability of establishment on severe sites. Long, shoestring-like roots have relatively little absorbing surface and also present difficulties in field planting. In addition to giving the individual plant more space for crown and root development, transplanting makes it possible for the roots to reach a greater amount of soil nutrients and moisture.

Transplanting requires precise organization and sufficient labor. The time of transplanting depends on many different factors, including time the seeds were sown, rate of seedling growth, climatic conditions, and immediate availability of potting materials or space in the transplant beds.

Seedlings of *Pinus halepensis* Mill., *P. brutia* Ten., *P. nigra* Arnold, and *Cupressus* spp. may be transplanted after the cotyledons cast off the seed coat and unfold completely, and the plumule begins to develop. By this time the stem of the seedling should be partly lignified and strong. This stage of growth is attained about two or three months after sowing, usually during early to midwinter. Transplanting may continue until the end of winter. Early transplanting is desirable to permit the seedling to recover from the shock of being moved and to attain the size required for field planting. If transplanting is done too late, the plants will not reach the necessary size before the end of the field-planting season during the following winter and will have to be kept in the nursery another year. Such seedlings occupy valuable nursery space, require extra labor for their care, and because of their large size when lifted are expensive to plant.

Eucalypt seedlings are transplanted about a month after sowing when they bear three or four leaves. Consequently, their transplanting must commence in early summer and be finished by midsummer, otherwise the transplants will be too small for planting during the most favorable season. *Casuarina* spp. are also transplanted at about this same season, at which time the seedlings are from 3 to 4 cm (1.2–1.6 in) high.

Acacias and other legumes are transplanted when the first leaves appear after the complete unfolding of the cotyledons. It should be re-

Fig. 3–4. Ten-week-old seedling of *Acacia cyanophylla* Lindl. The lance-olate phyllodes are the expanded petioles of the compound leaves.

membered that, although many acacias (e.g., *A. cyanophylla* Lindl.) develop true leaves after the unfolding of the cotyledons, these true leaves are soon reduced to flat expanded petioles (phyllodes) which carry on photosynthesis but are not true leaves (Fig. 3–4). In these species, the time of transplanting should be determined by observation of the succession of the different leaf forms.

No general rule for time of transplanting can be given to include all species grown in a single nursery, much less those of different nurseries. Usually transplanting should be done before the seedling has acquired a large, heavy root system but after it has developed a strong stem. This stage occurs just after the complete unfolding of the cotyledons and during the unfolding of the first true leaves. Species whose seedlings develop a strong taproot, such as oak (*Quercus* spp.) and carob (*Ceratonia siliqua* L.), suffer heavily from transplanting. Consequently, current practice is to propagate carobs in the nursery by sowing in receptacles and to regenerate oak by direct seeding in the area to be afforested. The usual practice with all species of stone pines is to sow the seeds directly in the field. However, *Pinus pinea* L. can be successfully transplanted into pots or field planted when the seedlings are three months old. When transplants that have been grown in pots are field planted, care must be taken not to disturb the soil containing the roots.

The time of transplanting varies with species and should be decided exactly according to the prevailing climatic conditions. The best weather is a cloudy day with a high humidity. These conditions are frequently found in some regions during the winter months. During the late spring, broad-leaved trees, such as the eucalypts, should be transplanted only during the early morning hours. As soon as the temperature begins to rise sharply the work must be stopped.

Drying of the roots during transplanting should be avoided. Therefore, before transplanting, the soil in the containers or beds should be thoroughly watered. Transplanting during the period of hot wind will result in low survival. Rootlets of the planting stock must never, under any circumstances, be exposed to the direct rays of the sun.

In hot weather the seedlings must be shaded during the first two or three days after transplanting. When large numbers of plants (even including eucalypts) are transplanted in the nursery, it may be necessary to work continuously throughout the day. This can be done with reasonable safety, if adequate shading is available to protect the seedlings. Shading may be provided by temporary, movable frames or by permanent lath covers.

The seedlings should be lifted from the seedbeds in such a way that a clump of seedlings, with sufficient soil to protect their roots, can be put into a receptacle and transported to the transplant area. If seedlings have been raised in cans, the cans are carted to the transplant area. As transplanting proceeds, small clumps of seedlings, with the soil still adhering to their roots, are taken from the can and wrapped individually in a piece of moist sacking. Care in handling seedlings is very important, and this work must be well supervised.

Transplanting into the soil or into containers is usually done with a dibble. The dibble is basically a pointed stick (Fig. 3–5). It is usually a piece of round wood or metal about 25 cm (10 in) long and 3 cm (1.5 in) in diameter, sharpened at one end and with a handle at the other A hole is made by pushing the dibble into the soil, then a seedling is removed from the clump; its roots are pruned by pinching with the fingernails to fit the depth of the hole prepared, and it is quickly inserted in the hole. The soil is pressed against the rootlet with the dibble. This work is usually carried out by women, who are more adept than men at this kind of task. When about 200 or 250 seedlings have been transplanted, they should be watered. If the seedlings are transplanted into cans, the seedlings should be lightly sprinkled with a watering can after approximately every dozen cans have been completed.

Cans and pots should be arranged in beds. To facilitate transplanting and weeding by hand from either side, the beds should not be more than 1–1.2 m (3–4 ft) wide. Footpaths between the beds should be 40–50 cm (16–20 in) wide. One seedling only is transplanted into each pot, but when cans are used the number of seedlings per can depends on

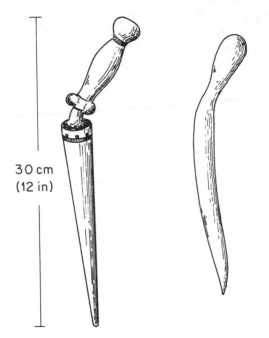

30 cm
(12 in)

Fig. 3–5. The dibble is used for making holes for transplanting seedlings.

the size of the can and the species. A convenient number for cans 24 × 24 cm (10 × 10 in) is generally 12 to 16 per can.

Transplanting into soil, rather than into receptacles, may be done rapidly and uniformly with a "transplant board." The transplant board is a surfaced board about 15 cm (6 in) wide, 2.5 cm (1 in) thick, and any convenient length between 1 and 2 m (3–6.5 ft). A thin narrow strip is nailed close to one edge, and this is notched at regular intervals to give the desired spacing between seedlings. Seedlings are laid in the notches with their tops against the board and their roots hanging down below it. The seedlings may be held in place by a string and rubber band stretched the length of the board over them, or by a clamp made by hinging a narrower, second board to the first by means of two handles about 30 cm (12 in) long fastened to the outside of the boards and at right angles to their long dimension (Fig. 3–6).

The boards are "threaded" with seedlings in a sheltered place and then taken quickly to the transplant area. The transplant board is held at ground level above a previously prepared ditch so that the roots of the seedlings hang in the ditch; usually they are held against the vertical wall of the ditch. The ditch is then filled with moist soil which is firmed about the roots. The string or clamp is released from the tops of the seedlings and the transplant board is removed. Simple transplant boards can be made of wood as described; however, some nurserymen prefer transplant boards of aluminum or other light metal because they are more durable and do not warp.

Transplanting is also done by specially designed machines. Several different types are commercially available. The transplanting machine usually consists of from one to five units, each of which is basically the same as a field-planting machine. A unit consists of a narrow, wedge-shaped double mouldboard plow that opens the soil momentarily as the machine is pulled along. The roots of the seedlings are placed in the slit by hand or by attaching them to clips on a wheel, which revolves and releases them in the slit. Up to 50 trees per minute can be planted by each operator (Fig. 3–7).

Potted and Balled Stock

In arid zones, foresters encounter great difficulty in successful field planting of naked-rooted stock. This difficulty, due to dry soil during and after planting, can be overcome by planting stock that has the root system contained in a ball of soil. The ball of soil retains moisture during transport and for a short period after field planting, and thus protects the roots from desiccation. In addition, the nursery soil forming the ball will inoculate the soil of the planting site with the necessary mycorrhizal

Fig. 3–6. The clamp-type transplanting board. (Photo Forest Service, USDA.)

Fig. 3–7. A four-row transplanting machine in operation in the Colorado State Forest Service Nursery. The naked-rooted seedlings are held by stiff leather clips near the edge of the planting disc.

fungi. Bare-rooted plants may suffer a "physiological shock" when lifted from the seed bed causing their metabolic processes to drop to abnormally low levels until new rootlets are formed, whereas these processes in balled plants continue virtually unaffected by transplanting, if the plants are properly handled. For these reasons, balled plants and those grown in containers usually show a much higher survival and a better growth rate than naked-rooted plants when planted in arid zones. The more arid the area, the greater is the need for using balled plants or container stock.

Potted stock is produced in the nursery either by raising seedlings in containers of various types or by transplanting seedlings into containers. The seedlings with a ball of soil encasing the roots may be removed from the container just before field planting; when certain containers are used, the container with the seedling is set in the ground. Containers for growing plants have been made from nearly every kind of material and in a great variety of shapes and sizes. All are designed to retain the soil around the roots of the seedlings until they are planted and thereby increase the rate of survival in field planting. This gives them their main advantage over naked-rooted plants. A disadvantage of most, if not all, receptacles is that if the plants are kept in them too long, the root system may be deformed by spiraling or in other ways.

Seedlings of many species such as eucalypts and pines grown by sowing the seed directly in receptacles are suitable for field planting in a year or less, if all environmental conditions are maintained at optimum levels. Three or four seeds are sown in each receptacle and about three weeks after germination the seedling are thinned leaving only one per container. If more than one vigorous seedling develops in a receptacle, it may be worthwhile to transplant the extra plants to other receptacles in which the seedlings have not developed well. The change from sowing eucalypts in seedbeds and later transplanting the seedlings into pots to sowing the seed directly in the receptacles has reduced the nursery time from 9 months to 6 months or less. This new procedure not only aids planning of nursery work, but also reduces costs. However, before abandoning the older method in favor of growing seedlings of any species by direct sowing in receptacles much research will be needed to determine whether such seedlings will be suitable for outplanting.

Species that produce long taproots immediately after germination, such as *Ceratonia siliqua* L. and *Acacia albida* Del., are grown in containers because, if these plants are grown in seed beds, their roots are likely to be severely damaged when they are lifted for field planting. Potted plants are also somewhat more tolerant of variable weather conditions than naked-rooted stock. In addition, their planting season can often be extended a few days or weeks longer than that suitable for naked-rooted plants. However, potted stock will not survive under conditions unfavorable for the species and one should carefully consider the environmental requirements of the species in relation to conditions on the prospective planting site before field planting.

Orders for large quantities of containers must be prepared well in advance of the time they will be needed. The selection of the type of container usually depends on the availability and cost of the raw material and manufacturing. A steady production of plants requires a large supply of containers, therefore the material for making containers should be easily and cheaply available close to the nursery. The price of the containers must be kept as low as possible, especially if the containers can be used only once, since this factor greatly affects the total cost of the planting stock. If containers are used several times, durability and rate of amortization must also be considered. Large-scale orders for containers should not be placed without extensive trial plantings of all the species to be raised and the investigation of their behavior in the nursery and the economics of their use.

In spite of the relatively high expense of planting balled stock, it will often prove more economical than the initially cheaper method of planting naked-rooted stock. The high rate of survival, plus early, uniform and rapid growth, reduce both beating-up (restocking) and tending operations.

The dimensions of the container affect both its weight and the volume of soil available to the plants. Small, light containers are to be preferred over large, heavy ones because they reduce the cost of transport and handling. Container size should be adequate for growing seedlings for one or two seasons. A container holding 0.6–0.8 liter (35–50 cu in) of soil is recommended. Larger containers will be required for special ornamental stock or for raising seedlings of species with long taproots, whose development would be adversely affected by root pruning. The shape of the container does not affect seedling development, but rectangular or hexagonal containers are advantageous because they can be placed tightly together without leaving open spaces between them, thus preventing the waste of irrigation water and the growth of weeds. One or two holes must be provided in the bottom of each container to allow excess water to drain away. The color of the containers may be an important factor in the growth of seedlings. In hot arid countries, light-colored containers are preferred to dark ones because they reflect more incoming radiation and minimize overheating of the soil. The container should also be of material that will have no adverse chemical effect on plant growth.

Many types of containers and techniques are used for producing planting stock. These can be divided into four groups according to the raw material used in their manufacture, size and shape, and method of use. The four groups are: wall-less containers, biodegradable pots, non-biodegradable pots, and "plug" units. Examples of wall-less containers are root balls, soil balls, and pressed soil blocks. Biodegradable pots include containers of paper, wood veneer, and recently some plastics. Non-biodegradable pots are those of metal and plastic, including the mini-containers developed mainly in Canada, such as the Ontario tube and the Walters' bullet. Plug units comprise all those containers from which the seedlings are removed and planted with the roots and soil (i.e. the plug) intact. Earthenware and concrete pots and metal cans are the traditional examples of this type whereas styroblocks, single cells, and "book" planters constitute the modern types.

Root Balls.   The simplest method of producing balled plants is to allow the roots of the seedling to grow throughout a confined volume of soil, forming a ball that will be held together by the root system, if the soil is not too sandy. This method is quite efficient and wherever suitable soil is available near the nursery it is widely used for raising balled stock of various pines, acacias, eucalypts, and species of *Casuarina* and *Prosopis*. This technique has all the silvicultural advantages of the more elaborate methods of producing balled stock, plus convenience and economy; the principal cost is only the small amount of additional labor required to separate and lift the balls.

The root balls are prepared by first laying out transplant beds of the same size as those normally used. The soil is removed from the bed and the bottom and sides are covered with asphalt paper or with cement. Each bed is then partitioned by bricks, boards, or planks, or by galvanized or tinned sheet metal, into many small square compartments containing 0.6–0.8 liter (35–50 cu in) of earth. One or more seeds are planted in the center of each compartment. Soon after germination all but one vigorous seedling are removed from each compartment. The roots of the seedling, restricted by the compartment walls, are forced to grow throughout the soil mass—forming a dense ball. When the seedlings are needed for field planting the dividing walls are removed, leaving each plant in its own separate root ball ready to be lifted and shipped to the planting site.

Soil Balls. Soil containing silt and clay and not over 50 percent sand may be pressed into a ball. Light soil, containing too much sand, should be mixed with a binding agent, such as straw, clay or manure. Sand may be added to soils containing too much silt or clay until just the right consistency is obtained. Before the ball is formed, a sufficient amount of water is worked into the mixture to bring it to the right condition of plasticity. When this condition has been reached, the moist earth can be gently squeezed by hand into a spherical form and it will retain its shape without exuding moisture. After each ball is cast or pressed in a simple mold it is usually placed in the sun and left until dry. One or two seedlings are transplanted into each ball and they are arranged in beds. The balls will keep their shape from three to six months under irrigation, root pruning, lifting, and transportation. Root pruning will be required, because without it the roots of seedlings frequently grow out of the ball and occasionally from one ball to another. If root pruning is not feasible, the seedlings will have to be planted out while still small. However, if the plants are not kept too long in the ball, they produce a root system without deformation.

In India, unbaked soil bricks have been used quite successfully in establishing trees on shifting sands. The bricks are made of a mixture of equal parts of clay, local soil (usually sand), and cow dung. The materials are pulverized, sieved, and kneaded with just enough water to give the proper consistency. Each brick is a frustum of a square pyramid 30.5 cm (12.2 in) high with top and bottom surfaces 10 and 15 cm square (4 and 6 in), respectively. A mold used for casting the bricks is made of wooden planks approximately 2 cm (0.8 in) thick, firmly dovetailed together. The inside dimensions of the mold are those of the bricks. A hole approximately 13 cm (5 in) deep and 3 cm (1.2 in) in diameter is made in the top of each brick by pushing a dowel into the compressed mixture in the mold. After removing the mold the bricks are dried for a day or two either in the shade or sun, depending on the local weather.

Three- to four-month-old seedlings are transplanted from the nursery beds into the hole in the soil brick. The bricks are arranged in closely packed rows, often in nursery beds that have previously been covered with a layer of leaves to keep the roots from penetrating into the natural soil. The soil bricks and the spaces between them are covered with sand to a depth of about 1 cm (0.4 in) to prevent erosion of the bricks during irrigation or rains. The sand in the bricks renders them sufficiently porous to enable the root system of the seedlings to ramify with ease, quickly filling the entire body of the brick; the cow dung holds the moisture as well as being an excellent fertilizer, and the clay supplies the cohesive property to hold the brick together. Field planting consists of transferring the bricks with their established and vigorously growing plants into 25 × 25 × 25 cm (10 in) pits. The slight hygroscopicity of the brick, by drawing moisture, helps the seedlings endure the dry season.

For planting eucalypts in Brazil, a method has been developed for molding rough hexagonal pots from a mixture of mud and straw by using a hand-operated soil press. In a single operation the press produces seven hexagonal pots 15 cm (6 in) deep and 6 cm (2.4 in) in diameter with a planting cavity about 2 cm (0.8 in) wide and 6 cm (2.4 in) deep. The daily output is as high as 2,500 pots per man. Large seed such as those of pine and acacia may be sown directly in the hole. With small-seeded species such as the eucalypts, seedlings are transplanted after filling the cavity with a mixture of soil and manure, or with compost (Fig. 3–8). In Portugal, a small press has been evolved for producing balled stock of eucalypts. Pots 12 cm (4.7 in) high and 8 cm (3.1 in) in diameter with a cavity 4 cm (1.6 in) wide and 5 cm (2 in) deep are produced one at a time. The amount of soil per pot averages less than 1 kg (2.2 lb). The daily output per worker is from 2,000 to 3,000 pots. In Morocco a light, hand press is used which produces two hexagonal blocks at one time. A crew of five workmen can produce 5,000 blocks per day and place them directly in the beds. (Fig. 3.9).

Many varieties of soil presses are commercially available. They are either hand-operated or provided with an electric motor, and can produce many different shapes and sizes of pots.

Where large peat deposits are available, peat balls have been prepared and successfully used. In a few countries, peat pots are made and sold commercially. In some areas, the peat is of such texture and consistency that it can be carved, as it is mined, directly into the requisite size and shape for use in the nursery.

Fig. 3–8. Hexagonal pots molded from mud are used in Brazil. (Courtesy FAO)

Fig. 3–9. Mud pots are made in Morocco from a mixture of straw, manure, and soil, or from forest soil only. (Photo S. Al Lozi)

The "brika" developed in Latvia is a peat ball-container combination in which the seedling's roots are sandwiched between two thin bricks of pressed peat. The two bricks are held together by a wrapping of perforated plastifoil, or by a special glue. The bricks used for pine are 16 cm high, 5 cm wide, and 1.5 cm thick ($4 \times 2 \times 0.6$ in); longer brikas are recommended for dry, stony sites. Brikas are soaked in a fertilizer solution to promote rapid growth in the nursery. Preparation of the brikas is partially mechanized. They are field planted after one growing season in the nursery either by machine or by using a specially designed dibble.

Earthenware Pots. Earthenware pots are among the best containers for raising balled stock, but their high initial cost plus about 20 per cent annual breakage often make their use uneconomical. Nevertheless, they are extensively used in arid-zone nurseries. Under favorable conditions and with careful handling, they may last six or seven years (Fig. 3–10). The conical shape of earthenware pots makes it easy to remove the soil mass containing the roots intact before field planting. However, due to their circular cross-section, even when they are placed as close to each other as possible, spaces where weeds can grow will be left between pots. A floor of concrete, sheet metal, or tar paper can be used under the pots to prevent weed growth.

Standard pots have a small hole in the bottom to permit drainage of excess water. This hole is usually covered with a small pebble, seashell, or potsherd to prevent the soil from trickling out, but this may also keep the roots from growing through the hole into the soil under the pot. If the root is confined to the pot, it will be forced to grow into an undesirable spiral knot. Therefore, it is better to allow the roots to grow out of the pots and prune them at least once, the final pruning is made about a month before field planting.

Pots, 8–12 cm (3.1–4.7 in) high, 9–13 cm (3.5–5.1 in) top diameter, and 4.5–7 cm (1.8–2.8 in) bottom diameter, are widely used for raising pines, cypresses and eucalypts. They have also proved very satisfactory for raising large seedlings of acacias for deep planting in moving sands. Several one- to four-month-old conifer seedlings may be grown together in a single pot. Usually, the pots are taken to the planting site, where the seedlings are planted individually with a ball of soil around their roots. Occasionally, the ball with the seedlings or transplants is taken out of the pot in the nursery, wrapped in paper, and packed in boxes before being taken to the planting area. This practice reduces the cost of transport and eliminates breakage of pots.

In India, *Prosopis* and *Albizia* are raised in bottomless earthenware pots that are about 15 cm (6 in) in diameter at the top and 10 cm (4 in) at the bottom. Species of these genera are also raised in cylindrical pots

Fig. 3–10. Types of containers used for sowing and transplanting in nurseries. (Courtesy FAO)

which are 7 cm (2.8 in) in diameter and 25 cm (10 in) long. Eucalypt seedlings in Rhodesia are transplanted into bottomless earthenware cylinders of about 15 cm (6 in) inside diameter. When the seedlings are about 15 cm (6 in) tall, they are field planted. The pots are not removed but merely cracked, and both pot and seedling are planted.

Concrete Pots. When earthenware pots or other types of containers are difficult to obtain or if they are very expensive, concrete pots may be used. These are much stronger than earthenware pots and, as a rule, last longer. A mixture of cement to sand in a 1 to 4 ratio is used. Large numbers of concrete pots can be made in a short time, using a mold similar to that used for making cement building blocks. They are cheaper to produce than earthenware pots because they do not require baking, use less expensive equipment, and the materials for their manufacture are easily available almost everywhere. In a few places, they are even cheaper than containers of waste metal. Concrete pots can be cast as frustums of cones or as square prisms; square pots are usually preferred because they can be tightly arranged in rectangular blocks. Concrete pots are also easier to handle, and therefore are more economical to use in the nursery despite the fact that they are heavier than earthenware pots and hold nearly twice the volume of soil held by circular pots of the same depth. Recommended sizes are 12 × 12 × 12 cm (4.7 in) for conifer stock and 9 × 9 × 11 cm (3.5 × 3.5 × 4.3 in) for broad-leaved species, such as the eucalypts.

To produce 500 large pots, 75 kg (165 lb) of cement are mixed with about 300 kg (660 lb) of fine sand. Two workmen can produce about 1,400 pots in a seven-hour workday. A few hours after they are cast, the pots are removed from the mold and placed on small wooden trays to cure. After they have hardened for a day, they are sprayed with water once daily for about twelve consecutive days. If they are used before completely hardened, seedlings are likely to become chlorotic because of an excess of calcium carbonate. Even after they have hardened, it is advisable to wash the pots thoroughly with clear water to remove any surplus carbonate.

Containers of Local Plant Material.   Bamboo tubes, leaf cups, and wicker baskets have all proved to be satisfactory for raising balled plants. However, their use is limited mainly to tropical countries where ample supplies of suitable materials can be found. If the cost of labor is low, these containers are strongly recommended because the material is cheap, and they are light and easily transported.

In dry tropical forest regions of India, leaf cups (donas) have been successfully used for raising teak. Seedlings are transplanted when they are 8 to 10 days old into donas which are made from leaves of *Bassia, Butea,* or *Diospyros.* Each dona is 12 cm (4.7 in) in diameter and 15 cm (6 in) deep, and has a perforated bottom. The donas are put on bamboo platforms 30 cm (12 in) from the ground, and for most of the day they are kept covered with thin nets of bamboo 2.5–3 m (8–10 ft) above the ground. After two to four weeks, when the plants are 10 cm (4 in) tall, they are pit-planted in the forest without being removed from the dona. Dona plantings have a higher survival rate and better height growth than "stump" plantings of teak.

In the Congo, Kenya, and Ethiopia, eucalypts and other exotics and indigenous trees have been planted in leaf baskets woven mainly from banana leaves.

The use of cane containers for plants is widespread, and excellent results have been obtained. In Malaya, tubes 10–14 cm (4–5.5 in) in diameter and 15–18 cm (6–7 in) long are preferred to larger ones. Smaller tubes, 10 cm (4 in) long and 8–19 cm (3.1–7.5 in) in diameter, split in halves before being filled with earth, are also commonly used. The two halves of each tube are held together by a string. At the planting site the tube is removed and the cylinder of earth holding the seedling is planted. The empty tubes are returned to the nursery and re-used. Because of their small size, the cost of transport to and from the planting site is very low. Species having rapid root development, such as *Pinus canariensis* C. Sm., cannot be transplanted before the roots emerge from the end of the tube, or the seedlings will be too small. During root pruning, the plants are lifted from the nursery bed and graded by size before the tubes are put back in the bed.

In east Africa, pots are made from bamboo of not less than 5 cm (2 in) internal diameter by cutting the stem into sections 45 cm (18 in) long. To provide a bottom for each pot, the lower end of each section is cut just below a node. A hole 1.5 cm (0.6 in) in diameter is bored through the nodal partition to permit drainage. The pots are then split lengthwise and one of the halves of each section is soaked for several hours in a 1.25 per cent solution of sulphate of ammonia. After the pots are reassembled by wiring, each pot has one treated and one untreated half. As soon as the seedlings are ready for transplanting, they are transferred to the tubes, which have been previously filled with a good soil mixture. Just before field planting, the halves of each pot are separated by cutting the wire. The roots of the seedlings will be found clinging to the treated half; this half with its plant is inserted into a hole made with a crowbar, to avoid damaging the roots. The hole is then filled, and the soil firmed around the roots. The other halves of the bamboo tubes are reused in the nursery.

Tubes of cane and sunflower stalks have been used as containers in the eastern Mediterranean region. The seedling is planted together with the tube, which eventually rots away in the soil. Excellent results have been achieved with Aleppo pine, *P. halepensis* Mill., and carob, *Ceratonia siliqua* L., in this type of planting. Sunflower stem tubes are about 25 cm (10 in) long and 2.5 cm (1 in) in diameter. They are filled with ordinary soil and fine humus, and then the tubes are packed tightly in a box and sown with two or three seeds. Only the best seedling in each tube is eventually planted in the field.

Veneer and Wood Residue Containers. Containers made of veneer or of sawmill residue, such as shavings, are often used in areas where planing mills and plywood plants provide a ready source of raw material. Wooden boxes made for other purposes can be used as plant receptacles, but these may at times have disadvantages of weight and size. However, where they are very inexpensive their use is fully justified. Veneer tubes, if made from scrap, are usually available at low cost. In treating the boxes or tubes with wood preservatives, care should be taken that the preservative does not seep or diffuse into the soil and damage or kill the seedlings.

It has become standard practice in South Africa to raise transplants in nursery trays, each containing 25 to 30 plants. The plants are conveyed to the site in the trays and individually lifted and planted with a planting trowel. Nursery trays and boxes are made of recovery wood of low grade and reject material. They are creosoted and may last for several seasons. Standard size is 30 × 25 × 10 cm (12 × 10 × 4 in). Individual plant boxes may also be used. If root pruning is needed, the trays are lifted just above the ground surface by placing them on laths, and a thin wire is pulled back and forth under the tray until the roots that have grown through the bottom of the tray into the soil are severed. Boxes measuring 12 × 45 × 66 cm (4.7 × 18 × 26 in) are used in Turkey for raising eucalypts in the nursery. The boxes are buried flush with the ground, a practice that greatly reduces watering costs.

Veneer tubes that are used only once can be produced cheaply in some localities. Such tubes can be unrolled cleanly without disturbing the soil or roots, and the plant and earth ball removed with ease, leaving the root system comparatively undisturbed. If desired, the tube itself can be planted with its seedling. The planted tube will rot in the soil within one season.

In Australia, 1 mm *Pinus radiata* D. Don veneer is cut into rectangles, which are rolled into tubes secured with one or two rubber bands. The diameter and length of tubes currently used range from 20 × 15 to 50 × 25 cm (8 × 6 to 20 × 10 in). Tubed seedlings are put out in boxes, where they remain until planted in the field. The tube, since it is cheap enough to be considered expendable, is planted together with the sapling and is left in the ground to rot. When tubes are used for raising eucalypt seedlings, two or three seeds are sown in each tube and grown in it till ready for planting in the field.

Veneer tubes have proved very satisfactory for raising planting stock in Malaya, where they have been adopted as a standard material for growing forest planting stock. Veneer, usually 1–2 mm (0.04–0.08 in) thick, of many species, peeled at local plywood factories, is used. The standard size for the rectangle is 35 × 22 cm (14 × 9 in). This is rolled into a tube 10 cm (4 in) in diameter by 22 cm (9 in) high. In Malaya, untreated veneers rot in about six months, but veneers impregnated with wood preservatives have been used three or more years without loss. The preservative treatment consists in soaking air-dried veneer for two minutes in 3 per cent copper naphthenate. There is some loss from splitting with use. However, split veneers can be reused by inserting a narrow strip of broken veneer inside the tube before filling it with soil.

After rolling, the planting tubes are secured by placing a thin galvanized wire ring about 10 cm (4 in) diameter (made in advance) over each end of the veneer. A handful of grass is pushed to the base of the tube, which is then filled with potting compost. The compost is consolidated by lifting the tube a few times and dropping it on a firm surface from a height of 5 cm (2 in). In planting out, the bottom wire is removed and the plant in the tube placed in a planting hole of the correct depth. After the hole has been about one third filled, the veneer tube is drawn up off the cylinder of earth containing the seedling.

Paper and Cardboard Containers. In recent years, there has been a growing interest in the use of paper and cardboard containers. Several advantages are cited for these containers: they are lightweight and easy to handle; the roots of the tree may grow downward because tubes of suitable depth can be easily produced; and the small tree and its container may be planted together, saving time and avoiding injury to the roots.

Many different methods have been described for producing tar-paper tubes. One of the easiest is to roll a rectangle of bituminous paper of suitable size into a tube and to fasten it at each end with a hand stapler.

Planting receptacles of asphalt paper with a square cross-section are also used. These receptacles are 12 cm (4.7 in) high and 5 cm (2 in) square. The asphalt paper is cut so that when it is bent, the four flaps protruding form a square which becomes the base of the receptacle. The flaps are sealed with asphalt and stapled to complete the assembly. The completed receptacles are collapsible and, therefore, easy to transport. A 25 m (82 ft) roll of asphalt paper is enough for 300 receptacles, and an experienced workman can make 125 receptacles or more per hour.

In the Colorado (U.S.A.) State Forest Service Nursery a potting system has been devised based on the assembly line concept. Potting is done in six steps and requires the services of six persons to operate the machine. Molds for shaping the pots are carried on an endless chain that moves past the workers. The first worker pushes a "square" of tar paper into the potting mold forming, in effect, a tube open on one side. The other workers, in turn, put the soil and seedling in the partly formed pot, add enough more soil to fill the pot, and then staple the sides together to form a square tube. The crew of six can pot 3,000 seedlings per day. Tar paper pots have two serious disadvantages; roots grow through the sides of the pots in the nursery making them difficult to handle and after field planting the tar paper restricts soil moisture from rain or irrigation from entering the tube.

A paper container system developed in Japan for growing sugar beet seedlings has been adapted by Finnish foresters for raising tree seedlings. In 1974 twenty-eight percent (175 million) of the seedlings planted in Sweden and Finland were grown in these containers. This system consists of an assembly of open-ended paper tubes, hexagonal in cross section and glued with an adhesive that is insoluble in water. Individual pots are joined to each other with a water soluble glue to form a honeycomb array of closely joined containers (Fig. 3–11). The irrigation water dissolves the glue that sticks the pots to each other while the individual pots remain intact and can be removed one at a time for planting. Three grades of paper are available; each with a different breakdown rate depending on soil conditions. Individual pots range in size from 2 to 10 cm (0.8 to 3.9 in) in diameter and from 3 to

13 cm (1.2 to 5.1 in) in depth. The size most commonly used for forest planting is approximately 4 cm (1.6 in) in diameter and 8 cm (3.2 in) tall and has an estimated breakdown time of 6 to 8 months. Each set of pots is received collapsed and is opened up by pulling the two ends apart so that the expanded set covers a tray measuring 34 × 94 cm (13.4 × 37.0 in). This set contains 336 pots or 1050 per square meter (98 per sq ft). The pots are filled with peat, soil, or compost and the material is slightly compacted before seeds are sown or seedlings transplanted into the pots. It is not necessary in planting to remove the pots. This is the only container system for which a full array of filling, sowing, handling, and planting equipment is commercially available.

Wood-Pulp Containers. Wood-pulp containers formed of unbleached wood pulp bound together with resin or some other adhesive are relatively new in horticulture. They are pressed into the desired shape in a mold. Unfortunately almost all of the containers commercially available are too shallow for forest nursery use. Some wood-pulp containers that are molded with six to twelve receptacles in one piece resemble egg trays. Seedlings may be field planted without removing them from the containers; their roots easily penetrate the soft material of the container. Further experimentation with this material is needed in forestry. It is cheap, relatively tough and light and appears to be very promising.

Metal Containers. Discarded cans are widely used for growing most evergreens, such as pines and cypresses, as well as carobs, eucalypts, and acacias. Since they are not porous, less water is required to grow plants in them than in other receptacles. Usually they are not too heavy, and their cost is relatively low where canned food is extensively consumed. Any empty food can may be used as a container for growing plants, provided its size is suitable. One to several holes should be punched in the bottom for proper soil drainage. The cans can be used only once because they are cut open to remove the seedling before planting. Cans may be planted out with the seedling, provided the holes at the base are large enough for the roots to pass through. The seedlings' growth will not be impeded because usually the cans will rust or corrode in a few years. Normally only one seedling is raised per can. Species with a taproot may be grown in large, tall cans. Large-size can openers for removing the lids are commercially available. However, several nurseries have devised their own can openers. These are of various types, but all have long handles to give leverage. In a few places it may be economical to make containers from the waste tin plate of canneries. Tinplate and other sheet metal containers can be produced in the nursery; the necessary tools are forming blocks, sheet metal shears, and hammers,

Seedlings of some species of *Acacia, Eucalyptus,* and *Casurarina* have been adversely affected by growing in galvanized iron containers; the symptoms were yellowing of the foliage, stunting of growth, and occasionally death. Root growth was normal until the roots touched the metal tube, whereupon progressive dying back of the roots occurred. Some evidence was found to indicate that excessive watering aggravated this condition. Rusty tin plates or uncoated steel tubes, whether rusty or not, were found to be satisfactory. A test of the suitability of metal containers prior to raising large quantities of plants is, therefore, strongly recommended.

Galvanized iron tubing, usually 15 × 15 × 5 cm (6 × 6 × 2 in), is in standard use in Australia to contain *Pinus radiata* D. Don seedlings. The tubes are made locally by rolling the sheet to form the cylinder and joining the two opposite, longer edges by a simple 1 cm (0.4 in) lock, or grooved, seam.

Disused jerricans and other types of petrol cans have been converted into two containers each by cutting the jerricans lengthwise, parallel to their wide, flat sides. Each half is approximately 36 × 32 × 9 cm (14 × 12.6 × 3.5 in) or 26 × 26 × 8 cm (10.2 × 10.2 × 3.1 in) and is large enough to accommodate several seedlings. Provision for drainage is made by punching holes in the base. Root pruning is done, as a rule, by lifting the can and breaking the roots that have grown through the drainage holes. Shallow containers have proved very successful as seedbeds for both conifers and eucalypts. For growing larger plants, a single container can be made from each jerrican.

If special containers for growing plants are to be ordered, a convenient size is 24 × 24 × 12 cm (9.5 × 9.5 × 4.7 in). Twelve to 16 plants can be grown satisfactorily in this size. In field planting the containers are transported to the site. The seedlings may be individually lifted with a planting trowel. However, a more common practice is to carefully invert

Fig. 3–11. The Japanese paper pot and plastic tray. Retaining clips on the right and stapling pliers on the left. (Courtesy Canadian Forest Service, Great Lakes Forest Research Centre)

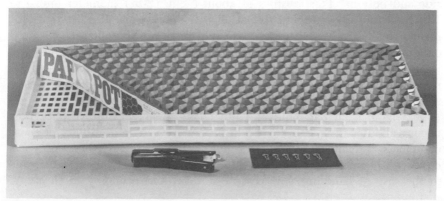

the receptacle near the planting holes. The receptacle is then removed, leaving the entire black ball of soil over the seedlings. Each plant is then cut from the soil block, separated by hand, and planted.

Plastic Containers. A recent development in the production of balled stock has been the introduction of plastic containers. These include polypots and minicontainers such as Ontario tube, the Walters' bullet, and plug units.

Polypots. Polypots, also known as polybags, polythene tubes, and plastic bags, have a number of advantages. They are light and compact, which reduces to the minimum the cost of handling in the nursery and transportation from the nursery to the planting site. They require little space for storage and are easily handled in the nursery during filling, sowing, root pruning, and lifting. Polypots do not become brittle with age and are not adversely affected by watering. If the polythene is 0.15 to 0.2 mm gauge (6–8 mil) or over, the pots will not deteriorate before the field planting season. However, the exposed upper edge of the pots may be slightly weathered by the sun. The plastic used is chemically inert and no adverse effects on root growth have been detected. Polypots have been successfully used in raising both transplants and directly sown seedlings.

Polypots can be purchased or, if plastic sheets are available, they can be prepared in the nursery in suitable sizes and shapes for different species. All that is needed is a knife to cut the sheets to size and a hot iron to seal the edges. They are quite inexpensive when made in the nursery, or when purchased in large quantities, and have been found in many places to be much cheaper than other forms of receptacles. Because of their economy they have tended to replace the other types of receptacles.

Polypots can be obtained in nearly any size desired. However, the most commonly used pots are 8 × 8 ×16 cm (3.1 × 3.1 × 6.3 in), made of 0.15 to 0.2 mm gauge (6-8 mil) plastic film, and seamed along the side and bottom. Plastic tubes of about 5-cm. (2-in) diameter and 5 to 10 cm (2 to 4 in) long, cut to size in the nursery, are also in vogue for raising small eucalypt seedlings. In field planting polypots can be used only once.

In Italy, particularly in Sicily, reusable plastic bags are employed for rearing both conifers and eucalypts. These bags are made of heavy gauge film and are approximately 10 cm (4 in) in cross section and 18 cm (7 in) long; each bag holds 1.3 liters (80 cu in) of soil. Eighty pots occupy about 1 sq m (1.2 sq yd) in the nursery. The durability of these containers is claimed to be over five years. Although these polypots cost slightly more than earthenware pots, they are cheaper to use due to the ease of handling, low cost of storage, and economy in shipping.

To avoid loss of soil during shipment, the top of the bag can be closed tightly around the stem of the plant by pulling a thread enclosed in the top seam. However, polypots that are used only once are preferred in most other countries because culling and sorting damaged bags is not necessary.

The lower part of each polypot is perforated with about 30 holes. The spacing and size of the holes is variable, however, holes 2 mm (0.08 in) in diameter have given good results in providing drainage and reducing root spiraling. Drainage holes of this size are also large enough for the egress of roots after field planting. The sides or bottoms of the bags should be slit or the container completely removed from the root ball before planting. Complete removal of the polypot is especially advisable when planting in irrigated areas to ensure that sufficient water will reach the roots.

The most serious disadvantage of the polypots is encountered when they are used for growing plants with strong taproots; once the developing taproot is constricted and forced to twist it usually remains deformed. Consequently, seedlings should not be kept in polypots too long. This means that the time of sowing seeds must be coordinated with the time of field planting.

Bags may be of any color, but white, transparent, and black are the most commonly used. It is claimed that white bags give the best results because they reflect part of the sun's heat and prevent excessive heating of the soil, thus reducing loss of soil moisture through evaporation. Seedlings grown in polypots of various colors have shown no difference in survival percentage or growth rate in the nursery.

After the tubes are filled, the soil should be lightly compacted. The polypots filled with soil are tightly packed in sunken beds in the nursery with their upper edge level with the paths. Seeds or seedlings may be planted in the pots either before or after they are put in the beds. By packing the bags tightly hardly any space is left among them for weeds to grow or for irrigation water to be lost (Fig. 3–12).

Various types of utensils and equipment have been devised for filling polypots with soil and to improve the efficiency of the operation. These include a long-necked funnel, a combined scoop and funnel, various types of soil hoppers with funnels attached, and a semi-automatic filling and planting machine used in Italy. The principal parts of this machine are a turntable, a soil hopper, and a grip to hold the seedling during planting (Fig. 3-13). A bag is clipped to the turntable with the roots of the seedling dangling inside it. The soil is then released from the hopper and falls around the roots holding them in their "natural" position. Once the bag is filled it is released from the machine. Four people using this machine can transplant over 400 seedlings per hour.

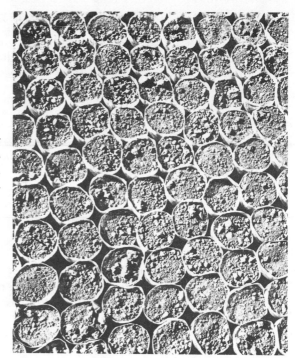

Fig. 3–12. Plastic containers filled with soil. These are used only once. (Photo V. U. Contino; courtesy FAO)

Fig. 3–13. A filling and planting machine for plastic bags used in Italy. (Courtesy FAO)

In Israel a soil receptacle-filling machine has been developed. It consists of a soil bin, a soil conveyor and the receptacle-filling part which can be used for filling tins, pots, or polybags with soil. The bin which holds the soil is fitted with a vibrator and sieves of the desired gauges for sifting the soil. The sifted soil is moved to the filling part of the machine by a conveyor and is poured into a funnel with one or two outlet tubes. If the containers to be filled are pots or tins, the receptacles are placed under the tubes and, when filled with soil, they are removed by hand to a platform on wheels, to be carted to the beds for placement. If the containers are polypots, the bags used are made with one side of the bag 2.5 cm (1 in) longer than the other forming a flap that is punched with two holes. The polybags are then mounted by threading the flaps on two parallel horizontal pins protruding from under the funnel, with the short side of the bag facing outwards. An air stream, directed through a pipe from a blower to the top of the first polybag in the stack, opens the bag which is just under the outlet of the pipe. The sack is filled by the soil released from the funnel and is snatched by hand from the pins. The next sack in the stack is in turn opened by forced air and filled. The speed of filling the polybags is regulated by controlling the amount of soil released from the conveyor, by the speed of the workers to stack the filled polybags on the platforms, and by their removal to the nursery beds. Four men are needed on a two-tube machine. One to shovel soil to the bin, two to snatch the filled polybags from the pins and stack them on the platform, and one, with the help of the soil shoveler, to cart the filled sacks to the nursery beds.

Studies of temperature requirements of some mycorrhizal fungi in northern Nigeria show that the maximum temperature that they can tolerate is about 34° C (94° F). Soil temperatures in plastic containers may exceed the maximum limit, if the containers are exposed to direct sunlight; mycorrhizae can then develop only on the shaded and cooler sides of the polypot. When seedlings grown in unshaded polypots are planted in the field, they either die or make extremely slow growth until mycorrhizae develop on the other roots. The plastic walls of polypots prevent the spread of fungi from one pot to another, so if the potting soil does not contain the required mycorrhizal fungi, it will be necessary to inoculate each pot with the proper fungi. In some nurseries the outer row of the bed of plastic pots is held upright and protected from the sun and drying by a border of earthenware or metal containers.

Mini-Containers. Techniques for growing seedlings in plastic containers with relatively small soil capacity have been tried in Ontario and British Columbia, Canada. The Ontario tube is a split styrene plastic tube from 1.4 to 1.9 cm (0.56 to 0.75 in) in diameter and 7.6 (3 in) long. Seedlings are grown under controlled environmental conditions in the greenhouse and field planted after 30 to 70 days, or occasionally the next spring, without removing the tube. However, due to the small size of the younger seedlings, growth rate and survival have been reduced by competition so that the trend has been to use the older and larger seedlings. Assumed, but not proven, disadvantages are constraint of root egress and stem girdling by the tube. About 7 million pine and spruce seedlings are currently being planted in Ontario in these containers.

The Walters' "bullet," developed in British Columbia, is a bullet-shaped receptacle of styrene plastic ranging in length from 7 to 13 cm (2.5 to 5.5 in) and usually with a top diameter of about 1.5 cm (0.6 in) (Fig. 3–14). The bottom is rounded to an acute point and a narrow slit extends the length of the receptacle ending in a hole that is just large enough to permit the passage of early roots. Seedlings are usually grown in the greenhouse or nursery for 1 year before outplanting. The bullets and seedlings are planted with the aid of a spring-powered gun

Fig. 3–14. The Walters' bullet is designed to be planted with a spring-powered planting gun. (Photo J. Walters)

that can hold up to 30 seedlings. The purpose of the slit is to weaken the container and allow it to be broken apart by the growth of the seedling. However, the seedlings are often not able to break out of the containers. Using this method high planting rates, from 2,000 to 6,000 seedlings per man-day, have been achieved.

These containers have such a small volume that in dry areas the soil cannot provide sufficient moisture for the seedlings after planting and before their roots can reach the moist soil outside the container. Consequently, they are not likely to be used in arid zones except in irrigated plantations or during periods of the most favorable soil moisture.

Plug Units. Favorable results obtained by removing the seedlings from the bullet containers and planting them with a dibble with the growing medium adhering to the roots led to the development of the plug method of planting by the British Columbia Forest Service. Four basic types of container systems are used for growing plug seedlings: styroblocks, multipots, single cells, and "book" containers (Fig. 3–15).

Fig. 3–15. Mini-containers. Single cell unit on left, styroblock in center, and "book" planter on right.

A typical styroblock unit is a molded block of expanded polystyrene plastic 35 cm wide × 51 cm long (14 × 20 in) containing 192 cavities. Each cavity is 2.5 cm (1 in) in diameter at the top and 11.4 cm (4.5 in) long with a 7.6 mm (0.3 in) hole for drainage at the bottom. The volume of each cavity is approximately 33 ml (2 cu in). Each block stands on two runners 1.9 cm (0.75 in) high which facilitates drainage and air circulation underneath the block. Roots that grow through the drainage hole are killed back by "air pruning." Each cavity has 4 vertical ribs designed to prevent root spiraling. Several different block and cavity sizes are available. Seedlings are grown under optimum conditions in the greenhouse for 3 to 12 months. Before the seedlings are shipped to the planting site they are carefully pulled from the styroblock with the plug of soil intact. Seedlings are planted in the field by inserting them into a hole the same size as the plug and which is made with a specially designed dibble. An average worker should be able to plant at least 1,500 seedlings per day. The styroblocks can be cleaned, disinfected, and reused.

The multipot system, which is similar to the styroblock system, was developed independently in Sweden. The multipot is a molded plastic gang unit of 67 cavities each 3 cm (1.2 in) in diameter and 8 cm (3.1 in) deep with a drainage hole at the bottom. Seedling culture is the same as that described for the styroblock system. Seedlings are transported to the planting site in the multipots. A modified planting mattock is used for setting out the seedlings. After the seedlings are removed for planting, the multipots are returned to the nursery for cleaning and reuse.

The single cell system produces a seedling plug similar to those of the styroblock and multipot. The basic unit is a molded plastic container 2.5 cm (1 in) in diameter and 12.4 cm (4.9 in) long with a 8.4 mm (0.33 in) drainage hole at the bottom. The individual containers resemble test tubes. Two hundred containers are held in a polystyrene rack 30 cm wide, 61 cm long, and 17 cm high (12 × 24 × 6.8 in). Culture and planting techniques are the same as those described for the styroblock system. An advantage of the single cell system is that non-stocked tubes can be easily replaced with stocked tubes resulting in maximum use of space and economy in production. The racks of empty tubes can be cleaned efficiently in a commercial dishwasher and reused.

The "book" container consists of a set of 4 or more containers molded from a thin plastic sheet into longitudinal pairs of container halves hinged (joined) at the bottom. To form the containers the two halves are folded at the hinge and brought together in the same way as a book is closed; hence their popular name. One size forms 6 containers 2.3 × 2.0 × 10.8 cm (0.9 × 0.8 × 4.25 in). Containers are held in shallow plastic boxes with open grid bottoms which permits drainage and air pruning of roots. Culture and planting techniques are similar to those described for the styroblock system. Book containers can be reused one or two times.

Propagation by Cuttings

Twig Cuttings. Some deciduous species, such as those of *Populus, Salix, Ficus,* and *Tamarix* are usually grown in the nursery from twig cuttings. Other species commonly propagated by cuttings include *Haloxylon ammodendron* Bunge and *Calligonum comosum* L'Herit.

Field planting of twig cuttings as a method of afforestation in arid regions is generally limited to riverine sites and to species that root the most readily from cuttings and whose propagation by seed is difficult or genetically inadvisable; e.g., poplars frequently hybridize and the seed may produce plants unlike the parent tree. Cuttings of most species, including conifers, may be rooted if they are first treated with auxin (e.g., indole-3-acetic acid) and kept in mist cabinets, but in current nursery practice, propagation by cuttings is restricted almost entirely to species that do not require special handling.

Although most pine species are difficult to root, cuttings of *Pinus radiata* D. Don have been grown successfully on a large scale in Tunisia. Twigs taken from the branches of trees approximately 160 years old were planted in perforated polypots in the nursery. The cuttings were protected from desiccating winds by permeable windbreaks and sprayed continuously by mist during the day. About 80 percent of the cuttings developed roots. The cost of the rooted cuttings using this method is equal to, or a little less than, the cost of growing plants from seed. In Australia 30-year-old trees grown from cuttings have shown about the same development as trees of the same age grown from seed. Cuttings of some species of eucalypts have also been propagated successfully using artificial mist.

In easily rooted species (see Table 3–2) that are grown in arid zones, propagation by twig cuttings (as opposed to root cuttings) is comparatively simple. Cuttings are best taken from dormant wood after the leaves have fallen, as with poplar, or after leaf growth has stopped, as with tamarisk. Cuttings taken in the spring are not always satisfactory, because they may produce leaves before rooting and thus reduce their vitality before the roots have become established. Therefore, to insure that cuttings will root before leaf development starts, they should not be gathered too late in the spring.

Table 3–2.   Some arid-zone trees propagated
in the nursery by cuttings.

Species	Remarks
Calligonum comosum L'Herit.	Easily rooted, also grown from seeds
Elaeagnus angustifolia L.	Easily rooted, also grown from seeds
Ficus sycomorus L.	Generally propagated by cuttings
Ficus spp.	Generally propagated by cuttings
Haloxylon ammodendron Bunge	Also grown from seed
Platanus orientalis L.	Difficult to root, generally grown from seed
Populus spp.	Easily rooted, propagation generally by cuttings
Salix spp.	Easily rooted, propagation generally by cuttings
Tamarix spp.	Easily rooted, propagation generally by cuttings

Cuttings are collected only at the time they are to be planted in the nursery, and they should be cut to the required size and planted as soon as possible. If immediate planting is impossible, the cuttings should be stored in moist, sandy soil at low temperatures to prevent development of roots during storage. Cuttings may be stored in boxes, in a manner similar to that used for seed stratification; however, burial in a well-drained, outdoor pit with a covering of moist soil is usually satisfactory.

The size of cuttings depends on the species. A length of 20–30 cm (8–12 in) is satisfactory for tamarisks, whereas poplar cuttings should have at least three or four buds. The minimum diameter may be about 1 cm (0.4 in), but cuttings of a diameter of 1–2 cm (0.4–0.8 in) generally root better. They should be cut to the correct length with small, well-sharpened scissors. As a rule, the cut should be below and as near to a bud as possible. In tamarisks, all the leaves should be removed before planting.

In planting the cuttings care should be taken to put only the lower end of the branch in the soil. For poplars and willows, the proper direction may be easily determined by observing the buds, which point upward, but with tamarisks careful inspection is necessary because it is often difficult to see in which direction the buds point (Fig. 3–16).

Cuttings may be planted either in late winter or in spring. Most cuttings are planted directly in the ground, although tamarisk cuttings are sometimes raised in small cans, plastic bags, or pressed-soil pots. The soil is prepared in the same way as for transplanting, and thoroughly watered before planting. The cuttings should be planted to a depth that will leave about 3 cm (1.2 in), or one bud, above the soil. A planting dibble of wood or iron of sufficient length can be used to make the hole in the ground, and the cuttings should be carefully introduced into the hole; afterwards, the soil should be firmly pressed around them and again thoroughly watered.

Raising Poplar Cuttings in the Nursery.   Special techniques have been developed for raising poplars from cuttings in nurseries. Cuttings are produced from one year old woody branches 10 to 12 mm (0.4 to 0.5 in) in diameter; small twigs and softwood cuttings are rejected. These branches are cut into 20 to 25 cm (8 to 10 in) lengths using a sharp knife or shears. The cut is usually made at angle to the long axis of the stem. To ensure a steady supply of cuttings, trees of the preferred clones may be grown in or near the nursery.

The cuttings are planted during the dormant season in ditches prepared by hand or machines. The ditches are made about 1.5 m (5 ft) apart and the cuttings planted in the ditch at 50 cm (20 in) intervals. The soil should be pressed firmly around the planted cuttings.

Fig. 3–16. *Populus* and *Tamarix* cuttings that have been prepared by overwinter stratification in sharp sand at 5° C (41° F) are planted in shallow trenches in the nursery. Colorado State Forest Service Nursery.

After one year's growth the stems are cut just above the base and used as material for additional cuttings. The rooted stock, known as "barbatells," may also be used for planting. Barbatells are usually left in place for an additional year or two: such plants after one year have 2-year-old roots and one-year-old stems and are designated as R_2S_1, and stock left for two additional years as R_3S_2. The R_3S_2 need slightly wider spacing than R_2S_1 to facilitate the frequent cultivation and irrigation needed to obtain fast and uniform growth. Only one stem and one leader should be left on each plant. All branches are pruned up to about 2 m (80 in) from the ground. To permit more plants to be loaded on each truck, all side branches should be removed in the nursery, not on the planting site.

Well grown R_3S_2 plants may reach more than 4 m (13 ft) in height and over 10 cm (4 in) in diameter, before they are lifted for planting out. A good height-diameter ratio is essential for nursery stock to be field planted. A curved sharp blade attached to a tractor is usually used for lifting these large plants. The blades cut the roots at a depth of about 30 cm (12 in). The lifted plants are then graded, labelled, and tied in bundles suitable for transport. Care must be taken during shipment not to damage these large plants. They should also be protected from desiccation by wrapping with straw or wet burlap.

Root-Shoot Cuttings. Seedlings of certain species, such as *Prosopis juliflora* (Swartz) DC, *Acacia cyanophylla* Lindl., *Dalbergia sissoo* Roxb., and *Morus* spp., are lifted from the seedbeds two to three months before the planting season when they are 1–2 cm (0.4–0.8 in) in diameter. The root system is cut back to about 15 to 20 cm (6–8 in) below the root collar and the stem to about 15 cm (6 in) above it. This root-shoot cutting is planted in a slightly tapered tube that is about 20 cm long and 10 cm in diameter (8 × 4 in). The cutting develops a strong root system without a taproot and is ready for field planting three months after planting in the tube. Root-shoot cuttings have several advantages over seedlings, transplants, or twig cuttings. They are more vigorous and hardy, and can better withstand drought and attacks by ants. They are also more easily transported and transplanted. These advantages suggest that root-shoot cuttings of other species, such as *Prosopis alba* Griseb., *P. nigra* Hieron., and *Aspidosperma* spp., should also be tried.

If moisture conditions are favorable, root-shoot cuttings may be planted directly in the field, where they should develop a root system and become established faster than twig cuttings.

CARE OF NURSERY STOCK

As soon as propagation and transplanting have been completed, the nurseryman is faced with another problem—the care of nursery stock, which may include seedlings in containers or rows; transplants in containers or rows; and cuttings, usually in rows but sometimes in pots. Where the stock is heterogeneous, many different techniques in irrigation, cultivation, weeding, and root pruning are required.

Diseases or insect pests are, fortunately, not common in arid-zone nurseries and, as a rule, the protection of stock is not difficult. Protection against damage by climatic factors, especially heat and drought, however, is of major concern. Irrigation and artificial shading are of course the principal protective measures, especially for sheltering new and valuable plant introductions. Generally speaking, with proper timing of seeding, transplanting, planting, and watering, artificial shading may be avoided, unless the nursery is located in an extremely hot zone.

Protection of Nurseries from Animals and Disease

Large Animals. Obviously, large animals, either wild or domestic, cannot be allowed to graze or browse in the forest nursery. Therefore, the nursery must be protected by fences that are strong enough to exclude these potential marauders.

Small Mammals and Birds. Care before and during germination must include the protection of seedlings against birds and small mammals. Containers and beds with seeds should be protected by screens of fine wire netting having openings no larger than 6 mm (¼ inch) if mice are to be excluded. Wooden or metal frames of a standard size to fit the seedbeds or to cover groups of containers and covered with wire netting are commonly used.

Wind-operated propellers or scarecrows placed around the sown area to keep birds away are generally successful for two or three weeks; shiny pieces of aluminum or tinplate, suspended on strings, and noise-making devices may be effective for a short time. Sometimes it may be helpful to have a man armed with a gun and blank cartridges patrol the area. Automatic "guns" that can be placed in various parts of the nursery as needed and made to "fire" at intervals are available commercially. However, some birds become accustomed to the noise and return to the nursery unless the placement of the guns is changed periodically.

The population of mice and other small mammals may be kept down by trapping or by using grain treated with strychnine, zinc phosphide, or other poison. Care should be taken to keep the poisoned grain away from domestic animals and song birds. The number of small mammals can also be reduced by clearing the surrounding area of the weeds in which they can hide from predators. Straw and litter mulches are particularly attractive to mice and other small mammals. Where beds are mulched with these materials the beds must be completely screened. Mixing poisoned grain with the mulch is also helpful.

Bird and small-mammal damage may be greatly reduced by the use of effective repellents. The two chemicals commonly employed are anthroquinone and tetramethylthiuram-disulphide 50 per cent. The latter is also effective at times as a control for damping-off.

Insects. Ants may steal eucalypt seed, or even seed of other hardwoods and conifers. Where termites are common in the area, the nursery soil should be kept free of all decaying wood. Heavy dosages of carbon disulphide before seeding will free the immediate area of termites, at least for a few weeks.

White grubs, the large, sluggish larvae of the May or June beetles (*Phyllophaga* spp.), often cause serious losses in tree nurseries. The larvae develop in the soil and feed on organic matter and the roots of plants. They may completely consume the roots of a seedling, leaving it standing, delicately balanced, on the base of the stem. The female is attracted to dense stands of low-growing vegetation, such as sod or seedlings in a nursery bed, where she deposits her eggs. Fortunately white grubs are quite sensitive to lack of soil moisture, and although occasionally troublesome in semiarid zones are not normally found in arid areas. White grubs may be controlled by application of 9 kg of chlorodane ° per hectare (8 lb/acre). Application of 10–20 per cent of this amount every

° Users of chlorodane and all other pesticides should comply with the latest national and local laws governing their application.

2 years will maintain the dosage level. Excellent control of white grubs may also be achieved by fumigating with 1 kg of methyl bromide per 10 m² (2 lb/100 ft²).

Cutworms, the larvae of moths of the family Phalaenidae [Noctuidae], cause considerable damage in some seedbeds by feeding on all parts of young seedlings and by severing some at the ground line.

Tip moths, larvae of the genus *Rhyacionia* [*Evetria*], may infest hard pines grown in nurseries from populations in neighboring plantations. The larvae kill the developing leader, stunting growth and producing a malformation of the stem. Beds that have been infested should be sprayed with an effective insecticide or fumigated for 2 hours with methyl bromide. All hard pine planting stock in areas where tip moths are present should be carefully inspected before shipping from the nursery.

Disease. Care must be taken in nurseries to detect diseased plants before the disease can spread. Exotic species are often more susceptible to diseases than native plants especially where the soil is wetter or drier than that of their normal habitat, or where soil pH is unfavorable. Some diseases are more active during certain seasons of the year and are more easily recognizable during that period. It is advisable to have repeated inspection because plants may appear healthy during one inspection and show disease symptoms a few days later.

One must be extremely careful when importing living plants from other areas not to import a disease along with the plants. The imported pathogens may be more damaging in the new area than in their native habitat, or they may spread to native plants. Occasionally native diseases cause more damage to the exotic species than to their native hosts.

Damping-off is a common and serious disease in virtually all forest nurseries. It is a pre-emergence and seedling disease caused by more than thirty different fungi. Some of these fungi attack the seed just as germination starts, whereas others infect the newly germinated seedlings. Many hardwoods are susceptible to the disease; oak, elm, and black locust are particularly so. Nearly all conifers planted in arid zones are also susceptible; however, *Cupressus* and *Juniperus* are resistant. Affected seedlings either topple over as though broken at the ground line, or remain erect and dry up. A watery-appearing constriction of the stem at the ground line is generally the visible evidence of the disease; decay occurs in the root as well as the stem.

Damping-off is favored by high humidity, damp soil surface, heavy soil, cloudy weather, too much shade, dense stands of seedlings which reduce evaporation, organic matter, high nitrogen, and alkaline conditions (generally a pH of 6.0 or higher). Warm weather increases its spread; consequently seed should be sown not too early in the autumn or too late in the spring, depending on local climate.

A number of cultural measures can be used to combat damping-off. One of the best preventive measures is to maintain a dry soil surface through cultivation. Another is to reduce the density of sowing and eventually to thin the seedlings to create better aeration at the ground line. Shading of the beds should be minimum, and during long periods of cloudy weather the material shading the beds should be removed entirely.

Chemical controls for damping-off are of three general types: soil sterilization, soil acidification, and treatment of the soil or seeds with fungicides.

Soil sterilization is quite effective in controlling pre-emergence damping-off, but much less efficient in combating post-emergence losses. The two most commonly used chemicals are formaldehyde (formol) and methyl bromide. Both chemicals are dangerous and should be handled carefully and according to the directions given on the labels. Standard dosage of methyl bromide is 50 to 100 gm per m^2 (1–2 lb per 100 ft^2) applied as the vapor under a polyethylene cover several days before seeding. Commercial 40 per cent formaldehyde may be used in water solution. The effective dosage is 80 cc per 5 liters of water per m^2 (¼ fluid oz/pint/ft^2). Formaldehyde should be applied 7 to 10 days before sowing. In addition to reducing the incidence of damping-off fungi, both chemicals give some control of nematodes and weeds.

Soil acidification is especially beneficial in arid-zone nurseries because of the natural tendency for soil alkalinity in low rainfall areas. Acidifying chemicals that have been used in tree nurseries include sulphuric acid, phosphoric acid, acetic acid, sulphur, aluminum sulphate, ferrous sulphate, and copper sulphate. Sulphuric acid has generally been the most satisfactory chemical for acidifying the soil. The amount needed to reduce the pH to an acceptable level (i.e., about pH 5.8) depends on the initial alkalinity and texture of the soil. Usually the equivalent of from 200 to 400 cc per square meter ($\frac{1}{16}$ to ⅛ fluid ounce per ft^2) of concentrated sulphuric acid is applied in dilute solution (2 per cent by volume).

Aluminum sulphate or ferrous sulphate applied in solution at the rate of 150 gm per m^2 (½ oz per ft^2) has given good post-emergence control. Dry aluminum sulphate crystals broadcast over the beds at the same rate and followed by irrigation are also effective. It is important that the solution reach the ground line where the infection exists. Seventy-five to 150 gm per m^2 (¼–½ oz per ft^2) of pulverized sulphur worked into the upper 15 to 20 cm (6–8 in) of the soil will maintain an effective pH longer than any of the other soil acidifying treatments. However, sulphur must be applied at least a year before seeding to avoid injury to seedlings.

Fungicides are single chemicals or combinations of two or more chemicals that are toxic to fungi but that, in the amounts used, will not harm seedlings. They may be applied to the soil or to the seeds before planting. The action of fungicides is similar to that of chemical sterilants, but less severe. Fungicides that are efficacious for controlling damping-off are commercially available under a variety of trade names. Some that have been successfully used in dry zones are thiram and captan; both are organic compounds. These may be applied as a dust or in water suspension directly to the soil before or after seeding. A number of other seed-protectant fungicides are also available; but those containing organic mercury compounds must not be used. Seeds are dusted with enough of the chemical to cover each one completely with a thin layer. Seed protectants are pre-emergence fungicides.

Pelleting or covering the seed with a thick protective coating of fungicides and binders has given better control of damping-off than seed protectant dusts. To form the pellet, the seed is first coated with a sticker of methyl cellulose or latex, then with the effective chemicals; after drying, the pellets are sown in the usual way. In addition to fungicides, rodent and bird repellants or fertilizers may also be included in the pellet.

Approved insecticides, fungicides, and animal repellants can be injurious to humans, domestic animals, desirable plants, honey bees, and fish or other wildlife if they are not handled or applied properly. Such chemicals must be selectively and carefully used, excessive application must be guarded against, and surplus chemicals and their containers must be disposed of as recommended by manufacturers and governmental agencies.

Several management practices are valuable in alleviating disease in the forest nursery. These include proper selection of the site and fertilization. Judicious application of organic nitrogen or phosphorus or potassium where these elements are deficient in the nursery soil has proved helpful in combating many diseases. Disease prevalence in nurseries is closely associated with deficiency or excess of soil moisture and soil aeration. Thus, adequate irrigation and proper drainage can have much to do with reducing disease.

Soil Fertility

Certain mineral elements must be available in every nursery soil or seedlings will not develop normally. If the soil is deficient in these mineral elements, or if the soil was depleted of its mineral nutrients by repeated production of plants, the seedlings will usually exhibit various symptoms indicating the lack of these essential elements. Occasionally a deficiency exists which is not indicated by visible symptoms and is revealed only by chemical analysis of plant parts. In arid zones the stronger and more frequent deficiencies appear in nitrogen, but sometimes potassium is deficient, and less often phosphorous is lacking in adequate amounts. Each of these elements, together with adequate amounts of certain other elements, produces a characteristic growth response. Proper application of the deficient elements is therefore extremely important in producing high quality planting stock.

Nitrogen. Available nitrogen in the soil comes from the decay of organic matter, nitrifying bacteria, rainwater after lightning discharge, and fertilizers. Nitrates and other nitrogen compounds are very soluble and easily leached from the soil. Despite the great amount of nitrogen in the air, few plants can use it unless it is in combination with other elements, as it is in fertilizers. Nitrifying bacteria that live in nodules on the roots of legumes and some other plants can use atmospheric nitrogen to make proteins which are later decomposed by other bacteria, ultimately producing nitrates. Mycorrhizal fungi are important in accumulating nitrates and supplying them to the roots.

The growth of stems and leaves is increased by nitrogen when supplies of other plant nutrients are adequate. Nitrogen is required in the production of proteins and chlorophyll; a healthy green color shows the presence of sufficient nitrogen. But the lack of green color does not always indicate nitrogen deficiency; e.g., manganese deficiency causes a yellowing of leaves. Insufficient available nitrogen is shown by stunting of the plant and undersized, chlorotic leaves which sometimes are tinted with red. Excessive nitrogen stimulates a too luxuriant growth; the whole plant becomes lush and soft, more susceptible to disease, and often does not harden before the autumn frosts.

Increased growth brought about by a good supply of nitrogen increases the demand on the soil for other elements, and deficiency symptoms of these may appear unless a properly balanced fertilizer is used.

Phosphorus. Natural phosphorus compounds in the soil are insoluble, but through chemical and biological action a small amount is made available to plants. The supply of phosphorus in nursery soils is usually quickly depleted and must be replenished by fertilizing. Availability of phosphorus is much influenced by acidity of the soil; the best range of pH is 6.0 to 6.5. In soils below pH 5.5 or above 6.5, soluble phosphates are changed to insoluble forms. In the alkaline soils of arid regions, especially those containing free calcium carbonate, soluble phosphates are converted into a nearly insoluble calcium phosphate which is barely available to plants.

Phosphorus promotes root development, particularly in the early stages of growth. It increases the production of chlorophyll and nucleic acids, which are needed for the conversion of starches into sugars and the assimilation of fats. Phosphorus is especially valuable in heavier soils that hinder root growth. If plants do not receive enough phosphorus, their root systems are stunted; this reduces their absorption surface and makes them less able to withstand drought and other adverse conditions.

Potassium.   Potassium is held in exchangeable form by clay minerals and organic matter, which slowly release it into the soil solution. Unless the soil is fertilized the amount of potassium available to plants is small; this is especially true of sands, other than those recently deposited by the sea, and of peats. High levels of nitrogen and calcium interfere with potassium assimilation.

Potassium apparently is involved in the production and breakdown of starches and sugars. Plants receiving potash fertilizers are less severely attacked by fungi and are better able to resist frost damage.

There is a direct relationship between potassium and water loss; plants that receive adequate potassium can better resist drought. This fact is extremely important in producing plants for arid-zone afforestation.

Fertilizer Requirements

Soils of arid zones usually have an excess or at least an adequate amount of calcium, magnesium, and potassium, but they are likely to be deficient in phosphorus and nitrogen. Deficiencies in sulphur and boron may also be found locally. The high alkalinity of calcareous soils interferes with iron absorption. Some species introduced into arid zones become chlorotic because of poor iron metabolism, although the actual iron content of the soil may be quite high.

Periodic soil analyses made by the specially trained technicians of a soils laboratory will be needed for proper soil management. The results of these tests, especially those for total nitrogen, available phosphorus, and available potash, will show the need for fertilizing if serious mineral deficiencies exist.

If the services of a soils laboratory are not available, much can be learned by small scale tests of fertilizer response and careful observation of the vigor, color, and evenness of seedling growth. Yellowing of foliage is likely to be due to a lack of nitrogen or immobility of iron, especially if there is an excess of lime carbonate. Purplish coloration may be the result of phosphorus deficiency, although in some species purple tinges are normal. Uneven growth, especially in newly established nurseries, may indicate the need for inoculation with mycorrhizal fungi.

The bulk of nursery stock produced in arid zones is raised in containers, and, if the soil is used only once, care must be taken to select a soil with good fertility.

The problem is entirely different where plants are raised directly in the soil. Even a good tract of land cannot be expected to maintain its fertility and productivity over many years without replenishing the soil

nutrients. Plant growth in hot arid-zone nurseries is unusually rapid because of the favorable climate and irrigation; it is especially rapid when
the plants are grown directly in the soil. The reduction of soil nutrients
by the nursery stock is very great because of the density of plants and the
long growing season. Rapid growth is made possible by a proper level of
soil nutrients. Because seedlings are removed completely at the end of
the production period, most soil nutrients are soon reduced far below
their optimum. The two most critical elements in maintaining nursery
soil fertility are nitrogen and phosphorus. Productivity can and must be
maintained by using fertilizers of one or more types which can be broadly
classified by origin as vegetable, animal, and chemical.

Fertilizers of Vegetable Origin.   The most common kinds of fertilizers of
vegetable origin are humus, green manure crops, and compost. Although
humus scraped from the forest floor may be obtained cheaply in some
places, it is generally unsatisfactory due to the weeds, damping-off fungi,
insects, small mammals, and other pests brought into the nursery by
its use.

Crop rotation in the forest nursery is an excellent practice. Different
tree species should be raised in sequence on a given field, followed by a
green manure crop every third or fourth year. The green manure crop
may be a legume, a grain, or another crop in keeping with local farming
practices. This crop is plowed into the soil while still succulent and well
before its seeds mature. The crop should be sown in the autumn or
spring, according to local custom, and turned over in the summer. A
heavy crop may be disced before plowing to ensure more complete in-
corporation into the soil. Plowing should precede sowing tree seed or
transplanting by at least one to two months. The green manure crop not
only releases its accumulated mineral nutrients to the soil when it decays,
but it also improves aeration and water relations by its bulking action.

Compost made in the nursery may be used, if suitable materials for
its preparation are available. Compost is prepared by making a pile
consisting of alternating layers of vegetable material or animal manure
and soil. Vegetable material may be hardwood leaves, straw, peat, or
leguminous plants, such as peas. Each layer, 10–20 cm (4–8 in) thick,
receives a small quantity of commercial fertilizer, principally nitrogen,
at the rate of 50–100 kg (100–200 lb) per ton of compost. The pile is
watered and allowed to decompose during which process the organic
material becomes crumbly and the carbon-nitrogen ratio is reduced. The
pile is usually turned over several times and may be ready for use after
six months.

Compost heaps are, however, expensive, and in normal nursery operations animal manures, chemical fertilizers, and soiling crops will be more
economical and more satisfactory.

Fertilizers of Animal Origin. Fertilizers of animal origin include not only farm manures but also bone meal, fish meal, dried blood, meat-and-bone meal, hoof and horn, and tankage. Only farm manures are commonly used in forest nurseries.

Animal manure is an excellent source of nitrogen and small amounts of other valuable plant nutrients. It is also very valuable in maintaining soil tilth and in increasing the water-holding capacity of the soil.

When animal manure is applied, it must be thoroughly rotted to reduce the number of viable weed seeds brought into the nursery and to prevent injury to the plants by the strong chemicals present in fresh manure. Because animal manure loses much of its nutrients by exposure to direct sunshine or through leaching by rain, it should be stored in a shed. If large amounts are to be used in the nursery, the construction of a concrete pit, protected by a roof, is recommended.

The amount required depends on the type of animal manure and on the level of soil fertility. One half to one cubic meter is needed per hectare (7–14 ft^3 per a). It is spread on the soil surface and immediately plowed into the soil. Animal manure is difficult to obtain in many countries because it is in great demand not only for fertilizing agricultural crops but also as a fuel, a situation that makes the price prohibitive for forest nursery use.

Chemical Fertilizers. Local requirements for chemical fertilizers (e.g., ammonium sulphate, ammonium nitrate, superphosphate, and so on) to supply the necessary nitrogen or phosphorus to the soil will vary. Often potash will also be needed. Although each required element could be added separately, it will usually be better to use a combined fertilizer and thus provide two or more essential nutrients in a single application.

Liming may be needed if the soil is deficient in lime. But lime deficiency is rare in arid-zone soils, and the need for liming is extremely unusual; too much lime rather than too little is likely to be the problem.

Commercial chemical fertilizers may be purchased in several forms: as powders, or crystals, or solutions of compounds containing the desired mineral nutrients. Powders and crystals may be the pure compounds, or they may be mixed with a bulking material to make application easier.

The composition and grade of combined fertilizers in terms of the three primary nutrients (nitrogen, phosphorus, and potassium) is shown by a three-part conventional numbering system, such as 15-30-15, 5-10-0, and so on. These numbers give the percentage by weight of total nitrogen, available phosphoric acid, and available potash. Therefore, a 15-30-0 fertilizer is incomplete because it contains only nitrogen and phosphorus. The percentage of mineral nutrients in some common commercial fertilizers is given in Table 3–3.

Table 3–3.　Percentage of mineral nutrients in some common commercial fertilizers. (Great Britain Ministry of Agriculture, Fisheries, and Food. Bul. 195, 1964.)

Fertilizer	Nitrogen	Phosphoric Acid	Potash
Sulphate of ammonia	21		
Ammonium nitrate and lime	21–23		
Potash nitrate	15		10
Superphosphate		18–20	
Ammonium phosphate	11–12	50–60	
Sulphate of potash			48–50
Dried blood	10–14		
Meat-and-bone meal	5–10	16 °	

° Insoluble tricalcic phosphate which slowly changes to soluble forms in the soil.

Excessive applications of fertilizers, especially some chemical fertilizers, can promote the growth of large seedlings with weak succulent stems and an abnormally high shoot/root ratios. Such seedlings are entirely unsuitable for field planting. Over-fertilization can cause losses in seed beds by raising the pH and favoring damping-off fungi, or by chemical burning. Heavy applications of ammonium sulphate and sodium nitrate can seriously reduce the number of plantable seedlings. But in contrast, under some conditions, over 1,000 kg per hectare (890 lb per acre) of 20 per cent superphosphate has been applied with entirely favorable results.

As previously indicated, iron deficiency is likely to be a problem in arid zones. Mild iron cholorosis may be counteracted by use of iron sulphate applied in a 1 per cent solution as a foliage spray, or to the soil in solution at the rate of 30 kg per 500 liters per hectare (27 lb/53 gal/a), or as dry powder or in solution at rates exceeding 750 kg per hectare (670 lb per acre) at the time of seeding. Because uneven distribution of fertilizers causes uneven growth of plants, even distribution is extremely important in the production of high quality stock of uniform size. Iron chelates have been used with considerable success in correcting iron chlorosis in some horticultural crops. However, treatment with iron chelates is still prohibitively expensive in forest nurseries even if no more than 15 to 20 kg per hectare (13–18 lb per acre) is used.

In some nurseries liquid fertilizers have been applied by pumping them through the overhead sprinkler system. Water soluble fertilizers can be placed in a sack that is hung in a barrel and the irrigation water passed through the barrel. Putting fertilizer in a sack will prevent clogging the sprinklers. The rate of application varies from 25 to 75 g per sq m

(0.7–2.2 oz/sq yd), depending on the fertilizer and species. Liquid fertilizers can also be applied with a sprinkling can or back spray. Generally only one application per year is required. Regardless of the method of application, it is absolutely essential that spray irrigation immediately follow treatment to rinse the chemicals from the foliage and prevent fertilizer burn.

Mulching

In nursery and afforestation practice, mulching may be defined as any artificial modification of the soil surface. Many methods are used to modify the soil surface using many different materials; these include soil mulching by ordinary cultivation and coverings of leaves, brush, straw, sawdust, grit, sand, peat, cloth, burlap, and plastic.

The primary purpose of mulching is to conserve soil moisture by lowering soil temperature and physically blocking the loss of water molecules. In arid-zone nurseries where irrigation is necessary throughout most of the year, mulching helps to reduce both the frequency of watering and the amount of irrigation water required.

Nursery practice generally prescribes that seedbeds be mulched to keep moisture in beds during seed germination. This is especially important in arid areas, where all coniferous species and small-seeded, delicate, broad-leaved species should be protected from the sun and wind as soon as they are sown. The surface soil must be kept moist throughout the period of germination. Therefore, seedbeds should be protected by a mulch to prevent drying and to help keep the surface soil adequately and uniformly moist.

Where seeds are sown in open beds, strewing brush over the bed immediately after seeding is one of the simplest ways of protecting it from wind and sun. Freshly cut coniferous branches can be used; care must be taken to distribute them uniformly over the bed. The brush must be removed when the seed begins to germinate. Similar materials commonly used in the same way prior to germination are hardwood leaves, coniferous needles, or weed-free hay or straw. Hardwood leaves that decompose quickly are preferred over the other materials. It is usually advisable to place branches, lath screens, or other material on a leaf mulch to prevent its disturbance by the wind.

Although the mulch is customarily removed as soon as germination starts, chopped straw may be left because the seedlings can grow through it. Several other types of mulching material that do not need to be removed during germination can be used to protect seedbeds against moisture losses. Sand, ash, charcoal screenings, sawdust, and wood chips all make good mulches. The main factors governing the selection of the mulch are availability and cheapness, but it will also be wise to select material that will improve the physical conditions of the soil and its fertility.

Sawdust and wood chips are among the most widely used mulches for covering seedbeds, but they must be used with care. These mulches may cause nitrogen starvation, increase in termite population, or damage by essential oils. However, damage is chiefly by toxic compounds similar to those used to preserve timber. These toxic materials may depress the growth of species other than legumes; the effect is temporary and closely associated with a decrease in available nitrates. Sawdust has no harmful effects, if it is supplemented by a heavy application of nitrogenous fertilizer. This is easily done since sawdust is an excellent absorbant of liquid manure.

Sawdust itself has little value as a fertilizer; its content of plant nutrients and their availability to plants are both low. Its main beneficial effects either mixed with the soil or used as a mulch are physical; it tends to loosen heavy soils and increase their water-holding capacity. It is also very effective in reducing evaporation from the soil surface. Care must be taken to prevent sawdust and seeds from blowing away. A practical method is to cover the sawdust with hay, straw, or burlap; these covering materials should be removed once germination starts. Under some conditions, sawdust mulch may reduce the need for watering by as much as 70 per cent. It also reduces weeding time and often induces fibrous root growth. Either hardwood or softwood sawdust may be used, depending on the pH requirements of the species raised in the nursery. Hardwood sawdust tends to increase soil alkalinity, and softwood sawdust to increase acidity.

Cheesecloth and burlap are widely used in protecting seedbeds prior to germination. Where nursery operations are conducted on a large scale, these materials are usually more satisfactory and often less expensive than covering with brush or mulching with leaves, because of the ease with which cheesecloth and burlap can be placed over the beds and containers and later removed. They have a distinct advantage over natural vegetative material since they do not contain weed seed. In large nurseries, burlap is unrolled onto the beds from a two-wheeled cart as the sowing progresses. As it is spread, a crew follows the cart and pegs the burlap to the edge of the beds. The advantages of cheesecloth and burlap depend chiefly upon the cost of material, length of service, and degree of protection. Cheesecloth gives less protection than burlap. Both are removed as soon as germination starts. Burlap is expensive, and to prevent rotting it should be treated with copper naphthenate, the only efficient preservative that will not kill seeds and seedlings.

Transparent moisture-proof cellophane has been used as a mulch. Cellophane, however, needs some other covering material to hold it in place. The exposed cellophane is easily torn unless burlap, wire netting, or other material is used to hold it in place. Tractor-drawn machines have been devised in Italy to spread the cellophane on nurseries. The cellophane is released from a spool and spread on the ground by a roller while two discs on each side cover the edge of the cellophane sheets with soil to hold it from blowing by the wind. Soon after the cellophane is laid on the ground, moisture will collect on its underside and drip to the ground keeping the seed and the soil moist, thus promoting even and complete germination. Burlap, used as supplementary covering over the sheet of cellophane, is protected from rotting by the cellophane. It remains in better condition and can be used longer than burlap placed directly on the soil. Although watering is not possible without removing the cellophane, the frequency of watering is reduced.

Mulching is a major factor in conserving moisture and regulating soil temperature when raising transplants both in beds and in containers. Water loss from soil, excluding drainage takes place through evaporation from the soil surface and through transpiration by tree seedlings and weeds. Weeding not only reduces transpiration, but it also loosens the surface soil, creating a mulch. The value of weed eradication as a means of conserving soil moisture is hardly to be questioned, but it is not yet clear to what degree a soil mulch is effective in conserving moisture.

It has often been asserted that a soil mulch conserves moisture by disrupting the capillary action of the soil in drawing up water from below, by shading the soil surface and lowering temperatures, and by reducing the surface wind velocity. In opposition to this idea is the contention that frequent disturbance of the soil exposes more moist soil to the air, thus bringing about an even greater water loss than occurs in undisturbed soil. It is certain, however, that soil mulches have been widely accepted in the general practice of cultivation, although their beneficial effect on plant growth is not necessarily or entirely attributable to the conservation of soil moisture. Improved plant growth may be due to better aeration of the soil, or perhaps to the increased activity of soil microorganisms following improved aeration.

In large nurseries, a straw mulch has advantages over soil mulches when transplants are grown in rows or beds; large quantities of straw are required to form an effective soil cover. Where seedlings are grown in rows in the ground, a good procedure appears to be to mow the weeds and spread the cut weeds between the rows. Covering the soil surface with loosely spread weeds will conserve soil moisture and reduce both the frequency and the amount of watering. Mowing should be done about three or four weeks before weeds mature their seeds; timely mowing may be expected to decrease the abundance of the second weed crop, since weed-seed germination underneath the mulch will be much reduced.

When nursery stock is raised in containers, any one of the mulches described may be used to conserve moisture. Weeding in containers either by hand or with selective chemical killers must completely eradicate the weeds. Mulching the containers will reduce competitive weed growth greatly. Sawdust and wood chips are most widely used; the harmful effects of nitrogen starvation can be easily prevented by applying a chemical fertilizer, such as ammonium sulphate.

Mycorrhizae

Mycorrhizae are intimate symbiotic associations of nonpathogenic fungi and the roots of forest trees and other plants. Many species of mycorrhizal fungi are known. In certain tree spieces, notably the conifers, the fungus forms a mantle over the absorbing rootlets. In other species, principally hardwoods, the hyphae actually penetrate the root tissues. In both types of mycorrhizae the hyphae radiate from the roots into the soil. It has been known for many years that pines cannot be grown successfully unless their roots are associated with the appropriate mycorrhizal fungi. However, pines are not the only trees that form mycorrhizal associations; indeed, mycorrhizae have been found on nearly all coniferous species and many hardwoods. The fungus apparently absorbs essential mineral elements and moisture from the soil and transports these to the roots. Some evidence also has been found that these fungi are able to tap nutrient supplies not ordinarily available to higher plants.

In general, mycorrhizal fungi are not exacting in regards to their host species and most of them can ally themselves with a great number of tree species, but a few are quite specialized. Many mycorrhizal fungi are adaptable to a wide range of climatic and soil conditions. For example, *Boletus granulatis* (L.) Murill. which is one of the common mycorrhizal fungi of *Pinus halepensis* Mill. in the Mediterranean basin, is also well adapted to the alkaline soils of La Pampa province, Argentina.

Often some of the species grown in forest nurseries are started from seed imported from distant regions. If compatible mycorrhizal fungi are not present in the soil these seedlings grow poorly or fail completely. Failures of this sort could be avoided if the proper mycorrhizal fungi were introduced into the nursery soil.

Where a nursery soil lacks the appropriate mycorrhizal species needed by the newly introduced trees, the soil should be inoculated with topsoil or litter taken from healthy natural stands or thriving plantations of the host species. This soil presumably will contain a population of the different mycorrhizal fungi required. Great care must be taken to avoid introducing harmful organisms along with the beneficial fungi. A thin layer of the inoculum is spread on the nursery beds or a small amount is mixed with the soil prepared for potting. Once the soil has become infused with the proper fungi, spreading of the mycelium is indicated by dark green foliage and accelerated growth of the seedlings.

If soil inoculum is to be transported over a long distance, it is advisable to keep the soil moist and, if possible, the time in transit should be limited to no more than two weeks.

Once the nursery soil has been inoculated, the fungi will remain in it and rarely will new inoculations be necessary. However, in nurseries where the soil is repeatedly sterilized, the fungicides used usually delay the development of mycorrhizal fungi or even kill them. If this occurs the soil must be reinoculated. Excessive temperatures also have an adverse effect on mycorrhizal development. Some species will not develop in temperatures above 35° C (95° F). Optimum temperatures for the most favorable development of mycorrhizae vary among the different tree species. In hot areas, pots on the outside rows in the nursery beds often fail to develop mycorrhizae normally because they are the ones most affected by the sun's heat. Good soil aeration is also needed for the development of vigorous mycorrhizae.

Irrigation

The object of irrigation of nursery stock is to maintain enough moisture in the root zone to enable the stock to make the desired growth. In arid areas, nursery stock obtains little moisture from precipitation; storage of rain water in the soil is almost nil and of no consequence whatever where stock is raised in containers.

The frequency and amount of irrigation depend on the rate at which water is absorbed by the roots and the water-holding capacity of the soil in the root zone. The rate at which nursery stock absorbs water is determined by the character of the stock and weather conditions. Stock characteristics include species, stage of growth, size, density, and whether it is naked-rooted or balled stock in containers. Weather conditions include temperature, wind movement, and air humidity. The amount of water available in the root zone is related to the depth of soil occupied by the roots (or the volume of soil in the containers) and soil characteristics—chiefly its texture, structure, and content of organic matter. Because so many variables are involved, establishing general rules for irrigation is impossible.

The depth of soil available to root growth and its water-holding capacity are the important soil factors governing the frequency and amount of irrigation that is required. If the subsoil is retentive—e.g., a sandy soil with a somewhat porous subsoil of firm sand or gravel—the amount of water lost by deep drainage is small, and the effects of a fairly heavy irrigation may persist for several days. Care should be taken, especially at the peak of the hot season and with fairly large nursery stock, to apply enough water during each irrigation period to moisten the soil completely to a depth of 30–50 cm (12–20 in). When nursery stock is grown in containers, the depth and porosity of the container itself and the characteristics of the potting soil must be considered. More water is needed for containers with porous walls than for those with impervious walls. If impervious containers are used, care should be taken not to over-irrigate or to permit an accumulation of excess water at the bottom of the container; good drainage of water from containers is of great importance.

Most of the water absorbed by the roots of nursery stock is lost through transpiration; only a small portion is used in photosynthesis and new tissue formation. The amount of water transpired and used varies greatly with the species. Plants absorb water most rapidly when they are in leaf and when making their fastest growth; absorption is less rapid as they approach the time of hardening or shedding leaves; and least rapid when they are dormant. Thus the volume of water applied in any one irrigation will depend on the time of year, the stage of development of the stock, and its size. Frequent and light irrigations are needed for seedlings just past the germination stage. Small amounts of water will suffice because the water requirement of such seedlings is not great.

Quantity of Water. Nearly all plants, even those with normally deep roots, will absorb most of their water from the upper layer of soil when water is available there. This phenomenon should be exploited to discourage deep rooting which will necessitate repeated root pruning or transplanting and render lifting and field planting difficult. Irrigation should aim, therefore, at limiting root growth of nursery stock to the upper 30 to 50 cm (12–20 in) of soil. Excessive irrigation that waters the soil to a greater depth should be avoided. During droughts, roots tend to grow into the deeper layers of soil which do not completely dry out, but if the plants are properly irrigated the roots can be made to grow within a shallow surface zone.

When plants are grown in containers, irrigation should wet the soil to the base of the container, since the depth of the container determines the depth of the root zone. If round earthenware pots are used, the spaces between the pots should be filled with soil and wetted during irrigation to reduce water loss from their porous sides.

Weather conditions strongly influence the rate at which plants use water, and also govern, to some extent, the lower limit to which soil moisture may safely be allowed to drop before irrigation water is applied. During cool, moist, calm weather evapotranspiration is low, and the slow movement of moisture through the soil to the roots is rapid enough to maintain turgor and plant growth. But during hot, dry, windy days potential evapotranspiration will exceed the rate at which moisture moves through the soil to the roots; a water deficit will occur in the plant and it will cease growth, wilt, and possibly die. Rapid movement of soil moisture to the roots during dry periods must be maintained by irrigation.

The method of distributing the water, whether surface, subsurface, porous hose, or sprinkler, will also influence the amount of water required. No irrigation method assures an absolutely uniform application of water, and regardless of method some areas will receive too much and others too little. The excess water will be lost by deep seepage or surface run-off. To prevent erosion, surface run-off must be avoided by careful irrigation or controlled by proper drainage. In most irrigation systems an appreciable amount of water is also lost by direct evaporation from the soil surface. Therefore, it is always necessary to apply more water than the seedlings will actually use. The amount of over-irrigation will depend on the irrigation method. For example, because furrow irrigation does not distribute the water as evenly as overhead sprinklers do, it requires more water.

The proper frequency of irrigation is estimated from the amount required during a single application and the rate of use under different conditions. Only short intervals, sometimes less than 24 hours, may be permitted between irrigations during extremely hot, dry weather; whereas longer periods are set in cool, moist weather and during the time of hardening-off of nursery stock. The exact time for irrigation can be determined only by an examination of the soil and by the appearance of the stock. Plants must be watered on schedule during the growing season; otherwise they may be severely harmed by drought.

The period of irrigation on each field must be long enough for the required amount of water to be absorbed by the soil. The proper length of time can be learned only by experience with the irrigation system, soil, and cultural practices in each nursery. Since the object of all land preparation and irrigation is the uniform distribution of water in the soil, the nurseryman should make certain that the water has penetrated deeply enough everywhere to moisten the soil in the whole root zone. Due to the high evaporation rate at midday, watering should be done either early in the morning or in the evening to minimize losses during and after irrigation. Most irrigation systems can be safely operated all night, provided that they are regulated so that the soil does not become waterlogged. Growth of most forest tree seedlings is slowed or the seedlings may even be killed by waterlogged soil because the excess water interferes with proper aeration of the roots. The optimum amount of water in the soil for best growth depends on soil conditions and species characteristics.

The various types of nursery stock require different irrigation practices. Naked-rooted plants grown in beds can be irrigated by any surface or overhead system, whereas plants grown in containers are usually watered by an overhead system. Adequate irrigation combined with long periods of warm weather promotes rapid growth of the planting stock. Because the cost of raising planting stock depends upon the time required for growing plants to the desired size, the intensity of irrigation should be regulated, if possible, so that most species will not remain in the nursery for more than a year. Broad-leaved species, such as acacias and eucalypts, that remain in the nursery for only 8 months, will need more intense irrigation than conifers, which may remain for 15 months. The desired size of stock should determine the timing and amount of irrigation. When plants have attained nearly the required size, watering should be reduced. Watering should be increased if for some reason, such as late transplanting, it appears that the plants will not attain the required size before the time for field planting.

The approximate total amount of water required for raising 1,000 plants is shown in Table 3–4. However, it appears that accurate data are

Table 3–4. Approximate total amount of water required to produce 1,000 plants.

Culture Method	Conifers (12 months)	Broadleaved (7 months)
	Cubic Meters (*U.S. Gallons*) Required	
Pots	30 *(7,900)*	12 *(3,200)*
Cans	15 *(4,000)*	8½ *(2,250)*
Beds	20 *(5,300)*	8 *(2,100)*

not available giving the volume of water required to produce a crop of coniferous or deciduous nursery stock. The amounts shown will, of course, vary with species, soil, and climatic conditions. Empirical observations indicate that at the peak of the hot, dry season, from 40 to 180 cu meters of water per day is required per hectare (4,300–19,200 gal/day/a) of saplings grown in containers. Intensive cultivation in beds and care in applying water to beds and containers may significantly reduce the amount of water needed.

Because the amount of water that will be needed also depends largely on soil characteristics and rate of infiltration, the soil and subsoil must be carefully examined before designing an irrigation system. The objectives of the system should be to supply water just fast enough to be fully absorbed by the soil and to bring the moisture content up to field capacity without waterlogging the soil. It is recommended that intervals between irrigations be so regulated that the soil moisture will not be reduced to less than 65 per cent of field capacity.

The amount of water that must be applied artificially varies with seasonal precipitation. In wet years, little supplemental irrigation will be needed during the rainy season, but during the dry season and in dry years daily irrigation will be necessary. Therefore, it is advisable to have sufficient water available throughout the year as insurance against unexpected drought.

The physiological process of hardening-off of seedlings is controlled principally by weather, especially temperature, light intensity, day length, and precipitation. Short days, full sunlight, cooler temperatures, and a reduction in available soil moisture promote hardening. Thus, in late summer and early autumn, about a month before the planting season starts, the amount of watering should be reduced and artificial shading removed to harden-off the stock. Only a small quantity of water will be needed to keep the trees in good health. Seedlings, especially those of conifers, should not be planted in the field after they have started new growth since many of them may die. An almost sure indication that a coniferous seedling did not become established after planting is the drooping of the new growth.

Once the tissues have hardened, seedlings can withstand severe frost or moderate drought without being killed. Normally, hardening occurs during cool, humid autumn weather. Growth and leaf formation is interrupted and is followed by natural defoliation in deciduous trees. The plants become dormant. Naked-rooted plants, especially deciduous ones, should be planted only when dormant.

Pumps. The type of pump and motive power used will depend on the quantity of water needed, the pressure desired, and the depth of the water table. Deep wells, of course, are expensive to operate, and their use should be avoided. If ditch irrigation is used, a pump of lower pressure will serve better than when irrigation is applied by means of an overhead sprinkler system. A great outlay for installation can be avoided, if the nursery is in an area where there is a large permanent supply of good water near the surface. Occasionally, pumping can be done from a lake, reservoir, or stream. Where the water table is within 3–9.5 m (10–31 ft) of the surface, and the water-bearing strata consist of sand or gravel, one of the most economical units is a horizontal centrifugal pump. This type is also well-adapted to pumping from open surface water in lakes or watercourses. Piston and rotary pumps also are used for shallow wells where the suction lift is not over 6 m (20 ft).

Vertical centrifugal and turbine pumps are the two most commonly used pump types in irrigation projects and in nurseries where the water table lies too deep for a horizontal centrifugal pump to be used. Although the initial cost is high, both are efficient, have great capacity, and develop all the pressure needed in a nursery. Weaker pumps may be used to fill a storage pond or tank of large capacity from which water can then be run by gravitation.

Irrigation Systems

In planning the layout of the irrigation system, the slope and configuration of the land surface, the character of the soil, the quantity of water available and the manner in which it is to be delivered must all be considered. The methods of irrigation adopted are based mainly on these factors. Much labor and expense can be saved by following a skillfully prepared plan for irrigation layout in the nursery. The construction of the system does not have to be completed in one operation but may be carried out over several years.

Whether naked-rooted stock or balled stock in containers is to be raised must also be considered in laying out the irrigation system. The type of nursery, too, influences the system to be selected, since the permanent nursery requires a much more elaborate and complete layout than does the temporary nursery. It is not possible to propose one standard plan of irrigation layout suitable for all nurseries in semi-arid and arid areas. Each nursery must adopt the plan and construction method that will best meet its needs and proposed objectives.

Many methods of irrigation are used in forest nurseries. These methods may be classified as follows:

1. Surface: flooding and furrow.
2. Subsurface.
3. Watering can.
4. Hose.
5. Porous hose.
6. Sprinkler.

Surface Irrigation

Flooding. Of the many methods of surface irrigation, only flooding (or border-strip) and furrow irrigation are recommended for use in forest nurseries. Both methods require careful site preparation. Areas to be irrigated by flooding must be leveled; those to be furrow irrigated must be brought to an even, gentle slope.

Flooding, or border-strip, irrigation is very useful for growing naked-rooted plants in large fields. In this method, the land to be watered is divided into strips by borders, i.e., low levees. Leveling is done with the same type of equipment used for land leveling. The border-strips are leveled from side to side and made to slope slightly from the head ditch to the far end. The lower end may or may not be terminated in a waste ditch. The water from the head ditch may be channeled successively from one border-strip to another, or into several strips at the same time. The width and length of each strip depend on the character of the soil and the gradient. A relatively large amount of water applied for a short time usually gives a uniform and economical application. The greater the infiltration rate, the longer should be the period of application and the shorter the length of the strip.

Where the land is nearly level, a system of level contour basins can be laid out along one or both sides of a ditch. Preferably the water is turned directly from the supply ditch into the basin, but sometimes it may be turned from one basin into another. This method is very useful for irrigating sunken seedbeds and small beds of transplants.

Although flooding may have less evaporative loss than sprinkler irrigation, it has a number of disadvantages. The low levees interfere with movement of machines, seedlings may be damaged by waterlogging or silt accumulation on their foliage, the surface pores of the soil soon become clogged with fine sediments, and a crust often develops on the soil surface.

Furrow Irrigation. Furrow irrigation may be used where naked-rooted stock is grown in rows. This method wets only a part of the soil surface and thus has a distinct advantage over flood irrigation in reducing evaporation.

The principal structure required in furrow irrigation is the head ditch or flume, from which the water may be diverted first into lateral ditches and then into the furrows adjacent to the rows of trees. The head ditch and the furrows must have sufficient gradient for the flow of water, whereas the laterals follow the contour. The head ditch and laterals are dug about 15 cm (6 in) below the surface with embankments about 15 cm high constructed on the surface on both sides of the ditch. To prevent water loss by seepage the ditch may be lined with clay, wood, sheet metal, or concrete.

Flumes of wood, sheet metal, concrete, or thin-walled metal pipes, although more expensive to install are generally far more satisfactory in the long run than earthen ditches. In permanent nurseries subsurface pipes are preferred because, unlike ditches or flumes, they do not interfere with cultivation.

The function of the head ditch or flume is to supply water to a system of short furrows that conduct the water to the plants. Several parallel head ditches or flumes are constructed at suitable intervals across the nursery area. The water may be taken from a ditch at check dams that create pools at required intervals along the ditch. Check dams may be either permanent or portable and placed at any desired point. They are commonly made of wood, metal, canvas, or plastic.

Where the head ditch is higher than the irrigation furrow, the water can be siphoned from the ditch to the furrow through a rubber hose or plastic tube. The flow is started by filling the hose or tube with water, closing one end tightly with the hand and dipping the other end into the water of the head ditch. When the closed end is lowered into the furrow and opened, the water will be siphoned without interruption as long as there is water in the head ditch. Several furrows can be irrigated at one time by using a siphon for each. Once the hose is in place a minimum of supervision is required.

If the main ditch is of earth, the distribution outlets may be temporary openings in the bank that can be opened and closed with a shovel. However, this procedure is not recommended because of erosion damage to the ditch walls. Another and safer method is to use short tubes of bamboo or metal that pass through the embankment.

It is usually possible to make a single outlet from the head ditch serve two or more furrows by curving the upper ends of the furrows to a junction point just under the outlet pipe. This arrangement reduces labor and also tends to reduce maintenance costs.

Where furrow irrigation is used the spacing between rows of seedlings varies from 40 cm to 1 m (1.3–3.3 ft). For most nurseries a row spacing between 50 and 70 cm (20–28 in) will produce the maximum amount of plantable stock. Spacing of the furrows must, of course, conform to the row spacing. Deep furrows, 10–15 cm (4–6 in) below the surface, and small streams of water reduce evaporation. The optimum length of furrows will depend on the slope, quantity of water available and soil type. As water flows down the furrow, its rate of advance gradually slows and eventually stops. Trees near the far end of the row will receive insufficient water if the row is too long. For most nursery soils a furrow length of 100 m (330 ft) should give all stock in the row adequate water. However, the exact distance that water will carry in the furrow must be determined for each field.

A modification of the furrow irrigation is known as the "corrugated method." The technique involved is that of sub-irrigation by small streams of water flowing through a series of narrow, shallow, parallel furrows, or corrugations. These are spaced so that during a relatively short period of water flow the lateral seepage from any two adjacent corrugations will meet. The general design and method of operation are similar to those of ordinary furrow irrigation. The corrugated method permits irrigation of rough, steep beds with small streams of water that reduce the danger of erosion. Although this method permits irrigation during the night without supervision, unsupervised irrigation is likely to result in considerable waste of water.

Subsurface Irrigation.   Subsurface irrigation supplies water directly to plant roots by seepage and capillary movement from porous tiles or concrete pipes. The distribution and application are accomplished by means of an elaborate system of butt-joined, unglazed drain tiles, or homemade concrete pipes that are laid just below cultivation depth. Subirrigation is claimed to be the least wasteful of water of all irrigation methods because water is delivered directly to the root zone. It is desirable to have a tight subsoil or hardpan below the tiles or pipes to reduce water loss by deep percolation.

Installation and maintenance costs of an underground system are extremely high, and seed germination in subirrigated beds is often poor and irregular because of drying of the soil surface. Consequently, this method is recommended only for very small areas, such as seedbeds or frames for rooting cuttings, and under favorable subsoil conditions. During the critical period of seed germination, supplemental irrigation by sprinklers should be provided.

Watering Can.   Watering cans of about 16 liters (4.2 U.S. gal) capacity are commonly used in small nurseries. Sprinkling nozzles with fine holes should be used before the seeds germinate and for a few days afterward. Nozzles with coarse holes can be used after the seedlings become established. Reservoirs, usually one half of a metal drum embedded in the soil, or water taps are spaced evenly in the nursery for filling the cans. The distance between the drums or taps should be approximately 40 m (131 ft) so that the water carrier does not tire nor waste time by having to carry water for distances over 20 m (66 ft). Very little water is wasted when watering cans are used since the water carrier can use the correct amount of water needed by individual plants and he can also irrigate the beds without wetting the paths between the beds.

Hose Irrigation.   Rubber or plastic hoses are still used for irrigation in many nurseries. Water taps to which the hoses are attached should be spaced at about 50 m (164 ft) apart. With this distance between taps the hoses should be 30 to 35 m (100 to 115 ft) long; inside diameter of hose is usually 2.5 cm (1 in). Water pressure at the nozzle must be sufficient to produce the necessary spray; long lengths and small hose diameters reduce nozzle pressure. Longer lengths of hose also tend to wear out quicker and are difficult to handle. Hose irrigation has the same advantages as the watering can plus not requiring time and energy to be spent in carrying water. Spray nozzles for hoses can be obtained with either small or large holes that aid in controlling the rate of application. The sprinklers with small holes are recommended when spraying small, delicate plants.

Porous-Hose Irrigation.   Irrigation by seepage of water through porous canvas hoses has been little used in forest nurseries, but it merits consideration.   In this method, water is pumped into a long, porous canvas hose which is closed at its far end.   After the hose is filled, and a slight pressure builds up inside it, the water oozes through the canvas.   There is no spray; the water simply escapes slowly through the canvas and flows freely over the ground on which the hose lies.   To permit a pressure buildup in the hose, the water should be conducted from the source to the field to be irrigated in metal pipes.   Rows should be about 1 m (3.3 ft) apart and the hose line laid between every other row.   A specially designed reel facilitates transport and storage of the canvas hose.   The advantages of porous-hose irrigation are the relatively small investment, economy of water, and low labor cost.   Slowness is its chief disadvantage.

Sprinkler Irrigation.   Sprinkler irrigation includes all of the various methods of applying water to nursery plants in the form of a spray that simulates rainfall.   The simplest and most common of these methods is sprinkling the beds by means of 4–8 liter (1–2 gal) hand-held watering cans or spray nozzles attached to rubber or plastic garden hoses as described above.   However, large nurseries that produce several million seedlings per year must use more sophisticated equipment.

Overhead systems and rotating sprinklers are the most common types of sprinkler irrigation employed in forest nurseries.   Moderate to high pressure is required to operate these sprinklers.   Such pressure is produced by high-pressure pumps or by the use of elevated reservoirs or water tanks.

When balled stock is raised in containers, overhead sprinkler irrigation is a highly desirable means of watering large numbers of plants.   The relative merits of furrow or flood irrigation versus sprinkler irrigation for raising naked-rooted stock have yet to be determined.   On very sandy soil, where deep-percolation losses from surface irrigation are large, sprinkler irrigation is suggested as a practical method of conserving water.   In any properly designed nursery, a high-pressure sprinkler system gives a more uniform distribution of water, better control of the rate of application, and minimizes soil washing and deep-percolation losses.   It also requires much less supervision and labor than either furrow or flood irrigation.   Its main disadvantage is the relatively high cost of installation, but this may be largely offset by the lower cost of land levelling, operation, maintenance, and the possibility of watering large amounts of balled stock with a minimum of labor.

Each application should be sufficient to wet the soil throughout the normal rooting zone.   Light applications, wetting only 3–5 cm (1.2–2 in) of the surface soil, will foster the development of shallow roots, producing low-grade stock that is easily killed by drought. High rates of application are likely to cause surface runoff and erosion. There is no evidence that sprinkling during midday is harmful, as many persons once believed. On the contrary, the cooling effect of such sprinkling is beneficial in protecting plants from extremely high soil temperatures. Of course, irrigation at night may be advisable to conserve water because the rate of evaporation is lower then. Sprinkler irrigation should find a wider application due to its higher efficiency in water use under ordinary weather conditions compared to surface methods. It also tends to improve the microclimate and leave the soil in a favorable condition.

Overhead sprinkling is not advisable in nurseries subject to continuous strong winds. Where strong winds are occasional it is better to irrigate in the evenings or nights after the winds subside. Well-planned windbreaks to reduce wind velocity in the nursery are recommended wherever strong winds are frequent.

Perforated-Pipe Sprinklers. In the perforated-pipe system distribution of water is made by thin-walled galvanized iron or aluminum quick-coupling pipe with small holes drilled along the upper side. When the operating pressure is 0.28–1.05 kg per sq cm (4–15 lb/sq in), the spray will cover a strip 6–15 m (20–50 ft) wide. Pipe is available commercially with a range in the size of perforations that will permit water to be applied at a rate of 1.25–5.00 cm (0.5–2 in) per hour. The holes must be spaced and arranged so that the entire strip is covered by the spray.

Installations may be either permanent or portable. If the installation is portable, the pipe is laid on the ground or supported on low posts, and when one strip has been watered, the pipe is moved to cover another strip. In the permanent installation several parallel lines of pipes are mounted on posts high enough to permit the workers to walk underneath. Adjacent lines are spaced 10–25 m (33–82 ft) apart.

Because perforated-pipe systems do not require high water pressure they can often be operated by utilizing the difference in elevation between the water source and the field to be irrigated. A difference in elevation of 1 m (3.3 ft) will produce a pressure of 0.100 kg per sq cm (1.42 lb/sq in). Perforated-pipe systems have been used with considerable success for irrigating both naked-rooted and balled stock.

Oscillating Sprinklers. The oscillating sprinkler system is a permanent installation that resembles the permanent perforated-pipe system just described. A better distribution of water is achieved by turning the distribution pipes back and forth about their long axes through an arc of 90° to 120° (Fig. 3–17). Usually the main line, which delivers

Fig. 3–17. A water-driven piston rotates the pipes of this oscillating sprinkler system in a 120° arc. (Courtesy Tennessee Valley Authority)

the water to the distribution lines, is buried beneath the soil surface. In a few nurseries the main line lies on the surface. The oscillating distribution pipes are parallel to the ground surface and extend from the main line at approximately right angles. They are usually elevated 1–2 m (3–6.5 ft) above the surface of the field by mounting them on wooden or iron posts spaced 5 m (16 ft) apart. The distribution pipes rest in roller cradles which allow them to be easily turned. When the system is in operation, the pipes are turned slowly and continuously back and forth by a small, water-powered engine or by a hydraulic oscillator. Small nozzles, through which the water is sprayed, are spaced along the pipe approximately 75 to 125 cm (30–50 in) apart. The parallel distribution lines are usually spaced about 16 m (53 ft) apart. If desired, the oscillating lines can be equipped with quick-coupling devices so that strips may be watered by moving successive lines.

The oscillating sprinkler system has been found to be well suited to forest nurseries and to give a reasonably uniform and frugal distribution of water. Installation of this system does not require leveling of the land, since the flexibility of the pipe will permit it to conform to a gently undulating surface and still be easily rotated. The installation cost for large areas is, however, likely to be appreciably higher and the rate of delivery of water slower than with other sprinkler systems, especially the rotating sprinkler.

Rotating Sprinklers. The rotating sprinkler system is a practical method for watering large nursery areas. This system has a much lower initial cost per hectare than the overhead, oscillating system. It is easily handled and can be operated and maintained at low cost. It usually requires only one main supply line through the center of the area to be irrigated. Distribution lines are spaced 15–30 m (50–100 ft) apart along the main line and at right angles to it. Distribution lines can be easily moved to new locations along the main after a strip has been watered. The distribution lines, and frequently the main line, lie on the ground surface. The surface main and the distribution lines are assembled from lightweight galvanized or aluminum pipes. Pipe sections commonly are 5–10 m (16–33 ft) long and are easily joined to each other by quick-coupling clamps. Single- or double-rotating sprinkler heads are spaced along the distribution line at intervals of 8–20 m (26–66 ft), depending on the available water and pressure. Sprinkler heads are set on short riser pipes. The length of the riser pipes is commonly 0.5–1.5 m (1.5–5 ft), depending on the height of the stock being irrigated. Risers and sprinklers can be placed only between sections of the distribution pipe; thus their spacing is governed by varying the length of the sections. In small nurseries, the distribution lines may be relatively permanent, but in large nurseries, a given line is operated in one position only until watering of its strip is complete, and then the line is moved to a new position on the main (**Fig. 3–18**). Small rotating sprinklers connected to distribution lines of rubber or plastic hoses are used for supplementary irrigation. They may constitute the only system of small nurseries.

Double-nozzle sprinklers are customarily used in forest nurseries. The diameter of the circular area irrigated by each sprinkler varies with pressure at the nozzle, discharge angle, and diameter of the nozzle opening. For example, under a pressure of 1.76 kg per sq cm (25 lb/sq in), a 40° sprinkler head with 3.97 mm ($\frac{5}{32}$ in) diameter nozzles will water a circular area 25 m (82 ft) in diameter and deliver 12.9 liters (3.4 gal) per minute. To assure full distribution of water, adjacent sprinkler patterns must overlap each other; the distance between adjacent sprinklers should not exceed 0.7 times the diameter of the wetted area.

Fig. 3–18. Rotating sprinkler irrigation of Russian-olive seedbeds. (Courtesy State Forest Nursery, Fort Collins, Colo.)

Rotary sprinklers require a higher pressure for efficient operation than do the perforated-pipe or oscillating systems. High capacity sprinklers spaced about 70 m (230 ft) apart are permanently installed in some nurseries. These are served by an underground distribution system. These sprinklers require a pressure of between 5.62 and 8.44 kg per sq cm (80–120 lb/sq in) and discharge 760 to 2,300 liters (200–600 gal) per minute over an area 120 m (400 ft) in diameter.

High-velocity winds have a greater adverse effect on the spray pattern of rotary sprinklers than on the pattern of perforated-pipe or oscillating sprinklers. The rotary sprinkler produces a fine mist which is blown away by the wind. If nozzles with too large openings are used to reduce mist, the large drops may pound the soil and wash it away.

Sprinkler irrigation has been used with some success to protect plants from frost injury. If the frost is not too severe, plants can be saved by sprinkling them continually until the danger of damage is past. However, during severe frosts sprinkling will result in a coating of ice encasing the plants and cause great damage.

Cultivation and Weeding

When the soil is in good physical condition, satisfactory growth of nursery stock may be expected. Cultivation is the technique of maintaining good physical condition of the soil in beds and containers during the growing season. It breaks the crust and permits adequate aeration and improves absorption of rain or irrigation water. Proper physical condition of the soil also promotes and sustains the activities of bacteria essential to maintaining fertility. Cultivation, furthermore, uproots and destroys competing weeds.

To obtain the optimum physical condition of the soil, cultivation should begin as soon as the upper layers have dried to just the proper moisture content to be brought to a fine tilth. The moisture content is especially important in clay soils because, if these are too wet, they may bake into clods, and if too dry they are hard and difficult to cultivate. Cultivation should be timed not only to improve tilth but also to eliminate weeds. Correct timing, therefore, requires careful observation of soil moisture and of weed invasion and maturity.

When cultivating between plants, the tools should not penetrate deeper than 10–15 cm (4–6 in) because deeper cultivation may damage the rootlets. A small garden tractor, equipped with a cultivating tool, can be used effectively to cultivate the wider spaces between plants. The area close to the plants, which cannot be safely cultivated by machine, may be cultivated by hand. Plants grown in containers are cultivated with small hand tools.

A weed is a plant growing where it is not desired. In forest nurseries or plantations, any plants other than those sown or planted are usually unwanted. Weeds compete for water and soil nutrients. They also block the circulation of air and may harbor insects and disease organisms. Where weeds are permitted to grow in the seedbeds, seedlings will be of poor quality; therefore, weed competition must be eliminated. The methods of ensuring a minimum of weeds in the nursery are: prevention, eradication, and control.

Prevention is the practical method. It is accomplished by making sure that weeds are not carelessly introduced into the nursery. Weed seeds or rhizomes may enter in many different ways: in the irrigation water, with soil brought in to fill containers or to replace the soil removed with balled plants, in manure that has not been properly composted, or on vehicles and machinery. Weeds on neighboring areas should be prevented from maturing to seed, and perennial weeds that reproduce vegetatively should not be permitted to spread. In Morocco, nursery beds and containers are sometimes watered a few days before the tree seed are sown so that weed seeds will germinate. Then the soil is allowed to dry and the weeds are killed.

Eradication is the complete removal of weeds and their seeds from the nursery.

Control is the process of limiting weed dissemination. There should be a balance between the costs involved in the control of weeds and the harm they cause to seedlings. Eradication and control are generally carried out as one operation in the nursery; the principal methods are manual, mechanical, and chemical. No one method is usually sufficient in itself to give a satisfactory and economical control of weeds, thus a nurseryman must be prepared to change from one technique to another when appropriate. Adherence to one technique only could lead to an increase in some weed species.

Manual or Mechanical Weed Control. Hand cultivation to remove weeds from among the plants is the standard practice in many countries. Weeds may be pulled out by hand, but usually hoes or trowels are used. A small garden tractor, equipped with such accessory tools as discs, cultivators, harrows, or rotary weeders, is often used in larger nurseries. Trees growing in containers must be weeded by hand. Weeds growing among the pots and cans should be removed by hand when the roots, which grow out of the containers into the ground, are pruned. The entire weed including the root system should be removed. This is especially important in controlling plants, such as Bermuda grass (*Cynodon dactylon* (L.) Pers.) or species of *Cyperus* that produce rhizomes or subterranean stems. Weeding should preferably be done before flowering, but certainly before seed dispersal. Weeds should be destroyed early before they begin to compete for water and soil nutrients and before their growth makes cultivation difficult. It is always easier and less time-consuming to remove young weeds.

A nursery is usually cultivated one to three times during the growing season. Proper timing will reduce the number of cultivations and thus the cost of the plants produced. The optimum number and timing of the cultivations must be determined individually for each nursery.

Although manual labor may be the most economical in small nurseries, it is generally more expensive (per thousand plants produced) than other techniques. Inexpensive mechanical methods are being increasingly employed wherever they can be used effectively. Most simple, mechanical equipment is quite efficient, having been developed over many centuries. Although the plow, the disc, and the harrow were developed for soil preparation, they are also extremely valuable for weed control. The hoe, rotary hoe, spring-tooth harrow, and cultivators with various types of shovels have been designed specifically for weed control.

Chemical Weed Control. Even with the best mechanical equipment, elimination of weeds is often still too expensive, and cheaper methods using chemicals are being adopted as new chemicals to suppress weeds are perfected.

Weeding among the tree seedlings in beds, between rows of seedlings, in nursery paths, or between rows of pots may be conveniently done with chemicals. Weeding chemicals should remain effective for a long time, but they should not be able to be diffused with the water and thus damage the planting stock.

Weed-killing chemicals are called herbicides. Many herbicides have been developed since 1945. Herbicides, despite their great utility in afforestation cause problems. Trees vary in susceptibility to chemicals according to the rate, method, time and number of applications, the species and age of trees, the soil conditions, and the weather. Herbicides that accumulate in plant tissue may reach toxic levels and cannot be used in nursery beds. Other herbicides may be poisonous to animals or plants. The principal types of herbicides are the contact, the sterilant, and the fumigant. Contact herbicides are of two types: non-selective and selective. The effect of the herbicides on plants is by inhibiting their action on physiological processes such as photosynthesis, translocation, and respiration; by adversely affecting the water balance; or by producing physical or chemical effects that alter the structure of the protoplasm. Damage or death of the plant is probably the combined effect of some or all of these factors.

Non-Selective and Selective Herbicides. Contact herbicides kill plants that absorb, or are covered by, the chemical. They are effective against annual weeds but destroy only the aerial part of the perennials. They are either selective or non-selective. A selective herbicide destroys certain species but causes little or no injury to others. Non-selective ones are toxic to all plants. However, any selective chemical, if applied in large enough quantities, will also kill all vegetation: thus, selective sprays may become contact weed-killers if improperly used. To avoid improper use, always follow the directions for application given on the package label.

Non-selective herbicides are used to control weeds on paths, along fence lines, and around buildings and storage grounds. Sodium arsenite has been commonly used for such weeding, but it must be used with extreme caution because it is highly toxic to humans and livestock.

Selective herbicides are available that will kill weeds but that will not injure tree seedlings or transplants.

Both types of herbicide may be used either as pre-emergence or as post-emergence treatments, depending on the chemicals employed. Pre-emergence treatment is the application of the herbicide to the soil before the germination of the tree seed; post-emergence treatment is the application after germination of the weed seeds, or the tree seeds, or both. Newly sprouted tree seedlings are more susceptible to certain herbicides than are older seedlings of the same species, therefore, use of such herbicides in newly sown seedbeds should be avoided.

Two non-selective, pre-emergent weed-killers that may be applied to seedbeds several days before sowing are methyl bromide and allyl alcohol. These chemicals are dangerous to use and must be handled with care. Most of the dangerous non-selective chemicals are being replaced, in most nurseries by newly developed, less dangerous chemicals. Nearly all of these new chemicals are selective herbicides, and in general they are cheaper and easily applied.

The selective herbicide most generally used for weeding conifer nursery beds is mineral spirit or white spirit of petroleum. Mineral spirits are sold under a variety of trade names. They cannot be used on some conifers (e.g., *Larix*) or on broad-leaved species because they will injure or kill them. Mineral spirits are quite effective on small weeds with less than 5 cm (2 in) of top growth, but are ineffective against thistle (*Cirsium*), quackgrass (*Agropyron*), large clover plants (*Trifolium*), and purslane (*Portulaca*). Mineral spirits containing from 10 to 20 per cent of aromatic hydrocarbons are usually sprayed full strength at the rate of 150–500 liters per hectare (15–50 gals/a). From three to eight applications are made during the growing season. The chemical may be used immediately after seeding, but should not be used during the first three or four weeks after germination. Mineral spirits should not be applied when the air temperature exceeds 27° C (81° F). Half-shade immediately after spraying is advisable, if the air temperature is high.

Two herbicides, 2,4 D and 2,4,5-T,[1] give effective post-emergence control for many broad-leaved weeds. They are selective and when properly used will not harm monocotyledons nor most conifers. Thus, broadleaved weeds, but not grasses, can be killed by spraying seedbeds containing conifers with water emulsions of either chemical. However, the selectivity of these herbicides is not absolute and a few coniferous species are harmed by contact with them.

Never use these chemicals to weed seedbeds of broad-leaved species!

These selective herbicides are most effective when the weeds are growing vigorously; consequently the best results are obtained during spring and early summer. Only low volatile esters should be used, and then only in a heavy (large drop) spray on windless days. Uniform rate of application by use of power equipment is recommended to prevent localized overdoses.

If sprayed on the soil between the rows of pine seedlings during cultivation, 2,4 D will inhibit weed-seed germination. This treatment is post-emergence to the pine seedlings but pre-emergence to the weeds.

A number of other chemicals, including copper sulphate, zinc sulphate, sulphuric acid, and sodium chlorate, applied either before or after sowing, give a considerable measure of weed control. Water soluble dry

---

[1] 2,4 D = 2,4 dichlorophenoxy acetic acid.
2,4,5-T = 2,4,5 trichlorophenoxy acetic acid.

chemicals, e.g., zinc sulphate, may be spread on the soil as a coarse powder. Rain or irrigation water will dissolve the chemical, and it will be absorbed by the roots of the weeds.

Formaldehyde, when applied as a 4 per cent solution at the rate of 4 liters per square meter (0.9 gal/sq yd) about 20 days before sowing, may be quite effective in reducing the number of weed seedlings.

The effect of many of these chemicals on the germination and early development of seedlings is variable, and they should not be used without trials. The only positive way to find out whether or not a recommended chemical is useful as a weed killer is to test it on small plots in the nursery and field. Not enough tests have been made with the different herbicides, tree crops, weeds, soil characteristics, and climatic conditions to furnish conclusive results for all nurseries.

By using the proper herbicide, hand weeding may be reduced by as much as 90 per cent during the growing season.

Sterilant Herbicides. The success of soil sterilization depends largely on the presence of a high concentration of a herbicide in the upper 10 cm (4 in) of the soil, because this is where most annual weed seeds germinate. In addition, for effective sterilization, the chemical must remain active in the entire rooting zone. The most commonly used sterilants are carbamates, triazines, amides, urea compounds, and phthalic compounds. These are sold under many trade names.

Sterilant herbicides may be applied in solution or in granular form as a dust. Many of them disappear rapidly because of repeated cultivation and through leaching by the large amounts of water used in nursery irrigation. Therefore, this factor must be considered in the cultivation or irrigation of the area because the length of time that the herbicide is retained in the upper layers of the soil determines how long weeds will be controlled by it.

Most sterilants remain active for from four to six weeks under normal conditions. The period varies with soil, moisture, amount used, and the chemical itself. Some sterilants are effective for only a week, others remain active for as long as two years.

Fumigants. Within the last few years, soil fumigants (lethal gases) have been used with great success in nurseries to eliminate weeds, fungi, nematodes, rodents, and insects. Some fumigants will eliminate all weeds for a year or more. They are especially valuable in destroying weeds that propagate by rhizomes or stolons, making it unnecessary to remove them by pulling up or hoeing.

Although many chemicals have been successfully used as soil fumigants, carbon disulphide (mainly for nematodes) and methyl bromide are the two most commonly employed. The chemical is injected under an airtight cover, usually a plastic sheet, that is pegged to the ground.

Methyl bromide is applied at the rate of 10 kg to 100 sq m (2 lb/100 sq ft). The cover is left in place for 24 hours. Methyl bromide is a colorless, odorless liquid or gas. It is poisonous to humans and livestock and neither should enter the fumigated area for at least 24 hours after the cover is removed. Carbon disulphide is frequently injected as a liquid into holes spaced 0.5 × 0.5 m (1.5 × 1.5 ft) over the field and driven to a depth of 15–20 cm (6–8 in). The gas diffuses easily throughout a soil with a low moisture content, loose structure, and high temperature.

Root Pruning

Root pruning or wrenching of nursery stock grown in beds, rows, or containers is a standard practice in most arid-zone nurseries. Both methods consist in severing the taproot or laterals to hold back top development or to encourage the development of a compact fibrous root system, particularly in taprooted species. Root pruning also improves top/root ratios, controls depth of root penetration, and makes lifting from nursery beds easier. Roots are often cut just before or during lifting of naked-rooted stock, and some cutting back of roots is done during grading.

When certain species have been sown in beds or rows, root pruning or undercutting has been a successful alternative to transplanting. Compared with transplanting, it saves time, labor, and nursery space.

Root pruning is confined mainly to taprooted species and to container-grown seedlings whose roots grow out of the container and penetrate the soil. It does not necessarily result in a compact fibrous root system in all species; and in some it has no effect on the number of laterals but affects only the rootlet replacements near the pruned surface. In other species, however, it is evident that root pruning promotes vigorous production of fibrous roots in the zone above the point of root severance. The severed root-ends should be left in the ground to decay so that their vital nutrient elements will be returned to the soil. Information is still needed on the effects of root pruning in different species and on seasonal variation of root growth and periods of dormancy.

When the roots and rootlets of seedlings are broken or pruned without removing the plants from the soil, the process is called wrenching. It is done by heaving the soil with a fork, or similar implement, or by partly lifting the plants and refirming. Seedlings from direct sowing in beds or rows can be root pruned in this way, and the expense of transplanting avoided. Experience shows that the plants with the best root and shoot development are produced in thinly sown beds, where the seedlings are undercut or wrenched at a depth of 10–15 cm (4–6 in). If undercutting is done during the right season (usually summer), the development of the plants will be satisfactory.

Taprooted species growing in the open are occasionally root pruned at a depth of 20–30 cm (8–12 in); this results in holding back top growth and promoting lateral root development. Root pruning can be used to retard the growth of plants which for some reason must remain longer than their normal time in the nursery. If these plants are not root pruned in the autumn, wrenching may be done in the early spring to retard growth during the next growing season.

It is the usual practice in planting naked-rooted stock to root prune the seedlings just before planting. Otherwise, long, dangling, unpruned roots are likely to be doubled back and crammed into the planting hole, which results in poor survival. Also it would be very difficult, even in light, sandy soils, to avoid cutting and breaking some roots during lifting.

Growth will be little affected if roots are pruned during the last few weeks before planting or during lifting. If root pruning is carried out well in advance of lifting, it leads to a better top/root ratio and more fibrous rootlets and also will tend to check active vegetative growth before hardening-off begins.

Root pruning and undercutting of naked-rooted planting stock growing in beds or rows may be done either by hand or by mechanical equipment.

Hand pruning of roots may be done by two men equipped with short-handled spades. The spades are inserted into the soil, at an angle of about 30° to 45° to the surface, on each side of a row or strip of seedlings. The angle will depend on the depth of pruning desired. The spades are pushed well under the plants, cutting off the taproots and the more vigorous side roots. Although this method is simple, it often results in roots of irregular size.

Small stock can be quickly root pruned with a large, heavy knife that is run obliquely under the row of seedlings from either side. This method can be practised only in light, loose soil that has no stones. The knife blade should be broad and sharp so that it will cut the roots easily when forced through the soil.

A U-shaped or horizontal blade has proved very satisfactory for root pruning large transplants growing in rows or strips. The bottom of the U is the cutting edge, and this may be as long as the width of the seedbed. The tool is thrust into the soil at the end of a row by two handles fixed 20–25 cm (8–10 in) apart. The cutting edge is drawn under the row of small plants 15–20 cm (6–8 in) below the surface. In nurseries that raise large numbers of naked-rooted plants, it will be economical to root prune with equipment drawn either by a draft animal or a tractor.

Root pruning is frequently done by the regular stock-lifting machine to which is attached a narrower and thinner blade than is used for lifting stock. A root-pruning machine drawn by a crawler tractor and using a sharp, serrated blade powered by an engine can also be employed for cutting taproots.

A clean cut with a sharp blade will favor proper healing of the pruned roots. Cool, cloudy days should be selected for root pruning, and plants should be irrigated immediately after pruning. Abundant irrigation is essential when the root pruning is carried out during hot, dry weather. If the soil is too dry, irrigation prior to pruning will also be necessary for best results.

Root pruning of plants raised in containers is a standard practice in most arid-zone nurseries. Rapid development of the root system occurs in the nursery during the dry season because of the high temperatures and irrigation. This intensive root growth usually results in part of the root system, or even the taproot, growing through the drainage hole of the container into the nursery soil. The rate of root growth and development outside the container depends on the amount of irrigation, the depth of soil in the container, and the size and number of drainage holes. It is the practice to prune periodically the roots that grow into the soil; one or more root prunings may be required during the season, depending on the rate of root growth. Container-grown nursery stock that is root pruned develops into stronger stock for afforestation than unpruned stock.

Potted seedlings, whose roots penetrate the nursery soil, grow rapidly and may be distinguished by their larger size from plants whose roots have been pruned or are confined to the container. Because the part of the root system growing in the soil must be cut away to lift the containers, these plants will have a disproportionate top/root ratio at planting time; the top is overdeveloped in relation to the remaining root system. In some broad-leaved planting stock, such as the eucalypts and acacias, an unfavorable ratio may be corrected by top pruning, but this is not possible in all species. Severe top pruning of conifers is not desirable. Therefore, to slow top growth, periodic pruning of roots of container-grown stock is necessary.

To maintain a favorable top/root ratio, the tops of the seedlings of some species are cut back to a height of about 30 cm (12 in). A movable wooden frame of the required height is used, and the seedlings whose heights exceed that of the frame are cut back. Top pruning by power mowers has successfully reduced the bulk and weight of some broad-leaved species without an adverse effect on field survival or form. Top pruning reduces damage from excessive transpiration after root pruning because transpiration loss and water absorption by the plant are brought more nearly into balance preventing critically high internal water stresses from developing. It also tends to produce sturdy, well-hardened plants of uniform size. Repeated top and root prunings have a more favourable effect on fast-growing nursery stock than on slow-growing seedlings. The frequency and timing of root pruning will vary with the size of the seedlings required and the objectives of afforestation. A seedling with a good top/root ratio based on dry weights is not necessarily a desirable seedling for planting. In addition it should have an abundance of fine absorbing rootlets, be of the required size, healthy, and vigorous.

A good top/root ratio for eucalypts is 1.5:2.0, depending on the species. The top/root ratio is determined by uprooting a sample plant as carefully as possible and washing all soil from the roots. The plant is then dried at 65° C (150° F) with 10 per cent relative humidity for 24 hours, or until it reaches a constant weight. The roots and tops are weighed separately and the top/root ratio is computed.

Tools used for root pruning nursery stock raised in containers are a sharp knife, pruning shears, or a bricklayer's trowel. Every pot or container is lifted, and the roots growing outside it are cut. Roots growing out of cans or boxes can be severed by merely lifting the containers and putting them down again, breaking most of the roots that have penetrated the soil.

Cans or boxes may also be placed on laths, leaving a space between the receptacles and the soil. The roots can then be pruned by two workers pulling a strong thin wire under the row of containers from both sides.

For pruning roots of balled stock growing in pressed soil, the most convenient tool is a sharp, bricklayer's trowel. Pruning of lateral roots is done by cutting the sides of the soil balls; then the roots are lifted and the taproot is cut. The trowel is also very useful for rearranging the soil balls in the bed after pruning.

Shading

High temperature, unless it is associated with drought, does not have very serious harmful effects on well-established hardened plants. Germinating seeds or plants that have soft, succulent stems are particularly susceptible to heat damage, however, even though adequate soil moisture is available. Injury may appear either as heat lesions on the stem at the ground level near the root collar, or there may be "burning" of the leaves or succulent tops. To avoid the harmful effects of heat in the nursery, techniques are used to produce sturdy woody stems as early in the season as possible; but until the young plants are robust enough to withstand heat, irrigation by overhead sprinklers and shading are helpful in reducing heat damage. Shading is not always a practical measure in large nurseries. Moreover, saplings planted in arid areas will usually be on sites exposed to full insolation, and nursery practice should aim at hardening the stock for the exposed planting site. Although intensive shading hinders hardening-off, occasionally there are circumstances that justify temporary shading of nursery plants.

Shading provides protection against heat and thus prevents damage resulting from high soil and air temperatures, but it cannot prevent excessive evaporation or drought. When soil moisture is, in fact, depleted to such an extent that it cannot be absorbed by the roots at the rate it is being lost by transpiration, the plants wilt, and if soil moisture deficiency is prolonged, the plants die. High temperature, low humidity, wind, and intense solar radiation will increase the rate of transpiration and intensify the casualties caused by low soil moisture. Restoration of soil moisture by irrigation is an absolute necessity to prevent serious drought damage. As previously pointed out, there is no evidence to support the belief that seedlings will be harmed by watering when the sun is shining.

Where soil temperatures are the same, heat injury to nursery stock is always more prevalent in coarse and sandy soils than in fine textured soils. This appears to be due to the greater reflection of heat from the sandy surface and the higher heat conductivity of the sandy material. The lower water-holding capacity of the sandy soils also makes it necessary to watch surface temperatures carefully, because heat injury may occur as soon as the surface of the soil has dried out, even though there is abundant moisture below the surface. The color of the soil in the nursery also has a bearing on the occurrence of heat damage; the darker the soil, the greater is the absorption of solar radiation, and the greater the danger of heat damage near the root collar. High soil temperatures, above 35° C (95° F) adversely affect development of mycorrhizal fungi. Shading helps to maintain favorable conditions for these fungi by preventing soil from reaching temperatures that might be lethal.

Shading Seedbeds. Shading of germinating seeds and new seedlings, either in beds or in containers, is standard practice in most arid-zone nurseries. It reduces the need for frequent irrigation. Too frequent watering is harmful, since it is likely to disturb the germinating seeds. To avoid the use of covers for artificial shade, or to reduce their use to a minimum, it is essential to sow the seeds in the proper season, either in the spring or in the autumn—avoiding the very hot days of summer— and to give the germinating seeds and seedlings a short period of favorable temperatures.

Seedbeds may be shaded by covering them with burlap or sacking, bamboo or lath screens, wooden slats, or brushwood. As soon as germination starts and the seedlings begin to emerge, the shade is either removed or reduced. Continuous shade is usually harmful. Good ventilation beneath the shading is essential to prevent or to lessen damping-off; therefore, the sides of the beds should be left open for air circulation.

Burlap used to protect nursery seedbeds during germination may safely be treated with copper naphthenate as a preservative. So treated, it is not toxic to the seedlings and may last four times as long as untreated material. Some organic dyes, such as copper oleate, copper tallate, and copper resinate, will extend the service life of burlap and are cheap. Copper-8-quinolinolate is an excellent fabric preservative, but perhaps too expensive for most nursery work.

Brushwood, tree branches, and palm thatch can be troublesome to use and probably cost more ultimately than is generally supposed. They are difficult to arrange to produce even shading, and time-consuming to remove and replace for watering, hoeing, and inspection. Care should be taken not to use branches or brushwood that may release seeds.

Good results are obtained by using bamboo or lath screens that reduce direct sunlight to from 50 to 60 per cent of its full value (Fig. 3–19). Rollable screens may be placed either on standard wooden frames covered with wire netting (which also protects the beds against birds or rodents) or on low supports connected by wire. This arrangement will permit the screens to be easily rolled back to reduce shade

Fig. 3–19. Bamboo screens used for shading seedbeds in Brazil. (Courtesy FAO)

and for cultivation, watering, and inspection. Sprinkler irrigation, preferably overhead, may be used after rolling the screens. It is convenient to have the length of screen in each roll the same as the length of the bed it is to cover; but rolls longer than 20 m (65 ft) are very cumbersome to handle. If a large quantity of screens is needed, it may pay to make them at the nursery.

Loose bamboo sticks or laths the width of the bed may be spread over it at the desired height on strong wire, supported by stakes.

In some countries, there is also available commercially a material woven of coarse, plastic threads in patterns of stripes or checks that will give a predetermined degree of shading. This material has several advantages, such as ease of handling, light weight, and small bulk for storage.

A satisfactory arrangement is to place the shade screens about 30–40 cm (12–16 in) above the beds on two parallel wires about 1 m apart. The wires are secured by nails driven into stakes and cross-pieces which are used only where necessary. The stakes should be treated with a wood preservative to prolong their service life and then driven into the ground until they are firm.

Shading Transplant Beds.   Because transplanting seedlings is a critical operation in the life of nursery stock, special precautions must be taken to avoid damage from heat and excessive insolation, especially when transplanting takes place during the hot, dry season. As has been said, the sowing of seeds should be timed so that the seedling will not have to be transplanted in the nursery during the hot weather. If, however, this cannot be avoided, devices are in use in arid-zone nurseries to provide shade during and immediately after transplanting. Whenever shading is used, it must be completely removed within one to three weeks after transplanting. For this reason primary consideration should be given to temporary shading devices and not to the permanent shading still practiced in several arid-zone nurseries. Experience has shown that well-established transplants make better growth when exposed to full sunlight.

Permanent Shading.   Transplanting may be carried out in permanent shade, but this is an expensive method because the stock must be moved into the open later. Lath houses or other shade huts must be made high enough to allow free movement of workers and to permit overhead irrigation. A lath house is usually built with a frame of strong timber and the top and sides, except for the doors, are covered with laths 2.0–2.5 cm (0.8–1 in) wide. The laths are spaced so that the distance between adjacent laths is equal to the width of the laths, giving 50 per cent shade. Insofar as possible, the laths should be aligned north and south, giving an even distribution of light and shade as the shadows sweep from west to east across the beds. As a rule, the completed house is painted for durability and appearance (Fig. 3–20).

Similar shade huts are made by building a frame of strong timber high enough above the ground to allow unhampered cultivation and watering. The main supporting poles are interconnected with lighter poles or wires upon which branches with leaves still attached are placed. By adding or removing branches it is possible to control the amount of shading. The sides of these huts are generally, but not always, open. The disadvantages of this type of shading material are that the coverage is not uniform and when the leaves dry, they fall and make the beds untidy.

Prefabricated lath frames with different spacing between laths are now used in Argentina. The frames are rectangular, 2 × 1 m (6.5 × 3.3 ft), hinged to each other, and fastened to the framing of the lath house. They may be put in place, removed, or moved to other lath houses easily. The different distances between laths makes it possible to alter the shade as needed.

The principal disadvantage of permanent shade huts is that the potted plants or the soil, pots, and plants for planting must be brought to the hut and then later taken outside for hardening. This is a cumbersome and expensive task, and many plants are destroyed in the shift to and from shade. It is for this reason that temporary shading devices placed over the beds in the nursery, which provide simple, cheap cover, are preferred.

Temporary Shading. In large permanent nurseries it may be worthwhile to have special portable devices which protect the stock from heat during and after transplanting, and which can be easily removed when the shade is no longer needed. Although permanent lath houses have been extensively used in nurseries, it is recommended that these or similar permanent shade huts, other than small huts for experiments, be discouraged for general use.

A very useful apparatus for shading transplants consists of light, mobile, wooden frames covered with burlap, canvas, or screens held 30–50 cm (12–20 in) above the ground by stilts. The dimensions of the frames should equal the width of the beds; when several are placed end to end the entire bed can be shaded. Four to six days after transplanting when the plants have taken root, the frames can be moved to other beds where transplanting is still in progress.

Natural Shading. Some shade can be provided for nursery stock by planting widely spaced trees. If, however, the saplings are raised in open beds or rows, the growth of stock may be considerably decreased

Fig. 3–20. Individually potted eucalypt seedlings in a permanent lath house in Chile. (Photo V. Bianchi; courtesy FAO)

by root competition for soil nutrients and moisture. In addition the spreading tree roots will interfere with lifting the stock, and the trees will be obstacles to machine cultivation. If the stock is raised in containers, natural shade by scattered trees is at times quite satisfactory. Shading can also be obtained by taking advantage of the shade cast by natural or artificial windbreaks. Windbreaks can be planted so that they will shade the transplant beds, at least during the afternoon. Rows of fast-growing shrubs may be arranged in patterns similar to windbreaks to provide shade.

It is well to remember, when shading nursery stock, that reduction of sunlight has a profound influence on tree form, often causing mild etiolation, succulence, and delaying hardening-off. Excessive shading will reduce the dry weight of the plant and cause the top/root ratio to be too high. Heavy shading may cause loss of vigor and deviation of the central axis from the vertical so that the plants tend to be "table-topped."

Greenhouses

In hot arid zones, greenhouses are not necessary and are rarely used, but in cold arid zones their use is increasing, especially for conifers which grow more slowly than hardwoods and for the production of container stock. Greenhouses can be environmentally conditioned to produce maximum seedling growth. Under such conditions and with proper fertilization conifers can be grown in 9 months that are equal in size and vigor to 3 to 5-year-old plants grown outside in a nursery.

Day and night temperatures in these greenhouses are controlled to meet the needs of each species for its optimum growth. Humidity is kept high and the soil in the receptacles regularly fertilized. In some greenhouses the CO_2 content of the air may be increased from 2 to as high as 7 times the normal atmospheric concentration to increase photosynthesis and growth. The sowing season starts when the days start being longer, so that the plants receive the advantage of the long days, or the normal day length may be extended by artificial illumination.

Greenhouse-grown seedlings have performed well after field planting. Survival and growth have been equal, or even superior, to those of comparable nursery grown stock.

Greenhouses are costly and expensive to operate, therefore the space in them must be efficiently used to produce the maximum number of plantable seedlings. This is generally done by using one of the mini-container systems. It is expected that with further development of the techniques of growing plants in the greenhouse the cost will be reduced and the risks of growing plants in open nurseries for 3-5 years under severe climatic conditions will be averted.

Inventory of Stock

This is an important operation that must be completed before planning the field planting program for the new season. Estimates of the number of seedlings, transplants, and container plants are made following standard sampling procedures. Each species, type, and age are counted separately and a record is kept of total seedlings and plantable seedlings. The size of the sampling unit and the number required for an acceptable estimate will depend on the uniformity and distribution of the plants. In general the greater the density, the smaller the area and the fewer the sampling units required. In small nurseries each bed or area is sampled, but in large nurseries only one-half of the beds or fewer are sampled. These beds of course, must be randomly selected for each category of stock. Care must be taken not to injure the plants during stocktaking.

Lifting, Grading, and Packing

Lifting plants for transport to the planting site should be carefully planned and well organized to be accomplished with maximum efficiency. The lifting crew should be trained in grading and selection of plants.

The optimum time to lift planting stock for a reforestation project depends on the field planting season. Stock for fall planting should be lifted only after it has completely hardened off, whereas stock for spring planting should be lifted before top growth starts. Hardened plants can be lifted through the winter, if storage facilities are available.

As a rule, before removal from the nursery, container-raised plants should be thoroughly watered to avoid desiccation during transport and before planting. There are no special problems when removing plants in containers, if the roots have been properly pruned.

Plants raised in beds or in rows may be lifted safely any time during the planting season. However, it is good practice to irrigate the soil from one to three days in advance to soften it so that it is suitable for digging, and to prevent tearing of the roots. When lifting is delayed until just before planting, the seedling is less likely to be damaged than when it is lifted earlier and stored.

Some pruning may be necessary before lifting and storing deciduous stock. Lifting, transporting, and planting of deciduous stock should be finished before the beginning of spring because the plant will break dormancy when warm weather arrives. Generally, lifting in early winter is preferable because the plants can be stored and be ready for delivery as soon as conditions permit planting. Also, by lifting early, the land needed for the next crop is freed, allowing ground cultivation or disposal of containers. Lifting may continue all through the winter when there is little likelihood of the ground freezing.

Naked-rooted plants may be dug with a sharp spade or a mechanical tree-lifter equipped with a U-shaped blade. The plants should be removed from the bed immediately after undercutting, and, for convenience in planting, long lateral roots should be cut back to a length of 10–15 cm (4–6 in) with pruning shears or a knife (Fig. 3–21).

Naked-rooted conifer stock is planted only in the less arid zones, but the general principles of packing for shipment are the same as described below for hardwoods with one important exception: the tops of conifers must be given free ventilation to prevent accumulation of transpired moisture.

As soon as they are lifted, the plants should be graded, counted, and tied in bundles of 50 or 100. The individual bundles are packed in boxes or crates, or several bundles may be tied together to make one large bundle which is wrapped in waterproof paper completely enclosing the roots and tops (Fig. 3–22). The bottoms and sides of the packages must be lined with moist peat, sawdust, shavings, or some other moisture-retaining material to prevent drying of the stock. Although fine sand retains moisture well, it is rarely used because of its weight. Just before the package is closed for shipment, the plants should be covered with a layer of moist peat or sawdust, and then thoroughly watered. If possible, packing should not be done until the day before planting because it is difficult to keep packaged stock in good condition for more than one or two days. About 500 fifteen-month-old coniferous plants can be shipped in a crate 40 × 40 × 60 cm (16 × 16 × 24 in).

A tractor-drawn and powered "seedling harvester" has been developed to speed the handling of stock in a California nursery. Two adjacent beds are dug in the usual manner and the machine carrying a crew of 4 or 5 pickers and 1 or 2 packers is drawn over the beds. The pickers pull, grade, and count the seedlings and place them on a conveyor belt where they are carried to the packers who prune the roots and tie them into bundles. To prevent drying the seedlings are shaded by a hood over the conveyor and kept moist by a mist spray.

Double handling and excessive transport costs can be avoided by grading and selecting the stock during and immediately after lifting in the nursery; thus, only plants of the required size will be sent to the planting site.

Grading of stock raised in receptacles that contain ten or more plants is difficult. Some of the plants may be unsuitable for planting, but the container must, nevertheless, be taken to the planting site, making the transportation cost per plantable seedling very high. Cans with more than 50 per cent of the plants missing or culls should be be sent to the planting site. Either the missing plants and culls should be replaced by healthy seedlings and left in the nursery for another season of growth, or the receptacle should be emptied and used for new seeding or transplanting.

In naked-rooted plants grown in beds or rows, grading is done mainly on the basis of stem diameter and development of the root system. Undersized trees and plants with badly stripped or broken roots or split stems must be rejected.

The root system of conifers raised in containers should be examined by pulling a few of the plants from the containers to note the length and development of the roots. Sturdy plants with a good stem and healthy color are to be preferred to tall, spindly, yellowish stock. The size of the plant is less important than its vigor, as expressed by healthy color and well-developed roots.

The best guide for grading nursery stock is the field survival of plants of various sizes. No universal grading rules can be given because the qualities required for survival depend upon the species and the planting site. Although stem diameter is a good indicator of seedling quality, it should not be used as the only criterion. Top/root ratio, health, vigor, and soundness of the plants must also be considered. Much bigger stock is required for sand dune fixation than for normal sites. For the affores-

Fig. 3–21. The blade of the mechanical tree-lifter is pulled the length of the bed about 20 cm (8 in) below the surface. As it moves, the soil is lifted and loosened permitting the stock to be easily pulled by hand. (Courtesy Tennessee Valley Authority)

Fig. 3–22. Seedlings being packed into bundles for transporting to the field. (Photo Forest Service, USDA.)

tation of heavy soils, mountainous areas, or eroded hills, sturdy plants are needed. For sand dunes, where deep planting is practiced, a tall stem is required because the roots often are planted at a depth of about 40 cm (16 in).

Any undersized plants with poor roots and conifers with unhealthy color should be discarded, no matter how great the need for stock, for they will have little chance of survival in the field. They are, in fact, the poorest individuals among plants raised under the most favorable growing conditions. Seedlings of unwanted species sent from the nurseries should not be used.

It is also considered bad policy and uneconomic to keep culls in the nursery for another year in the hope that they will develop into plantable seedlings. The culls often include plants with hereditary defects that cause them to succumb soon after planting even though they are two years old. If, however, there is a high percentage of undersized plants because of improper care or naturally slow growth, the plants may be left for another year in the nursery.

Storage of Planting Stock

All seedlings and transplants should be planted in the field as soon as possible after lifting. However, dormant stock, such as *Melia azeda- rach* L. and species of *Fraxinus, Acer, Pinus, Juniperus,* and *Cupressus,* may be easily stored for a few days by a procedure known as "heeling-in." The trenches prepared for heeling-in stock should be located in a cool, shady place and dug deeply enough to accommodate the roots of the seedling without bending. One side of the trench should be vertical and the other slanting. The bundles of seedlings to be heeled-in are laid on their sides in the trench with their roots toward the vertical side and their tops above ground level. Bundles are then untied and the seedlings spread out on the sloping side of the trench. The roots are covered with moist mineral soil taken from the vertical side of the trench; care should be taken not to cover the stems much above the root collar. If desired, a second layer of seedlings can be heeled-in on top of the first. The soil should be lightly packed about the roots and kept moist as long as the seedlings remain heeled-in. Seedlings can be stored by this method for only a short time in warm weather before top growth starts.

If, for any reason, stock must be kept for a few weeks before planting, it can be placed in cold storage at about 2° to 5° C (36°–41° F). One must never let the roots dry out during storage. Roots may be kept moist by maintaining the relative humidity in the storage room above 90 per-cent and by placing moisture holding material in contact with them. Excessive moisture such as that produced by mist sprayers can cause molding of the plants. If the climate is extremely dry the bundles may be put in polythene bags to prevent drying. However, it is advisable to keep the plants in the bags for only a short time to avoid molding. Plants must not be packed too tightly in the bag and they must be kept out of direct sunlight at all times. Bags should be labeled for proper identification of the plants. The bags can be used only once.

Heeled-in plants or balled-stock should be shaded; if they are shaded by a canvas cover, it should not be placed directly on the plants because the reduced ventilation may cause overheating. If cold storage is not available, planting stock may be kept, but only for a short time, in cool cellars or caves, or by wrapping in polyethylene film which is impermeable to water but permeable to carbon dioxide.

Transporting Planting Stock

No special problems are involved when transporting naked-rooted stock in bundles or crates. For transporting plants raised in pots, the pots should be carefully stacked to avoid shaking the soil loose from the roots during transport and losses of pots and plants by breakage. Cans should be placed in the trucks in layers, each one resting on the edge of two others in such a way that the underneath will not be damaged. This system may also be used when transporting potted plants, although loading will be more expensive because pots take up much more space. Special shelves for stacking pots or cans could be added to the truck, each layer of containers being placed on a shelf, with one shelf about 40 cm (16 in) above the other (Fig. 3–23). But even without any

Fig. 3–23.　　Truck with shelves for stacking and transporting potted plants. (Courtesy C. W. Chapman)

special shelves, three to five layers of cans are easily accommodated with careful handling and loading.

If possible, plants should be transported in the planting season on cool, cloudy, or even rainy days to prevent desiccation during transport. During shipment seedlings should be properly ventilated to prevent overheating. Crates or bales should be stacked in such a way that air movement among them is possible. Shipping schedules should be carefully planned to avoid delays and to allow proper disposition of the plants immediately upon arrival. As soon as the plants arrive at the planting site, they must be watered and, if necessary, heeled-in in a cool, moist, shaded place until they are needed for planting.

COSTS

The cost of growing nursery stock depends on many factors. These include size of the nursery, number of species grown, seed cost, age of stock, cost of labor, irrigation facilities, durability of containers, and facilities for cultivation. Even the size of the container has a considerable influence on the cost of the seedling. Large receptacles not only require more soil and more water, but it also costs more to handle the heavier containers in the nursery and to transport them to the planting site. There is a direct relationship between the diameter of a container and the final cost of the plant grown in it; therefore, it seems evident that a significant saving in production costs will result from even a small reduction in tube diameter.

Height growth for some species is less in the smaller polythene tubes than in the larger sizes, but this limitation can be overcome by fertilization.

In large-scale production of a relatively small number of species, expenses can be kept low per thousand of plantable stock, whereas costs of species grown in small quantities may be quite high. Pests and unfavorable climatic conditions may add to costs in spite of all efforts and care. It is difficult, therefore, to give exact data for calculating the costs of growing nursery stock. The information in Table 3–5 may nevertheless be useful.

Techniques of sowing and transplanting, and growth rate for various tree species suitable for planting in arid zones are given in Appendix C.

NURSERY RECORDS

Like any commercial undertaking, a nursery should have proper business practices, such as keeping inventories and cost accounts, and maintaining maps showing all facilities, including those below ground, such

Table 3—5. Number of workdays required
for growing 1,000 plants in nurseries.

Type of Work	Conifers (15 months old)	Eucalypts (8 months old)
Preparation of seedlings	0.3 workday	0.3 workday
Bed preparation	0.4	0.4
Arranging containers	0.5	0.5
Filling containers	1.0	1.0
Transplanting	1.2	1.2
Weeding	0.9	0.3
Watering	0.5	0.2
Root pruning	0.3	0.2
Overhead costs	0.3	0.2
Lifting and loading	0.5	0.5
Miscellaneous	0.3	0.1
	6.2	4.9

as the irrigation system. A job calendar should be developed to guide the timing of operations. All information on the daily operations of the nursery should be recorded in a journal. This should show the division of the fields for annual planting and rotation; seed received—species, origin, and quantities; seed sown—pretreatment, date, amount, and location; time of germination; irrigation and cultivation practices; time of transplanting; control measures for pests; quantities sent out and their destination—and, of course, the cost of these operations. All this information is indispensable for the continued successful operation of the nursery.

BIBLIOGRAPHY

ADAMS, R. S. Reforestation studies 1966. Annu. Rep. Calif. Div. For., Sacramento.
1967   21 p.
ALDHOUS, J. R. Nursery practice. G. B. For. Comm. Bull. 43. 184 p.
1972
BAILEY, L. H. The nursery manual. Macmillan, New York. 456 p.
1954
BEN-SALEM, B., and M. REYNDERS. Existe-t-il une périod optimale de plantation aux
1974   Mogodo? Repub. Tunisienne, Minist. Agric. Inst. Natl. Rech. For., Note
        Rech. 1. Ariana. 38 p.
BUSH, M. K. (editor). Lesoposadounyy material "brika." [Forest planting material
1974   "brika."]. Latvia Naucho-Issled. Inst. Lesokhoz. Problem, Riga. 136 p.
CLAUZURE, P. Utilisation des godets en polyéthylène pour les reboisements dans la
1956   région mediterranéenne. Rev. For. Fr. 8:769–784.
COSTIN, E., A. S. BALEIDI, M. EZZ, and M. BAZARA. Sand dune fixation and afforesta-
1974   tion in some semi-desert countries of the Middle East area. Pages 66–79
        in report on heathland and sand dune afforestation. FAO/DEN/TF 123.
        Food. Agric. Organ. U. N., Rome. 239 p.
DONALD, D. G. M. A study of the history, practice and economics of forest nurseries
1965   in South Africa. Univ. Stellenbosch, Ann. 40, Ser. A, No. 1. 70 p.

DUFFIELD, J. W., and R. P. EIDE. Polyethylene bag packaging of conifer planting
1959   stock in the Pacific Northwest. J. For. 57:578–579.
ENGSTROM, H. E., and J. H. STOECKELER. Nursery practice for trees and shrubs suit-
1941   able for planting on the prairie-plains. U. S. Dep. Agric. Misc. Publ. 434.
        Washington, D. C. 159 p.
EVANS, R. W. The evolution of a plantation technique for *Callitris introtropica* in the
1966   Northern Territory of Australia. Proc. World For. Congr. (Madrid) 6:1540–
        1545.
FAO. Forestry Research and Education Centre: The Sudan Final Report. FAO/SF:
1969   70/SUD 3. Rome. 170 p.
————. Institut de reboisement, Tunisie. Manuel pratique de reboisement. Établi
1974   sur la base des travaux de J. Marion et J. Poupon. FO:SF/TUN 11. Rapp.
        Tech. 2. Rome. 345 p.
GREAT BRITAIN, MINISTRY OF AGRICULTURE, FISHERIES, AND FOOD. Fertilizers for the
1964   farm. Bull. 195. H. M. Stationery Off., London. 90 p.
HANSBROUGH, T., and J. P. HOLLIS. The effect of soil fumigation for the control of
1956   parasitic nematodes on the growth and yield of loblolly pine seedlings.
        Plant Dis. Rep. 41:1021–1025.
HOLMES, G. D., and G. W. IVENS. Chemical control of weeds in forest nursery seed-
1952   beds. G. B. For. Comm., For. Rec. 13. London. 31 p.
KLINGMAN, G. C., and F. M. ASHTON. Weed science: principles and practices. John
1975   Wiley & Sons, New York. 431 p.
KOZLOWSKI, T. T. Physiological implications in afforestation. Proc. World For.
1966   Congr. (Madrid) 6:1304–1316.
KRAMER, P. J., and T. T. KOZLOWSKI. Physiology of trees. McGraw-Hill, New York.
1960   642 p.
KRÜSSMANN, G. Die Baumschule: ein Handbuch für Anzucht, Vermehrung, Kultur
1954   und Absatz der Baumschulpflanzen. 2te Auf. P. Parey, Berlin. 559 p.
LARSON, M. M. Effect of temperatures on initial development of ponderosa pine
1967   seedlings from three sources. For. Sci. 13:286–294.
LOW, A. J., and J. S. OAKLEY. Tubed seedlings. G. B. For. Comm. Leafl. 61. Lon-
1975   don. 17 p.
MATTHEWS, R. G. Container seedling production: a provisional manual. Canadian
1971   For. Serv. Inf. Rep. BC-X-58. Pac. For. Res. Cent., Victoria, B. C. 57 p.
MIKOLA, P. Afforestation of treeless areas. Unasylva 23(1):35–48.
1969
MONJAUZE, A. L'enveloppe de polyéthylène, vecteur des racines et instrument
1956   d'étude du développement radiculaire. Algér. Serv. For. Publ. 2. 10 p.
MULLIN, R. E. An experiment with wrapping materials for bales of nursery stock.
1958   Ont. Dep. Lands For. Res. Rep. 37. Maple, Ont., Canada. 31 p.
MULLIN, R. E., L. M. MORRISON, and T. T. SCHWEITZER. Inventory of nursery stock.
1955   Ont. Dep. Lands For. Res. Rep. 33. Maple, Ont., Canada. 64 p.
NIENSTAEDT, H., F. C. CECH, F. MERGEN, C. W. WANG, and B. ZAK. Vegetative
1958   propagation in forest genetics research and practice. J. For. 56:826–839.
OLIVE, C. L., JR., and C. B. UMLAND. Cost accounting in TVA forest nurseries.
1952   J. For. 50:831–833.
PHILIPPIS, A. DE, and E. GIORDIANO. Practice and research in nursery techniques in
1967   the Temperate Zone. Documents FAO World Symposium on Man-Made
        Forests and their Industrial Importance. Canberra 14–24 April 1967. Vol.
        1:205–247. Food Agric. Organ. U. N., Rome.
PIÉROLA, J. M., and F. DE SANZ-PASTER. Viceros de resinosas en Granada. Montes
1948   4:405–410.
ROTTY, R. Methods and machines used in North American nurseries. Unasylva
1960   14:17–38, 65–83.
RUPF, H., S. SCHÖNHAR, and M. ZEYHER. Der Forstpflanzgarten. 2te Auf. BLV
1961   Verlagsgesellschaft, München. 242 p.

SCHWALEN, H. C., K. R. FROST, and W. W. HINZ. Sprinkler irrigation. Ariz. Agric.
1953   Exp. Stn. Bull. 250. Tucson. 41 p.
SCHUBERT, G. H., and R. S. ADAMS. Reforestation practices for conifers in California.
1971   Calif. Dep. Conserv. Div. For., Sacramento. 359 p.
SCHUBERT, G. H., and K. B. LANQUIST. Mist sprayer improves seedling harvester.
1959   U. S. For. Serv., Tree Plant. Notes No. 38. p. 19–20.
SHEAT, W. G. Propagation of trees, shrubs and conifers. Macmillan, London. 479 p.
1948
SHIRLEY, H. L., and L. J. MEULI. Influence of moisture supply on drought resistance
1939   of conifers. J. Agric. Res. 59:1–21.
SHOULDERS, E. Seedbed density influences production and survival of loblolly and
1960   slash pine nursery stock. U. S. For. Serv., Tree Plant. Notes No. 42. p. 19–
        21.
————. Mycorrhizal inoculation influences survival, growth, and chemical composi-
1972   tion of slash pine seedlings. USDA For. Serv. Res. Pap. SO-74. Southern
        For. Exp. Stn., New Orleans, La. 12 p.
SILVICULTURAL CONFERENCE. Part I. Afforestation and soil conservation. Proc.
1960   Silvic. Conf. (Dehra Dun Dec. 1956) 9(I):291–397. India For. Res. Inst.,
        Dehra Dun.
SITTON, B. G., S. G. GILBERT, S. MERRILL, W. A. LEWIS, and W. W. KILBY. Pre-
1950   emergence treatment for weed control in the tung nursery. Proc. Am. Soc.
        Hortic. Sci. 56:197–202.
STEIN, W. I., J. L. EDWARDS, and R. W. TINUS. Outlook for container-grown seed-
1975   lings use in reforestation. J. For. 73:337–341.
STOECKELER, J. H., and G. W. JONES Forest nursery practice in the Lake States.
1957   U. S. Dep. Agric., Agric. Handb. 110, Washington, D. C. 124 p.
STONE, E. C., G. H. SCHUBERT, R. W. BENSELER, F. J. BARON, and S. L. KRUGMAN.
1963   Variation in the root regenerating potentials of ponderosa pine from four
        California nurseries. For. Sci. 9:217–225.
TENNESSEE VALLEY AUTHORITY. Operations manual for TVA forest nurseries. Tenn.
1954   Val. Auth., Div. For. Relat. Norris, Tenn. 57 p.
U. S. FOREST SERVICE. Seeds of woody plants in the United States. Prepared by the
1974   Forest Service, C. S. Schopmeyer, Technical Coordinator. U. S. Dep. Agric.,
        Agric. Handb. 450. 883 p.
VELASCO, F., and J. M. ALBAREDA. Estudo nutritivo de diversas repoblaciones fores-
1966   tales de coniferas en la España semiarida. Proc. World For. Congr. (Ma-
        drid) 6:1477–1483.
WAHEED KHAN, M. A. Improved methods and devices in nursery practice. Sudan
1965   For. Dep. For. Res. Inst. Pam. 28. Soba, Khartoum, Sudan. 28 p.
WALTERS, J. The planting gun and bullet: a new tree-planting technique. For.
1961   Chron. 37:94–95.
————. An improved plant gun and bullet: a new tree-planting technique. U. S.
1963   For. Serv., Tree Plant. Notes No. 57. p. 1–3.
WILLIAMS, R. D., and S. H. HANKS. Hardwood nurseryman's guide. U. S. Dep.
1976   Agric., Agric. Handb. 473. Washington, D. C. 78 p.
WRIGHT, E. Importance of mycorrhizae to ponderosa pine seedlings. For. Sci.
1957   3:275–280.
WUNDER, W. G. Planting Eucalyptus microtheca F. Muell. with and without poly-
1966   thene bags. Sudan For. Dep. For. Res. Inst. Pam. 30. Soba, Khartoum,
        Sudan. 22 p.

4

Afforestation

Establishing a forest on a treeless area or introducing a species to a forest area in which it does not occur naturally is known as afforestation. Afforestation may be done by direct seeding or by planting cuttings or tree seedlings reared in nurseries.

Natural regeneration is generally preferred to planting or artificial seeding where it is cheaper and where such regeneration can be expected to restock the area fully. Sites selected for planting in arid zones are rarely located in areas where trees, either natural or planted, have reached the seed production stage where natural regeneration can be relied upon to restock an area satisfactorily. Where restocking is incomplete and uneven, it will be necessary to plant the vacant areas and possibly to thin patches of dense natural regeneration in order to get the spacing required in arid zones. Due to these difficulties artificial regeneration is used almost without exception in arid zone forestry even where some natural regeneration can be expected.

FOREST PLANTING IN LOW RAINFALL ZONES

In arid and semiarid zones, trees are planted mainly as soil protection, as shelterbelts, as windbreaks to protect cultivated fields or cattle from sweeping winds and shifting sands, and for their aesthetic and amenity value. Although such regions may never before have been covered with sufficient trees or shrubs to form forests, savannas, maquis, or garigues, they may, by the planting of trees in suitable places, and with proper silvicultural treatment, be transformed from desolate and forbidding wasteland into productive and more habitable areas. While the aim of such planting may be mainly protective or aesthetic, it can be planned so that it will also produce poles, pulpwood, fuelwood, fodder, essential oils, or other minor economic forest products.

The soils in the planting area should be classified by a soil scientist and the best sites planted first. Topographic factors should also be considered in selecting the site for the initial planting. In the Northern

Hemisphere survival of seedlings in arid zones is generally better on north slopes than on other aspects because of the more favorable soil moisture there. Survival will be highest and costs lowest on the best sites and a successful plantation will give encouragement for further planting.

Even under favorable climatic and soil conditions, afforestation is always a costly venture. Under arid conditions planting is much more expensive than in humid climates because of the additional work required to create a favorable environment for the young trees. Faulty judgment in selecting the area to be planted and the species or provenance to be used, and improper techniques in land clearing, soil preparation, spacing, or cultivation will certainly increase the cost and could result in outright failure of the project. Subsequent treatment will be more expensive, and delayed treatment may not remedy errors committed in planting. For example, extra tilling of the soil late in the growing season, or thinning the trees, will not promote as favorable development of seedlings that are already stunted by compact soil or early competition as proper cultivation before and soon after planting, or adequate spacing during planting. In fact, if too many stunted or suppressed trees are found in a plantation, it may be more economic to abandon it or to start the plantation anew in the proper manner. The object is not merely effective sowing or planting but the ultimate success of the plantation.

It is well to avoid afforestation where it is evident that it will fail because of unsuitable site conditions and to concentrate efforts where they are like to be successful. Therefore, in areas with extremely low rainfall or too thin and poor a soil layer to permit successful tree establishment, protection of the soil by allowing vegetation to establish itself naturally is the only economic solution.

From the social aspect of afforestation, it might be well to consider the feasibility of establishing new communities in or near afforested areas, since such areas are usually thinly populated or uninhabited. Such communities must be sufficiently attractive to draw labor, and continuous work should be assured to keep the laborers from leaving. In countries where a large labor supply is available no attempt should be made to mechanize afforestation completely. Forestry can provide continuous work for the local population whose cooperation and understanding is necessary for the success of large scale afforestation. Afforestation can be carried out by laborers who are virtually unskilled but anxious to learn. These people can be trained so that they will be adept in the more exacting work needed later such as thinning and exploitation of the crops.

At first glance, the fundamental principles of afforestation by planting or seeding in arid zones appear to be the same in different zones or at least to be uniform within any given zone. Yet local conditions can so profoundly affect their application that suitable techniques must be devised for each zone. Different soil textures, the extent and kind of existing vegetation, the degrees of slope, the amount of rock outcrop, and the elevation will dictate different techniques and even determine the species to be used.

SELECTING THE SITE

It has been the practice in many arid countries to plant barren, steep, rocky, and dry areas because only land not needed for agriculture or grazing was designated as available for afforestation. Planting such areas was not only extremely costly but resulted in many failures. It is easy to understand why this policy had a discouraging effect on the sponsors of afforestation.

When large areas are available for tree planting, the sites to be planted can be chosen. Those sites most favorable for planting should be planted first. First choice should be the site that has the deepest soil, the least amount of competing vegetation, fewest rock outcrops, fewest gullies, the least slope, sufficient roads for communication and transport (especially during planting season), and adequate protection against grazing and fires. Obviously, it will be difficult to find sites with all these qualities, but the more positive factors the site has, the more probable the plantation's success and the lower the cost. If any desirable specification is lacking but can be met artificially (e.g., by eliminating competing vegetation, reducing slopes by terracing, stopping up gullies, building roads, or providing protection against fire and grazing), the decision to plant or not must be made after comparing the cost and the benefit to be derived.

PREPARING THE SITE

The site should be prepared before the prospective planting dates so that when the trees are brought from the nurseries they can be planted without delay. Preparation of the site for planting trees is done in essentially the same way as land is prepared for crops. The better the preparation, the better the results are likely to be. Preparation entails eradication of competing vegetation, leveling or terracing, and cultivating the soil. A disadvantage of such thorough preparation of the site is the increased danger of erosion, but this can be overcome by taking the necessary precautions.

Eradication of Vegetation

Growth and development of both natural and planted trees are predominantly dependent on soil moisture which is by far the most important single site factor in areas with long hot dry seasons. Factors affecting soil moisture, and hence tree growth, are soil quality and depth, soil texture, availability of nutrients, exposure, and the competition among plants for moisture. Partial or complete eradication of grasses, weeds, bushes, and trees, which will compete with the planted seedlings for soil moisture is required on all planting sites. Unwanted vegetation often has a high consumptive use of water and can quickly deplete the available soil moisture. Therefore, the drier the site the more important it is to eliminate competing vegetation. For example, an increase of about 100 percent in mean annual height growth for species of *Eucalyptus*, *Acacia*, *Prosopis*, and *Azadirachta* has been recorded in the Sudan in areas with only 350 mm (14 in) annual rainfall where the area was cleared of all weeds and well cultivated when compared to growth of these species on noncultivated areas in the locality. The manner of eradication of competing vegetation depends on the species and on the availability of labor, tools, and equipment, including herbicides.

Grass. When the competing vegetation is principally grass, it is advisable to plow the land to destroy the grass and produce the desired soil tilth before planting. Grass is usually chopped up and incorporated with the surface soil. Wide-bladed hoes are used when cheap labor is available. If mules or horses are available, grass may be plowed under or disced into the soil. In Spain, oxen have been found more suitable

Fig. 4-1. One yoke of oxen can prepare about 40 hectares (100 acres) a year (Spain). (Courtesy Henry S. Kernan)

than horses or mules because they are cheaper to keep and strong enough to pull a two-share plow to a depth of 25–30 cm (10–12 in) in loam soil. They are also more maneuverable on slopes (Fig. 4–1). One yoke of oxen can prepare about 40 hectares (100 acres) a year. Elsewhere a light, wheeled tractor is more commonly used. When tractors are available and can be kept in good repair, tractor plowing is an efficient way of eliminating grass and other vegetation.

On some planting sites, herbicides are used. But if roots or rhizomes are not completely killed by the chemicals, it will be necessary to uproot the living underground parts by hoeing or plowing.

Woody Vegetation. Many designated planting sites are occupied by degraded forests, woodland, or bush—i.e., savanna, maquis, garigue, or chaparral. On these sites a few scattered trees or tall bushes may be found, but such vegetation, whether dense or sparse, must be eliminated if the plantation is to succeed. Leaving trees or bushes and planting among them will result in early severe competition that will soon suppress or kill many of the seedlings.

In such areas, all trees should be cut, and any other saleable material, such as poles, posts or firewood, should be salvaged if it will yield a profit. Large trees are usually felled with two-man crosscut saws or with portable power saws. Small diameter material may be cut with axes or handsaws. The saleable material is then hauled from the site and stacked along the road for transport to the market. Remaining vegetation on the site is obviously of no economic value, and if it impedes reforestation, must be destroyed or removed. It is common, in clearing the remaining woody vegetation, to remove only the parts above ground. Where labor is available and not expensive, small lightweight axes or curved or straight hatchets (Fig. 4–2) are used. The hatchets may be either single or double-edged, which easily cut through the small stems of brushwood. Larger stems can be cut with full-sized axes or power-driven bush-cutting saws.

Brush burning has been effective under certain conditions, but foresters are reluctant to set fires deliberately in arid zones because of the difficulties of control. The air is normally dry and periods of high humidity are unpredictable creating a great risk that the fire will spread out of control. Where fire is used to destroy brush, one should remember that some species are more resistant to fire than others and that many species sprout vigorously after a fire and may have to be destroyed by other methods. Burning can affect the physical and chemical properties of the soil by accelerated leaching of minerals. Mineral nutrients may be temporarily increased after a brush fire, but this may cause a disproportionate increase in top growth compared to root growth making the seedling more susceptible to drought injury. In addition, the chemical changes in the soil may destroy some mycorrhizae.

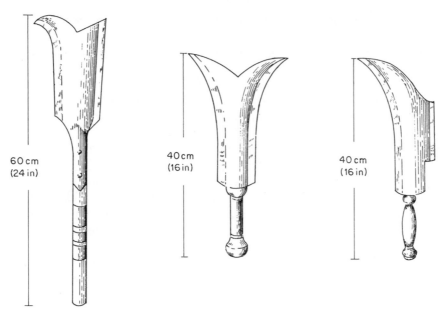

Fig. 4–2. Types of hatchets used for clearing land.

Heavy mechanical equipment, such as bulldozers and brushcutters, can be used. Bulldozers are used not only to work the surface soil, but also to remove the woody vegetation. Brushcutters, composed of heavy water-filled drums with sharp protruding angle-iron blades welded lengthwise to their sides, have been improvised locally. One or two such drums are hitched to a tractor and, as they are drawn along, they smash down and break off the vegetation.

Herbicides. Since 1950, herbicides have come into general use for killing unwanted vegetation on planting sites, and research is continually increasing their efficiency. Proper use of herbicides will greatly reduce the cost of eliminating unwanted, competing vegetation. In areas sprayed with herbicides, the dead vegetation acts as a mulch, and soil moisture may be significantly higher, particularly in the topsoil where the roots of seedlings grow, than in areas with native vegetation, or even in areas where the vegetation has been hoed out or scraped away. The differences in moisture percentages are greater during drought years than during years of normal or above average precipitation. Another advantage of chemical weed control is that one treatment is usually effective for two or more years, whereas mechanically treated areas are soon invaded by grasses and weeds.

Some herbicides are soluble in water and others in oil. Solutions or emulsions containing the herbicide can be prepared in such a way that they will adhere to the plant, eventually enter the sap stream, and be translocated to the aerial parts or the roots. Water solutions are more readily taken up by the roots, whereas oil solutions penetrate better through the leaves and bark.

Both selective and non-selective herbicides can be used. The two non-selective herbicides most commonly used are ammonium sulphamate ($NH_4SO_3NH_2$) and sodium arsenite, an indefinite mixture consisting principally of Na_3AsO_3 and $NaAsO_3$. Ammonium sulphamate is slow-acting but not toxic to humans or animals. It is generally applied to the individual tree by filling a frill girdle with the crystals, which are hygroscopic and dissolve in water absorbed from the air. Sodium arsenite is fast acting but highly toxic to humans, livestock, and wildlife. It is dangerous to entrust its use to untrained personnel. Sodium arsenite is readily soluble in water and is generally injected into the stem, or the ground near the base of the tree to be killed.

The selective herbicides most frequently used to kill broad-leaved woody plants are 2,4 D and 2,4,5-T or a combination of the two. The most effective against woody plants is 2,4,5-T. Use of these chemicals for weeding in nursery beds is discussed in Chapter 3. When selective herbicides are used to kill unwanted hardwoods on a planting site, they may be applied either to the foliage or, if the species has thin bark, to the base of the trunk. Basal spraying reduces drift of the chemical to other vegetation but increases the cost of application.

Selective herbicides disrupt physiological processes, especially respiration and mineral assimilation, in most broad-leaved plants to which they are applied. Because they are most effective when physiological activity is high, the best results are obtained by applying them in the spring, right after the resumption of growth. In regions of low rainfall, or where spring and early summer are dry, the best time to spray is after sufficient moisture has been received to stimulate rapid growth; thus in some areas midsummer may be the most favourable period.

The amount of herbicide used varies with the type of vegetation, the effectiveness of the herbicide, and the strength of the solution. For 2,4 D in water solution the variation between neighboring areas may be as much as 30–200 liters per hectare (3–20 gal/a).

The vegetation to be eliminated by herbicides can be sprayed from the ground using back-pack units that are pressurized or equipped with either a hand pump or by a pump driven by a light engine. Heavier spray units are usually mounted on wheels and pulled to the area by tractors. Hoses of different lengths are attached to the sprayer so that a large area of vegetation can be sprayed from one location of the unit. Spray nozzles should produce a mist or fog that will completely wet a plant approximately 4 m (13 ft) high with little waste.

Because it is impractical to spray large areas from the ground, they are sprayed from specially equipped planes or helicopters. Aerial spraying can accomplish as much in one hour as one man can in 300 days of brushcutting. Thus, it is cheaper than any other method of eliminating competing vegetation over large areas. Aerial spraying is economic only when the area is 200 hectares (500 acres) or more. In the United States, the cost of aerial spraying ranges between $12–$35 per hectare ($5–$14/acre). Ordinarily, the larger the area sprayed, the less the cost per hectare.

The boundaries of the area must be well marked so that they are clearly visible from the air. To minimize the drift of the herbicide into neighboring areas, aerial spraying must be done early in the morning, when there is usually little or no wind.

Because different types of vegetation react differently to different herbicides, and to different doses, methods of spraying, and periods of application, the reactions to all combinations and ranges of these variables must be carefully determined by experimentation to obtain the optimum mortality at the lowest cost. Mortality need not be complete over large areas; 90 per cent is considered quite satisfactory.

Herbicides are sold in stock solution under a variety of trade names. Each container must bear a label giving complete instructions for use and dilution in the field. These instructions should be carried out carefully and precisely and all precautions observed.

Pollution by Chemicals. Many chemicals that serve a useful function in forest management by reducing unwanted vegetation and controlling animal pests and diseases cause great concern among ecologists because of their undersirable side effects. Other than in nurseries, forest management activities in arid zones, especially in developing countries, have so far involved only minor use of herbicides and pesticides.

Many of the herbicides and pesticides used in forest management are toxic in varying degrees and are harmful if they come in contact with or are ingested by people and animals, particularly birds and fishes. The rate of decomposition of such chemicals varies and even chemicals with low indices of toxicity, if they do not decompose quickly after use, tend to accumulate to dangerous levels.

Chemicals used in an area may seep down to the water table or be carried to rivers and lakes by surface runoff. Some enter plants by absorption from the soil or through the foliage. Organisms that drink or come in contact with the chemically polluted water or consume the plants are subject to poisoning. Relatively little information on to toxicity and safe levels of concentration is currently available, therefore, if pesticides are used, every precaution should be taken to avert possible damage. Because control of unwanted vegetation by herbicides is more economic than by hand labor, particularly in countries where labor costs are high or where weed growth is rapid, the use of herbicides is becoming a standard practice.

Many herbicides used in forest management such as 2,4-D or 2,4,5-T or pesticides such as DDT, aldrin, endrin and other chemicals may persist in the soil, water, and plants after use and constitute a pollution hazard for weeks, months, or years. For fear of soil water, and plant pollution, many governments restrict the use of most herbicides and pesticides, or closely control them. New herbicides and pesticides with few side effects are now being developed. Some of these have shown promise in control of undesirable vegetation. Picloram, paraquat, and karbutilate have been effective in the control of brush, and results obtained by the use of dalapon, atrazine, and simazine have shown that low-cost control of grasses is practicable.

Recent studies show that if 2,4,5-T, which is one of the best selective herbicides, contains less than 0.1 ppm of a dioxin designated TEDD, the hazard of using it is very slight. This dioxin occurs as a by-product when the temperature rises too high during the synthesis of 2,4,5-T. TEDD is regarded as a carcinogenic and teratogenic toxicant. If the concentration of the dioxin is higher than 0.1 ppm in the herbicide used, there is danger that animals and humans accidently consuming it may suffer significant induction of fetal deformities or cancer. Findings of the studies, however, indicate that if the herbicide contains less than 0.1 ppm dioxin and is used in accordance with the directions on the label and governmental guidelines, there will be no appreciable hazard to humans, animals, or the general quality of the environment.

An important challenge to foresters is the maintenance of the productive capacity of land responsibly and economically by controlling undesirable vegetation and pests while still giving adequate protection to the environment.

Cultivation

Just as in agriculture, the soil to be planted or sown must first be cultivated to aerate the upper layer and enable it to absorb rain. Growth of trees in a plantation will be irregular unless the soil is thoroughly cultivated so that water can penetrate uniformly to the roots. If subsoil has been exposed in any of the previous work, it is advisable to cover it with topsoil. During soil preparation steep slopes may be terraced or formed into contour benches in order to catch the runoff and reduce erosion.

Soil may be cultivated by hand with wide-bladed hoes, by plowing, or by discing. If the soil contains many rocks, cultivation must be done by hand. Where there are no surface obstructions, the deeper soil may be plowed, disced, or subsoiled.

Cultivated Strips. Cultivation over the entire area is expensive and is used almost exclusively on level land for high-value crops. Consequently, only the strips to be planted are cultivated, and the intervening strips are left untilled. Partial cultivation is quicker and more convenient, as well as being cheaper.

In this method, strips previously cleared of natural vegetation are cultivated by hand or mechanical equipment, such as a tractor-drawn disc-plow. Generally, the width of the strip is that of the tractor-drawn equipment, although wider ones are sometimes preferred. The interval between two cultivated strips is generally equal to their width.

Disc Plows. Light vegetative cover can be efficiently broken up and mixed into the surface soil layers by disc plows. These discs are so constructed that in stony soil one disc can lift over an obstacle while the rest of the discs go on working, thus easing the strain upon the machine. The number of discs forming a single unit varies according to their diameter. The range is three to four discs 80 cm (32 in) in diameter up to ten discs 50 cm (20 in) in diameter. Disc plows must be heavy or weighted so that they will penetrate the soil to the desired depth. In favorable soil, one hectare (2.5 a) can be disced in an hour.

Agricultural plowing generally affects only the upper soil layers; but in afforestation, where deep-rooting trees are to be planted, ways have been found to obtain deep root penetration by thorough soil preparation.

Subsoilers or Rooters. Subsoilers are of two types: single-tooth or multiple-tooth (Figs. 4–3, 4–4). Each type can be operated with a low- to medium-powered tractor. A light single-tooth subsoiler weighs 75–150 kg (165–330 lb) and requires a 25–40-hp tractor to move it. The heavier, multiple-tooth types, which weigh up to 2 tons, may require a 90-hp tractor. The single-tooth subsoiler has an almost vertical tooth terminating at the bottom in a shoe, that makes a narrow angle with the horizontal. The tool works below the surface, and its forward motion thrusts the shoe into the ground. If it meets an obstacle, it dislodges it, or, if the obstacle is unbreakable, the subsoiler is moved backward and raised by pawls on the wheels and the obstacle is surmounted. In shallow calcareous soil, a 40-hp tractor pulling a single-tooth subsoiler can break one kilometer (0.6 mi) of soil at a depth of 40 cm (16 in) in an hour.

Under difficult soil conditions, rooters that work on the same principle as subsoilers are used. Rooters are larger, heavier, and more sturdily built than subsoilers and can loosen the soil up to a depth of

Fig. 4–3. This single-tooth subsoiler is set for a depth of 1.2 m (4 ft). Similar machines are capable of breaking the soil to a depth of 1.8 m (6 ft). (Courtesy American Tractor Equipment Corp.)

Fig. 4–4. The working depth of this five-tooth subsoiler is shown by the soil adhering to the teeth. (Courtesy American Tractor Equipment Corp.)

1 meter (3.3 ft) (Fig. 4–5). About 2 hectares (5 acres) can be prepared in an eight-hour day. During ordinary plowing, the different soil layers are mixed, but no interference with their natural sequence occurs with the use of rooters. Although rooter teeth may penetrate 60–80 cm (24–32 in) into the soil, depending on soil conditions and equipment used, they crumble the soil but do not mix it. A relatively small tractor under 40 hp is sufficient for plowing, but a rooter weighing 6 tons or more requires a tractor of at least 120 hp. The use of a subsoiler or rooters is advisable under conditions of extreme aridity and on heavy soils where root penetration and water infiltration are difficult. Use of these machines is also desirable on soils with a layer of accumulated calcium carbonate. Such a layer or "hardpan" is not penetrable by tree roots unless it is broken up by the rooter. Trees should be planted directly in the lines broken by the teeth of the subsoiler or rooter; pits need not be dug for setting in the plants.

Pits. Pits are artificially prepared shallow depressions or pockets in the spots where trees are to be planted. The soil in the pits is prepared by hoeing to improve aeration and accelerate infiltration of rain. Although the area between pits usually is not cultivated, pits are some-

Fig. 4–5. A heavy single-tooth rooter and stump puller mounted on a tractor equipped with a brush rake. (Courtesy Fleco Corp.)

times prepared on plowed fields or strips to create a still more favorable environment for the plants.

Pits may be 30 × 30 × 30 cm (12 in), but wider ones are preferred in the more arid regions. They are prepared just before planting or, preferably, just before the first rains. Pits should be filled with the best available soil to receive the seedlings.

On level ground, pits are dug in rows separated by the required spacing distance. The rows make cultivation easier, especially if animal or tractor-drawn cultivators are used. On slopes, pits may be staggered in such a way that they will catch all the surface runoff before gullies can be formed, or they can be placed on the contour and connected by ditches for even distribution of water. On rocky slopes, they are dug wherever convenient among the rocks, adhering as nearly as possible to the desired spacing.

One man should be able to prepare about 70 pits a day.

Experiments should always be carried out in new planting sites to determine the optimum size for pits and to find the least amount of soil working necessary to achieve satisfactory results; in a few places only the surface layer need be worked and then only enough to permit seedling roots to penetrate to the subsoil.

Mole Hills.   On rocky sloping areas in Israel, the soil of planting spots is loosened over an 80 × 80 cm (31 ×31 in) area down to a depth of 20 cm (8 in). Uphill from the planting spot a trench 80 cm (30 in) long, 25 cm (10 in) wide, by 25 cm (10 in) deep is dug to collect the surface runoff. Soil from the trench is piled on the loose soil of the planting spot to form a flat-topped mound resembling a mole hill. During the rainy season a slit is made in the center of the mound and a one-year-old pine is planted with its roots about 25 cm deep and the stem buried up to the first needles. The deep layer of loose soil permits easy penetration by roots, improves infiltration of water, and increases available soil moisture. Where mole hills have been used, survival and growth of seedlings has been good, however, this method has not been in use long enough to justify recommending it for large scale plantings. In using this method there is the danger that the soil will wash away from the mounds and expose the roots of planted trees. In addition, weeds which establish on the sides of the mounds are difficult to eradicate without disturbing the seedlings.

Scalping (Screefing).   In the United States removal of a square or a circle of sod or other vegetation approximately 30 to 45 cm (12 to 18 in) in diameter and about 15 cm (6 in) deep, together with the surface parts and root crowns of the vegetation is known as scalping. These scalped areas are spaced 2 to 3 m (6 to 10 ft) apart; trees are planted in them, either by the person doing the scalping, or by a planter who follows him. One man can prepare about 300 scalped areas per 8-hour day. Scalping is used principally on steep or rocky slopes where mechanical equipment cannot be used efficiently for site preparation.

Disposal of Debris

Uprooting live roots after removing the tops of the plants is essential, otherwise competition for space will quickly be renewed through new sprouts. In many countries uprooting is still done by hand, with the pick-axe being the tool most commonly used. Costs are often extremely high, but in some areas the roots may be sold as fuel-wood or for charcoal, thus defraying part of the cost. In dense oak scrub one man can clear 0.10–0.25 hectare (0.25–0.62 acre) per day.

Machines are now used more and more frequently in clearing, uprooting, and cultivating sites. Brush clearing may be done by a tractor with an angle-dozer blade that cuts off or uproots the vegetation and pushes it aside. On a slope, if the debris is pushed uphill and left in strips, it will provide some protection against erosion. If the brush is not well-developed, and if the soil is devoid of rocks, stumps, and gravel, the rotavator (a rotary disc fixed on a horizontal axis, whose rotation is powered by the tractor) may be used to clear the ground (Fig. 4–6).

Fig. 4–6. The discs of the rotavator, powered by the tractor, cut up the debris and incorporate it with the surface soil. (Courtesy Howard Rotavator Co. Ltd.)

To remove big roots and rocks a rooter having two, three, or more large steel teeth is often used. The teeth penetrate the soil to the desired depth which can be determined by raising or lowering the teeth by control cables connected to the tractor's winch. Such machines weigh between two and seven tons and must be drawn by crawler tractors of 30–120 hp. Heavy rooters of this type are not suited for work on steep slopes.

In using machinery to uproot vegetation or to level land, care should be taken not to bury the topsoil. After vegetation has been uprooted, the surface should be leveled to eliminate the large holes made where the roots were dislodged. Occasionally, underground hollows are formed after removal of rocks or roots. These must be found, filled, and leveled by discing, plowing, or harrowing to facilitate subsequent cultivation and planting.

Debris or slash resulting from the operations just described must be destroyed, not only to reduce fire hazard but also to facilitate planting. Disposal is commonly accomplished by controlled burning or by burying the debris in the soil.

Controlled Burning. Slash may be burned where it lies, or it may be piled or windrowed. A good knowledge of the behavior of fire and its control is essential to the safe use of fire as a silvicultural tool. Fires should never be started during windy, dry, hot weather, and never without properly prepared fire lines and an adequate crew to control them.

Burying. Debris can often be buried when heavy machinery is used to uproot unwanted vegetation during soil cultivation. The debris will rot more quickly after it is buried.

Windrowing. Windrowing or aligning the brushwood along the contour is necessary on sloping ground. It may be piled by hand or pushed by angle dozers. V-shaped dozer blades are often used to throw the brush to both sides of a strip along the contour. The cleared strip between the windrows should be wide enough to allow cultivation. Any living vegetation in the uncleared strips must be far enough from the trees planted in the center of the strip so that it will not compete with them. Brushwood left between the planted strips will help to protect the soil from erosion.

Lopping and Chipping. Lopping branches from logs and tops with hatches or axes, or reducing the slash to chips with machines, and then scattering the small branches or chips on the ground are other methods of reducing fire hazard and opening a site for planting. Lopping is usually cheap, but chipping is very costly.

WATER HARVESTING

Terraces

Before trees are planted or pits are dug on sloping ground, relatively level, narrow benches are formed along the approximate contour by digging soil from the uphill side and depositing it on the downhill side. A bench is known as a terrace, and its relatively flat surface is called the step. Usually the step slopes slightly downward into the hill, and after rains the runoff collects on the terrace. The width of the step varies according to the degree of the slope and the texture of the soil. The steeper the slope, the narrower the step and the shorter the distance between terraces. (Fig. 4–7.) If the slope is steep (20–30 per cent), and the step is narrow, it is known as a gradone. Usually gradoni are laid out 3–4 meters (10–13 ft) apart. A convenient width of a gradone is 1–1.5 meters (3.3–5 ft).

The purpose of terracing is to retard and collect all runoff between the terraces. If runoff is properly managed enough water can be added to the soil of the terrace to improve tree growth significantly. Terraces are essential on steep slopes where all woody vegetation has been completely destroyed and is not likely to re-establish before severe erosion occurs. Paradoxically in arid regions the danger of severe water erosion is great because of the scanty vegetative cover, and the fact that the meager rainfall characteristically is received in a few, sudden, brief, torrential downpours. Terracing provides an effective means of halting erosion, restoring the

Fig. 4–7. Schematic drawing of a cross section of a bench terrace, showing dug out portion at right, below the broken line, and the loose soil deposited at left, above the broken line.

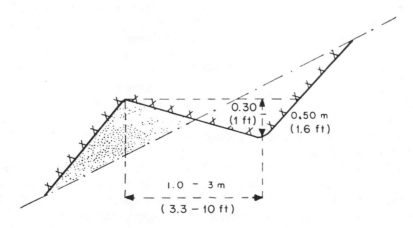

soil, and fostering the establishment of a vegetative cover. Terraces should be large enough to hold or carry the heaviest rain normally expected once every ten years. The terrace provides improved conditions for tree growth, because of the better soil moisture conditions. On extremely steep slopes where stones are available, walls may be built to support the sides of the terrace, but these are so expensive that they are seldom used. On extremely steep and easily eroded hillsides where stonewalled terraces are essential, they must be considered as part of the measures taken to protect the valley below. In a few places, abandoned orchards and fields with stonewalled terraces have been planted with forest trees, giving the impression that the walls were built for the plantation itself.

Usually, the walls of terraces are of earth and, if care is taken when building the terraces to preserve the topsoil and deposit it on the step and wall of the terrace, vegetation will quickly cover both surfaces. Eventually this vegetation must be hoed from the surface of the terrace so that it will not compete with the planted seedlings. The vegetation on the sides should be left undisturbed to prevent soil slippage and erosion.

When the sides of the terraces are of earth, they are made with a slope of between 1 to 1½ and 1 to 4. If possible, they should be covered with brushwood to protect them from erosion before natural vegetation begins to grow. Sides of terraces supported by stone walls are built to a slope of 1 m (3.3 ft) vertically for every ½ m (1.6 ft) horizontally. The walls should never be vertical, because they will crumble with the first heavy rains.

Terraces may be short—2–3 meters long—or they may be up to several hundred meters in length. If they are short, they can be scattered on the hillside wherever it is convenient, usually staggered at the required distances to collect the rainwater. Long terraces follow the contours of a hill and may encircle its crown (Fig. 4–8). However, where terraces are long, barriers should be left across the channel at intervals of 3–4 meters (10–13 ft), forming a series of troughs that hold the water and impede its flow along the channel. The earth barriers that separate the troughs are made slightly lower than the outer edge of the terrace. This allows overflow from one trough to the next during a heavy downpour (Fig. 4–9). In one day, a man can make a terrace about 10 meters (33 ft) long on steep and rocky sites, and 40 meters (130 ft) or more in good soil.

Often, instead of digging straight terraces along the contour, crescent-shaped ones (Fig. 4–10) are constructed. The two tips of the crescent point uphill. Crescent terraces, like straight terraces, are spaced at varying intervals depending on rainfall; the larger intervals being used in regions of little rainfall.

Fig. 4–8. Long terraces newly planted in Lebanon. (Photo V. U. Contino; courtesy FAO)

Fig. 4–9. Earth barriers to form troughs in the terraces. (Photo Forest Service, USDA)

Fig. 4–10. Crescent-shaped terraces sown with mixed species in Rajasthan.

Crescent terraces are sometimes staggered so that the water that passes between two adjacent upper terraces will be caught in the one below. They are always placed at right angles to the slope or to the flow of water. Crescent terraces can be made in deep erosion gullies. The steep sides of the deep gullies are smoothed off, slightly reducing the slopes, and are then protected with crescent-shaped terraces built along the contour at close intervals to check the rush of water.

Planting pits may be dug on the surface of the terraces or, especially where direct sowing is contemplated, continuous cultivated strips 40 cm wide by 30 cm deep (16 × 12 in) may be prepared.

In one day a man should be able to make approximately ten crescent terraces 3–4 meters (10–13 ft) long, each crescent having three or four pits.

Trenches for planting are prepared with machinery or by hand; pits are dug by hand where rocks or slopes make it inconvenient to dig long trenches. The distribution of the trenches or pits in the areas should be able to collect all the rain falling between the terraces, and the size of the trenches or pits should be large enough to hold the maximum rain water that collects in them.

In areas strongly susceptible to erosion, the distances recommended between terraces are shown in Table 4–1.

Terracing may be easily constructed using a tractor with an angle-dozer blade. The tractor moves forward and backward cutting a nearly flat surface approximately on the contour and pushing the soil down the slope. Level terraces are often made, but where heavy downpours occur, terraces should be built with gradient of 0.5–1 per cent. This small slope facilitates maximum infiltration and also insures drainage of the overflow into natural or prepared artificial outlets without damaging the terraces. The two types of terraces most commonly used in agriculture are the channel type and the ridge type. In afforestation the ridge terrace is the more frequent. This type is in essence a low (0.25–1 m; 1–3 ft), wide (4–10 m; 13–33 ft) contour ridge. It is ordinarily built by a tractor with an angle-dozer blade. Construction of a channel terrace usually requires the use of a tractor of a least 80 hp, whereas the ridge type is conveniently built by a smaller one of about 30–40 hp. Once built, the terrace itself may be plowed or sub-soiled along with the cultivated strips.

At times, small trenches or terraces are cut out with a tractor: these may be 2–3 meters (6.5–10 ft) long and 50 cm (20 in) wide. When made on slopes, they collect the soil that is washed into them.

A trench similar to the crescent terrace known as the "intermediate pit" has been used in the Arizona semidesert range. The pits are 1.5 × 2.5 m (5 × 8 ft) and 15 cm (6 in) deep and are made by a bulldozer using a modified blade. Average penetration of the 150 to 200 mm (6 to 8 in) rainfall was twice as deep in these pits as on adjacent flats and the vegetative growth of plants was far greater than in conventional pits.

Terraces are nearly impossible to maintain on deep sands. They are also unsatisfactory on stony soils and shallow soils over an impervious subsoil or rock.

Land clearing and soil preparation itself may sometimes be carried out in a single operation. For example, the angle-dozer that clears the land may at the same time draw a plow; land clearing and terracing also may be carried out as a single operation.

Table 4–1. Vertical and horizontal distances between terraces according to slope.

Slope	Distances Between Terraces, in Meters (Feet)	
	Vertical	Horizontal
3 per cent	2.0 (6.6)	67.0 (219.8)
6	2.5 (8.3)	42.0 (137.8)
10	3.0 (9.8)	30.0 (98.4)
15	3.4 (11.2)	23.0 (75.4)
25	4.0 (13.1)	16.0 (52.5)
35	4.5 (14.9)	13.0 (42.6)
50	5.0 (16.4)	10.0 (32.8)
80	6.0 (19.7)	7.5 (24.6)

Contour Strips

Where the steepness of the slope or the risk of erosion is not great enough to warrant building terraces, contour strips are recommended (Fig. 4–11). Strips 2 to 2.5 (6.5–8 ft) wide are laid out on the contour, and are clear-cultivated to a depth of 15 to 20 cm (6–8 in). No attempt should be made to change the natural slope of the land as in terracing. Between the cultivated strips, uncleared strips about 5 m (16.5 ft) wide are left. The cultivated strips are sown or planted to the desired spacing. To safeguard the new seedlings against competition from encroaching vegetation, adequate subsequent cultivation is imperative (Fig. 4–12).

Comparisons of seedling survival were made under semiarid conditions and three intensities of soil preparation: areas completely hoed to a depth of 10 to 15 cm (4–6 in); in pits 60 × 60 cm (24 × 24 in); and on terraces 1.5 m (5 ft) wide. For the average site the hoed areas showed greater survival and stronger seedlings probably because more moisture was retained in the soil. Lowest survival was in pits. On steep slopes and in areas with little rainfall terraces proved more favorable. Under these conditions seedlings growing on terraces were far stronger than those planted on cleared and hoed areas.

Méthode Steppique (Steppe Method)

To promote growth of trees in very dry steppe, some foresters advocate that the surface of the soil be modified by first breaking up and stirring the deep layers of the soil with rooters or large discs; then, widely spaced, roughly parallel embankments or ridges that follow the contour are built using the topsoil. The trees are planted along the crest of the ridges (Fig. 4–13) or better still on the lower half of the embankment facing the slope where the depth of moist soil is greater due to the accumulation of water after the rain. This method of soil preparation and planting is known as the "méthode steppique" or "steppe method" of planting. The purpose of this method is to maintain in the deep soil layers a reserve of moisture which becomes available late in the dry season when reached by extension of deep penetrating roots.

The depth of plowing should be judged carefully. If plowing is too shallow and the roots have access to the entire water reserve, they will drain the soil completely before the end of the dry season. The ridges, it is claimed, affect the microclimate in the plantation and allow the roots to put out abundant fine rootlets. The humus formed by the fallen leaves trapped between the ridges will also improve the soil. In this way, it is possible to reclaim areas of steppe by planting trees after concentrating all the usable soil in ridges or embankments, spaced according to the amount of annual rainfall. The lower the annual rainfall, the greater the distances between ridges. A rainfall of 100 mm (4 in) is

Fig. 4–11. General view of cultivated, contour strips in the Blida Atlas Mountains, Algeria. Strips were constructed with a maximum gradient of one-half per cent across a gullied slope five years before the photograph was taken. (Courtesy FAO)

Fig. 4–12. Hoeing eucalypts on contour strips. (Courtesy FAO)

Fig. 4–13. Hillside plantation of *Eucalyptus gomphocephala* A. DC in the arid zone of the Negev. Soil prepared according to méthode steppique. (Courtesy FAO)

equivalent to 100 liters per square meter (22 U.S. gal per sq yd) or to 400 liters of water per meter (97 U.S. gal per yd) run of trench, if the trenches are 4 meters (4.4 yd) apart.

In the low-rainfall steppe, similar methods are used by forming wide embankments with very wide spacing. A network of channels is made between successive ridges to direct the runoff to the planted trees and the lower embankment.

The larger the catchment area between the ridges, the more rainwater collects near the plants. This water soaks into the deeply cultivated soil. All calculations of the rainwater available to the plants must be based on the driest years of the area. Trees will die if rainwater collected near the tree in a dry year is not sufficient for its survival.

One of the disadvantages of this method is that the roots of the seedlings tend to run along the ridges and the trees grow well for a few years using the water in the moist ridges, but after the trees have grown, the amount of water available becomes insufficient for large trees and further development is checked and growth stunted, resulting in misshapen trees. In addition, soil from the slopes of the ridges washes away exposing the roots of the trees. Finally, weeding the slopes is difficult and removal of the weeds exposes the surface soil to further erosion.

Several methods can be used in arid zones to treat the soil surface to increase the flow of water into the channels leading to the planted seedlings. The most common of these treatments are:

a. Smoothing the land surface between the ridges to eliminate surface depressions and to prevent accumulation of water in puddles.
b. Compacting the soil to reduce permeability.
c. Impregnating or covering the soil with a non-permeable coating such as a petroleum mulch, wax, or a latex emulsion.

Judicious use of any of these methods can increase the yield of water several times. However, the decision to use one of the treatments should be based on careful consideration of the climatic and soil conditions prevailing in the area to be treated.

Where terracing and similar practices are new, time will be needed to prove that the costs are justified. Meanwhile they should be used on an experimental scale only. Where they appear feasible, they should be compared with the method of working the soil with a rooter and providing a simple network of canals leading the runoff to the trees. It is certain, however, that the soil should be worked deeply before planting, whichever system is used.

Before starting to clear and cultivate with mechanical equipment, a careful analysis of estimated costs should be made. Planting has to take place on a sufficiently large scale to make the fullest use of the equipment, and preliminary calculations should indicate that mechanization is cheaper than handwork. Frequently, mechanization will be more economic despite its high initial cost because it immediately stops erosion, or it greatly increases the rate of tree growth. Lost-time costs can be reduced if a repair shop and spare parts are readily available. It is more efficient to have units of at least two or three tractors working together under the supervision of a technically trained man, who will be able to check not only the progress of work but also the maintenance of the equipment.

SPACING

Trees do not grow naturally in extremely arid zones, even if soil and temperatures are favorable for growth, unless underground water is available. Where rainfall is scanty, trees are widely spaced and form a savanna or open park. Where rainfall is greater they grow closer together and with sufficient moisture they form a dense forest. The density of the natural forest is generally an indication of available moisture.

In dry areas only scattered trees survive. Seedlings that may start to grow in the intervening area almost invariably succumb to drought.

Competition for moisture between trees planted in arid zones must be avoided by wide spacing.

In an arid area it takes an extremely long time to reach optimum spacing by natural reproduction but by artificial reproduction optimum spacing can be achieved in a few years, if the site conditions and the requirements of the species to be planted are known.

It should be possible to determine the optimum spacing for a species based on the purpose of the plantation and the site conditions, especially soil factors, temperature, and amount and distribution of rainfall. Rainfall differences can be evaluated by study of isohyetal maps of the planting area. Isohyets are lines on a map that join points of equal rainfall. Isohyets can be used to establish the boundaries of zones for spacing of trees. For example, a planting area may be divided into four zones bounded by the 300, 400, and 500 mm annual isohyets. Spacing would be widest for the driest zone (under 300 mm) and decrease progressively for each wetter zone. Rainfall distribution could be considered by use of monthly or seasonal isohyetal maps. However, determination of the best spacing will require many trials over a period long enough to integrate the effects of all site factors.

To obtain trees with fewer, smaller branches, or trees with boles that do not taper much, species or genetic strains should be selected that do not inherently branch or taper in the open. Strains with these qualities are difficult to find, but a few such are available for various sites. The search for them, difficult, expensive, and time-consuming as it may be, is undoubtedly justified.

Planting densely to get small-branched trees and well-formed boles will necessitate early and uneconomic thinning. Furthermore, such plantings do not easily permit the cultivation so necessary in the first few years after planting.

There is no rigid rule for spacing in different sites. In rocky soils, the trees should be planted in pockets where the soil is sufficient. Consequently, in these soils the distances between plants will vary greatly. On terraces in regions with an annual rainfall of 400–600 mm (16–24 in) and with a long, dry summer, trees are usually spaced about 3 m (10 ft) apart. If the distance between terraces is more than 3 m (10 ft), scattered trees can be planted between the terraces in single pits.

In zones with 400–600 mm (16–24 in) of rainfall per year and on level ground with a good deep soil free of rock outcrops, plants, should be spaced about 2 × 2 m (6.6 × 6.6 ft) or 2,500 plants per hectare (1,000 per acre). The lower the rainfall and the longer the dry periods, the wider the spacing should be to reduce competition and avoid high moisture stress. It is well to remember that the amount of water available to a tree in a forest is proportional to stand density. For example, if plants are spaced 3 × 3 m (9.8 × 9.8 ft), there will be 1,111 per hectare (450 per acre) and they will receive 2.25 times more water than a similar plantation spaced 2 × 2 m (6.6 × 6.6 ft) with 2,500 trees per hectare (1,000 per acre) in the same rainfall area. The fact that the crowns of trees do not give the required shading to the root zone at wide spacing is a serious disadvantage, but relieving competition among roots for moisture is the deciding factor favoring the use of wide spacing. Where plants are widely spaced it is necessary to cultivate the soil to reduce competing vegetation, increase infiltration of rain water, and lessen evaporation from the soil. Extremely close spacing not only wastes planting stock, but also increases the cost of planting and imposes an additional cost of thinning at an early age. However, the total yield of a plantation can be increased by planting with moderately close spacing and thinning frequently after the trees are large enough to produce useful products.

Aleppo pine planted on a good site in the 400 to 600 mm (16 to 24 in) rainfall zone should be spaced 2 × 2 m (6.6 × 6.6 ft) or 2,500 plants per hectare (1,000 per acre). If the stand is thinned at the appropriate times, the stand will have about 500 trees per hectare (200/acre) at age 40 and nearly all of the trees removed will have been converted into useful products. The final density is approximately equal to that of a 40-year-old natural stand produced as a result of normal competition among the trees. Proper spacing at the time of planting and proper thinning eliminate competition and allow optimum growth during the entire rotation.

When mechanical cultivation is used, spacing must be adjusted to the width of the machinery. The minimum spacing can be no less than the width of the machinery plus the width of the row itself. Wider spacing should be multiples of machine width plus row width.

Close spacing of plants is sometimes practiced to avoid the necessity of replacing the dead plants. However, as previously indicated, this procedure is not recommended. Loss of a few trees is inevitable because of adverse weather, but losses can be minimized by skillful handling. If survival exceeds 50 per cent, replanting in the same season will not be needed.

SEASON FOR PLANTING

The proper season for seeding or planting varies with climate and species. The prevalence of desiccating winds, frost, snow, and severe drought must be known for each planting site because these dictate the season of planting. Seeds of some species are ready for sowing as soon as collected; some must after-ripen; and still others require pre-treatments before germination. (See Chapters 2 and 6.)

In arid zones where summers are dry and the maximum precipitation occurs in late autumn and winter, the best season to plant conifers, such as *Pinus halepensis* Mill., *P. brutia* Ten. or *Cupressus* spp., is the autumn, just after the soil has been soaked by the first heavy rains and while daily temperatures still favor root growth. Autumn-planted trees must have enough time to become established before cold weather stops growth and they go into winter dormancy. In the spring, as soon as temperatures are favorable for root growth, these trees can take imme-diate advantage of high soil moisture accumulated during the winter. Their roots will grow into the deep moist soil, and they can thus with-stand the subsequent long, summer drought. During the summer, roots in the dry upper layers of the soil grow slowly or cease growing com-pletely.

Trees that are not especially frost-hardy, such as most eucalypts, are usually planted in the spring, but only after the danger of frost is past.

Planting should not be attempted on hot dry days, during high winds, or in freezing weather. Mortality of seedlings whose exposed roots have desiccated or frozen is usually high. Newly planted seed-lings suffer more damage from winds and frost than well-established plants. The winds quickly dry out and kill the leaves and the top because the seedling's roots are still in poor contact with the soil parti-cles and cannot replenish the expended moisture. Frost may cause heaving of the ground, thus breaking the contact between root and soil, and may throw the seedling completely out of the soil.

On sand dunes, planting may be started after the first heavy rains of the season have soaked into the sand. Planting can continue through the winter until the last rains, provided dry winds or frosts do not occur. Seedlings should be planted in pits at least 30 cm (12 in) deep. Late planting is possible because sand retains the moisture well, and evaporation from the lower layers of sand is extremely slow.

In hot arid zones with the maximum rainfall during the spring and summer, the best season for planting is after the soil has been soaked by the first rains. This usually occurs between March and May, but occasionally as late as July.

Where maximum precipitation occurs during the winter, direct sow-ing is most successfully done early in winter, just after the soil has been soaked by rain, provided frosts do not occur after germination while seedlings are dependent on food stored in the seed or embryo. It is, however, safer to sow in late winter, allowing the seedlings to benefit from the accumulated winter moisture in the soil. Germination will occur when favorable temperatures are reached in the spring.

Seeds of *Haloxylon* and some conifers are broadcast on the snow during the late winter. Because seeds can be easily seen on the snow surface, a more complete and even distribution is possible than when seeding is done in other seasons.

SEEDING

The life of an infant seedling after it emerges from the seed is very precarious. In nature, even under apparently favorable climatic and soil conditions, great mortality of young seedlings often occurs. In arid zones, where germination conditions are typically unfavorable, losses are often great. Young seedlings are extremely susceptible to desiccation during the first few weeks after germination while their stems are still succulent. Unless seeds germinate in a bed especially favorable for seedling growth during their initial period of development, they soon succumb to desiccating winds. For the seedling to remain alive, the newly emerging roots must maintain constant contact with moist soil by growing into deeper and deeper layers where water and mineral elements are available. In arid-zone forests, millions of seeds may be shed into openings, but only a few may germinate, and most of these die early. Consequently, mature trees that originated from natural regeneration are extremely sparse.

Success in direct seeding depends heavily on the weather conditions and the suitability of the sowing method. If the method is wrong under a particular weather condition, no quantity of seed, no matter how large, can guarantee success. Success in direct sowing is also related to soil conditions, seed viability, provenance, the number of seed-eating animals, and plant competition. The seed sown must be of a provenance suited for the area. The germinative energy of the seed must be tested before sowing to determine the amount of seed needed to produce a stand of the desired density.

Direct Seeding versus Field Planting

The advantages of direct seeding are that it is cheaper, quicker, and requires less labor than field planting. Problems associated with growing, transplanting, storing, and field planting nursery stock are avoided. Root systems of trees established by direct sowing develop normally and do not have the spiralling and other deformities associated with poor planting techniques. As previously mentioned some species may be direct seeded during winter, and also later in the spring than would be considered safe for field planting. The principal disadvantage of direct seeding is the loss of seed and seedlings to birds, small mammals, insects, and fungi. It is also difficult to obtain uniform stocking so some parts of the area may need replanting and others require early thinning. Direct sowing should be restricted to the most favorable sites and not attempted on difficult sites.

Field planting has several distinct advantages over direct seeding. During the first few years nursery-grown seedlings are larger and more vigorous than seedlings from direct seeding, so they have a much better chance of survival. Seedlings can also be planted at whatever spacing is desired, and if a few simple rules are followed, a reasonably uniform stand will be produced. (Partial seeding does give some control of spacing.) Furthermore, the concern that seed may be lost to biotic agents, or not germinate under field conditions, is removed. When only a few seeds are available, such as in trials of some exotics, raising the trees in the nursery and hand planting in the field is much more efficient and reliable.

Direct Seeding

In direct seeding, the area where a forest is to be established is sown completely or partially with seeds of the desired species. Whenever it is reasonably safe to assume that a fair portion of plants will survive, direct seeding, which is comparatively cheap, is favored because of the great cost in setting up and operating a nursery, transporting and planting the nursery-reared plants.

In arid zones, direct seeding must be limited to species that develop deep roots quickly. Furthermore, such species are usually better suited to direct seeding than to nursery culture because the unavoidable severing of the roots when seedlings are lifted from the nursery bed can result in great mortality of field-planted trees.

Large seeds, such as those of Italian stone pine (*P. pinea* L.), may be sown directly in the field. As a rule, these seeds contain enough stored food to nourish the developing taproot as it penetrates to the deeper moist layers of soil. About 30 kg (3,500–4,500 seeds) of stone pine seed are sown to the hectare (27 lb, or 1,400–1,800 seeds/acre), and they require 20 to 25 days to germinate.

Some extremely small seeds are also direct seeded. In Kazakhstan (USSR), the saxaul (*Haloxylon* spp.) seeds, which are the size of a pinhead and remain viable for only a few weeks, are broadcast on the late snows. They reach the ground with the melting snow and germinate when temperature becomes favorable. Seed of the Sudan acacia or gum arabic (*Acacia senegal* Willd.) are broadcast on the floodwaters of the Nile. When the water recedes the seeds germinate and the roots grow quickly into the soil to the deeper, permanently moist layers.

Moisture is the most critical single factor for survival of the emerging seedling. Although excessive heat is frequently detrimental, its effect is usually minimized if soil moisture is adequate. Once the roots reach the moist layers of the soil, high temperatures are, as a rule, no longer critical. On the contrary, heat and moisture, together, generally promote fast growth.

The planting area has to be prepared for direct seeding the same as for field planting. All competing vegetation must be removed and the soil cultivated. In addition, to reduce depredations of birds and rodents, seeds should be pretreated so they will germinate in as short a time as possible after sowing. Finally, the seeds should be coated with chemicals, such as endrin, thiram, and anthroquinone, which repel birds and rodents. Each of these chemicals repels some animals more effectively than others. The most effective chemical should be determined by tests on the seed-destroying animals prevalent in the area.

Broadcast Seeding. Broadcast seeding is not commonly used in arid zones, unless seeds are cheap and easy to obtain. For afforestation, seed must be imported, frequently from distant regions. If, however, favorable climatic and soil conditions exist, broadcast seeding may be an economical and quick way of afforesting. Seed may be broadcast sown either from the ground or from aircraft. Both methods have been successfully employed for a number of species, including the sowing of *Haloxylon* previously described. Broadcast sowing from aircraft is economical if large areas are to be afforested, the seed is cheap, competition is minimal, the population of seed-eating animals is small, and weather favors at least moderate survival.

To ensure even distribution of seed, use of an inexpensive mechanical seeder and cross-sowing is recommended. In cross-sowing the area is covered twice using one half the required amount of seed each time. The second coverage is made at right angles to the first. If extremely small seeds are to be sown, they should be mixed with some lightweight bulking material, such as sawdust, bran, or vermiculite. Although sand will add the required bulk, it is usually not used because of its weight.

Partial Seeding. In contrast to broadcast seeding where the seed is scattered uniformly over the entire area, in partial seeding only certain selected and prepared spots or strips receive the seed. This method requires from one-half to one-tenth the seed needed in broadcast seeding. Thus, expensive seed, or seed that are difficult to obtain, if not used to grow seedlings in the nursery, should be spot seeded or strip seeded, but not broadcast seeded when sown in the field. Furthermore, only a fraction of the area is actually seeded. Consequently, the soil that will receive the seeds can be thoroughly prepared, and the seeds can be covered with soil after sowing. The best spots for sowing can be selected to avoid the waste that occurs in broadcast seeding when seeds drop on the barren rock or are caught in vegetation. Two general methods of partial seeding are used, planting in strips and spot planting.

Strip Seeding. The area to be planted may be prepared for seeding by clearing and cultivating parallel or contour strips. These strips are approximately 1 m (3 ft) wide and 2–4 m (6.5–13 ft) apart, center to center. The seeds are sown in a single line at the desired spacing down the center of the strip.

Spot Seeding. Rather than preparing a continuous strip, small spots about 1 m (3 ft) in diameter are thoroughly prepared at the desired spacing. Spacing should be flexible to take advantage of the best microsites for sowing. The sower places the predetermined number of seeds in a shallow hole and covers them with soil. The number of seeds per spot should be large enough to ensure one or two established seedlings per spot. The number varies with the expected germinative energy and expected survival; for many pines 10–15 seeds are adequate. Before planting, the seeds should be treated with an animal repellent, and to prevent damping-off, with a fungicide. Treated seed should be coated with aluminum powder which will reduce losses to birds and also clearly indicate that the seeds have been treated. Small conical or dome-shaped barriers of ¼-inch wire mesh can be placed over the seed spots to protect them from animals. These screens are usually about 10 cm (4 in) high and 10 cm wide at the base. Screens are very expensive to make and they must be removed after germination so that they will not hamper growth of the seedlings. Protective screens have been used mainly on experimental plots.

Seeds are sown to a depth equal to approximately twice their diameter. The covering soil should be free of stones. If the seed is covered too shallowly there is a risk of loss, especially through drying, and if it is sown too deeply, the growth of the seedling may be hampered.

A dibble is occasionally used in direct seeding of large seeds, such as acorns. It is pushed into the soil forming a hole into which the seed is dropped. The seed is then somewhat crudely covered by pushing the dibble into the soil again near the first hole and forcing it closed. To compact the soil about the seed further, the soil should be lightly trodden around the dibble hole.

Long-necked funnels or seeding sticks are often used in much the same manner as the dibble. The funnel neck is driven into the ground to the depth required for seeding. Seed is dropped through the funnel, which is then withdrawn, and the hole stamped closed. There are several varieties of these funnels. In one, a quantity of seed is placed in the funnel and the number of seeds to be planted in each spot is released by a lever. Although similar in construction, agricultural seeders or "drills" are seldom used for afforestation in arid zones.

Seeding mortality is usually high when direct seeding is used in arid zones. Often a high percentage of seed germinates, but few seedlings survive the drought, hot winds, and sunscald of the first summer.

Where many seeds germinate and the soil is wet, it is advisable to start cultivating about two or three months after germination. Cultivation is conveniently done with a two-pronged hoe. If more than two or three seedlings are found per spot, all but one should be removed.

By the end of the second summer the density of established seedlings should be apparent, and they can then be thinned to the desired spacing. Unwanted seedlings should be pulled out with care to avoid disturbing the roots of the remaining plants.

If, because of one or two years of favorable weather conditions, direct seeding has been successful in an area, it should not be assumed that this system of afforestation will always be suitable there. A short period of unfavorable conditions may prevent germination or kill the seedlings. Such losses can upset the normal planting program, unless plans have been made for field planting nursery-grown seedlings.

FIELD PLANTING

The object of all planting is to obtain a forest of the desired species, at the determined spacing, in a short period, at reasonable cost. Even with well-prepared, nursery-reared plants in a well-prepared site, using suitable tools, this task is not easy in arid zones. However, proper selection of tools and technique will increase the rate of survival and reduce the cost of plantation. Attention to details in planting is of the greatest importance, perhaps more important than the method itself.

In arid zones where humidity is low and transpiration high, the danger that newly planted, bare-rooted plants will wilt is great. From the moment seedlings are lifted from nursery beds they undergo an increase in internal water stress which may persist for several weeks after planting. After planting, their roots, which usually are damaged during lifting, must grow and become active enough to make up the water lost through transpiration and re-establish the normal internal water potential. Tree planters must adopt practices most suitable for maintaining high physiological vigor in the planted trees. In choosing species one should be concerned with drought resistance mechanisms of plants that prevent desiccation resulting from excessive transpiration. The ability of plants to withstand drought depends mainly on their ability to absorb water through their roots and to reduce water loss through their transpiring surface. Tree survival in dry habitats shows a close relationship between the spread of the root system and the extent of the transpiring surfaces of the plant.

The roots of seedlings to be planted must be continually in contact with moisture from the time they are lifted in the nursery until they are planted in the field. Soil moisture in the upper 10 cm (4 in) of areas covered with low vegetation is frequently below the wilting point, and often contains little moisture to a depth of 50 cm (20 in). On cleared areas, the moisture content of the upper 10 cm of soil may be low, but below this depth adequate moisture for seedling growth is usually present. On these areas only natural or planted seedlings that can develop roots deep enough to reach the moist soil can survive. Large, vigorous seedlings and balled plants can extend their roots a short distance into dry soil and can sometimes reach moist soil, if the distance is not too far. If water absorption is reduced because young, growing rootlets and mycorrhizae are destroyed in handling stock, survival will generally be low. Planting results indicate that seedlings with mycorrhizae survive better after planting than seedlings without mycorrhizae. When the seedlings lack mycorrhizae it is possible that indigenous fungi may form mycorrhizae in time to prevent first-season mortality.

The size of the aerial portion of the plant especially its transpiring surface should be in proportion to the ability of the roots to absorb water from the soil and make up transpiration losses after planting.

The roots of the seedlings to be planted are usually pruned to remove damaged or excessively long rootlets so that the root system will fit the size and shape of the planting hole. Lateral roots that are crammed into the planting hole may spiral or wrap around each other or the central taproot. Such spiraling often occurs where the soil around the planting hole is too compact for root penetration. As the roots increase in diameter the spiraled roots choke off the movement of the sap and cause stunting and even death of the affected trees.

The tops of hardwood planting stock can be pruned to remove damaged shoots and to reduce the transpiring surface. Although top pruning may be used with some species of conifers such as *Juniperus* spp., it is not recommended for pines.

To maintain a favorable water balance for a few weeks after planting, the stomata may be artificially blocked or induced to close by application of antitranspirant compounds. Several different chemicals are sold for use as antitranspirants. Many antitranspirants merely form a coating that covers or plugs the stomata. This action not only retards transpiration but also impedes CO_2 uptake which causes a decrease in photosynthesis and growth until the substance breaks down. Unfortunately, use of antitranspirant coatings has not been particularly successful in increasing survival, so plant propagators are turning to metabolic inhibitors that cause stomatal closure by affecting the enzyme systems.

Effects of such compounds on plants disappear in a few weeks and the stomata resume normal action.

Naked Roots

Roots of naked-rooted seedlings are, of course, more susceptible to injury during lifting and planting than roots of balled seedlings, which are well shielded by the surrounding ball of earth. Moreover, roots of balled seedlings are continually in contact with the moist soil of the ball, from the time they are taken from the nursery until they are planted in the field. This enables the new rootlets to grow quickly into the new soil.

In the favorable areas with moderate rainfall, naked-rooted seedlings have a fair chance of success. But in more arid areas, their probability of survival is diminished, giving a distinct advantage to balled seedlings.

In northern Portugal, where rainfall is the heaviest, naked-rooted seedlings are used. Southward, as the climate becomes more arid, they are used on the more favorable sites, and balled seedlings on the less favorable. Still farther to the south, under even less rainfall, only balled seedlings are used. Because the costs of producing, transporting, and planting balled seedlings are so high, they can be economically used only where their rate of survival is significantly higher than that of naked-rooted seedlings.

Naked-rooted stock is lifted in the nursery only when weather forecasts indicate favorable planting conditions. The seedlings are packed in bundles of 25–50 and are transported to the site in crates or bales. Long shoestring-like roots should be pruned back before packing. Roots must be kept continually moist, either by placing damp moss or similar material around them in the crate or bundle, or by dipping them in a slurry of mud. If weather conditions turn unfavorable, the seedlings should be stored in their crates in cool buildings, cellars, or caves. When conditions are favorable, the crates may be opened and the bundles distributed to the planters, who place them in wet sacking. The roots must never be exposed to the sun or wind before planting. The seedlings may be carried in pails, baskets, or bags hanging from the shoulder. As brief a time as possible should elapse between lifting the seedlings and field planting. If, for any reason, the seedlings in a crate are found to be damaged, the seedlings in it should be discarded.

As soon as naked-rooted, broad-leaved plants are brought to the planting site, they should be heeled-in and watered. When they are needed for planting, a few bundles at a time are taken out of the heeling-in trench, and the roots immediately covered with wet sacking. Depending on their size, as many as 50–200 seedlings can be carried at one time by one man.

Although exposing naked roots to the sun or wind is not as damaging to deciduous trees as similar exposure is to conifers, exposure should be avoided. Hardwoods, as well as conifers, should be planted as soon as possible after lifting.

Planting Methods

Regardless of the method used in field planting, the soil in the spot where the seedling is to be set must be cultivated and the competing vegetation removed. Site preparation should precede planting by a few days to a few weeks.

Slit Planting. This method of planting naked-rooted plants is to make a wedge-shaped slit in the soil with a planting bar, spade, or similar tool. The depth of the slit depends on the length of the roots. Long, dangling roots should be pruned to approximately 20–30 cm (8–12 in). The slits are made 5–10 cm (2–4 in) deeper than the length of the roots from collar to tip. Planting bars are of various shapes and dimensions, but basically they consist of a heavy, iron bar handle with a spade-like bit about 2 cm (0.8 in) thick on top, tapering to a sharp edge at the bottom, 8–10 cm wide, and 25 cm long (3.1–4 × 10 in). The bit is pushed into the ground with the foot to the depth required. The handle of the planting bar is then moved back and forth to widen the upper part of the slit. The roots are lowered into the slit, and care is taken to prevent them from catching on the sides of the hole and curling upward. The slit is closed and the soil is pressed back around the roots by inserting the bar again into the soil near the planted seedling and with a lever action forcing the planting slit closed. The soil is trodden firmly around the plant to ensure contact between the roots and the moist soil (Fig. 4–14). Unfortunately the slit has an hourglass shape in longitudinal section, which makes it difficult to obtain good root-soil contact at the bottom of the slit. The firmness of contact can be tested by a gentle pulling on the seedling.

In Spain, a planting spade known as the "plantamón" has been devised in which the vertically lanceolate blade is 25–35 cm high (10–40 in) and 20–25 cm wide (8–10 in). The thickness of blade is 1 cm (0.4 in) at the top, two thirds of the way down it increases to 3–4 cm (1.2–1.6 in) and it tapers to a sharp edge at the bottom. To open a planting hole, the plantamón is pushed into the ground to the full length of the blade. When the handle is then moved back and forth, the thickest part of the blade acts as a pivot, and the tapered sides of the blade form a rectangular hole in the soil (Fig. 4–14). After placing the seedling and filling the hole with soil, no air pockets are left. Greater success in seedling establishment is claimed for the plantamón, compared with other planting tools, especially when the laborers are inexperienced.

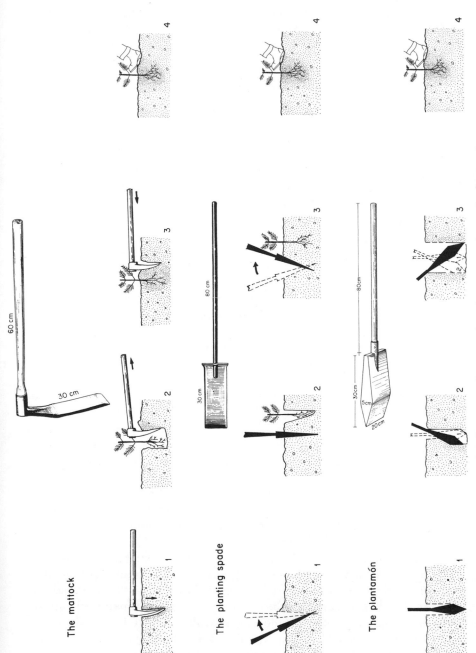

Fig. 4–14. Slit planting with mattock, planting spade, and plantamón.

Slit planting is fast. A crew of two, one making the slit, the other planting, can, under average conditions, plant about 1,000 trees a day. Because it is not advisable to use this technique for plants with delicate roots, it should be limited to tough-rooted plants and cuttings. This method is recommended when growing conditions are the most favorable and both labor and the planting stock are cheap. It is generally not suitable for hardwoods because even a one-year-old hardwood seedling has too large a root system. Furthermore slit planting is not suitable for sands or for heavy clays.

Hole Planting. In this method a hole is dug, large enough to accommodate the roots after they are spread out in their original positions. A shallow depression, or basin, usually not over 1 m (3 ft) in diameter and slightly lower than the adjacent surface, may be formed around the seedling to collect the rain. A wide variety of tools are suitable for digging the holes. The spade and hoe are the tools most commonly employed in field planting. The type and size of tool that will usually be the most satisfactory depends on the texture of the soil. For example, in sandy or sandy loam soils, wide-bladed hoes are used, but in clay or stony soils, narrow-bladed hoes are the most efficient.

The seedling to be planted is held by the stem near the root collar, with the roots not quite touching the bottom of the hole. The hole is then filled by carefully working the soil in among the roots and at the same time spreading the roots in roughly their natural position. Filling the hole is usually done by hand or with the hoe. After the hole is filled, the soil should be firmed about the roots by lightly treading on the loose soil near the seedling (Fig. 4–14). Two men working as a team can plant about 500 seedlings a day.

Powered hole diggers are also used. These may be attached to tractors (Fig. 4–15) or they may be small portable diggers (Fig. 4–16). The tractor powered digger is used on gentle slopes or flat areas which are free of rocks. Portable diggers with engines of about 3 hp weigh approximately 10 kg (22 lbs). The digging auger is from 5 to 30 cm (2 to 12 in) in diameter and may be used under a wide range of planting area conditions. Portable diggers can be used on any planting site where a person can walk. If the auger hits a rock or other obstruction, it will stop while the motor continues to run, thus protecting the operator and the machine from harm. This type of hole digger is operated by one man but larger machines that require two men to operate them are available. One man using a hole digger with a 15 cm (6 in) diameter auger can dig over 200 holes, 40 cm (16 in) deep, in clay soil in an hour. Operating the digger for one hour requires about 1 liter (0.25 U.S. gal) of fuel; a mixture of gasoline and oil. Two men operating the larger machine with a 30 cm (12 in) auger can dig about 250 holes,

Fig. 4–15. Auger for planting. (Courtesy FAO)

Fig. 4–16. Portable power digger. (Courtesy FAO)

30 cm (12 in) deep, in dry clay soil in an hour. Where powered augers are used, survival is usually higher than where holes are dug with hand tools; probably because larger and deeper holes are dug with the machine than normally be dug by hand.

Balled Plants. Balled planting stock is transported to the field in crates holding 25–50 units. A crate of balled stock can usually be carried without difficulty by a team of two. If the stock has been grown in pots, the plants are usually removed from the pots, wrapped in paper, and placed in crates. Almost any paper that is large enough will be satisfactory. Both waste paper and new paper are used. Two men can carry twice as many balled plants without the pots as with them. Plants grown in plastic bags are handled in the same way as balled plants wrapped in paper. Removing the plastic bags increases survival. If they are wrapped well, their survival equals that of seedlings transported to the site in pots. All balled seedlings should be thoroughly watered before planting. Watering may be done as soon as the seedlings reach the planting site or just before actual planting. Soaking the balled roots in fertilizers may also improve survival and early growth. Although balled plants should be planted before growth starts, they can be safely planted afterwards, if soil moisture is satisfactory, or if it is kept so by watering.

The planting site should be cleared of competing vegetation and the soil cultivated before the seedlings are brought to it. The planting hole is dug or bored sufficiently deep and wide to accommodate the ball. The hole should be approximately 10 cm (4 in) deeper than the height of the ball. Just before the plant is placed in the hole, the soil at the bottom of the ball is loosened and some of the lower roots are freed. The root collar is positioned slightly below the ground surface. The seedling is held with its stem vertical and the root ball hanging down. The ball should not rest on the bottom of the hole. While the seedling is being held in this position, the soil is pushed into the hole from all sides with a hoe. The soil is pressed tightly against the ball. The surface is then smoothed.

One man should be able to plant 100–150 trees a day; a team of two can plant 350.

Dibble Planting. Dibble planting of greenhouse-grown seedlings is especially efficient in planting small seedlings with correspondingly small root systems. Three-month-old seedlings, grown in shallow boxes, or flats, are sometimes used in planting. A flat $20 \times 20 \times 7$ cm ($8 \times 8 \times 3$ in) may hold from 200 to 250 seedlings. The seedlings are carried to the planting site in the flat and set out early in the planting season. A dibble is used to punch a hole in the soil. After loosening the soil in the receptacle, the seedling is grasped between finger and thumb and pulled out. The roots are then let down into the hole and the soil pressed around them using the dibble and feet as previously described.

Planting three-month-old seedlings requires skilled workers. The method has been used successfully in North Africa, where seedlings were closely spaced, so that even a low survival percentage gave satisfactory coverage. The advantage of using such young seedlings is their low cost and the ease of planting. One man can plant about 1,000 seedlings a day.

Machine Planting. Planting also may be done with specially constructed planting machines (Fig. 4–17). One type basically consists of a plow that opens a furrow, a trencher that forms the holes, excavating

Fig. 4–17. Machine planting of rooted stock of *Haloxylon ammodendron* Bunge in Kazakhstan, USSR.

fins which loosen the soil, and filling irons which push the excavated soil back into the trench and around the tree roots. The seedling roots are lowered into position by the planter. The wheels of the machine help to firm the soil around the roots. Planting machines are not commonly used in arid zones, but they may occasionally be employed on moist sites. Planting machines are not suitable for planting balled stock.

Machine planting requires the same strict adherance to details of planting as hand planting. Litter, slash, and other debris must be removed from the area because they can interfere with machine operation and cause improper planting. The coulter and trencher must be adjusted to permit the roots to be fully extended. The packing wheels must be so adjusted that the soil is packed firmly around the trees. Roots should be kept moist and shaded in the container, and only a small number of plants should be taken from the container at one time to insure that they are fresh and show no evidence of drying before planting.

Explosives. In a few localities, explosives have been employed to prepare planting holes in limestone or to break a hardpan. After a hole is made with a crowbar, the explosive charge is placed in it and detonated. Because the explosion usually scatters the soil and makes a clean hole, soil for planting may have to be brought in from a nearby area.

Moisture Harvesting and Conserving Measures

Kraft Paper. In arid planting sites in Oregon, where dense herbaceous vegetation is expected to grow and compete for soil moisture with the newly planted seedlings, sheets of paper mulch have been successfully tried to eliminate or reduce such competition and improve survival.

Kraft paper sheets about 60 × 60 cm (24 × 24 in) were used. An X-shaped cut, just large enough to allow the seedling to pass through is made in the center of the sheet; after planting the sheet is placed on the ground with the seedling protruding through the cut. The sheet is then held down by overturned sod or stones.

Polythene Aprons. Experiments with polythene aprons to catch the atmospheric moisture and divert it for use of plants and also to suppress weed growth around young trees have been carried out by the Food and Agriculture Organization of the United Nations in some arid countries. The aprons are sheets 50 × 50 cm (18 × 18 in) with a hole in the center of the apron through which the plant grows. The apron is held in place on the ground by stones or earth. Various colors and film thicknesses were tried, but it was found that color made little difference in the growth of plants. If the film was strong enough to last one year, it was considered satisfactory. In similar tests by the U.S. Forest Service in New Mexico, the plastic aprons were found to be durable enough to last up to five years. Rainwater caught on the apron is funneled to the hole in the center and through it to the soil. Soil moisture under the aprons has been found to be considerably higher than that in the soil around plants without aprons. Soil moisture conditions were the most favorable in soil in large planting holes that was thoroughly prepared before placing the apron. In these trials the use of polythene significantly increased the survival and height growth of the planted seedlings. Hand installation of plastic sheets around individual plants is costly and the expense must be weighed against the risk of failure, the cost of replanting, and the slower growth of unprotected plants.

Stones. If light-colored stones are available, they should be placed around the newly planted seedlings to minimize evaporation of water from the adjacent soil. Dark stones are unsatisfactory because they absorb heat that can scorch seedings (Fig. 4–18).

Fig. 4–18. Cultivated strips (Spain). Only the strips to be planted are cultivated. Note white stones placed around the seedlings to minimize evaporation of water. (Courtesy Henry S. Kernan)

Wood Shingles.   In some regions of the United States, namely in the Great Plains, Rocky Mountains, and California, wooden shingles have been placed in a semicircle around newly planted conifers on exposed sides, or sometimes on all four sides to protect the plants from heat, intense solar radiation, and drying; results in increasing survival have generally been favorable.

Twig Shading.   Newly planted seedlings can also be shaded with twigs if these are available in the vicinity. Seedlings should be completely shaded by the twigs; if their tops show above the twigs, the effect of shading on survival is not so pronounced.

Gravel Mulch.   Infiltration and soil conditions are markedly improved by applying a layer of about 5–7 cm (2 to 3 in) deep of gravel around newly planted seedlings. It greatly reduces the need of watering, eliminates weeding, and improves seeding vigor. The chief problem is cost, except on sites where suitable gravel is readily available.

CARE OF PLANTATIONS AFTER PLANTING

Recruiting or Replacement

Usually some mortality after planting can be expected either because of improper handling of the planting stock or because of adverse weather. If planting is done early in the season, it may be possible to replace the dead plants with fresh ones in the same season. Dead or dying plants can be recognized easily. Conifers turn down near the tips; they become yellowish, gradually changing to brown, and begin to lose their needles. In broad-leaved plants the stem shrivels, and in both broad-leaved plants and conifers, if the stem is scratched, it will be found to have turned brown. Occasionally, plants with some degree of these symptoms may survive, consequently it is advisable not to uproot those thought to be dying, but to plant new ones near them. Sometimes seeds can be sown directly, close to the dying plants.

Large-scale recruiting is expensive because all the planting operations must be repeated for a relatively small number of plants. Unless the mortality is extremely high, it is usually inadvisable to replant. This is especially true where the number of survivals over the entire area is sufficient to form a scattered, open forest. With eucalypts or other fast-growing trees, recruiting is useless after the first year, since subsequent replacements are nearly always suppressed by neighboring trees.

It is advisable to have the planted area inspected by trained staff three to four weeks after planting or seeding. These men should carry fresh plants with them and replace dead or dying plants, particularly where mortality is concentrated in one locality. Enough plants of the same stock as that planted should, therefore, be left as a reserve in the nurseries. The number to be reserved can be gauged from observed failures in similar areas. Plants not used for replacement are kept in the nurseries for planting the following year.

Watering

In zones where rainfall is low, special preparations should be made to plant as soon as the soil is soaked. If, however, the beginning of the rainy season is delayed, it is better to plant and to water the seedlings immediately after planting. This practice is very costly and is probably justified only in low rainfall areas, when a planting season might otherwise be lost. In localities of uncertain rainfall, two or three waterings of about 2 liters (2 qts) per seedling are required to ensure establishment and adequate root development. When rain eventually comes, the seedlings will thenceforth depend on it for growth.

The expense of watering is warranted for roadside and other amenity plantings. Watering should be done immediately after setting in the young trees. During the first season after planting, water may occasionally be applied to ensure establishment of the saplings and to increase initial growth. Roadside plantings usually must be watered during the first two or three years because the seedlings are exposed to the hazards of road traffic, road maintenance, grazing, and people. Plantings, such as windbreaks and shelterbelts, laid out to protect unirrigated fields and orchards, should also be watered occasionally to ensure rapid establishment. The expense of watering is recovered in subsequent years by increased yields because of the more favorable environment produced by the trees.

Watering at intervals of 2 or 3 days and heavy and thorough enough so that the water penetrates deep enough to reach the root zone, is much more beneficial than superficial light waterings at frequent intervals. However, irrigation should not be so heavy that the soil becomes waterlogged. Most trees do not grow well in saturated soil, because the excess water impedes root aeration.

In India a high percentage of survival of plants was achieved in extremely arid regions by placing porous earthenware tubes or jars in such a way that their bottom was near the roots. The receptacles are filled with water when empty. In southern Spain bamboo tubes are used in this way. One man can fill 1,500–2,000 tubes in one day (Fig. 4–19).

In recent years "drip" irrigation has come into use in extremely arid regions to water roadside trees or the trees in small parks. The basic principle of this method is to supply water to the individual tree one drop at a time. The system consists of a hose, usually plastic, which is clamped to a faucet and is laid beside the trees in the row to be irrigated.

Fig. 4–19. Bamboo tubes with their bottoms near the roots are filled with water to irrigate trees in extreme arid areas in the south of Spain. (Courtesy Henry S. Kernan)

Several sections of hose may be clamped together, but to reduce the number of coupling clamps needed, long lengths of hose should be used. Nipples, or similar devices to regulate the flow of water, are inserted into the hose near each tree to be irrigated. Nipples, available commercially, have a range of hole sizes that will permit regulation of the drip to less than 1 liter (1 qt.) per plant per day; high water pressure is not needed. Nipples are easily removed to permit cleaning or changing if they become clogged. The water allotted to each tree slowly seeps into the soil and moves into the root zone by gravity and capillarity. Because the main movement is downward, moisture remains near the tree being irrigated. Little water is wasted; none runs off the surface, and only minor amounts are lost by evaporation from the small area of wet soil exposed. After a brief training period, the average forest worker can learn to operate the system and to adjust the rate of application to nearly the amount of water needed by the plants with a minimum of waste. Plants irrigated by this method never suffer from either lack of moisture or from saturated soil. Growth of plants watered in this way is the best per unit of water applied of any of the irrigation methods. The saving in water, compared to other systems, is from 30 to 50 percent. Installation costs are also cheaper than for most other systems. Moderate topographic differences do not cause any difficulties in the use of this method.

Water may be transported to the site on pack animals, by cart, or by motor vehicle. Even where local supplies of irrigation water are available, distribution ditches or pipes are not needed unless it is intended to irrigate the trees for a long time. Cultivation and dry-farming techniques must also be practiced to increase the water absorption of soil, to reduce competition from weeds, and to reduce evaporation.

Cultivation and Weeding

Losses in artificial regeneration represent a great waste. The large investment in planting, therefore, justifies a considerable expenditure to protect the young plantation. These added expenses are part of the cost of the plantation. The greater the danger of loss from atmospheric, edaphic, and biotic agencies, the greater the expense of practices employed to ensure success of the plantation.

In arid zones, the most important cause of failure is insufficient soil moisture. Summer rains rarely penetrate the soil to any appreciable depth, and soil moisture is quickly depleted by evaporation and the transpiration of competing vegetation.

Where water for irrigation is scarce and costly, reliance must be placed on dry-farming techniques. Six weeks to two months after planting, weeds are usually large enough to compete for water with the newly planted seedlings. The tree seedlings should by then have grown enough new roots to be established. Therefore, the best time to start cultivation is about six to eight weeks after planting. The roots of all weeds must be dug out. A narrow-bladed hoe is perhaps the most efficient tool for cultivation. During the first two or three years after planting it is essential that the area around the trees be kept absolutely free of weeds.

By crumbling the surface soil, hoeing not only reduces competition but also minimizes the effects of insolation. The rough surface in itself produces shade, thus reducing evaporation. Hoeing reduces the adverse effects of soil cracking. In especially heavy soil, the soil commences to crack as soon as the hot weather starts. Unless impeded by hoeing, soil moisture evaporates from the cracks, drying the soil throughout the root zone and causing high seedling mortality.

Where seedlings are in rows, the entire intervening strips can be cleared of weeds. Cultivated strips should extend for 1 m (3.3 ft) on each side of the planted row. If the seedlings are not in rows, weeds growing within a radius of 1 m around each plant must be dug out. If it rains after the first hoeing and the weeds commence to grow again, it is advisable to cultivate a second time about three months later. Cultivation must be completed before the weeds produce seed. If the rains come late in the first year, newly germinated weeds may be easily and cheaply destroyed with a rake. Elimination of weeds from the site by the second hoeing is also beneficial in reducing the danger of fires.

A third hoeing during the first year after planting will be necessary if the weeds grow again after the second hoeing, or if the soil begins to crack. By properly timing the first and second hoeings it is often possible to avoid the necessity of a third.

In one day a man with a hoe should be able to destroy all the competing weeds around 150–200 plants. Land that is reasonably level and free of major obstructions may be cultivated with a disc harrow or other cultivating machine. Wherever machines are used the utmost care is needed to prevent accidental injury to small trees.

PROTECTION FROM GRAZING AND FIRE

Plantations must be protected from grazing animals. Costly and laborious planting should never be undertaken where animals are allowed to graze or where open grazing is permitted by law.

Goats will damage any forest trees that may be planted, regardless of species, and thus must be excluded from the planted areas. Sheep, cows, and horses may be allowed to graze in the plantation after five to ten years, depending upon the rate of growth of the trees. But even with trees that are old, grazing should be controlled and permitted only while adequate edible grass remains. Once the grass has been grazed down and depleted, sheep and cattle will browse on the young trees. In addition, excessive grazing may cause soil erosion even in a forest.

In many countries wild animals such as deer often cause great damage to plantations. Where large game animals are likely to damage young plantations by browsing, especially experimental plantations of exotic species or where new silvicultural techniques are being studied, it is advisable to spray the seedlings with repellents. The repellents should be mixed with resin adhesives to hold them on the plants. If properly applied, repellents can protect the trees from browsing animals for a year or two. Approved animal repellents are commercially available in many countries. When these chemicals are used in the field, current laws and regulations governing their use and the manufacturer's directions should be carefully followed.

Young plantations are often damaged by small mammals. Several species, including rabbits, mice, moles, and porcupines may damage or even destroy plantations, if they are not controlled. Damage caused by these animals can be reduced by thorough site preparation, use of repellents, poison bait, or by trapping and hunting. Complete site preparation is extremely effective in small mammal control since it eliminates their food supply, protective cover, and nesting sites.

Reduction of wildlife populations to protect forest plantations must be done only in accord with the wildlife and game laws that apply to the area.

Adequate provision should also be made to protect every plantation from fire. No plantation or forest area is immune to fire. A single fire that starts because of inadequate fire prevention and lack of supervision can result in the total loss of the plantation.

Forest fires may start anywhere. The degree of risk is controlled principally by climatic factors. Generally the lower the humidity and the higher the temperature of the air the greater the risk. All those responsible for fire fighting should be especially alert during hot, dry periods with strong winds.

The most disastrous effects of fires in arid zones have occurred in brush-covered areas where both the brushwood and the forest floor have been completely destroyed. The aftermaths of such fires have frequently been costly debris-laden floods.

Many fires are purposely started for a variety of reasons. Shepherds burn the dead vegetation on grazing areas to produce fresh grass for their livestock, farmers use fire to clear new ground for cultivation, and hunters start fires to chase game out of the bush; unless they are controlled, such fires can easily spread into plantations. Nearly all fires are due to the public's carelessness and disregard of the most basic precautions. Education of the public in proper fire prevention principles is essential.

In young plantations, ground fires that burn through the grasses and shrubs left on the area will destroy the young trees. The most severe fires occur during the rainless season, from the time the vegetation begins to dry until eventually the drought is broken and the rains return. Fires frequently start outside the plantation, and unless the plantation is surrounded by a wide cleared strip over which fire cannot leap, it is always in danger of being destroyed.

When large, continuous areas are planted, it is desirable to subdivide the area into units each no larger than 10–15 hectares (25–37 acres), separated from each other by firebreaks. Firebreaks should conform to topography and natural firebreaks, and they should be made either on the crests of ridges or run directly up and down the hills. Firebreaks should be strips 8–10 m (25–33 ft) wide, from which all flammable material has been removed. They must be kept clean of dead vegetation; this is especially critical during the dry season.

The techniques practiced in clearing land for cultivation also are used to eradicate vegetation from the firebreaks. Since 1955, increasing use has been made of herbicides for such eradication. This technique may prevent regrowth of vegetation for as long as two years.

Firebreaks are occasionally planted with fruit trees or eucalypts, which are low in flammability. If fruit trees are planted, the area around the trees must be thoroughly cultivated.

Roads or even narrow paths that have been hoed and cleared of vegetation, and thus are free of flammable material, will stop most surface fires. But whether it is wide or narrow, the firebreak alone is not an assurance of complete safety against a spreading fire. This is especially true when the fire is driven by strong winds. Then the spread of the fire must be stopped by proper use of fire-fighting tools and equipment. Simple tools are often adequate. For example, where the ground is covered with dry leaves or pine needles, rakes are the best tools for clearing a narrow firebreak to stop an approaching ground fire.

Grass fires are usually extinguished by beating the fire into the ground with wet sacks or with beaters made by attaching strips of sacking or canvas to long handles. Often a grass fire can be controlled by shovelling sand directly on it. Where water is available, it can be sprayed on the fire with a hand-pump to supplement the other methods. Fire fighters must be able to reach the fire as quickly as possible after the alarm has been given. Consequently, good roads and paths permitting access to every section of the plantation are a prime necessity.

PROTECTION FROM INSECTS AND DISEASE

The study of forests in arid zones has revealed few really serious insect pests or fungal diseases of trees. Perhaps this is due in part to the fact that dry climates do not favor dense stands or growth of underbrush, environments where harmful insects and pathogens often breed in humid climates.

Insects

Many kinds of insects can be found throughout the dry zones; every area has its own indigenous population and often one or more exotic species. Many of these insects live in or on shrubs and trees and, since they depend on these plants for food and shelter, cause some minor damage. Although the endemic insects of dry zones may be from widely separated families, all are acclimated to the local environment. Insects are but one part of the complex, interacting flora and fauna of an area. Natural forests in any area exist in "dynamic equilibrium" with their environment, including the native insects.

Of the many insects to be found in dry zones, relatively few species harm trees, and damage by an individual insect species is usually confined to a single tree species. In a normal, balanced forest, insects are not conspicuous, generally limiting their activity to trees or branches that are weak, dying, or dead. This normal, endemic population should not cause any undue anxiety when discovered. However, during years of severe drought in arid zones many trees become weak and are then severely attacked. Under these conditions the insect population may increase to such magnitude that healthy trees are heavily attacked and are unable to resist the combined onslaught of thousands of insects. Vigilance is required to detect the possibility of such epidemics in their incipient stage. When such an outbreak occurs it should be immediately reported to the forest entomologist and steps taken at once to combat the infestation before it spreads farther. In reporting an outbreak of insects one should state where the pests occur, the extent of the area affected, and the abundance of the insects.

Harmful insects are of many types and habits, and no part of a tree is immune from attack. Insects may be classified by the part of the tree attacked or the damage inflicted. The principal types include borers that create tunnels by chewing their way through the wood and the bark beetles that mine galleries in the cambial tissue. Some insects consume the leaves and are classed as defoliators, whereas members of another class suck the sap from the leaves, twigs, or thin-barked stems. A few insects attack the roots, and still others infest the fruit, cones, or seeds. Great differences in life cycles and host preference occur among the various classes. Some complete their life cycle in only a week or two, and other species require several years. Most insect species prey on a single, or perhaps two or three closely related, host species; only a few insect species attack a dozen or more plant species.

In combating an insect epidemic foresters should look first for a possible ecological imbalance that might have caused the outbreak. If such an imbalance is found, it should be corrected or reduced as much as possible before applying other controls. Ecological imbalance is likely to be great in plantations, especially during the first few years. Thus, danger of an insect epidemic is greater in most plantations than in comparable natural forests. The necessity for insect control should be thoroughly and carefully considered when planning new plantations. Plans for the control of infestations must be practical and economically justified.

Techniques that may be employed in new plantations to avert or control an insect epidemic fall into three categories: phytosanitation, biological control, and chemical controls or insecticides.

Phytosanitation. Many species of harmful insects seek cover in the weeds, brush, and trees that often are found on or near the area to be planted. Such undesirable vegetation should be eliminated by cultivation, burning, or application of herbicides (See the discussion of eradication of vegetation).

Another important phytosanitary measure is the inspection of nursery stock for insects and disease before transport to the planting site. All infected stock must be removed and destroyed.

Biological Control. Every destructive insect has its natural enemies that man can sometimes employ in controlling damage. These control agents may be other insects, birds, small mammals, nematodes, bacteria, or viruses. A natural enemy of a destructive insect can occasionally be found in the plantation, or one may be introduced from other regions. Biotic agents that are introduced must not harm beneficial insects, other animals, or economic plants. The success of biological control depends upon the discovery of an enemy of the harmful insect, and the possibility of economically rearing it in sufficient numbers to achieve control. Discovery and rearing of an effective biotic agent usually require painstaking and expensive work, but once the proper one has been found, biological control may be the most economical method.

An important advantage of the biological method over the use of insecticides, and one that should not be overlooked, is the complete absence of harmful chemical residues that could contaminate the environment.

Insecticides. Chemicals that kill or check the spread of insects may be sprayed from the ground or air, or applied to the infested trees in a variety of other ways. Halting the spread of insects with insecticides is often expensive, not only because of the cost of the chemicals, but also because the trees frequently must be sprayed several times before an outbreak is controlled. However, this method is the only practical way of quickly suppressing isolated outbreaks.

Some of the more commonly used insecticides are benzene hexachloride, carbaryl, malanthion, parathion, lindane, various arsenic compounds (such as lead arsenate), and nicotine sulphate. All must be carefully handled to avoid injury to humans, domestic animals, beneficial wildlife, and plantation trees. The use of DDT and related insecticides is not permitted in many countries.

Some Important Insects of Arid Zone Plantations. Of the serious insect pests affecting forest plantations in the Mediterranean basin, one is an exotic and two are endemic. One of the latter attacks trees in irrigated plantations.

The eucalyptus borer (*Phoracantha semipunctata* Fabr.) in an exotic which was brought into the region from its native Australia. It has also been introduced into New Zealand, South Africa, Argentina, and Chile. The adults are strongly attracted by cut logs, but they also attack the weak, dead, or dying eucalypts, especially those suffering from drought. The borer may spread to neighboring healthy trees, but there the larvae are usually killed by exuding gum. Recommended measures to reduce the damage caused by the borer are: cut eucalypts in the winter when the beetles are less active; remove weak, dead, or dying trees immediately; if possible, irrigate the plantation during droughts; and in the summer use trap trees, which should be removed, debarked, and burned after one month exposure.

The pine processionary caterpillar (*Thaumetopoea wilkinsonii* Tams) is indigenous to the Mediterranean basin. It attacks several species of pine but is especially damaging to plantations of Aleppo pine, Canary Island pine, and brutia pine. These insects may defoliate a single pine tree or a tract of forest. They build nests on the trees for their eggs and these plus the defoliated trees form large ugly eyesores on the forest landscape. Scales from the wings of the processionary moths may cause severe irritation of the skin and eyes of people in the vicinity of an infested area. Methods of combating this pest include: 1. Spraying with a pesticide such as 0.2 percent Dimecron (Phosphamidon 50). 2. Cutting and burning or burying branches that bear the eggs. This method is most efficiently used for young, low trees. 3. Injecting the stems of trees with insecticides that will be absorbed, translocated, and deposited in the needles which will be eaten by the caterpillars. Diptagen (Trichlorfon 60), Rogor (Dimethoate 38), and Dimecron are insecticides used as systemic poisons in this way; they become effective in about 8 to 13 days after injection and their toxicity lasts for several weeks. 4. Burying an insecticide such as Di-Syston in a shallow furrow dug around the infested tree. This insecticide will be absorbed by the roots and its effect is similar to that of the injected systemic insecticides.

Both the eucalypt borer and the processionary caterpillar can be controlled successfully by insecticides, but usually at great expense. Attempts have been made to control the processionary caterpillar by biotic agents, but with little success to date.

Capnodes (*Capnodis miliaris* Klug.) are also native to the Mediterranean basin where they cause considerable loss in irrigated plantations of poplar and willow. The larvae bore tunnels under the bark of the young trees at the root collar and the base of the trunk. In plantations where the trees are weak because of inadquate irrigation, capnodes may kill even large trees. *Populus nigra* L., *P. alba* L., and *P. euphratica* Oliv. are particularly susceptible, but a few of the other poplars, notably a subspecies of *P. deltoides* Bartr., are quite resistant to attack. Therefore, only resistant strains should be used where capnodes are present. Poplar and willow plantations should be copiously irrigated to foster strong trees whose rapid growth of bark can close the tunnels and suffocate the larvae.

An ambrosia beetle (*Platypus sulcatus* Chapuis) has caused considerable damage in forest plantations in arid zones of Argentina. The beetle bores galleries deep into the stems of trees. It attacks a large number of species including cedars (*Cedrus* spp.), elms, eucalypts, poplars, willows, black locust, and baldcypress. No satisfactory control has been found, but infested trees should be immediately removed and destroyed. Greater use of less susceptible species is also recommended.

Diseases

Relatively few fungal diseases occur in dry climates since low atmospheric humidity does not favor development and spread of fungi. However, in irrigated plantations and the more humid areas in arid zones diseases occur that are destructive enough to cause concern. Diseases usually develop slowly in dry climates and are not easily detected until they are well advanced, by that time they are difficult, often impossible, to control. Constant vigilance is required to detect the first signs or symptoms as early as possible and to report the infection to the forest pathologists. Adverse environmental conditions weaken trees and are among the most important factors favoring infection. Edaphic factors such as deficiency or excess of water, too high or too low pH, poor aeration, and lack of essential mineral elements promote the spread of pathogens. Some soil management practices and most silvicultural treatments improve growing conditions in plantations and are therefore measures that help to control the spread of disease.

To overcome symptoms of mineral deficiency, it may be necessary to fertilize the soil or inoculate it with mycorrhizal fungi. Soil aeration can be improved by plowing or discing. Drainage of wet sites may also be needed in some areas.

Opening a plantation to the sun and wind by light pruning and, if necessary by thinning, will help to create conditions unfavorable for the spread of fungi. Careful inspection of planting stock is necessary to prevent the introduction of diseases into the plantation. Some pathogens in the soil may be checked by fumigating, however, pathogens in the soil are so difficult to deal with that conversion of the forest to non-susceptible species is recommended.

TOOLS

In many countries, machinery has been found to increase efficiency and lower the cost of afforestation. However, the use of machines is often difficult because of steep slopes, rocks, logging debris, or stumps. The machines, therefore, must be extremely strong and rugged; consequently they are expensive. Furthermore, suitable machines are not commonly available from commercial sources.

Often afforestation projects are initiated chiefly to alleviate unemployment, and mechanization reduces the opportunities of employment.

Many operations cannot be performed by machinery; consequently manual labor, using relatively simple tools, must be employed.

If suitable tools are not available and tools designed for other purposes are substituted, efficiency may be lowered and the cost increased. Many types of tools have been designed to accomplish different functions. Tools that appear suitable for one function in one country may or may

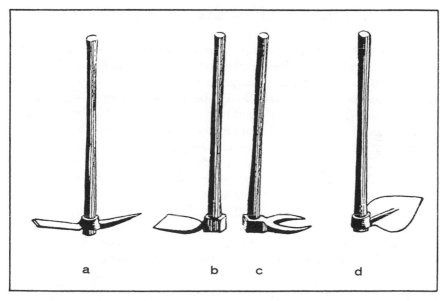

Fig. 4–20. Digging and hoeing tools (a) pick-mattock, (b) wide-bladed hoe, (c) two-pronged hoe, and (d) arrow-bladed hoe.

not be suitable for the same function in another country. Furthermore, laborers are not always willing to exchange a tool to which they have grown accustomed for an unfamiliar one. Nor do they readily admit the efficiency of a better designed tool on its introduction. Yet, after some practice with the new tool, they often discover that they prefer it to the old (Fig. 4–20).

Tools should always be kept in good working condition. They should be strong and no heavier than necessary. Blades should be of the length and width suitable for the job and be properly ground or sharpened. Sharpening equipment should always be available in the field. Handles should be of the proper length and thickness, smooth and well-shaped for balance and handling, and correctly fitted. Extra tools should always be kept in the field. Many hours may be wasted if a tool is broken and cannot be immediately replaced. Well-kept tools greatly increase the efficiency of labor.

If tools are improvised and made by local craftsmen, standard specifications should be insisted on.

At times, it is possible to find multipurpose tools. A hoe, e.g., may be designed to be used effectively for hoeing, digging holes, and planting. For this, the blade must be carefully made to meet the needs of all these tasks.

CONSTRUCTION OF ROADS AND PATHS

A good network of roads and paths is, of course, necessary for efficient plantation management. Before planting, the area should be subdivided into plantation units based principally on topography. The units may vary in size, but ideally each should be approximately 40–50 hectares (100–125 acres). Each area should be directly accessible by a path or road. A forest road in a plantation needs only sufficient load bearing capacity to carry the vehicles used in transporting plants and labor. The main road may be visualized as an axis running as nearly through the center of the plantation as the topography permits. From it lateral paths are built to permit ready access to all units.

It is essential that traffic should not be hampered by the weather. Therefore, the main road should be properly drained and surfaced to eliminate mud in the rainy season and to protect it from blowing sand in the dry season. The road's gradient should not exceed 9 per cent. In hilly and mountainous country, plantation roads are approximately 2–2.5 m (6.5–8 ft) wide and are usually prepared in the same manner as terraces. Cuts on the uphill side of the road are made into the hillside, and the earth removed is used to fill in on the downhill side of the road. On steep slopes the sides of the roads may be reinforced with stone-masonry retaining walls that are generally laid dry.

Paths are constructed in the same way as roads but usually are not as wide. Ordinarily, the maximum gradient of paths is 9 per cent, the same as for roads. However, under certain conditions, their gradient may be as much as 15 per cent for short distances. On steep slopes, they should have strongly built retaining walls and a good drainage system so that they will not be washed away by heavy rain. They should always be maintained in good order, even when not in constant use. Paths may be kept free of weeds by spraying with herbicides, such as potassium chlorate (1 kg in 15 liters of water for each 75 m²; 2.75 lb in 5 gal water per 1,000 ft²).

STORES AND SHEDS

It is advisable to erect movable stores and sheds in the center of the plantation. The size of store or shed depends on the magnitude of the undertaking. The store may house the records of the plantation, as well as the seeds, tools, spare parts, sharpening equipment, herbicides, fire-fighting apparatus, and first-aid equipment. The shed is to protect the laborers from the weather and is especially appreciated during heavy rains. The store should be no more than 1–1.5 km (0.6–1 mi) from the planting area.

COST OF AFFORESTATION

It is extremely difficult to give average figures for the cost of afforestation. Expenses are likely to vary greatly according to the type of land, the site preparation involved, the number of trees to be planted per hectare, the cost of recruiting, maintenance, and protection. Obviously, where terracing is needed, hand construction will be very costly and may involve as much as 400 man-days per hectare (160/acre). However, this cost can be substantially reduced by using suitable mechanical equipment. Of course, if the land is level, terracing is unnecessary.

The data in Table 4–2 are for plantations in the Middle East, where all

Table 4–2.　Cost of afforestation.

Operation	Man-Days per Hectare	(Acre)
First year:		
Clearing of land	15	(6)
Preparation of soil (pits, strips)	25	(10)
Planting, recruiting	15	(6)
First hoeing and weeding	25	(10)
Second hoeing and weeding	20	(8)
Firebreaks, paths	5	(2)
Total	105	(42)
Second year:		
Recruiting	15	(6)
Hoeing and weeding (twice)	30	(12)
Firebreaks	5	(2)
Total	50	(20)

operations are carried out by hand. Man-days for each operation vary greatly with the kind of soil, the degree of slope, road availability, the amount and species of vegetation growing in the area, the efficiency of labor, the techniques employed, and the mechanical equipment used.

Data for the cost of afforestation in seven different countries or regions are given in man-days, or their equivalent, in Table 4–3.

Table 4–3.   Cost of afforestation in different countries.

Country	Method of Planting	Man-Days per Hectare	(Acre)	Per Cent
Argentina	Mechanized + plants	150	(61)	100 *
Middle East	Manual labor	155	(63)	103
Spain	Plow (oxen + labor)	170	(69)	113
Brazil	Mechanized + plants	250	(101)	167
Mexico	Manual labor + plants	270	(109)	180
India	Manual labor + plants	300	(121)	200
East Africa	Manual labor + plants	450	(182)	300

* Argentina taken as 100 per cent.

It is obvious from Table 4–3 that cost figures for one region are not applicable to another region, even if the work is standardized. Costs also vary greatly in the same country and for different years in the same area.

The profitability of afforestation depends on its purpose. In some plantations for the production of paying crops, where the full use of every working day and the efficiency of labor are critical, the use of suitable tools and careful selection of the proper site may be the difference between loss and gain. The absolute value of plantations established to protect people, houses, other structures, roads, fields, or canals from floods, sedimentation, or soil erosion, is often difficult to assess. No monetary value can be assigned to afforestation initiated mainly to create employment in underdeveloped, overpopulated, rural areas and, of course, the monetary worth of forests planted for aesthetics and amenity values cannot be calculated.

No two countries have the same demand for the produce extracted from forest plantations. The market prices, the cost of extraction, and conversion to the final product vary in each locality. Furthermore, although a plantation may have been initiated to produce a certain commodity, this may not be in demand when the product is ready to be extracted ten or twenty years later.

Yet, whatever the purpose, an extension of forest areas in any region will assure more employment in the future, and some use will always be found for forest products. It is safe to assume that the yearly increment per hectare in a plantation on average soil, with a rainfall of 500–600 mm (20–24 in) a year and a long rainless season, will be between 2 to 5 m^3 (140–360 ft^3/acre) of wood in the form of poles, posts, pulpwood, firewood, or whatever final product is extracted. The net returns from such plantations will depend, therefore, not only on the expenses incurred in planting, extraction, and conversion to the final product but also on the local price of such commodities at the time of the extraction.

PREREQUISITES FOR SUCCESSFUL PLANTATIONS

Afforestation in arid zones is difficult and costly, therefore failure must be avoided. For a successful plantation certain prerequisites must be met; among the most important are:

a. The species selected for planting should produce a valuable product or benefit.

b. The species selected should be suited to the ecological conditions of the site and be of a good genetic strain.

c. Plants selected should be vigorous and sturdy.

d. Site selected should be of good quality.

e. The site should be well and deeply cultivated before planting.

f. Populations of destructive biotic agents should be controlled.

g. Planting must be properly executed and any losses during the first few years should be replaced.

h. Enough water, either from rain or irrigation, for normal growth must reach the root zone of the trees.

i. Plantations must be protected from fire, wind, illicit felling, and grazing animals.

j. Proper silvicultural procedures for the species must be used.

BIBLIOGRAPHY

AHMAD, S. D. Afforestation on dry hillsides. Proc. World For. Congr. (Seattle 1960) [1962] 5(1):370–375.

AL'BENSKH, A. V., and P. D. NIKITIN (editors). Manual of afforestation and soil
1967 melioration. (Agrolesomelioratsiya, 3rd ed. enlarged and rev., Moscow, 1956.) Transl. from Russian by A. Gourevitch. Israel Program for Sci. Transl., Jerusalem. (TT 66–51098). 516 p.

ALDON, E. F. Soil ripping treatments for runoff and erosion control. Pages 2–24 to
1976 2–29 in Proc. Third Fed. Inter-Agency Sediment. Conf., Denver, Colo., Mar. 1976. Sedimentation Comm., Water Resour. Counc., [Washington, D. C.].

ALDON, E. F., and H. W. SPRINGFIELD. Using paraffin and polyethylene to harvest
1975 water for growing shrubs. Pages 251–257 in Proc. Water Harvesting Symp. (Phoenix, Ariz., Mar. 1974). ARS W-22. U. S. Agric. Res. Serv., Berkeley, Calif.

ALLARD and PERROT. Reboisements industriels au Maroc. Rev. For. Fr. 4:399–407.
1952

BARTON, J. H. How much does it cost to plant trees? For. Farmer 14(2):4–5.
1954

BENTLEY, J. R., and K. M. ESTES. Use of herbicides on timber plantations. U. S. For.
1965 Serv., Calif. Reg. and Pac. Southwest For. Range Exp. Stn. San Francisco and Berkeley, Calif. 47 p.

BESSER, J. F., and J. F. WELCH. Chemical repellents for the control of mammal dam-
1959 age to plants. Trans. North Am. Wildl. Conf. 24:166–173.

BHIMAYA, C. P. Role of checkdams in afforestation areas. Indian For. 86:711–718.
1960

BHIMAYA, C. P., R. N. KAUL, B. N. GANGULI, and P. N. BHATT. Experimental af-
1964   forestation of rocky refractory sites in the arid zone. Indian For. 90:160–
        163.

BILAN, M. V. Root development of loblolly pine seedlings in modified environments.
1960   Stephen F. Austin State Coll., Dep. For. Bull. 4. Nacogdoches, Texas. 31 p.

BOUVAREL, P. Sur le boisement et l'amélioration des forêts en Macédoine Yougoslave.
1955   UNESCO Tech. Asst. Spec. Rep. 3. Paris. 45 p.

BROWN, A. A., and K. P. DAVIS. Forest fire: control and use. 2nd ed. McGraw-Hill,
1973   New York. 686 p.

BYTINSKI-SALZ, H. Two important tree borers in Israel. FAO Plant Protect. Bull.
1952   1:38–39.

CHAPMAN, G. W. Afforestation techniques in Cyprus. Unasylva 6:160–165.
1952

DAVIDSON, D. F. The evolution of direct sowing techniques of reafforestation in
1960   Cyprus. Arbor (Aberdeen) 3(4):28–30.

DAVIS, K. P. Forest fire control and use. McGraw-Hill, New York. 584 p.
1959

DE BELLIS, E., and B. CAVALCASELLE. Control of the pine processionary caterpillar
1967   with *Bacillus thuringiensis* Berliner. Documents FAO World Symposium on
        Man-Made Forests and their Industrial Importance. Canberra 14–24, April
        1967. Vol. 1:205–247. Food Agric. Organ. U. N., Rome.

DIETZ, D. R., and J. R. TIGNER. Evaluation of two mammal repellents applied to
1968   browse species in the Black Hills. J. Wildl. Manage. 32:109–114.

DOST, F., J. WITT, M. NEWTON, and L. A. NORRIS Statement on 2,4,5-T and TCDD.
1975   J. For. 73:410–412.

EDMINSTER, T. W., and G. E. RYERSON. Machines for clearing land. Pages 103–107
1960   *in* Power to produce. U. S. Dep. Agric., Yearb. Agric. 1960. Washington,
        D. C.

FAVRE, R. Y. Las coniferas en la forestación de zonas semi-aridas, metodos, sistemas
1961   y mecanizacion de tareas. [Proc.] Primera Reun. Reg. Coniferas, 24–29
        Abril 1961 p. 274–282. Asoc. For. Argent., B. Aires.

————. La forestación, factor significativo en la recuperación de zonas aridas. Proc.
[1962] World For. Congr. (Seattle 1960) 5(1):375–378.

FLINTA, C. M. Prácticas de plantación forestal en América latina. FAO For. Dev.
1960   Pap. 15. Rome. 499 p.

FAO. Bibliography on savanna afforestation. Rome. 381 p.
1962

————. Savanna Forestry Research Station, Nigeria. Tree physiology. Based on
1970   the work of A. L. McComb. FO:SF/NIR 16. Tech. Rep. 3. Rome. 48 p.

FRANCE, DIRECTION DES EAUX ET FORÊTS, COMITÉ CONSULTATIF DES REBOISEMENTS.
1953   Techniques du travail du sol. Etude Com. Consult. Rebois. 3. Paris. 16 p.

————. Materiels mecaniques de reboisement. Etude Com. Consult. Rebois. 8.
1955   Paris. 20 p.

GIORDANO, G. Mecanización en las repoblaciones con fines industriales de la madera.
1954   Montes 10:8–12.

GOOR, A. Y. Sand dune fixation in Palestine. Palestine Dep. For. Annu. Rep. Ap-
1947   pendix I. Jerusalem. 8 p.

————. Forestry in Tripolitania. Emp. For. Rev. 27:80–82.
1948

————. Advances in reforestation and afforestation practices in arid and semi-arid
[1962] zones. Proc. World For. Congr. (Seattle 1960) 5(1):339–343.

————. Tree planting practices for arid zones. FAO For. Dev. Pap. 16. Rome.
1963   233 p.

GORDON, D. T., and R. D. COSENS. Slash disposal and site preparation in converting
1952   old-growth sugar pine-fir forests to regulated stands. U. S. For. Serv., Calif.
        For. Range Exp. Stn., For. Res. Note 81. Berkeley. 7 p.

GOSWAMI, P. C. A note on contour trenching and soil moisture in afforestation sites.
1960 Indian For. 86:198–204.

GOUJON, P. Industrial tree planting in Morocco: a plan to provide roundwood sup-
1963 plies for a pulp factory. Unasylva 17:2–12.

GRASOVSKY, A. J. [A. Y. GOOR]. Forest policy in Cyprus. Emp. For. J. 19:219–225.
1940

HALL, N., et al. The use of trees and shrubs in the dry country of Australia. Aust.
1972 Gov. Publ. Serv., Canberra. 558 p.

HALPERIN, J. The control of the pine processionary caterpillar Thaumetopoea wilkin-
1968 soni Tams by systemics, with special reference to stem injection of phosphamidon. Z. Pflanzenkr. Pflanzenpathol. Pflanzenschutz 75:591–604.

HARRIS, H. K. Slash disposal by dozer, Northern Rocky Mountains. Fire Control
1958 Notes 19:144–154.

HEIDMANN, L. J. Use of herbicides for planting site preparation in the Southwest.
1969 J. For. 67:506–509.

HERMANN, R. K. Paper mulch for reforestation in southwestern Oregon. J. For.
1964 62:98–101.

HETH, D. Growth of Alepo pine plantations in Israel. Israel Agric. Res. Organ. Div.
1976 For., Leafl. 55. Ilanoth. 32 p.

HILEY, W. E. Conifers: South African methods of cultivation. Faber and Faber,
1959 London. 123 p.

HUDSON, R. B., and R. M. JONES. Tree establishment in semi-arid areas. J. Soil
1963 Conserv. Serv. N. S. W. 19:162–167.

JACKSON, J. K. Project 37: plastic aprons. [FAO] PA/1/SAM and PA/2/SAM. 8 p.
1968

JIMENEZ-CASTELLANOS Y CONDE, A. Repoblaciones sobre terrenos calizos de poco o
1964 nulo suelo vegetal. Ensayo sobre la solución del Barrón de Acero. Montes
20:87–90.

KAUL, R. N. (editor). Afforestation in arid zones. Monogr. Biol. 20. W. Junk
1970 N. V. Publ., The Hague. 435 p.

KELLER, T. Some physiological implications of anti-transpirants. Proc. World For.
1966 Congr. (Madrid) 6:1456–1461.

KERNAN, H. S. Reforestation in Spain. N. Y. State Univ. Coll. For., World For. Publ.
[1966] 3. Syracuse, N. Y. 52 p.

KHAN, K. N. Afforestation in arid tracts. Pakistan J. For. 1:74–84.
1951.

KING, N. L. Tree-planting in South Africa. J. S. Afr. For. Assoc. 21:1–102.
1951.

KLINGMAN, G. C., and F. M. ASHTON. Weed science: principles and practices. J.
1975 Wiley & Sons, New York. 431 p.

LAFFITTE, J. C. Conceptos sobre forestación en el Uruguay. Asoc. Ingen. Agron. Rev.
1949 21(86/87):32–36. Montevideo.

LANE, R. D., and A. L. McCOMB. Wilting and soil moisture depletion by tree seed-
1948 lings and grass. J. For. 46:344–349.

LAURIE, M. V. Tree planting practices in African Savannas. FAO For. Dev. Pap. 19.
1974 185 p.

LEONT'EV, A. Pesčanye pustyni Srednej Azii i ih lesomeliorativnoe osvoenie. [The
1962 sandy deserts of Soviet Central Asia and their reclamation by forests.]
Gosizdat U.S.S.R., Tashkent. 160 p.

LETOUZEY, R. Technique d'afforestation en zone subaride au Cameroun. Bois For.
1961 Trop. 77:3–12.

LILLIE, D. T. Control of Arizona chaparral with 2,4,5-T and silvex. J. Range
1963 Manage. 16:195–199.

MACÍAS ARELLANO, L. Reforestación: teoría y práctica. Sec. Agr. Ganad. Dir. Gen.
1951 For. y de Caza. Mexico. 330 p.

McCOMB, A. L., and J. K. JACKSON. The role of tree plantations in savanna develop-
1969 ment: technical and economic aspects with special reference to Nigeria.
Unasylva 23(3):8–18.

MEŠTROVIČ, Š. [Use of mechanical soil preparation for establishing forests in the
1964 Mediterranean area.] Sum. List 22 (3/4):124–133. [Serb., e.]
MONJAUZE, A. Le reboisement sur rootage en plein et sur bourrelets. Rev. For. Fr.
1960 12:1–25.
———. Progrès dans les méthodes de boisement et de reboisement dans less zones
[1962] arides et semi-arides. Proc. World For. Congr. (Seattle 1960) 5(1):344–
352.
MOULOPOULOS, C. High summer temperatures and reforestation technique in hot and
1947 dry countries. J. For. 45:884–893.
NEWTON, M., and L. A. NORRIS. A discussion on herbicides. J. For. 73:410–412.
1975
PELED, N. Molehills: a new planting method for hill afforestation. La Yaaran 11(1):
1961 20–22 (Hebrew); 41–40 (Engl.).
PHILIPPIS, A. DE. Sulla tecnica di preparazione del suolo per il rimboschimento in
1939 clima caldo-arido: indagini sperimentali. Milizia Nazionale For. Pubbl.
R. Stn. Sper. Selvicoltura 6. Firenze. 44 + [24].
PICCAROLO, G. La meccanizzazione nella pioppicoltura. Cellul. Carta 4(4): 9–14.
1953
PISARENKO, A. Mechanized afforestation of mountain slopes in the U.S.S.R. Proc.
1966 World For. Congr. (Madrid) 6:1744–1749.
POND, F. W., D. T. LILLIE, and H. R. HOLBO. Shrub live oak control by root plow-
1965 ing. U. S. For. Serv. Res. Note RM-38. Rocky Mount. For. Range Exp.
Stn., Fort Collins, Colo. 2 p.
POURTET, J. La mécanisation des repeuplements artificiels. Rev. For. Fr. 2:564–569.
1950
———. La mécanisation des travaux de reboisement. Rev. For. Fr. 3:38–46.
1951
———. Les repeuplements artificiels. Éc. Nat. Eaux For., Nancy. 242 p.
1951
PUTOD, R. Les reboisements en pays méditerranéens par repiquages de jeunes semis.
1948 Rev. Eaux For. 87:334–355, 402–423.
RADWAN, M. A. TMTD wild mammal repellent: review and current status. For.
1969 Sci. 15: 439–445.
SAATÇIOGLU, F., and B. PAMAY. 20 ans de boisement d'Eucalyptus a Karabucak,
1959 près Tarsus. Rev. For. Fr. 9:438–448.
SACCARDY, M. Notes sur le calcul des banquettes de restauration des sols. FAO
1950 Subcomm. Mediterr. For. Probl. 15 p. (Mimeo)
SCHOENENBERGER, A., and C. BALDY. Essai de projection pour les reboisements en
1970 Tunisie du nord. Ann. Inst. Nat. Rech. For. Tunisie 4(6). 15 p.
SCHUBERT, G. H., and R. S. ADAMS. Reforestation practices for conifers in California.
1971 Calif. Dep. Conserv. Div. For., Sacramento. 359 p.
SCHUBERT, G. H., L. J. HEIDMANN, and M. M. LARSON. Artificial reforestation prac-
1970 tices for the Southwest. U. S. Dep. Agric., Agric. Handb. 370. Washington,
D. C. 25 p.
SHAH, S. A. Afforestation technique in kotar areas of Gujarat. Indian For. 94:791–
1968 794.
SHEIKH, M. I., and A. MASRUR. Drip irrigation—a new method of irrigation developed
1972 at Pakistan Forest Institute, Peshawar. Pakistan J. For. 22:446–462.
SHOULDERS, E. Mycorrhizal inoculation influences survival, growth, and chemical
1972 composition of slash pine seedlings. USDA For. Serv. Res. Pap. SO-74.
Southern For. Exp. Stn., New Orleans, La. 12 p.
SLAYBACK, R. D., and D. R. CABLE. Larger pits aid reseeding of semidesert range-
1970 land. J. Range Manage. 23:333–335.
SMITH, D. M. The practice of silviculture. 7th ed. John Wiley & Sons, New York.
1962 578 p.
SPRINGFIELD, H. W. Mulching improves survival and growth of Cercocarpus trans-
1972 plants. USDA For. Serv. Res. Note RM-220. Rocky Mount. For. Range
Exp. Stn., Ft. Collins, Colo. 4 p.

STOECKELER, J. H. The United States of America. Pages 268–346 in Afforestation in
1970 arid zones, R. N. Kaul (editor). Monogr. Biol. 20. W. Junk N.V. Publ.,
The Hague. 435 p.
STOECKELER, J. H., and P. E. SLABAUGH. Conifer nursery practice in the Prairie-
1965 Plains. U. S. Dep. Agric., Agric. Handb. 279. 93 p.
STONE, E. C. Root growth characteristics of coniferous nursery stock related to field
1966 survival potential. Proc. World For. Congr. (Madrid) 6:1461–1467.
STUART SMITH, A. M. Practice and research in establishment techniques. Documents
1967 FAO World Symposium on Man-Made Forests and their Industrial Im-
portance. Canberra 14–24 April 1967. Vol. 1:205–247. Food Agric.
Organ. U. N., Rome.
TURPIN, P. Tools and equipment for planting and reforestation. Food Agric. Organ.
1957 U. N., Div. For. Inf. Pap. 3. Rome. 33 p.
―――. Techniques de reboisement. Proc. World For. Congr. (Madrid) 6:1298–
1966 1303.
VELASCO, F., and J. M. ALBAREDA. Estado nutritivo de diversas repoblaciones fores-
1966 tales de coniferas en la España. Proc. World For. Congr. (Madrid) 6:
1477–1483.
VIDAL, J. J., and I. N. COSTANTINO. Iniciación a la ciencia forestal. Salvat, Bar-
1958 celona. 547 p.
VIDELA PILASI, E. O. Estudio economico para un plan de forestation con especies del
1965 genero Eucalyptus en suelo premontanos de la Republica Argentina. Montes
21:153–163.
WARE, L. M., and R. STAHELIN. Growth of southern pine plantations at various spac-
1948 ings. J. For. 46:267–274.
WITTERING, W. O. Weeding in the forest. G. B. For. Comm. Bull. 48. London.
1974 168 p.
WOODS, F. W. Converting scrub oak sandhills to pine forests in Florida. J. For.
1959 57:117–119.
WOOLSEY, T. S. French forests and forestry; Tunisia, Algeria, Corsica, with a trans-
1917 lation of the Algerian code of 1903. John Wiley & Sons, New York. 238 p.

5

Special Plantations

MAJOR TYPES OF PLANTATIONS

Plantations in arid zones are expensive and difficult to establish, therefore all plantations should serve justifiable needs. The decision as to which type of forest plantation is to be established in an arid area depends on the object of the plantation and the ecological conditions prevailing in the area. The object of a forest tree plantation is usually to obtain from it the maximum benefits that are likely to fulfill society's comfort and needs. As a result, the forester is confronted with competing objectives: (a) the need for more wood, (b) public demand for more forest land for recreation, and (c) concern for environmental conservation. To allay the concern for environment and to meet the demand for recreation, silvicultural practices often must be modified so that certain areas of the forest can be used for recreation, and so that the management of all areas will be in harmony with the public's concern for environmental conservation.

The objects for which forest tree plantations are established are many and assigning priorities will depend on how well and to what extent each fulfills society's needs.

Four major types of plantations that may be established are:

1. Production plantations. These plantations are established to yield a tangible and economically valuable product. The product may be timber, poles, posts, and pulpwood, or minor forest products such as fuelwood, charcoal, cork, fodder, honey flowers, tannin, gums and essential oils.
2. Plantations for environmental improvement. Plantations of this type include groves, windbreaks, and shelterbelts. The object of these plantations is to protect people, cattle, homes, orchards, and crops. This may be accomplished by moderating the damaging effects of hot or cold winds. The benefits derived from such plantations are not only direct physical protection from the winds but

also indirect economic returns such as higher livestock gains and increased crop yield due to the improved microclimate in the protected area.

3. Soil stabilization plantations. These include plantations to stabilize moving sand dunes, reclaim mining wastes and swamps, and to conserve the soil of fields. Economic returns from such plantations are to be found in the new areas of productive land made available by protection or reclamation, and in saving valuable topsoil of fields from erosion.

4. Amenity plantations. This type includes trees planted in parks and gardens, along roadsides, to reduce noise and to beautify the homestead or landscape. The object of amenity plantings is to make living conditions more pleasant and to give more pleasure and comfort to vacationers. The importance of forest trees in recreation grounds both for local inhabitants and for tourists has increased rapidly in most arid zones; so much so, that now many forests which were originally established to meet other objectives are being converted into recreation grounds.

Single Use and Multiple-Use Plantations

In some areas plantations may, for the good of the community, be planted to achieve one objective only. However, whenever possible plantings should be designed to serve two or more purposes. The object of such multiple-use plantations should be the harmonious and coordinated use of as many resources as possible. When a plantation is managed for multiple use, ordinarily not all objectives can be achieved equally. Consequently, the primary purpose of the plantation must be pursued with the least detriment to the secondary or other aims of the plantation. In a forest established for the production of major or minor forest products, other objects might be the protection of livestock and crops, providing recreational opportunities, or enhancing aesthetic values. These plantations should be managed on a sustained basis, wherein all the uses are properly blended and balanced, and where consideration is given for the present and future social and economic needs of the community—maintaining at the same time a balance in the environment.

An intensive analysis is needed to establish the relative priority of the objectives of a plantation. This will help to assure that the limited funds and manpower available are dedicated primarily to the higher priority objectives.

Once it is decided what benefits are to be derived from a plantation, the primary object of the plantation should be the guide. Only tree species that produce the greatest benefits expected from the plantation and can thrive under the ecological conditions prevailing should be used. For example the blue-leafed wattle, *Acacia cyanophylla* Lindl., is a small spreading tree and is one of the best species to use for binding sand. In contrast to this blackwood, *Acacia melanoxylon* R. Br., is an erect slim-trunked tree usually planted for the production of lumber and is not suitable for sand dune fixation, whereas the value of *Acacia senegal* Willd. is mainly as a producer of gum arabic. Each of these three acacia species should be used only in plantations where it best meets the desired objective. Since the wood of all three species can be burned for charcoal, charcoal production may be considered a second objective of the plantation.

It is worthwhile to note that every type of a plantation serves more than one purpose. Because all trees act as wind barriers and give shade, it can be said that all types of plantations improve the microclimate near them. Leaves or pods of many trees are used as fodder. The wood of most trees can be used as fuel and the aesthetic value of trees is, of course, always present. Although the secondary purposes are important, the primary objects of the plantation must be kept well in mind when planting and managing a forest.

The types of plantations determine not only the species to be used but also their mixture, arrangement, and spacing in the plantation. The techniques used in planting also vary with the type of plantation desired, and the intensity of cultivation is dictated by the expected benefits and crops.

Planting trees with the main object of obtaining large, quick returns warrants the allocation of favorable sites and the use of intensive cultivation; whereas planting trees for the fixation of dunes may require no more intensive silviculture than the subsequent protection of the area planted.

PRODUCTION PLANTATIONS

Plantations established to produce timber, poles, or posts are likely to become increasingly important. In the arid-zone countries where natural forests can produce only a fraction of what is required, the demand for such products will rise as the needs of an expanding and developing population increase (Fig. 5–1).

Foresters have been forced to adopt a new outlook for land use in arid zones, and consequently some of the greatest changes in reforestation and afforestation have evolved in the last two decades. One of the principal changes has been the establishment of plantations known as "forest-tree orchards."

Forest-Tree Orchards

Many arid-zone foresters have started to shift plantations to better pasture and agricultural lands—lands which, until recently, no for-

Fig. 5–1. A mixed plantation. Foreground, *Ceratonia siliqua* L.; background, *Cupressus sempervirens* var. *pyramidalis* Nyman and *Pinus halepensis* Mill.

ester could obtain for planting trees. In most arid zones, there is a desperate need for arable land. For centuries lands in these areas have been overexploited, and in many places much valuable land has been lost through misuse. What arable land is left is usually thought to be essential for agricultural produce, but it is also the best land for growing forest products which, if they are not grown in the region, must be imported. Because they are bulky and expensive to transport, producing them in the region becomes economically attractive. Such plantations could supply the wood and wood-products required in the area. These products now are either extracted from the depleted natural forests or imported, or, because they are so expensive, are not available to the rural population at all.

In many arid countries a change of policy took place after it was shown that forest crops may yield greater returns per hectare per year than many agricultural crops on land of the same quality. Land users' objections to reserving the better land for forest and non-food crops is fading; in fact, farmers frequently grow cotton, flax, and tobacco on good agricultural land. These crops are grown wherever they are more profitable to grow than are food crops.

Planting forest-tree orchards is done to meet the demand for forest products which cannot be obtained from poor natural forests or from plantations on steep, rocky slopes, and depleted lands. Forest-tree orchards are plantations on productive soil, and the techniques used might be described as semi-horticultural and semi-silvicultural. New techniques have been evolved in these plantations, and further improvements can be expected.

Problems are certain to arise in planting, tending, and harvesting these plantations and in utilization of the products; when they do, solutions must be found. In man-made forests utilizations of the products can be planned before afforestation commences.. However, later on changes may occur in the needs of the people in the area in which the trees are growing. Such developments can necessitate a partial or complete change in the system of management, or even conversion of the plantation to a different species.

The possible utilization of thinnings must be carefully considered before embarking upon an afforestation program aimed at production of large logs. A market or use must be found for the small material removed in thinnings, if the plantation is to succeed.

Because forest-tree orchards are planted on good agricultural soil, they should be intensively cultivated and planted with species which, under the climatic conditions existing in the area, will respond favorably to the treatment and which will produce above-average quantities of good quality wood in a relatively short time. Such production is needed to compensate for the use of the better soil and the costs involved in intensive cultivation. If a tree is to grow fast and produce more wood, it must have access to optimum levels of soil nutrients. Where the soil is not naturally rich in nutrients, it should be fertilized.

When the first forest-tree orchards were established (c. 1945), much of the planting was to supply poles and fuel. In recent years, attention has been devoted to planting for the production of pulp and timber, and in some countries timber from such plantations constitutes a significant portion of the wood used.

Many of the main principles and precepts involved in establishing a successful tree orchard are based on new concepts and advances in knowledge. The most important principles and precepts are given below.

Site Selection. As experience of planting has widened and evidence has accumulated of the effect of site differences on performance of tree growth, the importance of carefully selecting sites with good soil has become increasingly appreciated. In regions where planting must be on poor soils, such as the savanna of Africa or the campo de carrascas in South America, the problem will be to select the best available land in generally poor areas.

In such areas the initial growth is at the expense of the site's inherent fertility and continuation of a high level of productivity will require reserves beyond the capacity of the site to provide them, hence the need for artificial fertilization of the site. Even on better sites it is necessary to improve site conditions in order to get good growth of trees.

The site selected for a plantation of fast growing trees to be managed on a short rotation should be capable of sustaining the desired rate of growth. Before an area is finally selected for this type of plantation, the physical and chemical properties of the soil must be carefully examined. The area chosen should have a deep, good quality soil that is free of rocks so as not to interfere with the frequent cultivation required for aeration and retention of moisture. Important chemical properties to be considered are the amount and availability of essential minerals, the presence of harmful chemicals, and the pH of the soil solution. Soils in arid zones are often alkaline and good growth of most arid zone species occurs in the pH range of 6.0 to about 7.0. This is the most favorable range of pH for the absorption of essential mineral elements by the roots. If the pH of the soil is above or below this range, certain fertilizers can be used to bring the pH to the desired level. Nitrogen applied as urea tends to raise the pH of the soil temporarily, whereas nitrogen applied as ammonium sulphate usually lowers the pH. These chemicals should be applied with caution and tested on small areas before being applied to the entire plantation.

Ground Preparation. The main advance in ground preparation has been the greater realization of the benefits accruing from thorough pre-planting cultivation, including deep plowing and subsoiling, especially on the more arid sites.

Planting. The main advance in planting is the use of better plants—usually balled and thus well preserved in freshness till planting. Planting early in the rainy season will ensure receiving the maximum benefit of precipitation.

Tending. Tree orchards should be well tended, especially by weeding and discing. In the drier areas, cultivation and weeding operations have to be concentrated in the relatively short rainy season and immediately afterwards.

Spacing and Thinning. By using data about the rate of growth of quick-growing species in arable land, the appropriate distance between the trees at various ages which will allow them to grow to timber size in the most profitable manner can be calculated. As a result of such studies, trees are now not only spaced more widely, but are thinned more drastically than formerly. There should be no suppressed trees in forest-tree orchards—only dominants and codominants.

Trees must have adequate space for their roots. The growth rate in diameter or volume is determined by the amount of water available for each tree. Trees compete for root space with weeds and with the trees growing nearby; competition starts soon after they are planted. If some trees are removed, the roots of the remaining trees spread into the vacant areas. Where competition for water is keen, as it is in arid zones during a long dry period, the growth of the trees is restricted by the root space. Before planting, the rows and the spacing interval of the trees in the rows should be marked by flags, stakes, or stones so that the rows will be straight and parallel. Crooked rows make cultivation with machine or animal drawn equipment difficult. Where tractors are used, a row marker, which is a small disc on a boom attached to the tractor, provides an easy and accurate way of maintaining position between parallel rows.

Given adequate growing space, trees will develop and increase in diameter quickly. The same or a greater volume and increment of timber may be obtained per hectare from a small number of widely spaced trees as from a large number of closely planted trees, provided the roots of the widely-spaced trees reach all the available water and mineral nutrients in the area. For this reason the density of planting and the rate of thinning depend on the quality of site, the rainfall, and the extent and method of cultivation.

For fair-quality arable land in a region of from 400 to 700 mm (16–28 in) of rainfall during 5 months of the year, the best spacing for eucalypts and pines is 3 × 3 m (10 ft). Annual height growth of trees planted in the average well-cultivated soil in regions with 600 mm (24 in) of rain may be 0.5 to 1.0 m (1.6 to 3.3 ft) or more for some pines and 1.5 to 2.0 m (4.9 to 6.6 ft) for eucalypts. The rotation of a eucalypt plantation is based on the growth for 12 years.

Protection. Vigorous plants do not succumb easily to insect or disease attack, and the insects or diseases that do appear are usually easier to control. Similarly, fires are easier to detect and check in plantations with adequate firebreaks.

Mycorrhizae. Mycorrhizal fungi may be carried to plantations on the roots of seedlings taken from the nursery or the soil of the plantation may be inoculated by using soil brought from natural stands or established plantations of the host tree. In dry soils the mycelium of the mycorrhizal fungus may dry out and die. Because of this mycorrhizal deficiency is often experienced in arid zones.

Some mycorrhizal fungi are adapted to many host species, whereas other fungi are specialized. Soils taken from healthy natural stands or thriving plantations will most likely contain a population of the different mycorrhizal fungi needed.

Most pine species will not survive without suitable mycorrhizae and they differ very little from each other with respect to the fungi forming mycorrhizae. In contrast, it appears that most species of *Eucalyptus* and *Cupressus* do not need mycorrhizae for survival.

Soil Fertility and Fertilization. Trees require adequate supplies of many elements for healthy growth: nitrogen (N), phosphorus (P), and potassium (K) are usually required in fairly large quantities but other elements, including the trace elements, are also needed in greater or lesser concentrations for vigorous growth of various tree species. In arid zones, soils are often either deficient in the amount of the required nutrient or the proportions that are available are not properly balanced for optimum growth. Chemical analyses are made to determine what elements occur in the soil and in what concentrations. The elements that are deficient or absent should be applied to the soil as fertilizers.

Appraisal of a soil on the basis of a chemical analysis is, however, insufficient to indicate the type and dosage of fertilizer required. An evaluation which takes into account the microbiological, physical, mechanical, and hydrological characteristics of the soil in the root zone is a more precise indicator of its potential for producing tree crops. Fertilization of the soil based on this evaluation should lead to increased growth of trees and indirectly to lower susceptibility to disease. Either organic or inorganic fertilizers can be used in plantations.

Organic fertilizers such as manure, compost, and litter are occasionally used in small plantations but are seldom used in large plantations because they are bulky and difficult to obtain in great quantities. Moreover, organic fertilizers generally contain elements which are already found in soils in large enough concentrations, or they may not contain all the required elements in the amounts needed for proper balance of nutrients.

Inorganic fertilizers are usually preferred in forest plantation because they are cheaper, easier to handle, and only the needed elements are added to the soil. Frequently more than one element is applied not only because they are deficient in the soil but also because of their interaction; for example, nitrogen and phosphorus are both more available to the plants when applied together than when applied singly.

In relatively small plantations with good access by roads, inorganic fertilizers are applied to the soil either in water solution from spreaders drawn by animals or tractors, or as dust from blowers. In larger plantations fertilizers are pelleted and spread from the air by specially equipped fixed-wing aircraft or helicopters.

For greater economy fertilizers are applied at the same time as either site preparation or tree planting. In Australia it was found that fertilizers produced the most rapid growth when applied at the time of planting or soon afterwards. This was attributed to stimulation of root growth enabling them to exploit the site rapidly. The induced rapid growth rate continued until restricted by weed competition, indicating how important it is to control weeds on fertilized areas to obtain maximum growth rate. No significant advantage is gained by dividing the fertilization among several small applications. The ultimate value of the early response to fertilization rests upon its persistence through the rotation and its effect upon total volume production. Delaying fertilization reduces production, and the difference in the growth rate between fertilized plantations widens with time.

Not all species respond equally to fertilization, in fact, the degree of response varies among genotypes within the same species. Additional yearly volume increment of 25 percent and more has been recorded in poplar, eucalypt, and pine plantations that received proper fertilization.

Although fertilizers may leach deeply into the soil after rains or irrigation, some still continue to affect growth for several years after application. This is explained by the fact that nutrient elements absorbed by the roots are incorporated into the wood and tissues of the tree. These are returned to the soil when dead leaves, twigs, fruit and other parts drop to the ground and decay. Cycling of these elements lengthens the duration of the effect of the applied fertilizers on the growth of trees. The number of years fertilizers remain effective after application depends upon the type and quantity of fertilizers applied, the nature of the soil, climate, drainage, tree species, and efficiency with which the nutrient cycle functions. The influence of the fertilizer occasionally persists as long as 10 years or rarely even up to 20 years which is longer than the rotation of most quick-growing species under intensive cultivation. A balanced application of the needed elements in a production plantation of quick-growing species may reduce a 10 or 12-year rotation by a year or more.

If in a few years after planting an area, which according to its soil, analysis contains all the necessary elements in balanced concentration, many plants have deformed branches or leaves that are chlorotic, abnormally colored, or dying, and if such symptoms are not caused by bad drainage, it is an indication that required elements are present in the soil in a form in which they cannot be absorbed by the plants and are therefore not available to them. These elements must be applied to the soil in a form that can be absorbed by the rootlets. In alkaline soils, which are prevalent in arid zones, solubility of iron is greatly reduced, thus decreasing its availability to the plant; lack of iron is indicated by chlorosis of the leaves. Availability of manganese, copper, zinc, and boron is similarly affected by high soil alkalinity. Iron deficiency can be counteracted by applying heavy doses of ferrous sulphate. If the treatment is effective, the trees will regain a healthy green color. Nitrogen may increase plant growth only during wet periods when ample soil water is available. For example, nitrogen fertilization of Aleppo pine had a significant effect upon diameter, height, and volume growth on sites deficient in nitrogen, only if water was readily available.

In applying fertilizers it is not economically advisable to try to obtain the maximum increment possible by lavish use of expensive fertilizers and costly methods of application, but rather to get a profitable return from economical techniques and fertilizers.

Effects of Fertilization on Environment. Foresters and agriculturists are quite generally concerned about the effect fertilization may have on the pollution of lakes, streams, and ground water by chemicals carried in surface runoff and seepage. Few investigations have been devoted to the environmental impact of fertilization on this type of pollution; yet it is clear that fertilization of an area causes complex and dynamic changes within the ecosystem of the area. The risk of pollution is high for both nitrogen and phosphorus fertilization; whereas, potassium fertilization is thought not to cause many problems in water ecosystems. The rate of the change in the ecosystem caused by pollution depends on the kind of fertilizer used, rates and timing of application, and the total area involved. Failure to evaluate and consider the potential effects of fertilization on pollution of water supplies may rightly result in public censure.

Species Suitable for Forest-Tree Orchards

The variety of species used, especially of eucalypts and pines, has been considerably enlarged. This has been brought about by a desire for diversity as a protection against the risks of monoculture, the need to extend plantations to new sites and climatic regions, and the growth performance of some species. The species most likely to be profitable should be planted; these do not necessarily have to be native species. Usually, fast-growing species, even if exotic, are selected for planting. Fast-growing species are dependent not only on their own individual genetic capacity for growth, but also on the concurrence of this factor with favorable environmental conditions and on the improvement of growth conditions by proper silvicultural techniques. Care must be taken not to be misled by a species which initially gives high level of production, but which may eventually prove to be not entirely suited to the site.

It is commonly believed that the soil is impoverished by plantations of exotic species, but no such generalization should be made. Growth of exotics, in some regions, may slow down or even stagnate after a few years, but this may be due to a mineral deficiency that existed in the soil prior to planting, or to a multitude of other factors. In Australia, Monterey pine plantations were revived by the application of phosphates and by adding traces of zinc sulphates to the soil, and in East Africa boron was added to the soil of *Eucalyptus* plantations. Sometimes the lack or presence of the proper mycorrhizae, i.e., tree roots inhabited by certain fungi, may control survival and future growth of exotic trees in their new environments.

Eucalypts.   There are over 600 species of eucalypts, almost all of which are native to Australia and Tasmania, although the genus is also represented in Java, Timor, New Guinea, New Britain, and New Ireland. They dominate about 95 per cent of the forest area of Australia. In their native habitat, eucalypts grow in a variety of climates and soils, from the hot deserts to the cold mountain slopes. A great assortment of products can be obtained from them because of the enormous range in tree characteristics and wood properties within the genus.

The species growing in the more arid zones generally yield timber and pulp, and, although the wood is not of high quality, many of them meet the technical requirements of local industry.

The particular advantage of some species is their rapid growth. They have been widely planted in mild climates outside Australia, and species likely to succeed have been tried in most arid zones of the world. In general, successful plantings have been made in all but the cold arid zones. Successful irrigated groves of *Eucalyptus globulus* Labill. have been planted in cold arid zones on the mountains of Peru at an elevation of 3,000 m (9,800 ft). The wood produced is used mainly for mine props and firewood. Eucalypts that grow in cold Australian climates (minimum of about $-20°$ C [$-4°$ F]) require high rainfall.

Eucalypts should be planted in pure stands. They respond favorably to intensive cultivation, and if, in addition, they are grown in the proper climates and edaphic conditions their increment is phenomenal. In nutrient poor soils fertilization is of great value for improving their growth rate especially of the younger eucalypts. In spite of the nutrient removal from the soil by the trees, these plantations do not deteriorate site productivity.

The practice of planting in pits and hoeing around the plants for only one to two years after planting, which is done in many places, does not normally give good results. In Morocco, e.g., eucalypts were planted in this way in zones of *Pistacia lentiscus* L., where the yearly rainfall is 500 mm (20 in), with 75 per cent occurring between November 15 and January 15. Fifty per cent of the plants died within the first two years, and the rest did not develop well. Four years later, more trees of the same species were planted in a similar area, under intensive cultivation, and as a result establishment was almost complete and these trees outgrew those of the original plantation in a short time. Encouraged by the results obtain from intensive cultivation, foresters planted 70,000 hectares (173,000 acres) of eucalypts in Morocco between 1950 and 1960, with similar excellent results.

Deep plowing and repeated cultivation are essential to success. In the more arid zones, the "méthode steppique," which originated in Algeria, may be used. In areas with less than 500 mm (20 in) of rainfall a year, height growth of 1 m (3.3 ft) or more per year is attained by *E. sideroxylon* A. Cunn., *E. camaldulensis* Dehnh., *E. gomphocephala* A. DC, *E. occidentalis* Endl., *E. tereticornis* Sm., and others, and the volume increment may be 10 m³ or more per hectare per year (143 ft³ [715 bf]/acre/yr).

In areas with 500 to 700 mm (20–28 in) rainfall, the trees reach a height of from 3 to 4 m (10–13 ft) by the third year, after which they need less cultivation and care. The rotation is between 9 and 12 years and production is between 100 and 150 m³ per hectare (1,400–2,100 ft³ [7,100–10,700 bf]/acre/yr). The plantations are clearcut, and the coppice, if well cared for, can be cut on a 10-year rotation, producing 10 to 15 m³/ha/year (140–210 ft³ [715–1,100 bf]/acre/yr). The coppice can be maintained for six or more consecutive rotations without deterioration of the rootstock, provided the soil is good and the cutting and tending are properly carried out.

In exceptionally favorable environments, such as in Adana, Turkey, on drained, swampy land, or along irrigation canals, productions of over 30 m³/ha/year (430 ft³ [2,100 bf]/acre/yr) have been recorded.

The best results are generally obtained with *E. camaldulensis* Dehnh. However, the provenance of the species is most important. Trees of one provenance will do well in one region and fail almost completely in another.

Some species are better adapted to the more arid regions than others. A few species classified by their resistance to aridity are listed below:

Arid zones: Species for regions with less than 275 mm (11 in) annual rainfall: *E. brockwayi* C.A. Gardner, *E. oleosa* F. Muell., *E. salmonophloia* F. Muell., and *E. torquata* J.G. Luehm.

Species for regions with more than 275 mm (11 in) annual rainfall: *E. astringens* Maiden, *E. leucoxylon* F. Muell., *E. occidentalis* Endl., *E. sideroxylon* A. Cunn., and *E. tereticornis* Sm.

Semiarid zones: *E. camaldulensis* Dehnh., *E. tereticornis* Sm. (for non-calcareous soils), *E. astringens* Maiden, *E. corynocalyx* F. Muell., *E. gomphocephala* A. DC, *E. maculata* Hook., *E. melliodora* A. Cunn. (resists cold), *E. occidentalis* Endl., *E. rudis* Endl., and *E. sideroxylon* A. Cunn.

Semiarid zones with irrigation and an expectation of economic returns: *E. astringens* Maiden, *E. camaldulensis* Dehnh., *E. gomphocephala* A. DC, *E. leucoxylon* F. Muell., *E. maculata* Hook., *E. occidentalis* Endl. (saline soils), *E. paniculata* Sm., *E. rudis* Endl., *E. salmonophloia* F. Muell., *E. salubris* F. Muell., *E. sideroxylon* A. Cunn., and *E. tereticornis* Sm.

Semiarid zones with alkaline soil: *E. gomphocephala* A. DC, *E. leu-coxylon* F. Muell., and *E. sideroxylon* A. Cunn.

The production of mine props, poles, construction timber, and, in some places, cellulose from eucalypt plantations has brought great benefits to many arid-zone countries. Some eucalypts produce good tannin (*E. astringens* Maiden, *E. occidentalis* Endl., and *E. brockwayi* C.A. Gardner) and others honey-flowers (*E. melliodora* A. Cunn. and *E. camaldulensis* Dehnh.).

Pines. Pines are very valuable introductions to certain arid zones. In nature many pine species are confined to comparatively small areas. It was formerly believed that their diffusion to other parts of the world was precluded by the presumed unsuitability of other areas. However, when artificially introduced into new areas, many of these pines grow and regenerate as well as, and sometimes better than, in their native habitat.

Although pines growing in the more temperate zones produce better timber, those pines, even of inferior qualities, growing in arid and semi-arid zones have been of great value. *Pinus pinaster* Ait. of the proper provenance and *P. radiata* D. Don, where aridity is not extreme, have helped to create a more favourable balance of timber import-export in some countries. *Pinus halepensis* Mill. of the Mediterranean basin, and its close relatives, *P. brutia* Ten. of the Middle Eastern Mediter-ranean and *P. eldarica* Medw. of the arid zones of Georgia (USSR), are great favorites for planting. They may produce only from 2 to 6 m³/ha/year (30–85 ft³ [145–430 bf]/acre/yr), but their wood is pre-ferred to that of *Eucalyptus*. They respond well to intensive cultivation. Those species growing in the arid zones of the United States, such as *P. ponderosa* Laws., *P. coulteri* D. Don, *P. jeffreyi* Grev. & Balf., and others, and the pines of Mexico, e.g., *P. cembroides* Zucc., have not been given proper trials as exotics, although in some localities individual trees and small plots under intensive cultivation show a growth potential of over 10m³/ha/year (143 ft³ [715 bf]/acre/yr).

Poplars. It is customary in all arid zones of the world to grow poplars (and willows) along the banks of rivers and watercourses, along canals, or on irrigated land. Poplars require abundant moisture and do not grow well unless ample supplies of water are available. They are very responsive to climate, particularly to high temperatures. Within limits, the hotter the temperature the faster they grow, provided adequate moisture is available. In arid zones unless water is supplied continu-ously, die-back occurs.

The species commonly planted are *Populus nigra* L. and *P. alba* L., or clonal varieties of these species. A clone is a group of plants derived from a single individual by asexual reproduction, usually vegetatively.

All members of a clone have the same genotype and consequently tend to be uniform. Poplars are still planted in many countries with intervals of 1 m (3.3 ft) or less. In plantations, there may be several thousand per hectare. They are propagated by cuttings taken from neighboring trees and planted directly on the site. The trees are cut when they reach a usable size; occasionally they are harvested after the fourth year when less than 5 cm (2 in) in diameter (Fig. 5–2), but the usual rotation is from 8 to 12 years.

Poplar plantations are found in Patagonia, in northern Chile, in Mexico, Spain, the Middle East, and India—in fact, along watercourses everywhere in the arid zones, including the cold arid zone. However, poplars do not grow well between latitudes 30°N and 30°S. Their poor growth is attributed to the absence of a long photoperiod (day length) in these latitudes.

Poplars are also planted either in clumps or as windbreaks (Fig. 5–3) in irrigated vegetable gardens and irrigated fruit orchards, where they benefit from the intensive cultivation and irrigation given to the main crop. They are also planted in pure plantations and given intensive cultivation and irrigation. Under such conditions, an annual increment of 20 m³ (700 ft³ or 3,500 bf) or more per 1,000 trees may be expected.

Fig. 5–2.   Poplar roofing poles in Afghanistan.   (Courtesy FAO)

Fig. 5—3. A windbreak consisting of a single row of poplars (*Populus* sp.).

To have a successful plantation in hot zones, the plants should be selected from a clone that has been well tested in the region and is resistant to insect attack. Plants should be reared in the nursery for 2 to 3 years and brought to the planting area when they are 4–6 m (13–20 ft) high. The area to be planted should be deep plowed and properly leveled. Planting holes should be large, the soil fertilized, and spacing should be wide: 5 × 5 m (16 ft), 6 × 6 m (20 ft), or even 7 × 7 m (23 ft). Normally, fewer than 500 trees per hectare (200/a) should be planted. The annual consumption of water per hectare for irrigation is often between 1,500 and 2,000 m³ (160,000–214,000 gal/a, or ½–⅔ acre ft), depending on the rainfall. This amount is much more than the standard agricultural crops require. It is, therefore, only with full knowledge of the expenses to be incurred that such plantations should be undertaken in arid zones. The cost of producing poplars in arid zones may be 10 to 15 times the cost of production in more humid climates. Under favorable conditions it is possible to produce trees up to 50 cm (20 in) in diameter in 15 years, but such growth is very rare in arid zones. However, in regions where the cost of transportation is a major expense of imported timber, such plantations may be economical.

In places some farm crops especially legumes, are grown between the rows of poplars during the first 3 to 4 years after planting to improve the structure and the fertility of the soil. The return from such crops also helps to pay part of the expenses of the intensive cultivation and irrigation. Such crops help check soil erosion where the area is flooded either naturally or by irrigation. The area must be repeatedly cultivated when it is not covered by crops. Hybrid poplars are not generally good producers of timber if left unattended but are very productive if well cultivated and cared for.

The aim should invariably be to have all the poplars succeed and make the plantation a success in the first year. If, however, some plants die during the first year, they should be replaced at the beginning of the second year with plants of the original stock kept in the nursery for just this purpose.

The poplar clones that are recommended for intensive management are *P. deltoides* Bartr. (eastern cottonwood) and the Euramerican hybrids (×*Populus euramericana* (Dode) Guinier), "I-214," "I-488," Campeador, and others.

A clonal variety of black poplar, which apparently originated in the Po valley of Italy, but was developed in Chile, has been introduced into Argentina, South Africa, and Israel and is now propagated in these countries as a windbreak tree. This clone is commonly known as "Chile." The Chile retains its leaves almost all year, especially where winters are mild, and new leaves usually develop before the old leaves drop from the trees in early spring. The branchlets are thin and start at ground level and grow upward at an angle of 45 degrees. On good soil and with ample water (1.5 cu m [40 cu ft]) per tree per month, they can grow as much as 4 m (13 ft) in height per year during the first 2 to 3 years after planting. If planted in suitable soil, well-spaced and intensively cultivated and irrigated, the Chile makes an excellent windbreak in relatively short time. The Chile is a delicate tree and is susceptible to attack by insects and diseases. *Capnodis miliaris* Klug. feeds on the roots and causes the death of many trees, especially if the trees are not well tended.

Roots of the Chile are relatively long and thin and often spread into neighboring cropland. If they are severed during cultivation of the fields, they produce suckers which must be destroyed by additional cultivation or by spraying with an herbicide.

New introductions of poplars have not always been successful. *Populus deltoides* Bartr. and several of the Euramerican hybrids have had severe setbacks where the cultivation and irrigation were not adequate, e.g., in Iraq, Syria, Lebanon, Uruguay, and Argentina. The plantations were severely damaged by insects that attacked trees which were weakened because of lack of proper cultivation.

Insects and Diseases in Poplars. Poplars planted in arid sites which are not completely suited to them are often plagued by insects and diseases. The different species and varieties, or even clones, of poplars are particularly sensitive to environmental differences and grow well only on certain sites. Care should be taken when planting poplars to select clones based on their environmental requirements since strong vigorous trees can usually repulse insect attacks. The success or failure of plantations will depend on how well the site meets these requirements. Alkaline soils or water, shortage of water even for a brief period, and inadequate cultivation can weaken trees and lower their resistance to insects and disease. Keeping trees vigorous and strong is one of the best ways to minimize damage by many species of insects. Poplars are attacked by many insect species; some attack the bark, others the cambium, still others bore tunnels into the wood. Some insects are confined to the roots, others attack the upper stem and branches and still others feed on the foliage. Many cause only minor damage but a few severely damage or kill the trees. Any insects seen attacking the trees should be reported promptly and specimens of the insect together with samples of the damage done to the tree should be sent to an entomologist for identification.

Where ants or termites attack poplars, a clean field devoid of stumps and dry vegetation will help to reduce their population. In India castor cake powder is spread around ant nests to kill them.

An unusually large number of fungi species have been reported to occur in irrigated poplar plantations in arid zones. The humid air rising from irrigation water and the heat in the area favor the spread and growth of fungi. Fortunately few of the diseases caused by the fungi are of great pathological significance, if silvicultural treatments are proper.

Protection of Poplars from Animals. Farm animals can cause great damage to the green bark of young poplars and also to their leaves, if they can reach them. Young trees should be protected by piling thorny branches around them or by erecting tree guards. It has been found that painting the trunks with a mixture of lime and cow dung gives protection against cows and lime and horse dung against horses, but unfortunately similar application of goat dung does not deter goats.

Deer are extremely destructive to poplars. They are fond of the bark and especially the shoots of some clones. Plantations and nurseries of such clones should be fenced if deer are likely to get to the trees.

Where rabbits and hares nibble at the bases of young poplar trees, crowns of thorns or sleeves of wire netting afford good protection.

Small animals, especially field mice and some insects, attack the roots and root collars of young trees; this weakens them so that they may be blown down. To prevent large scale losses by field mice, it is advisable to keep the area around the base of the trees, or even the entire plantation clear of herbage. This will aid in their natural control by predators.

Poison bait, chiefly zinc-phosphide placed underground so as to avoid accidentally poisoning farm livestock is often effective.

In some countries, wild boars damage the roots of both young and old poplars. These animals should be trapped or shot in accordance with the game laws of the area.

Financial Aspects of Forest-Tree Orchards

It is evident that the change in land-use policy in arid zones has come about after carefully evaluating the economics involved, especially the following:

1. The cost of transporting bulky forest products is high compared to the cost of transporting non-perishable agricultural commodities, such as wheat and lentils. Thus, there is an economic advantage in producing such items as firewood, posts, tree supports, poles, and fruit boxes locally in plantations and importing the agricultural products that might otherwise have been grown on the plantation area.
2. The plantation can be so situated that the forest produce is near the area where it is to be used. If necessary, a suitable sawmill or crate plant may be set up near the plantation.
3. Trees grown in orchards are uniform in size. This simplifies harvesting because the trees all reach the desired size at the same time and most of the trees are usable. *P. radiata* D. Don or eucalypts, may reach the proper size for pit props in 7 to 9 years.
4. Because of the rapid growth in orchards, the required round wood can be produced on a small area. Large annual increments per hectare are recorded in such plantations, whereas the increment in regular plantations ranges from only 1 to 2 m^3/ha/year (14–29 ft^3/acre/yr). Eucalypt orchards have shown more than a tenfold increase over regular plantations.
5. Short rotations and quick returns on the money invested are the aims of planting forest-tree orchards. Where the rotation of some tree crops is from 7 to 10 years, an annual interest rate of from 6 to 7 per cent is realized on the investment. In normal plantations, with a rotation of over 70 years, returns of between 1 and 2 per cent are considered satisfactory.

In the Andes of Argentina, in excellent apple-producing country, apple trees were uprooted and replaced with poplars. These produced the wood shooks required for shipping crates. Prior to this, crates had been imported from Brazil, a distance by rail and sea of over 3,000 km (1,850 mi). The sawmills are set up on the grounds and are manned in their spare time by the laborers who cultivate the orchard. One hectare (2.5 a) of poplars planted as a windbreak or plantation produces enough wood to provide crates for the apples harvested from 10 hectares (25 acres) of orchard.

In Chile, vineyards have been uprooted and planted to *Pinus radiata* D. Don. These plantations now produce wood for crates, pulp, and other valuable products. Timber from these plantations is now exported.

The increase in specialized plantations in arid zones is mainly the result of improved tree-farming methods. The owners of the lands consider such planting an economic venture and regard the trees as a crop. They find the new silviculture that is recommended much easier to understand and practice than the old, complicated, orthodox type of silviculture recommended for the scrub forests or for planting in poor land. These farmers willingly plant eucalypts, poplars, or pines when such plantations are more profitable than other crops.

Fuelwood Plantations

Because wood is bulky in relation to its calorific value, and is expensive to cut and transport, it has been replaced in arid zones to some extent as a source of heat by oil, electricity, and coal where these are available. However, over 100 million people living in arid zones depend almost entirely on fuelwood and charcoal for heating and cooking, and in many regions, the demand for firewood exceeds the supply. The average yearly use of fuelwood per person is estimated at 1.5 cu m (50 cu ft) which is more than the average annual growth per hectare in arid zone plantations. Cutting of enormous quantities of wood has caused complete devastation of large areas of woody vegetation in the vicinity of villages and people have at times had to haul fuelwood from a distance of over 150 km (93 miles).

In many regions fuelwood is so scarce and expensive that people use cattle dung as fuel. This they collect in the field, thus depriving their already impoverished lands of the fertilizer so badly needed. The demand for fuelwood is likely to continue and special fuelwood plantations are the best means of meeting it; many such plantations have already been established in arid zone countries.

Fuelwood plantations can be established where land and moisture are available, and if such plantations are properly conceived, managed, and protected, they can be perpetually self-renewing.

The area, or areas, to be planted should be large enough to grow wood for a continuing supply of the fuelwood needed in the area. Fuelwood plantations are usually managed on rotations of about 10 years. The length of the rotation however, depends on the quality of soil, amount of moisture available, the species used, and the intensity of cultivation. The plantation should not be far from the settlement in which the wood is to be used and it should be well guarded against illicit cutting. In some districts of the People's Republic of China for example, young plantations have been destroyed by people desperate for fuel; thefts have occurred soon after the trees were planted and even before they were well established.

The area selected for planting should be cleared of competing vegetation by plowing, discing, hoeing, or by the use of herbicides. The entire area should be cultivated, not just around the plants. Proper cultivation and elimination of competing vegetation may increase the increment of trees by 2 to 6 times.

Such plantations should obviously be of species that grow quicker and produce higher calorific values than the native species that were destroyed. Such plantations can restore the equilibrium between man's needs for fuelwood and the supply of this crop in the vicinity.

Spacing in the plantation depends on the species selected, the quality and depth of soil, and the amount of rainfall, or in irrigated plantations, on the amount of water used. Wide spacing is usually recommended in non-irrigated plantations.

The choice of species for firewood plantations is great (See Chapter 6). However, the principal species planted in arid zones for fuelwood are:

In Mediterranean climate: *Acacia arabica* Willd., *Acacia cyanophylla* Lindl., *Casuarina equisetifolia* Forst., *Eucalyptus camaldulensis* Dehnh., *Eucalyptus globulus* Labill.

In semiarid summer rainfall areas: *Cassia siamea* Lam.

In irrigated plantations: *Dalbergia sissoo* Roxb., *Morus alba* L.

In sub-desert sandy areas: *Haloxylon ammodendron* Bunge., *Tamarix aphylla* (L.) Karst.

In cold arid zones: *Ailanthus altissima* (Mill.) Swingle, *Gleditsia triacanthos* L., *Juglans* spp., *Platanus* spp., *Robinia pseudoacacia* L., *Ulmus* spp.

On the better sites, poles and posts can also be grown and extracted from fuelwood plantations. These are generally more remunerative than the sale of fuel, but production of fuelwood is the primary object of these plantations and they should be managed to supply this commodity as long as the demand exists.

Irrigated Plantations

In arid areas, where rainfall is insufficient for the commercial production of timber, economic considerations may favor the establishment of irrigated plantations. In arid zones, poorly forested or devoid of timber, the need frequently arises for wood to be used locally, mainly for fence posts, roofing poles, and fuelwood. This need can often be satisfied by planting fast-growing trees in irrigated plantations. Because of

a

Fig. 5–4. Fuelwood being taken to market in (a) Iraq, (b) Nepal, and (c) Libya. (Photos courtesy FAO; (a) by C. H. Holmes, (b) by S. Theuvenet)

their rapid growth, compared to unirrigated trees, such plantations result in a considerable increase in production and a reduction in the length of rotation. The production of fuelwood in plantations under intensive cultivation is usually an important requisite for the reclamation and development of underdeveloped zones. When wood from plantations is made available, there is less illicit felling and destruction of the remaining natural vegetation. In fact, in some areas, soil reclamation and conservation programs can succeed only if a source of wood has been made available (Fig. 5–4). The same also applies to pasture improvements, because, by the correct selection of species, trees that will produce not only wood, but also leaves and pods for fodder, can be grown under irrigation. Irrigated plantations also offer the possibility of increasing the financial yields of semiarid and arid lands in areas where wood and tree products are much in demand.

On the technical side, the two main points to be considered with regard to the establishment of irrigated plantations are the availability and suitability of water and soil.

Irrigation projects in some areas, where lake or river waters are used, have brought a large proportion of the original arid scrub or desert under cultivation and converted it into productive agricultural land. Where this occurs firewood supplies are likely to diminish. Consequently, a certain percentage of the irrigated land should be allotted to trees to meet the domestic and industrial demand for wood.

Plantation areas must be selected with consideration of their accessibility and the adequacy of water supply by canals. Irrigated plantations should also be suitably situated with respect to the centers of consumption and, of course, close to existing roads or railways. The land should be level and free from mounds and depressions. These simple but essential requirements cannot be ignored if maximum production consistent with minimum outlay is to be achieved.

The land to be planted should be carefully surveyed and a contour map showing relatively small differences in elevation should be prepared. This is most important because, without a detailed contour map, it is impossible to fix the position of the irrigation channels. From this map, the area can be subdivided into sectors, quarter sections, and parcels; the distribution system can be plotted; and all practical arrangements can be made to reduce the necessity for terracing to a minimum. The layout and design of these channels may be very complicated and should, whenever possible, be entrusted to an irrigation engineer, who knows how to calculate properly the size of channels, their gradients, and their discharge. In practice, irrigation is impractical unless the area being considered has undergone a preliminary grading. This work should also be based on the contour map. Preparation is obviously easiest on land with only a slight slope, which will permit irrigation without excessive velocity of water flowing in the ditches.

After the area for irrigation is cleared of all obstructions, such as trees, scrub, and rocks, it is graded to a uniform slope. The initial grading is followed by the replacement of any topsoil removed with the final smoothing off of the surface. Then the ditches for irrigation and drainage are dug; their banks will also serve to limit the areas irrigated. Land clearing, grading, and digging are conveniently done with heavy mechanical equipment, when available.

Irrigation. Under certain circumstances, watering of forest-tree plantations in semiarid and arid areas is warranted. The techniques of establishment and subsequent cultivation of such plantations closely follow dry-farming practices. In areas where rainfall distribution is known to be irregular, or where the rainy season is late and tree planting may not be delayed further lest the season be lost, watering may be done immediately after setting in the young saplings. During the first season after planting, occasional waterings may also be applied, either to ensure the establishment of the saplings or to increase the initial growth.

Watering is usually confined to the first two or three years, and the low rates of water application bear no relationship whatsoever to the great expense involved in laying out a water-distribution network.

If the establishment of irrigated plantations is continuous, irrigation throughout the whole rotation of the stand constitutes the most important cultural technique, both for establishment and for subsequent growth.

Some plantations may be irrigated during the rainy season when other fields need not be. The plantations are then flooded from gullies to supplement the yearly rainfall. The added moisture results in a higher increment on the trees. Such floodings are common in poplar plantations near the banks of gullies and rivers. Other plantations require that sufficient amounts of water be available throughout most of the year, especially during the dry season.

As a rule, the establishment of forest plantations can be undertaken only where there is surface water, i.e., water from rivers or lakes. In view of the relatively low value of the forest products, engineering works should be kept at a minimum. Only in exceptional circumstances should water be pumped from wells. Favorable conditions for the establishment of irrigated plantations exist where rivers pass through arid valleys. Usually, water for irrigated forest-tree plantations is not made available until enough water has been diverted for agricultural production. But, with proper planning, it is generally found that, after the water requirements of irrigated fields and orchards have been met, some additional land may be put under irrigation to produce trees. The development of additional water resources from rivers and lakes for forestry has to be based on a study of the discharges of the streams involved as well as on the quantities needed for the proposed plantation. Available data show that trees require twice as much water as most irrigated agricultural crops, but the requirements diminish when the fertility of the soil rises, and trees on the better soils may need only 30 per cent more. The size of the trees also influences their need for water; the larger the trees become, the more water they need.

It may not always be possible to obtain an adequate supply of sweet water, and the effects of salinity on both the soil and the trees must be considered (Fig. 5–5). The chemical composition of the soil as well as that of the irrigation water must be determined in the planning of irrigated plantations before a suitable species can be selected. Usually water containing less than 100 ppm of sodium chloride is suitable for irrigation of most forest trees. A few species can tolerate between 100 and 600 ppm, but if the salinity exceeds 600 ppm, the water is not suitable for most species growing on ordinary soils. However, it is reported that on extremely porous soils some species can tolerate considerably higher concentrations than this. Some chemicals are very harmful; e.g., boron is highly toxic and no more than one part in two million should be present in the water. In Kuwait, where rainfall is less than 150 mm (5 in) a year, *Eucalyptus* spp. and *Tamarix* spp. have been planted and fair growth obtained by irrigating with purified sewer water.

Except for sandy soils, any moderately flat land, including areas with a slight slope, is suitable for irrigated tree plantations. Irrigating large plantations by sprinkling is costly, involving the construction of an elaborate water-distribution system, using pipes capable of carrying water under pressures of from 1.5 to 4 atmospheres.

In arid zones, bottom lands are often saline, and special techniques of soil improvement and management may be required before forest

Fig. 5–5. Irrigated plantation of *Casuarina* near Baghdad. Note white deposition of chemicals along sides of ditches.

trees can be grown. Usually the bottom land along rivers consists of deep, fertile, alluvial soil; such land may already be under irrigation for agriculture. Marginal lands farther from the river may also be used with profit, but these may require some reclamation, such as leveling, scrub eradication, and the removal of noxious salts from the soil. Excess salts are removed by the use of large quantities of water to leach them out and by the improvement of drainage. In areas where a large percentage of sodium occurs in the soil, calcium can be substituted for the sodium by the addition of gypsum.

The rate and amounts of water application can vary widely, according to climatic and soil conditions, as well as according to the tree species planted. In parts of central Asia, in light Chestnut soils, only one irrigation a year may be required. This is done by intercepting the runoff from heavy showers or melting snow in the spring and spreading it over the plantation. Only in exceptional circumstances is it possible to maintain a plantation exclusively with the help of spring-flood irrigation. In the Sudan, good results have been obtained with *Eucalyptus microtheca* F. Muell. by irrigating for only two to three months after the end of the rains instead of irrigating throughout the dry season. This technique tends, in effect, to increase the length of the rainy season.

In order to effect watering of forest plantations in the Sudan where water is scarce and the annual rainfall is between 200 and 450 mm (8–

18 in) with 4 rainy months, a minimum watering schedule has been evolved to fit a climatic regime in which surplus water is available during the rainy season. During the six months that include the four rainy months, in addition to the rainfall, fortnightly waterings of 1,000 cu m per ha (14,300 cu ft per acre) each are carried out during the first year of the plantation. A few additional waterings are recommended to promote quick growth, especially during the hot dry season. After the first year fewer waterings are necessary where the water table is high.

In some irrigated plantations, such as in those of the Punjab, watering is done at intervals varying between every 5 and 14 days, according to the soil, the weather, and the development of the plants. In central Asia, about 12 to 15 irrigations are made during the first year from April to August. The number of irrigations is reduced from 4 to 6 in the third year and only 2 to 4 in the fifth. At each watering, between 500–900 m^3 of water are used per hectare (53,000–96,000 gal per acre). Where saline or alkaline land is to be reclaimed by irrigation, large amounts of fresh water will be required.

Great attention should be given to proper irrigation, as faulty watering is likely to restrict root development. Excessive fluctuation in water supply may lead to the death of part of the root system, which will lower resistance to disease, insect attack, and strong wind. Beneficial effects including leaf flush, leaf fall, and hardening-off can be controlled by manipulating the time of irrigation.

Several irrigation methods may be used, and it is advisable to leave the choice of method to the irrigation engineer.

Surface Flooding. Surface flooding from head ditches, or "wild flooding," is used mainly in areas with gentle natural slopes that require little preparation of the soil surface. In this method, water spreads evenly from the main ditches. Roots of plants growing in waterlogged soils are deprived of oxygen. Although some species and ecotypes can endure flooding longer than others, few can withstand long periods of flooding without adequate aeration of their roots.

Border System. Ditches run along the upper edge of each parcel to be irrigated. Parcels are usually rectangular; the water flows down the whole surface into the drainage ditch at the bottom. The strip is bounded on each side by earth banking 20 cm (8 in) high, running at right angles to the distribution and drainage ditches. The length of strips from the distribution ditch to the drainage ditch may be 100–120 m (330–400 ft) and the width 10–30 m (30–100 ft). The width selected should involve the least expenditure on grading.

Contour Flooding. Under this system each strip is watered by the overspill from small channels running laterally from a distribution channel which follows the general slope of the ground, but which is raised slightly above it. The overspill channels are between 20–30 m (65–100 ft) in length, the space between them varying from as little as 2–3 m (6.5–10 ft) on highly permeable soils to as much as 20 m (65 ft) and above on other types. Excess water is collected in drains. This method distributes the water more satisfactorily than the border system, reduces losses of water, and is applicable to surfaces with slopes of up to 20 per cent. But it needs accurate grading of the land.

Herringbone Method. This system differs from contour flooding only in that the laterals run at an angle from the feeder ditch descending the slope.

Inundation Method. The ground is flooded either for short periods or for several days. This is the system used with river water, which usually transports fertile silts. Solid banks divide the land into carefully leveled basins. The area of each basin may be up to several hectares. Where the land has but little slope, this procedure makes it possible to irrigate easily and cheaply.

Infiltration Method. With this method the water is not spread over the whole surface, but infiltrates laterally through the sides of channels that have only a very slight inclination. The channels are 10–15 cm (4–6 in) deep and 100–200 m (330–660 ft) long. The interval between channels varies from 40 cm (16 in) for permeable soil to 20–30 cm (10–14 in) for less permeable soil. This method is best suited to soil of medium permeability.

A new method of furrow irrigation is recommended in the Sudan. The furrows are ridged on each side with a plough that pushes the soil to both sides. Ridges are 20 cm (8 in) high making the effective depth of the furrows 35 cm (14 in). The furrows are spaced at 6 m (20 ft) intervals and the trees are planted on the flats between the furrows. The spacing between trees is 3 m (10 ft) in the direction at right angles to the furrows. Water from the open ditch infiltrates into the flat and trees planted near the ridge and to a distance of 3 m (10 ft) from it are almost equally vigorous. A saving of one-half to one-third in water used is effected by this system compared to ordinary ditches spaced at 3 m (10 ft) intervals. Under this system, trees usually grow faster and are of better form than in furrow and flood irrigation systems.

None of these systems can be carried out until additional engineering work has been done to bring the water to the site selected for the plantation. Engineering works include storage reservoirs, canals, diversion works, weirs, and measuring devices. Their planning and execution, therefore, should be left to the irrigation engineer.

Choice of Species. Only native trees or exotics that have been grown many years in the region should be used in irrigated plantations because they will have to withstand the extreme droughts that can be expected to occur after they receive the initial irrigation at the time they are planted. In selecting the tree species to be planted, account should be taken of the objectives of the plantation, the suitability of the trees selected to local climatic and soil properties, and the amount of water available. No complete list of trees suitable for irrigated plantations can be given here. Obviously, large-scale planting should be done only after careful experimentation in which both species and amounts of water required have been tested. However, trees commonly grown in irrigated plantations in arid areas include:

Hot arid areas: *Dalbergia sissoo* Roxb., *Morus alba* L. (often mixed with *Dalbergia*), *Gleditsia triacanthos* L., *Casuarina equisetifolia* Forst., *Acacia arabica* Willd., *Prosopis spicigera* L., and *Eucalyptus* spp.

Temperate and cold arid zones: *Ailanthus altissima* (Mill.) Swingle, *Robina pseudoacacia* L., *Ulmus pumila* L., *Gleditsia triacanthos* L., *Platanus orientalis* L., *Juglans regia* L., *Populus* spp., and *Salix* spp.

Although no general rule can be prescribed for the choice of species, a few miscellaneous observations and suggestion may be helpful. For example, *Dalbergia sissoo* Roxb. does not grow well on alkaline or sandy soil, which is more suitable for species of *Tamarix, Melia,* and *Prosopis.* In certain areas, where only limited water supplies are available for forest plantation, the introduction of xerophytic species is necessary in the interest of water economy. Suitable trees for planting under those conditions in descending order of water requirements are: *Melia azedarach* L., *Morus alba* L., *Khaya senegalensis* (Desr.) A. Juss., *Eucalyptus camaldulensis* Dehnh., *Casuarina equisetifolia* Forst., *Tamarindus indica* L., *Cassia siamea* Lam., *Albizia lebbek* (L.) Benth., *Dalbergia sisso* Roxb., *Tamarix aphylla* (L.) Karst., *Eucalyptus microtheca* F. Muell., *Acacia nilotica* (L.) Del., *Conocarpus lancifolius* Engl., *Acacia senegal* Willd., *Acacia farnesiana* (L.) Willd., *Prosopis juliflora* (Swartz) DC. Although this list showing the order of water requirements may not be exact under all circumstances, it can be considered a reasonable approximation. There is some question whether it is possible to grow shisham (*Dalbergia sissoo* Roxb.) timber and mulberry (*Morus*) fuelwood in the same area. Experience has shown that in mixed plantations mulberry tends to suppress the shisham. Both species produce high yields of fuelwood when grown in pure stands. Mixing of trees and shrubs can be useful in creating green belts, nut- and fruit-bearing plantations, and shelterbelts. This method is used in cold and arid zones, such as Central Asia, for establishing shelterbelts. If it is desired to mix species, it is done by rows rathers than within rows. In growing eucalypts or poplars, or any other tree to be managed as coppice, only pure stands should be established.

Establishment and Planting. After the area has been leveled and prepared for irrigation, a working plan is made to set out the planting and lay down the details of nursery, road, and other work to be done. The whole forest is then divided up into as many annual planting blocks as there will be years in rotation. Thus, when planting for the last year is finished, there will be a complete series of age gradations on the ground for working the clear by felling or coppice systems. The rotation depends on the number of years the trees take to reach the required size, according to the objective of the planting. Planting should always start at the head of the watering channel—not at its tail. Land not yet planted may be used for temporary agricultural cultivation.

Irrigated plantations are established either by sowing or by planting, according to species and soil conditions. Direct sowing is carried out with species such as those of *Dalbergia, Robinia, Ailanthus,* and *Juglans.* These are species that have either a deep root system or large seeds of high germinative vigor.

Sowing is done on the berm of the irrigation trenches. The time of sowing depends on climatic conditions, as well as on the germination characteristics of the species concerned. Although, in irrigated plantations, sowing theoretically can be done all year round, high or low temperatures are likely to prevent proper germination during part of the year. In hot arid zones, the best time for sowing would be either the beginning or the end of the rainy season. In continental climates, it should be deferred until the spring frosts are over. The seeds are covered lightly with crumbled earth, which easily becomes moist for several centimeters above the actual water level of the trenches, because of the absorbent quality of the soil.

Several tree species are established by planting seedlings or balled plants raised in nurseries. When balled plants are used they are not watered for about a week prior to planting to make the ball of earth more compact. Consequently, the area should be irrigated soon after planting. A few species including those of *Robinia, Dalbergia,* and other genera may be established by planting root-shoot cuttings, known as "stumps." Stumps can be produced easily and cheaply in nurseries by taking large seedlings and cutting them 15 cm (6 in) above and 15–20 cm (6–8 in) below the root collar. Nursery plants of some hardwood species like *Azadirachta indica* A. Juss. and some acacias are pruned about 30 cm (12 in) above the root collar and 30–40 cm (12–16 in) below the root collar. These are set out in the planting holes with the root collar at ground level. Seedlings planted with their root collars below or above ground level tend to have slower height growth and lower survival.

Direct broadcast sowing may result in dense crops of seedlings, which require early and expensive thinnings, whereas the stand formed from planted stumps is properly spaced from the start. Such stands may need no thinning until the yield is saleable and, what often is most important of all, they need less water and less care. In addition, where there is crust formation, stumps forced 20 cm (8 in) into the ground can easily penetrate the upper crusty layers and have more water reserve for dry weather or when canal water fails, as sometimes it may. Therefore, stumps will usually succeed where direct sowing might fail.

When stumps are planted in the Punjab, water is let into the trenches and, as soon as the sides are moist, a workman sets stumps or saplings in them. In stiff soil, a planting rod or crowbar may be required to make a hole, but, if the ground is moist, stumps can be pushed slowly into the ground. Immediately after the planting, the trenches are again filled with water. In the Sudan an irrigation cycle of two weeks is used and the amount of water given per irrigation cycle is about 300 cu m per ha (4,290 cu ft per acre) which is equivalent to 780 mm (31 in) of rainfall per year.

Planting distances vary, but spacing is usually rather dense compared to that of unirrigated plantations because water is no longer the limiting factor. Distances in central Asia are often 35–70 cm (14–28 in) within the row and 70–80 cm (28–32 in) between the rows. In India and the Punjab, the usual planting distance for trees is 1.8 m (6 ft) apart in trenches 3 m (10 ft) apart.

Culture. During at least the first two years after establishment, the young tree crop has to be thoroughly weeded if the plants are not to be suppressed by weeds. Indeed, very extensive weed growth is to be expected during this period because of irrigation. Weeding in irrigated plantations is of major importance. Not only do weeds and grasses suppress the plants, but they clog the water trenches and impede the flow, and the root competition by weeds robs the trees of both moisture and soil nutrients. Weeding may be done by hand or by animals or tractor-powered equipment in the intervals between irrigation channels. Tractor-powered equipment is usually preferred because it may be operated at low cost, especially where the land has been prepared by leveling or terracing prior to planting. Weeds that do not grow again once they have been uprooted may be left on the ground to serve as a mulch, and thus reduce the amount of irrigation water required. It may also be desirable and good practice to plow these weeds into the soil to increase its organic matter. Mulching of soil favors root development of young seedlings close to the soil surface by improving moisture conditions and by mitigating temperature extremes. By the end of the second or third year, the canopy of trees should be dense enough to suppress the weeds, but tolerant weeds may then establish themselves in the plantation, and a further weeding may be required to control root competition. During the first two years, agricultural crops can be grown between the rows of trees, and the weeding can be done by the farmers.

Soil cultivation is of the utmost importance on irrigated plantations. It is good practice to loosen the soil during the time between irrigations to increase the aeration and the rate of water infiltration and to help microbiological development. Deep ridging by tractors gives excellent results with clay soils. Superficial cultivation by harrowing or discing not only loosens the soil surface and promotes the decomposition of organic matter, but also removes weeds. Such cultivation may be done with horses or camels. In central Asia, cultivation between the rows is done five to seven times in the first year; in later years, only one or two annual cultivations may be required. However, cultivation is expensive and usually must be done by hand because cross-cultivation by tractor- or animal-powered equipment may interfere with the layout of the irrigation network.

Financial Aspects. From the preceding discussion it is evident that irrigated plantations generally call for a large investment of funds for the layout and maintenance of the irrigation network. This investment is in addition to the actual irrigation (including water and labor) and soil cultivation. Another factor, often overlooked, is the cost of the land itself. Although irrigated plantations supply large quantities of fuelwood and timber for local consumption, products that otherwise would have to be hauled over long distances, the question arises concerning the financial returns from intensive plantations. Experience in arid areas has shown that irrigated plantations are profitable in terms both of revenue and of timber yield. Plantations of *Dalbergia sissoo* Roxb. in the Punjab show a high mean annual increment of wood (up to approximately 8 m³ per ha [115 ft³ or 575 bf per acre]) with substantial profit. A comparison of the output during the first and second rotations shows a marked improvement in the yield during the second rotation. This trend will probably continue for at least three to four rotations. Irrigated poplar plantings in arid zones may be expected to produce an increment of over 20 m³ per ha per year (290 ft³ [1,400 bf]/acre/yr).

There is ample evidence to show that irrigated plantations and canal-bank plantings have a definite favorable influence on agricultural yields in the adjoining areas, since the trees act as windbreaks. In the Near East, central Asia, and South America, yields of various crops have shown significant increases owing to the sheltering effect provided by irrigated plantations. Increases of up to 70 per cent of cotton yield have been observed in central Asia, while yields of various crops have increased by as much as 200 per cent in the fourth year after establishment of the protective plantation.

Canal Plantations

Plantings along canals are similar in many respects to irrigated plantations. Tree planting along canals is important in arid and subhumid areas for the production both of fuelwood and of timber. Such plantations are irrigated by the water seeping from the canals; their very existence is based on the temporary or permanent availability of water in the canals. Canals may carry either irrigation, drainage, or flood-discharge water; or they may serve other purposes, such as regulation of the water flow, carrying water to storage reservoirs, or movement of ships and barges between rivers and lakes. Canal plantations usually occupy narrow strips bordering existing canals.

When designing a canal plantation, the requirements may be the same as for the design of irrigated plantations with respect to climatic and soil conditions and to supply and quality of water. However, it should be remembered that the only water supply available to the trees is seepage from the canal into the root zone. Some water loss from the canal is to be expected, but such loss by lateral seepage may be compensated for by the value of the timber produced. In some places it is cheaper to grow trees and thus utilize the seepage water rather than prevent seepage by canal linings of concrete, asphalt, or other material. But, even when trees are planted along canals, it usually is not possible to prevent some water loss by deep seepage below the root zone, and transpiration by the trees may increase seepage losses. However, plantations along canals that have not been lined for the prevention of water losses are one of the cheapest ways of producing timber in arid areas.

The proper selection of tree species is important for canal-bank plantations. A species that may be quite satisfactory in an irrigated plantation may not be suitable for canal plantings. In fact, the choice of species must take into account both the particular character of the plantation and its purpose. The roots of the trees should strengthen the banks of the canal, and the trees should keep the canal and its banks well shaded in order to suppress weed growth and reduce evaporation from both the ground and the canal. Species that tend to increase water seepage through the sides and bottom of the canal should be rejected. These species usually have roots or rootlets that die leaving tubelike cavities in the soil, allowing seepage of water. Where canals have an intermittent flow, such as flood-discharge canals, only trees able to adjust to varying water levels in the soil can be used.

Species that reproduce by suckers, such as *Robinia pseudoacacia* L., should not be planted along canals. Their habit of extending roots toward the bank and their prolific suckering from damaged roots makes them unsuitable. Strongly suckering poplars should be avoided also. Within the same species, the suckering habit often varies with the climate; the hotter the climate, the stronger the habit. *P. nigra* var. *italica* Muenchh., *P. alba* L., and Euramerican and balsam poplars, are useful species, and occasionally they can be planted farther away and separated from the canal bank by rows of species with deep root systems.

Acer negundo L., because of its dense root system, is good for strengthening banks and may be used in any place where the banks are likely to break. Other species suitable for canal plantations in hot arid areas include teak, mango, *Eugenia jambolana* Lam., *Azadirachta indica* A. Juss., *Tamarindus indica* L., *Albizia* spp., and *Acacia catechu* Willd. In more temperate areas, the most useful trees are usually poplars and willows.

Generally, it is found that once the trees have been established, and if the canal has no special anti-seepage lining, soil moisture from seepage is sufficient to support trees without further irrigation. Soil moisture samples will readily show the width of the strip that can be planted on either side of the canal.

Usually, two or more rows of trees can be planted with sufficient spacing to permit mechanical cultivation. Because the roots should be planted in the moist layer, depth of planting is the most important single factor on which successful establishment depends. Some additional water from the canal can be provided without difficulty when the trees are planted, and during the first year, to ensure establishment. In extensive plantations, it may be worthwhile to have a mobile water pump to provide additional irrigation during this time. Subsequent cultivation within and between the rows may be needed to suppress competing weeds.

Plantations for Minor Forest Products

Plantations that yield minor forest products are usually multipurpose. They produce fuel and fodder, fuel and tannin, and so on. The choice of products depends on the need and the suitability of the region to grow the species that produce them. As the return from such a plantation is small, the soil quality in the site selected should be such that it could not produce other crops with greater returns.

Fodder Trees. Too little has been done to save fodder trees from destruction or to select suitable ones for arid-zone plantations. When grass is scarce, especially in years of drought, grazing animals may have only the branches and leaves of fodder trees to live on. The leaves of some trees are very palatable for cattle, sheep, or goats. They may also have a suitable chemical composition and digestibility that make good fodder. Leaves of some species contain as much as 20 per cent of crude protein.

Several species of *Prosopis* are well known as fodder trees. *Prosopis spicigera* L., e.g., is protected and cultivated in northwest India and Pakistan. The branches are normally cut for fodder at a rotation of three to five years, but in drought years additional branches must be cut to save the cattle from starvation. Pods and leaves of *Acacia arabica* Willd. are readily eaten by cattle, and this species is planted in India and Pakistan both for fodder and for fuel. In Argentina, *Prosopis alba* Griseb., *P. nigra* Hieron., and other species supply pods which are highly palatable and nutritive, and the leaves of some species are eaten by cattle. These trees also produce valuable posts and timber. They grow in extremely arid areas on saline soil where other fodder plants are rare. A related species, *Prosopis tamarugo* F. Phil. (tamarugo), grows on salt flats in Chile.

In southern Morocco, bordering the Sahara, *Argania sideroxylon* Roem. & Schult., growing on sand and rocks, is heavily browsed by goats, indicating that this might be a useful fodder species. *Haloxylon* spp. are browsed by camels in extremely arid zones and two species have been sown over large areas in the Usbek (USSR).

Brachychiton populneum (Schott) R. Br. has been found to be not only useful as a reserve supply of fodder, but also as shelter and as an ornamental. A number of other species, including *Robinia pseudoacacia* L., *Morus alba* L., *M. nigra* L., and *Salvadora* spp., have been similarly used.

Honeylocust (*Gleditsia triacanthos* L.) and carob (*Ceratonia siliqua* L.) grow in hot, dry climates where their pods are valuable fodder for animals. The pods of different varieties of these two species differ in the amount of sugar and other nutritive elements that they contain, so only varieties with high yields should be planted. The amount of fodder also varies, and some varieties of carob produce as much as 1 ton of pods per tree a year.

In general, fodder from trees is particularly important in arid zones for meeting abnormal conditions of food scarcity. Fodder from trees is likely to continue in demand during certain critical seasons as long as the cattle population remains excessive, and until measures are taken by cattle owners to ensure the preservation of adequate stocks of other fodder during the dry season (Fig. 5–6).

When improving the range, it is advisable to leave all fodder trees. These will serve as a fodder reserve and shelter. When planting shelterbelts to protect animals from the cold, sun, and wind, or the soil from desiccation, it is advisable to choose species that bear fruit, pods, or leaves palatable to animals.

Fig. 5–6. An acacia tree reserved for shelter of cattle. The other trees have been lopped for fodder.

Honey Trees. It does not pay to raise trees solely as honey plants. The most that can be done is to encourage the growing of good nectar and pollen-producing trees for other purposes; honey products will always be of secondary importance.

When planting honey species, it should be remembered that not all species flower at the same time nor for the same length of time. Whereas some may be in flower for a month or six weeks only, others will produce flowers for more than seven months in the year. Some species blossom in winter, others bloom in summer; and some may even flower unexpectedly out of season. Exotics may not flower in their new environment in the same season as they would in their native habitat. Therefore, when trees for honey production are selected, they must be those that can be expected to blossom collectively for as long a period as possible. The flowering periods of some arid-zone species are given in Table 5–1.

There are areas in the Mediterranean basin in which species of *Arbutus* spp. flower during March and April. *Elaeagnus* spp. flower during May and June, and the exotics *Grevillea robusta* A. Cunn. flowers in June and July; *Eucalyptus camaldulensis* Dehnh. flowers in March and April and

Table 5–1. Flowering period of some tree species used for honey production in arid zones.

	J	F	M	A	M	J	J	A	S	O	N	D
						Month of the Year						
Arbutus andrachne L.			M	M								
Cercis siliquastrum L.			M	M	M							
Elaeagnus angustifolia L.				M	M	M						
Eucalyptus camaldulensis Dehnh.	V		M	M						M	M	V
Grevillea robusta A. Cunn.						M	M					
Schinus molle L.								M	M	M		
Prosopis juliflora (Swartz) DC					M	M	M	M				
Schinopsis lorentzii Engelm.		S	S	S								
Aspidosperma quebracho-blanco Schlecht.									S	S		

M = flowering in the Mediterranean Basin.
V = flowering in Victoria, Australia.
S = flowering in South America.

again in September and October. Thus, in such areas there are trees that bloom during 8 months in the year, from March to October.

PLANTATIONS TO IMPROVE THE ENVIRONMENT

Living conditions in the arid zones are harsh. In many dry regions of the world the perennial shortage of water and the severe climatic conditions are intensified by strong hot or cold winds which sometimes blow relentlessly for days on end. In such areas trees give shelter from the sun and winds and are valuable catalyzers for the improvement of the local environment in general.

Plantations of trees ameliorate temperature extremes, reduce wind velocity, and raise soil moisture and atmospheric humidity by reducing evapotranspiration and temperatures in the area protected by the trees. For these reasons forest tree plantings having as their primary object the improvement of the microclimate of the areas they shield, are becoming increasingly appreciated by society and common in many arid regions. These plantings also beautify the landscape, protect recreation areas, help to abate noise, and screen industrial plants.

Multi-purpose plantations designed to meet several objectives have been tried in the past without giving complete satisfaction, particularly when the design did not satisfy the requirements of the species in meeting those objectives. It is, therefore, advisable to establish plantations to satisfy but one primary objective. Variations in design may be used to fulfill a subordinate objective, provided this does not interfere with achieving the primary objective.

Three principal types of plantations are made with the primary object of improving the environment: groves, shelterbelts, and windbreaks.

Groves

Groves are groups of trees that are either growing naturally or that have been planted around farmsteads or country homes. Where groves are available, people normally select them as site for building their houses and where natural groves are not present, they may be created by planting.

Planted groves may be of any size, so long as they cover the area to be shaded. Groves should be watered for the first few years after planting to promote rapid growth. Livestock may rest under the trees during hot days, so it is wise to protect the trees against damage by the animals. Groves have become a sign by which habitations can be recognized on the wide, open landscape in many countries. The state of the trees usually reflects the efforts of the people living in the grove to improve their well-being and comfort.

Any project for planting around a homestead should be carefully planned in advance and should take into consideration the proposed location of all trees and shrubs with due regard to the position of telephone lines, power lines, sewers, and ditches.

Trees used in establishing groves are often taken from natural forests in the vicinity, but local species do not always have the qualities desired for grove trees. Consequently, many tree species with more suitable qualities have been introduced into the different arid zones of the world. Qualities desired in species to be planted where the sun and winds are hot are long boles without branches near the ground to allow wind flow and wide-spreading crowns which retain their leaves most of the year to provide shade. In addition trees should be long-lived and have strong branches resistant to wind damage. The root system should not be too spreading and the tendency of some species to produce suckers from the roots is undesirable.

If winds are severe and continuous, and especially where deep snowdrifts are deposited in the winter, windbreaks should be planted on the windward sides of the farmstead at some distance from the grove and the living quarters to slow the wind and to keep snowdrifts out of the farmyards. Evergreen shrubs or trees with low branches should be planted in these windbreaks.

The particular species selected for planting will depend on its site requirements and on the ecological conditions prevailing in the area. Recommended species are listed at the end of this chapter.

Shelterbelts

The principal distinction between a windbreak and a shelterbelt is size. A windbreak is a protective planting of trees, shrubs, or herbaceous plants around a garden, a house, or an orchard, whereas a shelterbelt is usually a barrier of trees protecting fields.

Semiarid zones do not support natural forest; at best, the woody vegetation consists of scrub trees, generally growing in a more or less open formation. The trees themselves are not, as a rule, straight or very tall, and they do not form a high forest.

In open parks and woodlands of arid zones, where pasture is to be improved and trees and shrubs have to be removed, it is advisable to leave bands of trees and shrubs at proper distances and directions to form windbreaks to protect the pasture and the soil.

The semiarid zones are natural grazing land rather than forest land, but, unfortunately, most of them throughout the world have carried cattle, sheep, goats, and camels in a greater number than the land could endure. As a result the vegetation has deteriorated, and its grazing capacity has been still further reduced.

Excessive grazing also results in soil erosion by both wind and water. To stop erosion, it is essential to improve and increase the cover of grasses, shrubs, and trees, all of which contribute to the protection of the soil. Properly managed fields, therefore, must support the vegetation necessary for their own protection. Trees, however, in addition to their role in reducing soil erosion also protect the fields from desiccating winds. The value of the protection given by trees to cultivated fields, grazing animals, homes, and farm buildings is now generally recognized, although difficult to calculate in monetary units.

Shelterbelts of trees in semiarid zones not only improve the conditions of the fields and livestock, but also supply some forest products, especially fence posts and firewood, so greatly needed in such areas. In fact, the revenue from shelterbelts of properly selected species planted on more favourable sites may be higher than the net proceeds from other forms of land use.

Principles of Wind Shelter. Shelterbelts protect crops from being blown down and physically damaged; they prevent soil from blowing away; they help to reduce the evaporation of soil moisture and the transpiration of plants; and, by reducing wind movement, they reduce heat losses and effect some control over temperature by leveling extremes. Windbreaks may be used to shelter cattle from strong winds and provide shade to protect them from the hot sun. In villages windbreaks are valuable for protecting factories and machinery against damage by blowing dust and sand. Furthermore, their aesthetic value in an otherwise treeless landscape should not be minimized especially where such belts are around lawns and villages. In general, the more extreme the climatic conditions of any region, the greater is the need for windbreaks and the greater their value.

Windbreaks and shelterbelts are of great importance to agriculture, arboriculture, and animal husbandry, especially during dry hot or cold seasons.

The modern concept of protective belts originated in the early 1890's. Since then, immense strides have been made in the study of shelterbelts, yet much is still unknown. However, these studies have shown that shelterbelts counteract adverse climatic conditions, principally by reducing the wind velocity.

Fig. 5–7. Leeward distance of wind protection is proportional to height of barrier. (After Read, USDA Agriculture Handbook 250)

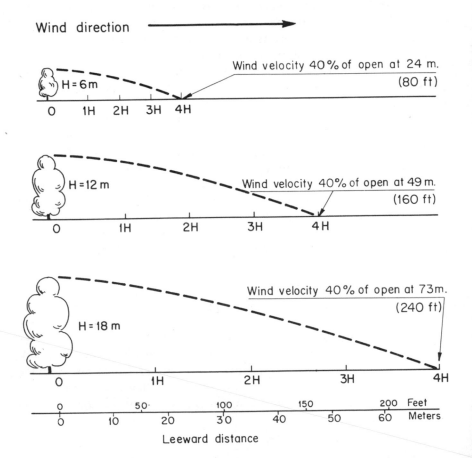

The obvious physical injuries that animals and plants may sustain from wind are, of course, serious, but physiological effects may also be significant; e.g., if cows are not protected from strong winds they will produce less milk. Furthermore, most people find high-velocity winds that blow without interruption for several days extremely disturbing psychologically.

Tests have shown that the depth of the sheltered zone is largely dependent on the height of the trees (Fig. 5–7). When the wind strikes the shelterbelt, part of the air current passes through the trees and is broken up into minor turbulences, another part hurdles over the belt, and the remainder is deflected well above it. Wind is slowed before reaching the shelterbelt; the reduction in velocity begins at a distance equal to about nine times the height of the trees. When the wind reaches the barrier its average speed has been reduced to about 70–80 per cent of its original velocity. On the lee side of the shelter, the speed continues to diminish and reaches its minimum from one to five times the trees' height beyond the belt. From this point the velocity increases, eventually regaining its original speed. Wind velocity is reduced for a maximum distance equal to about 25–30 times the height of the trees; the actual distance depends on the original wind speed and the design of the windbreak. Hence, some effect of the shelter on wind speed can be felt on both sides of the barrier in a zone whose width is about 35 times the height of the trees. (Fig. 5–8)

The effectiveness of different species and types of wind shelter should be studied in new planting areas. Windbreaks of the same design, but of different species, may have greatly different effects—as will windbreaks of the same species and design, but in different localities. For example, tests of varieties of *Cupressus sempervirens* L. indicate that, in the vicinity of a shelterbelt of *C. sempervirens* var. *pyramidalis* Nyman, the wind is reduced to a far greater extent than with shelterbelts composed of *C. sempervirens* var. *horizontalis* (Mill.) Loud. Between 40–50 m (130–160 ft) from the windbreak, the protective effect of *C. sempervirens* var. *horizontalis* (Mill.) Loud. is definitely better. A windbreak of *C. sempervirens* var. *pyramidalis* Nyman is windproof; one of *C. sempervirens* var. *horizontalis* (Mill.) Loud. is permeable.

The protective effect depends on the direction of the wind flow and the angle it makes with the shelterbelt. The effect does not change appreciably until the angle between the long axis of the shelterbelt and wind direction decreases to approximately 50°. If, however, the angle is reduced further, the protective effect diminishes rapidly. Therefore, the direction of the prevailing damaging wind for any area should be studied closely.

In the zone of protection of a shelterbelt, both air and soil temperatures are generally higher by day than those of the unprotected areas.

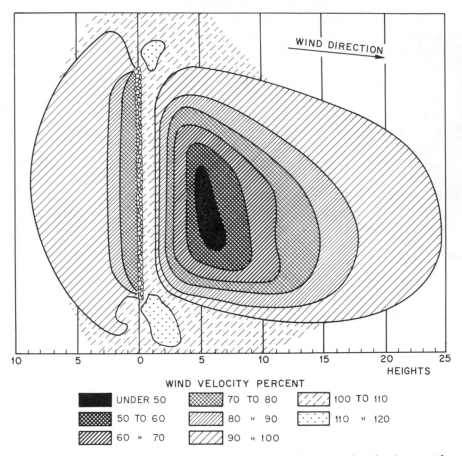

WIND VELOCITY PERCENT

■ UNDER 50	▨ 70 TO 80	▨ 100 TO 110
▨ 50 TO 60	▨ 80 " 90	▨ 110 " 120
▨ 60 " 70	▨ 90 " 100	

Fig. 5–8. The actual field protection of a windbreak 19 heights long, with an average density of 50 per cent. The wind was measured 40 cm (16 in) above ground. (USDA Farmers' Bulletin 1405)

At night in cold climates both soil and air temperatures near the ground in the protected zone are slightly warmer, about 1 to 2° C (1.8–3.6° F), than in open areas and in warm climates cooler by about the same amounts. In general, the benefits of shelterbelts are greatest during extremely cold or very hot, dry weather.

The reduction of transpiration and evaporation of water considerably improves the water economy of sheltered pastures. Such pastures characteristically favor heavier, sleeker cattle. Shelterbelts protect soils against being blown away, particularly fine-textured and sandy soils. They also prevent the loss of humus and keep it in the area where it can be incorporated into the mineral soil.

The best criteria of the value of shelterbelts are the size and quality of the harvest from a sheltered field compared with the harvest from an unsheltered one. In general, yields are markedly higher in sheltered zones and are decidedly so in years of drought. An increase in yield of over 100 per cent has been observed in protected areas. (Fig. 5–9) In order to obtain the optimum effect from a windbreak it must be correctly located and designed. Yet there is no assurance that the effect of a windbreak will always be beneficial. In some areas where air movement is blocked, temperatures near the belts may rise high enough to damage crops.

In dry farming areas reduction of evaporation from the soil surface by shelterbelts could be of paramount importance and make the difference between success and failure of a crop. In areas where water availabilty is likely to limit expansion of irrigation programs, the water saved by reduced evaporation, and which could then be diverted to other areas, might be as significant as in increase in crop yield per unit area.

Wind shelter is usually not an end in itself, but simply a means of increasing production, either quantitatively or qualitatively. Every windbreak removes land from production and, as a rule, reduces crop yield in a narrow, bordering zone. Furthermore, shelterbelts should be well

Fig. 5–9. Cross section of crop yield on fields under shelterbelt influence. (After USDA Production Research Report 62)

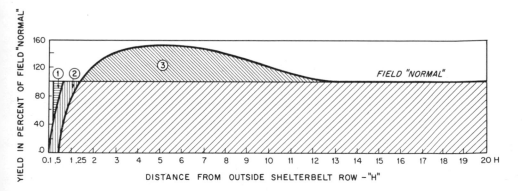

LEGEND

Area ① yield that is normally lost at a field edge not adjacent to a shelterbelt.
Area ② yield that is lost due to shelterbelt influence.
Area ③ yield that is gained due to shelterbelt influence.
Area ③ minus ② is the net influence of the shelterbelt.
    H = 1 unit of a tree 13m (43ft) high.

cared for and fenced, and, because they are costly, they are justified only when the increase in production on the cropped area, over a long period (especially in dry years), is appreciably greater than the lost yield caused by using productive land for the windbreak.

Design of Shelterbelts. Planting a windbreak around a garden or at right angles to the direction of the most severe winds is a simple operation. The windbreak should consist of a single row of trees or double row of trees and shrubs planted at appropriate distances, according to the species. Rapid growth of the windbreak may be expected as a result of the irrigation, manuring, and cultivation of the crop which the trees are protecting.

Shelterbelts require a more careful layout than windbreaks. Although single and double rows of trees are sometimes used, shelterbelts generally consist of several rows. Shelters are mainly of three types: (1) windproof—a solid wall of live plants, (2) permeable—allowing some air flow, (3) porous—with gaps.

The permeable type is generally considered to be the best. This type gives good protection to the area on the leeward side while permitting

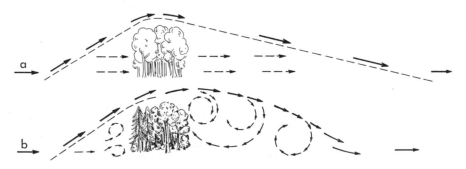

Fig. 5–10. Flow of wind over (a) a moderately penetrable, and (b) a dense shelterbelt. (After R. W. Gloyne; courtesy Forestry Commission, London)

some air to flow through the barrier (Fig. 5–10). Of course, the air flow through the shelter must not be so great that it will cause physical damage (Fig. 5–11). A 20 per cent wind flow can be permitted through small and evenly distributed openings without fear of damage. When winds are continuous and very high, the first line of trees should form a closed barrier.

The effectiveness of windbreaks changes throughout their lifetime; it generally increases until the trees reach maturity and then declines as they pass maturity, lose vigor, and their crowns open up. For maximum effectiveness over a long period, the species selected for planting should be fast-growing and long-lived.

On plains and rolling hills, shelterbelts should be planted on the crests of the ridges, wherever these run within 40° of the direction desired.

The principal problem in designing a series of belts is to achieve the maximum protection for the minimum sacrifice of land. The long axis of the belt should be across the path of the prevailing winds, but if the direction of the winds varies, some compromise, or perhaps protection

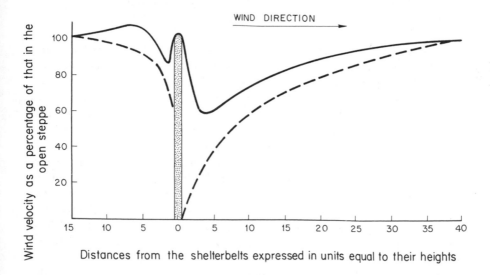

Shelterbelts "open" throughout their height — partly permeable to wind.
Shelterbelts "dense" throughout their height — impermeable to wind.

Fig. 5–11. Protective effect of shelterbelts of varying permeability. (After R. W. Gloyne; courtesy Forestry Commission, London)

from all directions, may be necessary. Wherever possible, regardless of wind direction, shelterbelts should first be planted along the roads.

The most common design consists of a chessboard pattern. The entire area is thus protected from every side, provided the right distance between the belts is maintained. The distance between the belts is controlled by the nature of the site as well as by the mature height of the species to be planted.

The design of the shelterbelt depends on its purpose. If the shelter is to protect animals from the cold wind, it should be U-, V-, or X-shaped (or other shape) with the opening on the side opposite the direction from which the cold wind blows. A triangle with any of its points facing the cold wind is also an effective design. Trees forming such shelters should have live crowns down to the ground for the maximum effect in preventing the wind from blowing through.

If the main purpose is to protect animals from the sun, any shape is satisfactory. A square 100 × 100 m (330 × 330 ft) has been commonly accepted. If, however, the shelter is to protect pasture from desiccation by dry winds, long belts should be planted at right angles to the wind. A multi-purpose shelter might be formed by windbreaks laid out as a hollow rectangle 200–400 m long and 50 m wide (660–1,300 × 165 ft).

It was formerly believed that shelterbelts should have a triangular profile in cross section. High trees were planted in the center row, forming the apex of the "roof." These were flanked on each side by successively shorter trees and finally by shrubs; the lowest shrubs formed the margins of the belt. It is now accepted that a rectangular cross section is adequate, even for belts two to seven rows wide, provided one or two of the rows of trees retain their foliage down to the ground.

A wide wooded belt prevents wind damage. Such wooded areas may have some influence on the local climate, but their specific shelter effect is limited to the area planted. Therefore, a large number of narrow parallel shelterbelts aligned in the proper direction and planted the proper distance apart is preferable to one large wooded area. The best width for a belt is four to ten rows composed of trees and shrubs whose crowns retain their foliage down to the ground.

The stronger the hot, prevailing winds in the area, the greater the number of rows needed in the shelterbelt. In the most adverse situations, 10 to 15 rows are planted, but where the prevailing winds are not strong, the number may be reduced to 2 or 3. If the trees can be irrigated, the number of rows can be reduced to a minimum of 5 or 6 where winds are strong. The area occupied by a shelterbelt varies from 1.5 to 3.5 percent of the area to be protected depending upon how adverse the prevailing conditions are.

Spacing in the shelterbelt depends upon the species, however, in arid zones more space is needed for each tree than would be required for the same species when it is planted in humid climates. The spacing and arrangement of the trees must be a compromise between the space required for good growth of the individual tree and the density needed to make an effective windbreak. In practice seedlings are planted very closely to obtain early closure of the crown. Spacing is usually about 3 m (10 ft) between the rows with the trees 2 m (6.5 ft) apart in the rows. This spacing is wide enough to allow easy cultivation with machines without damaging the trees. Shelterbelts are often planted with more rows than might be thought necessary because of the possibility of loss of trees through windfalls and insect attack.

The distance between belts depends on the expected velocity of the wind and the purpose for which the belt is planted. If winds over 100 kph (60 mph) are frequent and fruit orchards are to be protected, belts should be planted about 100 m (330 ft) apart. In zones where the velocity is 40–60 kph (25–35 mph) and pasture is to be protected, 0.5–1 km (0.3–0.6 mi) between belts is recommended. But regardless of the distance between the belts their effect in reducing wind velocity is not cumulative. On dry-farming land and on slopes steeper than 3 degrees, the belts follow the contour lines and, therefore, they will also help to reduce soil erosion.

The techniques employed in plant propagation, site preparation, planting, and cultivation, all of which are extremely important in successful establishment of shelterbelts, do not differ from those used in general afforestation.

Choice of Species. It is advantageous to use only one species to simplify planting and management. At times, two or more species must be used because of a soil difference or because one species alone will not give the required shelter. For example, eucalypts alone do not give adequate protection because the lower part of the bole is branchless. This characteristic makes eucalypt plantations, when viewed from a distance, appear as a floating canopy on stilts (Fig. 5–12). If eucalypts are used in windbreak planting, a second shrubby species or short tree is required to give complete shelter (Fig. 5–13). Shrubby species of eucalypts or other species may be used for this purpose; in Uruguay tamarisk is planted, and in the Sudan, bamboo. The bamboo is harvested at regular intervals to provide small poles and to stimulate new growth.

However, instead of planting two species, a full shelter of eucalypts can be obtained by cutting alternate rows of trees. The low coppice of the most recently cut rows will complete the shelter.

If browsing animals are likely to damage the windbreak, the shrub species for the outer row should be unpalatable or armed with thorns or prickles. *Acacia farnesiana* (L.) Willd. and species of *Myoporum*, *Pittosporum*, *Tamarix*, and of the Cactaceae may be used. If these or similar plants are not used, the shelter must be properly fenced or the animals will browse away the lower branches and destroy the effectiveness of the windbreak. Fencing is expensive, and corner construction is the most costly part of fencing. Therefore, to reduce the cost per hectare, wide plantations with as few corners as possible should be made.

Fig. 5–12. *Eucalyptus* spp. shelterbelt for cattle in Uruguay.

Fig. 5–13. Windbreak in Uruguay; below, *Tamarix* spp.; above, *Euca-lyptus* spp.

Tree species selected for shelterbelts should meet most, if not all, of the following specifications:

1. Be adaptable to soils of different origins and in particular to the soil in which it is to be planted.
2. Be able to develop strong, deep, root systems because extensive horizontal surface roots will compete with crops that the trees are supposed to protect.
3. Be fast growing, tall, of uniform shape, with live branches and foliage to the ground.
4. Be long-lived and capable of providing effective protection for over 50 years with minimum care and maintenance, unless the objective of the shelterbelt is of a short term nature.
5. Be resistant to drought, frost, extreme temperatures, windthrow, snow breakage, insects, and diseases.
6. Be easy to establish.
7. The crowns should be of the density, permeability, and shape to conform with the protective purpose of the shelterbelt.
8. Produce timber of usable quality, fodder, or some other economically important product.
9. Not reproduce easily from suckers or from seed, as such trees may become weeds.
10. Retain their leaves, at least partially, throughout the year.
11. Not be host to fungi, insects, or other pests which may attack the neighboring crops.

Not all of the specifications which pertain to growth habits and products can be found, or are even needed, in a single species, but a combination of primary and secondary trees and shrubs can be planted to obtain the ones which are the most desirable.

Although it is advisable to use native species for windbreaks and shelterbelts, if they fulfill the requirements, the district in which the shelter is to be planted should be searched for exotics that have been grown successfully. Any of these that appear suitable for planting in shelterbelts should be selected for trials. Many trees that grow well in arid zones are unproductive, and wherever possible, these should be avoided. Various species of *Acacia, Casuarina, Schinus,* and *Grevillea* are often used, but they should not be planted where better species can be grown.

A few of the more common species that have been used in different regions for windbreaks and shelterbelts are listed in Table 5–2.

Species that have been planted successfully in shelterbelts in the arid zones of the Soviet Union and which are worthy of trial elsewhere are: *Acer tataricum* L.; *Fraxinus pennsylvanica* Marsh. [*F. lanceolata* Borkh.]; *Populus alba* L. [*P. bolleana* Lauche] in irrigated belts; *Salix arbuscula*

Table 5–2.   Common species in shelterbelts and windbreaks.

Species Planted Mainly in Shelterbelts

Hardwoods
Acacia cyanophylla Lindl.
 A. *melanoxylon* R. Br.
 A. *salicina* Lindl.
‡*Acer tataricum* L.
 Celtis occidentalis L.
†*Eucalyptus brockwayi* C.A. Gard.
 E. *camaldulensis* Dehnh.
†E. *dundasi* Maiden
†E. *gracilis* F. Muell.
†E. *salubris* F. Muell.
†E. *sargenti* Maiden
‡*Fraxinus pennsylvanica* Marsh.
 Populus bolleana Lauche
 Prunus virginiana L.
 Quercus macrocarpa Michx.
 Q. robur L.
 Robinia pseudoacacia L.
Salix arbuscula L.
 Ulmus americana L.
 U. parvifolia Jacq.
‡*U. pinnato-ramosa* Dieck
 U. pumila L.

Conifers
†*Callitris glauca* R. Br.
 Juniperus virginiana L.
 Pinus brutia Ten.
 P. canariensis C. Sm.
 P. halepensis Mill.
 P. ponderosa Laws.

Species Planted Mainly in Windbreaks

Populus spp.
Salix alba L.
†*S. arbuscula* L.
 S. humboldtiana Willd.
Tamarix articulata Vahl

Cupressus arizonica Greene
 C. *sempervirens* L.
 C. *macrocarpa* Hartw.

Species Suitable for Low Shelterbelts

Acacia longifolia (Andr.) Willd.
A. cyanophylla Lindl.
 Acer negundo L.
 Caragana arborescens Lam.
†*Elaeagnus angustifolia* L.
†*Tamarix gallica* L.

Species Suitable for Temporary Windbreaks

Crotalaria juncea L.
Pennisetum purpureum Schumach.
Rhus coriaria L.
Ricinus communis L.

---

* On sandy soils or dunes
† On saline soils
‡ Planted successfully in the arid zone of the U.S.S.R.

L. on saline soil; and *Ulmus pinnato-ramosa* Dieck on eroded slopes and degraded areas.

Arrangement of Species in Shelterbelts. Where the shelterbelt is to contain more than one species, the different species should be arranged to produce the desired density in the upper and lower levels of the belt. Short-lived species should be planted where their removal will not interfere with the remaining trees in the belt. Whenever possible each row of trees should be of a single species and these rows should be arranged to avoid suppression of one species by the species in the adjacent rows.

Care of Shelterbelts. In areas open to grazing, all belts should be fenced to protect the plants. For belts that are to be managed on a short rotation for poles, posts, fuelwood, and so on, the fence should be permanent and well maintained. For belts to shelter animals from the sun, the fence may be removed as soon as the trees are large enough to escape damage by cattle.

Quick and even growth of trees may be obtained by repeated cultivation between the rows. Weeding and cultivation during the first few years after planting are absolutely essential; cultivation once or twice a year during the life of the stand is also advisable. Rapid growth may also be stimulated by manuring.

It is important that trees planted in shelterbelts have deep roots rather than spreading shallow roots which extend into the neighboring fields. Spreading shallow roots of shelterbelt trees will compete for moisture with the roots of the adjacent crops. To prevent this competition, the roots of the sheltering trees that enter the field may be severed by digging a ditch 1 m (3.3 ft) deep parallel to the belt at a distance of 2 m (6.6 ft) from it. The ditch is then refilled with soil; however, since new roots will soon grow into the filled ditch, it will be necessary to repeat this procedure annually.

Where the soil is deep and without rocks, a tractor-pulled knife, which can be thrust to a depth of a meter or more into the soil by a hydraulic or compressed-air piston, can be used to cut the competing roots. This task can be done quickly and can be repeated twice a year if necessary.

In very arid zones, trees will not grow without irrigation; even xerophytic trees will need some watering. All shelterbelt trees should be watered during the first year or two to ensure early growth and establishment of the plants. Watering is usually done with rubber hoses connected to a portable tank. The number of waterings and the amount of water applied depend on the aridity of the area, the soil characteristics, and the species and size of the trees planted. About four to six waterings per year [each tree receiving about 10 liters (2.6 gal) at each watering] is considered sufficient for trees planted on sandy loam in areas that receive 150–200 mm (6–8 in) of rain annually and have an 8-month dry season.

Trees may have to be irrigated permanently in very arid zones. Where agriculture is practiced in dry regions, the windbreak trees may be planted along irrigation canals.

Protection and Renovation of Shelterbelts.   Because the establishment of shelterbelts is so costly, it is most important to protect and manage them properly to ensure that their effectiveness will be maintained for as long as possible.   Due to the very nature and purpose of shelterbelts, they are exposed to severe environmental stresses especially those caused by winds, drought, and temperature extremes.   Such exposure can cause serious physiological and physical injuries resulting in the premature decline in vigor of some trees.   Some of the symptoms that indicate loss of vigor are dropping of leaves, reduced live crown, and loss of lower branches. The net result of such losses is an increase in the porosity of the windbreak.   The incidence of insect and disease attacks also increases with the weakening of the trees.   Trees may be so weakened that individual trees or even clumps of trees die and must be removed.   Gaps in windbreaks due to loss of trees or the increased permeability of the crowns of the weakened trees greatly reduces the effectiveness of the barrier.   When this happens it is necessary to fill in the openings as soon as possible. Occcasionally it may be possible to stimulate crown development of weak trees by discing, irrigating, or fertilizing, but often such efforts are futile. If the species sprouts, coppicing may possibly be induced by cutting. Gaps produced by the removal of dead trees should be filled by planting or by natural seedlings, if they occur.

Recently there has been a trend towards establishment of narrow windbreaks due to increased land values and taxation.   Thus, when renovating old plantings the number of rows may be reduced and broad-crowned hardwoods replaced by narrow-crowned conifers.

SOIL STABILIZATION PLANTATIONS

Erosion

Flash floods, loss of topsoil, and gully erosion are typical features of the arid-zone environment, and control of erosion is a serious problem to be solved in land management.   Two characteristics of arid zones increase the severity of floods and erosion—scanty vegetative cover and deluges that release tons of water in a single short-lived cloudburst.

Cloudbursts do not occur entirely at random, but are commonly associated with mountains which cause sharp, localized upthrusts of air.   They are also characteristic of arid regions where strong, convectional updrafts are caused by surface heating.   Even in zones with an average annual rainfall of only 300 mm (12 in), convectional storms may produce sudden and heavy rains of short duration. Rainfall of as much as 50 mm (2 in)—one sixth of the yearly total—has been recorded in less than an hour in such zones.

If the mountain slopes exposed to recurring torrential rains and cloudbursts have been heavily grazed or the tree cover burned or indiscriminately cut down, a protective vegetative cover may be almost completely absent. As a result water moves over the surface unimpeded, infiltration is reduced, and runoff is considerably accelerated. The rushing water picks up the topsoil and carries it to the valleys below. Thus, the level valley bottoms consist largely of rich alluvial soil brought down by erosion from the mountains. It is on just such rich soil that many agricultural communities have developed, but it is also in the valleys that disastrous floods so often occur, causing vast destruction.

Occasionally after an unusually heavy rainstorm, a moving mass of wet earth slips down the denuded slope, carrying boulders and the remaining trees with it. In some areas much valuable agricultural land has been buried under a thick layer of sterile earth and boulders from such mass erosion, or by flood deposits. Flood damage is not caused so much by the actual flood waters, as by the debris and mudflows. If the flood waters could be prevented from picking up debris, or if the debris could be separated from the flood waters, controlling the waters by providing channels would not be too difficult.

Mechanical Control. Protective dams and outlet channels are often constructed in the bottom of gullies. These structures are intended to arrest the flow of mud and debris during floods, or to divert them from valuable properties. Regardless of the extent of these structures, however, their effect is generally negligible unless other protective measures are also applied to the catchment area. As the runoff slows down on reaching the plains, the sand, gravel, and boulders which it is carrying, are deposited. These soon clog the channels and fill the basins behind the dams, forcing the flood waters from their normal course. Preliminary measures in erosion control must include the reseeding of denuded lands, control of grazing, adequate fire protection, and the provision of contour trenches and ditches planted with trees or grass.

Contour trenches are usually short, but if they must be made long, they should be separated into short lengths by earth partitions spaced at regular intervals. Each trench thus consists of a series of basins with large capacity, that will retain all or most of the surface runoff, even following a heavy rainstorm. If the trenches do not stop surface runoff completely, they will, at least, reduce it to a minimum. Newly constructed trenches should be planted with suitable trees and shrubs as soon as possible after the first rains to ensure the rapid establishment of an effective vegetative cover.

Fig. 5–14. Terraced slopes (gradoni) for erosion control in Spain. (Courtesy FAO)

Trench terraces, or gradoni (Fig. 5–14), have proved satisfactory in preventing runoff, provided their construction is started from the top of the watershed. Controlling the headwaters is the most important consideration in erosion control, and upon it will depend the success of the program. A large number of trench terraces, each draining a strip, prevents the accumulation of runoff. Once the water accumulates and begins to spill over the trenches, no obstacle will prevent it from running down the slope, carrying the soil with it.

The trench-terrace system provides improved conditions for plant growth. Loss of topsoil is stopped by the terraces and available soil moisture is significantly increased because all precipitation and runoff are caught and held until they soak into the soil. Thus, in selecting trees to plant on these terraces, those with higher moisture requirements than trees normally planted in the same district may be selected. *Pinus halepensis* Mill. and eucalypts have been successfully planted in areas that receive only 300 mm (12 in) of rain annually. There is, of course, the risk of extremely dry years, when all the rain received in the catchment trench of a tree is not enough to keep it alive.

Gullies that form on the hills need not be terraced, but dams or barriers should be built across them. These dams may be stone walls, logs, brushwood held by pickets, or anything that will hold water back and will produce a hard face on the lower side, which the water cannot wear away. To prevent the water from cutting a new channel around or under these check dams, their ends should be built well into the banks and the foundations dug deeply into the bed. The beds of the gullies below the dam should be paved with stones or protected by a brushwood apron to prevent erosion (Fig. 5–15). The top of each dam in a gully should be higher than the base of the next one above it, so that a series of level strips will be produced as silt is deposited. After the gully banks are smoothed, they should be planted with herbaceous plants and trees to stabilize them.

Fig. 5–15. Gullies protected by brushwood in Spain. (Courtesy Henry S. Kernan)

Vegetative Control. No matter how expertly made, mechanical structures in themselves cannot stop erosion; they must be combined with proper vegetation controls. However, check dams, terraces, diversion channels, or other mechanical controls of runoff are frequently required for successful forestation of severely eroded areas. Although vegetative controls alone might halt erosion, no control method can succeed unless overgrazing, fire, and excessive cutting are eliminated. Removal of these initial causes is an administrative matter, but it must be done before control is attempted.

The basic principle of vegetative control is to establish a plant cover over the eroded area as quickly as possible. Even in humid zones it is difficult to find plants that will grow on the poor subsoil of badly eroded sites, and in arid zones the problem is compounded by scanty annual rainfall that is often received in one or two violent cloudbursts.

Grasses (e.g., *Saccharum aegyptiacum* Will. and *S. munja* Roxb.), vines or other herbaceous plants should be among the first to be planted on severely eroded and gullied sites. After these have become established, trees and shrubs may be planted over the entire area, including the gullies.

Species suitable for erosion-control plantings will usually be those of the temporary seral stages of succession, rather than those of climax species. Most hardwoods require some preparation of the site before planting, but many conifers can be planted successfully with little or no site preparation. On severely eroded sites, where the raw subsoil is exposed, it may be necessary to protect and improve the soil with a mulch of straw, litter, or animal manure to ensure establishment of trees and shrubs.

Suitable species for erosion control will vary from region to region and may include exotic as well as native species. In most places native species should be favored, but in a few localities some exotics, especially certain eucalypts, grow better than the indigenous species.

Many of the species recommended for general planting in the arid zone can be used in erosion control. However, the species listed below are among the most useful when planted in their proper climatic zone:

Acacia arabica Willd.
A. catechu Willd.
A. cyanophylla Lindl.
Casuarina spp.
Cupressus sempervirens var. *horizontalis* (Mill.) Loud.
Dalbergia sissoo Roxb.
Elaeagnus angustifolia L.
Eucalyptus camaldulensis Dehnh.
E. hemiphloia F. Muell.

E. occidentalis Endl.
Pinus spp.
Prosopis juliflora (Swartz) DC
Robinia pseudoacacia L.
Tamarix spp.

To control streambank erosion and to form live hedges in gully bottoms, easily rooted woody plants, such as *Dalbergia sissoo* Roxb. and various species of *Populus, Salix, Vitex,* and *Ficus,* are often established by planting unrooted cuttings.

Although spacing in erosion-control plantings is usually 1 m (3 ft) or less, it may be as much as 2.5 m (8 ft) and still produce an effective cover. Spacing should be close enough to achieve early crown closure, but not so close that the trees will be stunted or killed by competition.

Planting technique is essentially the same for erosion-control plantings as for other plantations in the same locality. If the entire catchment cannot be planted in one season, the highest portions should be planted first. All cultivation and planting lines should follow the contour. Because of the poor site, either potted or balled stock should be used. Fertilizing the trees when they are planted will improve survival.

The area must be fenced to exclude grazing animals and unnecessary travel across it by man. Increased protection from fire, disease, insects, and unauthorized use will be needed. It should never be assumed that a gully or an eroded area that has been planted has permanently healed and that protection is no longer needed. It takes centuries to develop even a thin layer of topsoil and for the vegetation permanently to stabilize soil movement.

Dune Fixation

Dunes, almost devoid of vegetation, constitute moving waste areas that are a constant menace to fertile soils, to towns and villages, to roads and railways, to telegraph lines, and to almost everything lying in their path (Fig. 5–16). Moving dunes may consist of coastal sand deposited by the sea, or they may be formed inland from sand produced by rock disintegration.

Coastal dunes are formed of sand thrown upon the shore by wave action during storms. When the sea recedes and the sand dries, it is picked up by the wind and blown away from the shore or along the coast.

Inland dunes are formed of sands produced by the weathering of rocks, mainly sandstones. The fine particles, such as silts formed by weathering, may be carried long distances away by the winds while the heavier and larger sand particles are moved only a short distance where they tend to accumulate and form dunes. Many regions of the world

Fig. 5–16. In Argentina, sand dunes that covered one road only 10 years before are menacing a new road more than 10 m (33 ft) higher up. (Courtesy Dr. J. Morello)

with dry climates are faced with the problem of sand dunes. Scarcity and variability of rainfall also contribute to dune formation because under such conditions vegetation is either absent or too sparse to bind and hold the sand in place.

Both coastal and inland dunes are usually low in fertility and present an extremely poor habitat for vegetation. Coastal dunes near salt water are saline, whereas inland dunes are usually alkaline with a pH range of 7 to 8.5. Both types of dunes carry hardly any organic matter and they are usually deficient in nitrogen, phosphorus, and potassium. Salty coastal dunes may support an open vegetation of scattered salt tolerant plants such as *Atriplex* spp., *Tamarix* spp., *Ammophila* spp., and *Artemisia* spp. Inland dunes, if not over-exploited may have scattered trees and shrubs such as species of *Acacia* and *Prosopis* and grasses such as *Ammophila* spp., and *Saccharum* spp.

Regrettably, man himself, is to a great extent, responsible for the destruction of vegetation which covers and protects the sands by unrestricted cutting of firewood and by permitting overgrazing by livestock. Once the vegetative cover is destroyed, the winds can start moving the unprotected dunes and threaten the existence of homes, cultivated fields, woodlands, and communications. To stop the movement of dunes one must establish a mantle of vegetation on them. Various species of grasses, shrubs, and trees can be planted on the dunes to give them the necessary protection from the wind.

When planning dune fixation, the forester must study the characteristics of the sand; the strength, frequency, and direction of the winds; the amount, duration, and distribution of rainfall; and the composition and density of the natural vegetation on or near the dunes. Usually, the movement of the dunes is related to some extent to one or more of these factors.

Sand holds moisture well. Even where the rainy season is only three months long and the total rainfall is less than 200 mm (8 in), moist sand may often be found at a depth of 50–60 cm (20–24 in). However, the infiltration rate of water into sand varies considerably with the degree of purity of the sand.

Sand movement is most pronounced during strong, dry winds, and great movement may occur during a short period of high velocity desiccating winds. When the atmosphere and the soil are the driest, sand is blown steadily over the surface by the prevailing winds. Where movement of sand hills was not checked, records show that some moved over 1 meter (3.3 ft) in a single month.

Technique of Fixation. The basic principle in dune fixation is to immobilize the sand long enough to enable either natural or planted vegetation to establish itself.

Sowing tree seeds directly on dunes has failed almost universally. The seed germinate freely while the sand is saturated with rain, but the seedlings are immediately cut off by the abrasive action of sand grains blown over the surface, or they are buried by drifting sand. One of the few examples of successful establishment by direct seeding has been carried out in Soviet Central Asia. There, *Haloxylon aphyllum* Minkw. and *H. ammodendron* Bunge have been established by sowing directly on the snow or on the soil immediately after the snow melts. The roots of the newly germinated seedlings follow the descending soil moisture until they reach the water table. Where the sand is immobilized by a snow cover this technique appears to be practical.

Natural vegetation will invade the dunes only if their movement is completely checked, and there is sufficient vegetation in the vicinity to supply seed. The usual practice is to erect long, low barriers of planks, branches, mats, sacks, or any other available material to check the movement of the sand. These barriers are usually about 1 m (3.3 ft) high. When a barrier is covered by the moving sand, it is raised or a new one is erected on the accumulated sand. Eventually a mound is built up that can provide shelter for plants on its leeside. Several lines of parallel barriers must be erected at close intervals [about 40 m (130 ft)

Fig. 5–17. Stems of *Imperata* spp. and *Aristata* spp. erected to form a grid-like barrier to stop the moving sand. *Acacia cyanophylla* Lindl. planted in center. (Courtesy FAO)

apart] and at right angles to the prevailing winds. If wind direction is variable, cross-barriers are erected, forming a grid pattern (Fig. 5–17). The sand within the grid squares is usually stable enough to allow any natural vegetation in the vicinity to seed in and establish itself. Grazing animals must be completely excluded, and the barriers must be well maintained until the vegetation has become established.

Occasionally, where there are trees and shrubs in the vicinity, the dunes have been covered with a light continuous layer of branches or cut shrubs merely scattered on the surface. Trees have then been planted in openings in the covering. Holes for planting are dug with wide-bladed mattocks or augers. Some plantations, especially of acacias, have been successful, but others have failed because the brush was blown away by the wind leaving the area without protection.

Instead of using non-living or dead materials (such as planks and branches) for the barriers, sand-binding grasses or cuttings of quick-growing trees and shrubs can be planted. These should be planted deep in the sand when it is wet and unlikely to move before the roots begin to spread. The planted rows should be closer together than the lines of mechanical barriers because vegetation gives less protection from the wind. Once the grasses or other plants have become established, they will soon spread and bind the sand. Grasses are able to maintain themselves by natural seeding.

Sand dunes can be immobilized by spraying them with crust-forming chemicals, such as bitumen, plastic, and polymeric emulsions. These chemicals are patented products and are sold under a variety of trade names. The instructions of the manufacturer should be carefully followed as to dilution strengths and other handling procedures. The crust formed by these chemicals is but a few millimeters thick and is brittle enough to allow germinating seedlings of dune grasses sown before spraying to emerge through it. The crusts are permeable to rain water after seedling emergence, but solid enough to hold the sand in place for up to 2–3 years, if it is not trampled on too much.

In Libya a bitumen mulch is sprayed on some areas before planting. Spraying is done immediately after a rain or a dew heavy enough to provide the soil moisture needed for seedling establishment. The equipment consists of a steel sled fitted with a large tank to hold the bitumen. Two long, antenna-like pipes with spraying nozzles extend from the tank to each side of the vehicle. The bitumen is heated to 80°C (176°F) before being pumped through the sprayers. A heavy duty tractor is used to pull the sled. The spray produces a continuous thin sheet of bitumen about 2 to 3 mm (0.08 to 0.12 in) thick and covers the surface of the sand in a strip up to 25 m (82 ft) wide. Usually about 5 hectares (12 acres) can be covered in a day, but under favorable conditions one unit can cover 10 hectares (25 acres) a day. From 2 to 4 tons of bitumen are required to cover 1 hectare (2.5 acres). The mulch lasts for about 3 years. Tree planting is done using conventional methods. Survival has ranged from about 50 to 70 percent. This method may result in satisfactory survival, but other vegetative cover does not grow in abundance and fixation of dunes is not as dependable as with traditional methods. With the increasing cost of petroleum products this method is likely to prove too expensive for widespread use.

Ammophila arenaria (L.) Link is one of the most successful binding grasses, but *Saccharum aegyptiacum* Will. and *S. munja* Roxb. are also planted extensively on bare dunes. *Ricinus communis* L., from which castor oil is obtained, has been used effectively on dunes in Morocco. *Calotropis procera* (Dryand.) Ait., *Calligonum* spp., and *Artemisia monosperma* Delile are other valuable plants for dune fixation. Fertilizers have been used in Australia to encourage quick growth of some grasses and a good response has been indicated. Nitrogen in the form of sulphate of ammonia [100 kg per ha (100 lb per acre)] applied to an

Ammophila plantation at the time of planting was found to be the most economical method of application.

Although pre-fixation is still part of the standard control method, recently developed techniques may make it unnecessary in many localities. It has been found that the early failures on bare sand occurred chiefly because most of the plants used were too small, and they were either completely buried or their roots were exposed when the sand blew away. However, if large stock, 0.8–1.2 m (2.5–4 ft) tall is planted with 40–60 cm (16–24 in) in the sand and about 40 cm above ground, the normal movement of the sand is rarely great enough to cover the plants or to expose their roots.

The plants, such as *Acacia cyanophylla* Lindl., that are to be used in the new method should be grown in temporary nurseries located among the dunes where water is available and where there is some protection from the wind (Fig. 5–18). The seedlings are started in cans and, as soon as practicable, transplanted into pots filled with a mixture of soil, sand, and manure. Copious irrigation is required, and to conserve water the pots should be sunk into the sand to reduce evaporation. By the end of the year the seedlings will be over 1 m (3.3 ft) high, and the soil in the pots will be filled with a dense mass of roots. Early in the second half of the rainy season the plants can be transported in the pots to the planting site. After the seedling is removed from the pot, the ball of roots should be soaked in water. The seedling is then

Fig. 5–18.   Sand-dune nursery in Gaza.

planted with its roots at the bottom of a pit, 40–60 cm (16–24 in) deep, which is then filled with sand to ground level. This leaves about 40 cm of the top above ground. Recommended spacing is 2.5 × 2.5 m (8 ft), or about 1,600 plants per hectare (650/a).

Other techniques were used to establish the Euramericana hybrid poplars, ×*Populus euramericana* (Dode) Guinier and I-214, on active dunes in Yugoslavia and in the Argentine pampas under an annual rainfall of 500 to 750 mm (20 to 30 in). Holes 8 cm (3 in) in diameter and 1.5 to 2.0 m (4.9 to 6.6 ft.) deep were dug with soil augers at a spacing of 5 x 5 m (16 x 16 ft). Poplar plants 4 m (13 ft) tall were inserted into these holes and the sand stamped back into the holes with the heel. The moisture retained near the roots at depths over 1.5 m (5 ft) is adequate for good growth. These plants can tolerate wind and shifting sand and in about 3 years the dunes are stabilized. One man can carry out the entire planting operation. Where this method is to be used, it should first be tried on a small area to make sure that the water table is not too deep to supply moisture to the roots.

This method of planting tall, potted plants in deep pits has proved to be economic because all the costly pre-fixation of the dunes is unnecessary, and the costs of maintenance and replacement are greatly reduced.

Choice of Species. The first stage of dune fixation is complete when sand movement has been checked; this can generally be accomplished within three years of planting. By this time, if the area is well protected, a deep layer of leaves and twigs transformed into humus will have been deposited. With careful management and if climate permits, the dunes may be planted with more valuable species. The species selected should be those that will not only produce firewood, charcoal, tanning materials, poles or posts, or be useful to beekeepers in the locality, but under favorable conditions, also produce timber.

Tree species for dune planting must be capable of growing in dry sand which is deficient in nutrients and which has a great fluctuation of surface temperature. They must be able to withstand wind, abrasive action of moving sand, and, if near the sea, salinity. The seaward edge of plantations is always ragged and windblown. Within the protection of the first few rows of scrubby trees, taller trees may be established close to the sea, but once they grow appreciably above the protection of the seaward trees, their leaders will be killed. Thus, beginning with the short scrubby trees near the shore, tree heights increase inland to near normal, producing a distinctive, streamlined stand profile.

Species suitable for dune fixation must also be highly drought-resistant and have well-developed root systems capable of deep vertical penetration to reach the lower moist layers of soil, or produce roots with considerable horizontal spread which can take maximum advantage of the scanty precipitation and surface condensation. Choice of tall species must be limited to those that develop deep root systems and are wind-firm. The species chosen must also be capable of withstanding frost or high temperature, or both; many xerophytes that have been tried have failed because they were not hardy.

Plants that have been successfully used for dune fixation are *Acacia* spp. (especially *A. cyanophylla* Lindl.), *Tamarix aphylla* (L.) Karst., *Pinus pinea* L., *Elaeagnus angustifolia* L., *Haloxylon aphyllum* Minkw., and *H. ammodendron* Bunge (Fig. 5–19). Other species may be success-ful under the special conditions that prevail in certain kinds of sand, but surprisingly the only eucalypt that has been reported to give good re-sults is *E. gomphocephala* A. DC, planted in Morocco.

In Cyprus, *Pinus pinea* L. is preferred over *P. brutia* Ten. for plant-ing on fixed sands because it is straighter and more resistant to wind damage. Experiments are being carried out in most arid-zone countries with many untried species, especially with various Australian mallees. These are short, multiple-stemmed eucalypts that grow mainly in sands and in the deserts. In a foredune plantation in Tunisia where the rainfall is about 700 mm (28 in) a year *Pinus pinea* L. produced 3 to 4 cu m/ha/yr (43 to 57 cu ft/A/yr) and *Eucalyptus gomphocephala* A. DC 8 cu m/ha/yr (114 cu ft/A/yr).

Where temperatures do not drop to freezing, the slow-growing *Proso-pis spicigera* L. may be planted; it may yield leaf fodder and fuel.

Fig. 5–19. Planting rooted stock of *Haloxylon ammodendron* Bunge on dunes in Kazakhstan, USSR.

Other species of *Prosopis* have been planted on dunes in several widely separated countries. Some species bear pods which are valuable as fodder, others produce only fuelwood.

In Kazakhastan, U.S.S.R. *Salix caspica* Pall., a quick growing shrub up to 3 m (10 ft) in height, is extensively used for dune fixation where underground moisture is not too deep. *Tamarix ramosissima* Ledeb., *T. laxa* Willd., and *T. szovitsiana* Bunge are salt tolerant species that are planted in this region to control moving sands and as windbreaks. When the branches of these tamarisks are covered by sand, they produce adventitious roots and numerous shoots so that in time the plant develops into a large, abundantly branched shrub. Blowing sand which is caught in the branches, builds up into a mound that may reach a diameter and height of 10 m (33 ft). In Mongolia where fresh water is near the surface, *Salix matsudana* Koidz. has been planted to fix moving dunes and for production of timber and fuel. In Afghanistan *Tamarix laxa* Willd. and *T. leptostachis* Bunge have been planted extensively on sands.

Stabilization of Mining Waste

Underground Mining. In the arid zones of many countries, mining has created enormous piles of broken or pulverized rock waste from which the minerals have been extracted. These waste dumps remain barren and, unless stabilized, threaten to bury the neighboring fields and buildings by slippage or by wind and water erosion. Mine dumps are among the most difficult sites to vegetate even in humid climates, and in arid zones they present the extreme in adverse conditions. The rock material composing the dumps ranges in size from the texture of coarse sand to clay. In some strip-mined areas, it may consist of large stones and large, jagged rock fragments. All of the material is sterile, completely devoid of organic matter, and with poor water-holding capacity. In low rainfall zones nearly all the precipitation it receives evaporates, leaving behind an accumulation of harmful chemicals near the surface. Waste material is typically strongly acid; the low pH resulting from the oxidation of iron pyrites or other minerals. If the mine dump is composed of sand-like material, this tends to blow over the surface, cutting off any trees that may be planted.

The technique of establishing vegetation on mine dumps is, in many respects, similar to that employed in dune fixation. Plants cannot be grown on the dumps until the severe adverse conditions are ameliorated. The acidity can be reduced, or neutralized, by sowing lime over the area just before planting. Because of extreme dryness, and in order to leach the harmful chemicals from the surface layers, irrigation may be required during the early stages of establishing a vegetative cover. However, to prevent further erosion the water must be applied at an exceedingly slow rate—a rate that does not exceed the rate of infiltration. Blowing of the fine rock material over the surface can be prevented by erecting low mechanical barriers, the same as is done in dune fixation. On some dumps in South Africa, the cut stems of reeds have been thrust into the ground to form low, parallel, closely-spaced windbreaks along the contours. A second series of windbreaks is made at right angles to the first series and extends up and down the slope. Thus, the two series divide the entire area to be vegetated into hundreds of small paddocks.

The first cover plants should be mainly grasses and spreading legumes. After the surface is stabilized, trees may be introduced. The vegetation will gradually add organic material to the substratum, eventually producing a "soil" capable of supporting vegetation indigenous to the surrounding region.

Experiments in vegetating some gold-mine dumps in South Africa have been quite encouraging. Several mine dumps have apparently been successfully vegetated using the site improvement measures described and direct seeding with a mixture containing many species. This mixture contained clover and other herbaceous legumes, some 16 species of grasses including grains that served as nurse plants, and two tree species. The two tree species were *Acacia baileyana* F. Muell. and *A. melanoxylon* R. Br. which after four years had become established in sufficient numbers to form a park-like stand.

Surface Mining. Revegetation of surface mined areas is especially difficult in arid zones, but if such areas are not treated, they may remain barren for decades. Problems associated with coal mining illustrate those associated with surface mining of other minerals. Coal seams are buried from a few to several meters under an "overburden" of soil and rock. The overburden is removed by enormous power shovels and piled down-slope from the coal seam, creating a series of parallel ridges of overburden ("spoil") bordered by a final, deep, unfilled cut. Spoil consists of boulders and broken rocks, nearly devoid of fine particles. Spoil usually has a pH below 5 and is deficient in available plant nutrients, especially nitrogen. Information on treatment of surfaced mined areas in arid zones is scanty, but the following procedures can be recommended: (1) Remove the topsoil and stockpile it for future use. (2) Shape and smooth the spoil banks and fill in the cuts. Make sure that the sites have proper drainage to prevent ponding after heavy rains. Terrace and contour strip the slopes to prevent erosion and to harvest the available water. (3) Spread the topsoil over the prepared area as evenly as possible. (4) Fertilize the planting sites based on deficiencies shown by soil analyses. Heavy applications of nitrogen and probably phosphorus will be required. These should be applied in prilled (pelleted) form rather than in solution. (5) Use container stock and follow the procedures recommended for erosion control. Mulching or use of plastic aprons is highly desirable. (6) Irrigate immediately after planting; plants will probably require watering during the first year or two. Drip irrigation is recommended due to its economical use of water.

Though it may often be necessary to revegetate spoil banks as quickly as possible using grasses, these will compete severely with shrubs or trees that may be planted later. So where erosion is not a problem, woody plants can be planted directly on the site. The following are suggested for trial within their respective temperature zones: black locust, acacia, green ash, Russian-olive, pea tree, hybrid poplars, junipers, and pine. The legumes should be planted first and underplanted later with other species. On extremely arid sites choice will be limited to desert shrubs such as species of *Atriplex, Artemisia, Chrysothamnus, Ephedra,* and *Sarcobatus.*

Afforestation of surface mined areas is extremely expensive and is undertaken primarily to reduce erosion, sedimentation, and water pollution, and to improve aesthetics. However, in time, many treated areas should yield some minor products such as fuelwood and also provide cover for wildlife and areas for recreational use by the public.

Swampland Plantations

The purpose of planting trees in swampy areas is to produce timber on land that will otherwise remain unproductive. Poorly drained soils may be found on wet plains, in swamps, and frequently along the margins of lakes and rivers. Such soils occur in virtually all arid-zone countries. These soils tend to have a high organic content, often deposited as peat. Because soil moisture in the hot arid zones is the most critical factor in good growth, these moist lands, if properly planted, may produce high yields. In fact, almost continuous growth may be expected on permanently moist, or even periodically flooded, lands.

Planting in swampland should be preceded by a soil analysis that will disclose the nature of the soil solution. Brackish or saline swamps are found in many places in the arid zones, and the composition and amount of soluble salts will determine the possibility of afforestation and greatly influence the choice of species.

Few species can grow on swampy soil with their roots in stagnant water. Consequently, the afforestation of bogs and swamps should be preceded by the construction of a properly planned and carefully engineered drainage system. Success in planting swamps usually depends on whether or not the topography of the surrounding area will permit their drainage into a permanent watercourse. Often the swamps may be drained and thus made highly productive by digging ditches in a simple herringbone pattern. These conduct the water into the main discharge ditch which traverses the lowest levels of the bog.

Many different species of tamarisk, all of them tall shrubs or trees, may succeed on slightly saline soil without drainage. *Acacia cyanophylla* Lindl., *Eucalyptus gomphocephala* A. DC, *E. occidentalis* Endl., and *E. cornuta* Labill. can tolerate salinity up to 5,000 parts per million. *Prosopis tamarugo* F. Phil. and some other species of *Prosopis* do well on highly saline areas. These species produce pods that are valuable for fodder.

However, the afforestation of swamps can be justified economically only on non-saline soils because only on these soils can good yields be expected. Suitable species for non-saline swamps include *Taxodium distichum* (L.) Rich., *Casuarina equisetifolia* Forst., and some eucalypts, such as *Eucalyptus camaldulensis* Dehnh., *E. robusta* Sm., *E. saligna* Sm., *E. sideroxylon* A. Cunn., *E. hemiphloia* F. Muell., *E. globulus* Labill., *Dalbergia sissoo* Roxb., and *Acacia arabica* Willd.

The most valuable forestry use of many wet lands after drainage is for poplar plantations, provided the proper species or clones can be found for the particular zone and conditions. Willows found growing naturally in a locality are frequently useful indicators of the suitability of the site for poplars. Poplars normally require deep alluvial soil for rapid growth to timber size, but such soils when drained are, of course, also suitable for agricultural crops. If there is need for arable land, poplars may be restricted to rows along the canals, or to windbreaks, or plantings in odd corners.

Soil preparation for planting begins by establishing the necessary drainage system. Open drains may be dug by hand, using spades for cutting the sides and for lifting and spreading the cut soil. Drains may also be cut by large, tractor-drawn plows. The smallest drains are usually 25–30 cm (10–12 in) deep. The slope of the drain should be about 2 per cent so that the water collected will flow by gravity into the larger discharge channels. If possible, the drains should be constructed parallel to each other with the distance between drains varying according to the amount of water to be removed.

After drainage, the remaining vegetative cover should be burned before the area is planted. Wherever possible, drainage should precede planting by several months. Planting is done in the usual way, but special care must be taken to clear all vegetation from around the planted trees by repeated hoeings because weeds grow profusely in these wet areas and are likely to suppress the newly-planted seedlings. Ditches must be kept clear for proper drainage because the roots of most trees will not develop if the soil is waterlogged for a long period.

The fight against malaria is closely associated with swamp afforestation. If the soil is effectively drained, the growing trees will use any excess water, and the area eventually will become unfavorable for breeding of mosquitoes.

Plantations on Saline Soils

A characteristic of arid zone soils of great importance is the presence of salts, mainly of Na, Mg, and K, which at times form hardpans at or just below the surface of the soil. Where these salts occur in the soil horizons, improper irrigation, clearing land for cultivation, and overgrazing can reduce productivity of the soil. Capillary action and fluctuations of the water table bring the dissolved salts to the surface or just below it where the salts are deposited when the water evaporates. Due to such salt deposits, many areas that produced agricultural crops in Iraq, Australia, and California had to be abandoned because they were no longer suitable for agriculture.

Some of the areas described above and areas that are naturally saline can be planted to forest trees, if the amount of salt in the soil is not too great and the salt is not toxic in weak concentrations. However, one should avoid planting in saline soils whenever possible becase of the difficulties in preparing the soil. In order to reduce the concentration of salts, it is advisable wherever possible to flush or wash out the salts by flooding the area with fresh water, then after the water has soaked through the soil to plow and plant. Where salt pans are thin and near the surface, and where the lower horizons are not too salty, planting holes can be dug through the pans. Species which are resistant or tolerant to salt must be selected for planting in such areas. Not all species are equally tolerant to the same salts or to the same amount of a given salt in the soil.

Species recommended for planting on saline soils include: *Callitris glauca* R. Br., *Conocarpus lancifolius* Engl., *Elaeagnus angustifolia* L., *Eucalyptus brockwayi* C. A. Gardner, *E. dundasi* Maiden, *E. gomphocephala* A. DC, *E. gracilis* F. Muell., *E. occidentalis* Endl., *E. oleosa* F. Muell., *E. salmonophloia* F. Muell., *E. salubris* F. Muell., *E. sargenti* Maiden, *E. spathulata* Hook., *Gleditsia triacanthos* L., *Haloxylon ammodendron* Bunge, *Prosopis tamarugo* F. Phil., *Salvadora persica* L., *Tamarix gallica* L., and *Zizyphus jujuba* Lam.

AMENITY PLANTATIONS

Amenity plantations include planting to beautify the landscape, parks for recreation, and roadside plantations. Such plantations are made popular by governments and societies by declaring "Arbor Days," by the distribution of pamphlets, and by writing articles in the press on the subject. Such propaganda is used to get public cooperation. Without popular cooperation such plantations have little chance of success.

In an arid zone, "beautifying" the landscape usually means changing the countryside from its normal brown color to green, or "greening" of the landscape.

Parks for Recreation

Areas with special natural scenic beauty are in many places developed, managed, and protected as recreation grounds or parks. Where such natural parks are not available, recreation grounds may be established by converting natural forests or plantations or by planting trees on suitable areas. Parks of this kind are in great demand in arid zones. These parks should be planned to conform to the demand and tastes of the local inhabitants and of the tourists who come to enjoy the park and contribute to the economy of the area.

The most obvious requirement of recreation grounds in arid zones is for shelter from the sun and dust. Where trees are not growing naturally, shelter may be provided by planting trees in favorable sites. However, it should be pointed out that the view taken by some people that planting a bare area with trees or shrubs (i.e. "greening" the area) makes it more beautiful is not shared by everyone. Many who live in deserts prefer a bare landscape, and even some who live in forested areas prefer open vistas. Yet people who live in an area devoid of trees often learn to appreciate the beauty of planted trees and to appreciate the comfort they give without having to rationalize the presence of trees as an attraction to increase tourism. With these facts in mind, suitable areas of reasonable size that have scenic or historic value should be reserved and developed by planting trees to meet society's needs for recreation.

Although it is generally agreed that judicious tree planting under most circumstances beautifies the view, it does not follow that beauty is achieved by every forest plantation. Certainly planting row after row of one or two tree species over large areas, broken only at intervals by firebreaks, is not an ideal way to improve the aesthetics of a locality. Such plantations are not only unnatural but monotonous. If such areas are to be converted into parks, silvicultural practices must aim toward improving them aesthetically.

The needs and fancies of people change so rapidly and often so drastically that predicting what their requirements might be by the time a new plantation is mature is usually impossible. Many woods planted early in this century to produce fuel are being converted to satisfy other needs because better, cheaper, or more convenient fuels are available in the area. Changes in the silvicultural treatment of plantations must be made continuously to harmonize with the changing demands and styles of society. For example, recreation is emerging as a major forest use in many arid areas.

The Changa-Manga plantation in Pakistan was established to supply fuel to the railway, but now the plantation is an intensively managed, multiple-use forest with recreation as its greatest contribution. Thousands of people come to picnic and rest in the area every year. In Israel tens of thousands of hectares that were planted with forest trees, primarily to supply small sawlogs and poles and to beautify the scenery, have, to a great extent, been converted to parks for the enjoyment of the local population and tourists.

In general, chaparral and scrub vegetation does not provide adequate or good recreational opportunities. However, in California, in response to public demand, foresters and land managers have been able to transform some sites within the chaparral type into attractive picnic areas and campgrounds. Sites selected are either "ecological islands" within the chaparral or former timber sites which were clearcut and invaded by brush. Such sites are suitable for planting shade trees including species with attractive foliage and flowers. Wherever possible, these small parks are located near roads and a good water supply that can be economically developed.

In preparing these sites for planting the brush must be removed and the soil thoroughly prepared using machinery. Trees are planted at 3×3 m (10×10 ft) spacing and the area kept free of weeds for at least three years after planting. A clean plantation reduces the fire hazard in this area of high risk and thus helps to insure the success of the project. The size of the area should be no larger than can be adequately taken care of with existing personnel and resources. Species of proven adaptability to dry sites are used, but there still is some mortality and so each spring before new sites are planted the losses in the previous year's plantings are fully replaced. In just a few years the area is turned into an attractive new recreation ground.

The task of the forester in converting a natural forest and especially a plantation into a recreation area is not usually easy because often the existing species on the site and their arrangement and spacing are not suited for the new objective. To convert natural forests, which are usually badly degraded in arid zones, or to transform a plantation into a park requires great skill. The aim should be to create a stand which will appear to the public to be a natural forest. Sites in a dense plantation to accommodate campers can be created by thinning, but these sites to be aesthetically acceptable should give the appearance of natural openings. Disturbances arising from misuse of campfires or trampling of vegetation must be controlled so that they will not permanently damage the flora and fauna of the area.

Most people prefer a mixture of shrubs and trees. In most places one can usually find several suitable shrub and tree species of different colors, shapes, and heights from which to choose and which will blend with the natural landscape. Clumps of trees of varying sizes and shapes together with large and small open spaces to fit the natural contours are usually more pleasing to the eye than unbroken forests. Choice of species should not be dictated by the value of the trees for timber, nor planting expenses weighed by the value of the wood produced. Costs of turning a plantation, especially one which is poor aesthetically, into a recreation ground are high. Improving the landscape may enhance land values, but economic justification of recreational areas must increasingly take into account aesthetic benefits and the intangible gains in the health and well-being of the people.

Trees may be cut in such areas if, by cutting them, the landscape is improved. The felled trees should be utilized, if possible, but trees must not be cut just because their product is needed or has an economic value.

To accommodate picnickers and campers, roads, paths, camping sites, fresh water sources, fireplaces, sanitation facilities, tables, and benches must be provided in the parks. These should be so designed that they will harmonize with the newly created landscape.

Roadside Plantations

Many reasons may be cited for planting trees on roadsides between towns and in the towns themselves. Trees increase the comfort of travellers by providing shade and attractive surroundings, and they also relieve monotony, an especially important reason in arid zones. Although most people generally find all trees pleasant and agreeable to view, individual tastes differ and planting should not be limited to a single species. Where practicable, species having foliage and flowers that exhibit a broad range of colors at different times of the year should be chosen. These may be planted in groups or in desired mixtures. Trees may also be used to introduce contrasts and to screen unattractive fields, as well as to beautify the vista and make a locality more attractive. Roadside trees may occasionally become an important factor by alleviating an unforeseen timber shortage. In fact, roadside trees are frequently considered a part of the national forest-planting program. Such trees may be managed and harvested by sections of the road on a rotation determined by a management plan.

Traffic is aided by proper planning so that the trees will mark the direction and width of the road. They may protect the road itself against moving sand or act as a windbreak for adjacent fields. Trees along roads may produce edible fruit, yield pods for feeding animals, furnish food and shelter for birds, or, when in bloom, be valuable in beekeeping.

Species should be carefully chosen. Only native trees, or exotics whose value has been tested, should be selected to meet the principal objective for the planting. At times, it is difficult to meet both the aesthetic and the economic objective, but a compromise can usually be found. Meeting the aesthetic objective is much less of a problem in arid zones where trees are few because any tree that is planted cannot fail to add to the beauty of the landscape.

To be adaptable to roadside planting, a species should:

1. Be suitable to the soil and climate of the area so that it will have good growth and a healthy appearance.
2. Be able to grow in the open, often on soil modified during road building.
3. Be capable of developing a strong root system, but should not develop roots which may hamper road traffic, nor should the roots spread into the neighboring fields or cause damage to drains or to foundations of buildings.
4. Be resistant to damage by automobile exhaust gases.
5. Be resistant to parasites and climatic agents, such as direct sunshine, heat, wind, or snow.
6. Be easy to establish, have fast growth, and be of uniform shape.
7. Have full crowns; but if the trees have branchless boles, more than one row should be planted, so that the patches of light between the boles, which may be dazzling to drivers, are eliminated.
8. Be resistant to damage arising from road accidents.
9. Produce timber or other economically important products.
10. Not reproduce from suckers.

Only a few species meet these requirements and are considered suitable for roadside planting in arid zones. In mountainous areas, conifers, plane trees, and poplars are generally used. In the plains, with 400–500 mm (16–20 in) of rain annually, poplars, carob, and species of *Casuarina, Grevillea, Eucalyptus, Fraxinus,* and *Robinia* are often planted; although some of these species may need supplementary irrigation. Under more arid conditions, *Tamarix* spp. and some species of *Eucalyptus, Acacia,* and *Prosopis* may be planted.

Often the only purpose of roadside planting is to beautify the landscape and make living conditions more pleasant. Every species has its own particular value in this type of planting, but in arid zones the choice is limited to relatively few. Where flowering trees are desired, *Delonix regia* (Bojer) Raf., species of *Jacaranda, Melia, Cassia, Tecoma, Grevillea, Acacia,* and some of the eucalypts might be planted.

In the parts of the semiarid zone having the most rainfall, deciduous trees are preferred because they interfere less with the drying of the road after rains. In the drier parts, evergreens may safely be planted because storms are brief and are almost always followed by dry weather. If roads are likely to be slippery when wet, the trees should not overhang the roadway too much because they will hamper drying. Overhanging can be avoided either by planting the trees farther from the road or by using trees with fastigiate crowns.

Although modern taste is inclined to favor irregularity and variety in roadside planting, in order to simplify management a single species is often grown over long stretches of a roadway.

Because of the close relationship between road construction and maintenance of roadside trees, cooperation between public-utility departments and the departments in charge of roadside planting is essential. Such cooperation is particularly important when planning the layout of the plantation to make certain that the trees will not interfere with telephone and telegraph lines, sewers, water mains, or other public utilities.

Planting trees with a small interval between them and close to the road should be avoided. Trees should be planted far enough from the road to permit the road to be widened, if this becomes necessary, and with sufficient distance between trees for construction of culverts. The distance between trees in the row will depend on species and many other factors, but the average is about 6 m (20 ft), and this distance is recommended for most plantings. The interval chosen for the final spacing may appear to be too wide when the plants are young; if this is true, a faster growing species may be planted between the main trees as a temporary measure. The temporary trees should be removed long before they can adversely affect the growth of the trees in the main planting.

Allowance for maximum visibility on curves and at crossings should be made when designing the layout. If two or more rows of trees are to be planted on each side, the rows should be far enough apart to permit mechanical cultivation; crowding must be avoided. Because conventional shade avenues may prove to be inordinately expensive or even impracticable, it is considered better to adopt a system of shade groves at reasonable intervals along the road. Their aesthetic effect can be very striking in a flat and otherwise barren landscape.

Two- or three-year-old conifers may be planted, although such seedlings are quite small. Most broad-leaved species one or two years old are large plants, and such plants are recommended where they might be damaged by browsing cattle or broken and mutilated by people, especially by children at play.

After planting, the trees should be protected by tree guards from possible injury. Tree guards should be strong and well anchored in the ground. They are made to protect the trees for a long period and are subject to destruction by traffic, grazing animals, children, and adverse weather. Guards are usually made of metal strips or wooden laths. In some places, metal drums, open at both the top and bottom, are placed over the young trees; the sides of the drums are perforated to permit aeration. Brick towers, with many openings in the sides, are commonly built around newly planted trees. Occasionally, after a tree is planted, a trench 1 m (3.3 ft) wide and 1 m deep is dug around the tree, isolating it on an island of soil. Thorny branches may be placed in the trench, or on the island, for added protection against goats and camels. In places, thorny plants, such as *Euphorbia* spp., *Opuntia* spp., and some acacias, are planted along the roadside where trees are to be established. When these thorny plants become large enough to give protection, trees are planted in their midst (Fig. 5–20). When the tree outgrows the protecting plants, the thorny plants are killed.

Trees should be protected against wind by binding them to steadying stakes. When securing the tree to a stake, slack should be left in the ties to allow for wind movement.

Fig. 5–20.   A catalpa tree protected by cacti (*Opuntia*) in Ethiopia. (Photo A. J. Urbanovski)

Rapid growth is usually desirable so that the protective effect will be quickly obtained. A young tree occupies so much less space than a fully grown one that it is often difficult to envisage its mature form. It is even more difficult to picture the root system; however, arid-zone trees generally need considerably more space below the ground for their roots than is required above ground for their crowns.

Quick growth may be obtained by watering saplings during the first two years. This is usually done with rubber hoses connected to a tanker. About four to six waterings per year should be given and each tree should receive about 10 liters (2.6 gal) of water at each watering. In arid zones, trees may have to be irrigated throughout the rotation. Swift development may also be stimulated by manuring.

Thorns or brittle branches, such as those of some eucalypts, are likely to cause accidents. The peculiarities of the tree species used should be known. Laws on the responsibility of owners for any injury or nuisance which trees may cause should be carefully studied before plans for roadside and other amenity plantations are completed.

Noise-Abating Screens

Loud noise from road traffic, factories in residential areas, recreation areas, and schools is a form of environmental debasement popularly called "noise pollution." Such noise is extremely disturbing and may be harmful to the health of persons in the afflicted areas. Trees planted in such areas and along highways can greatly reduce the noise of machinery and traffic when it is projected through them. To accomplish this, a screen of shrubs backed up by tall, dense-crowned trees has been found to be quite effective. There does not appear to be much difference among species in their ability to reduce noise levels, provided that the deciduous varieties are in full leaf. For the best results trees and shrubs should be planted close to the noise source rather than close to the area that needs shielding. A distance of at least 30 m (100 ft) between the noise source and the area to be protected is desirable. The recommended width of noise-suppressing tree belts varies with the intensity of the noise, but ordinarily it should be from 6 to 30 m (20 to 100 ft).

AIR POLLUTION AND SELECTION OF TREE SPECIES

Air pollution in some areas near population centers or heavily traveled highways is known to cause serious damage to plant life. Estimates of economic losses due to air pollution are difficult to make; this is especially true of damage to amenity and landscape plantings where the aesthetic values are incalculable. In many arid areas where industrial settlements have developed around mining operations or where factories and smelters emit toxic fumes into the air as in Broken Hills, Australia and near the oil refineries of the Middle East, there is a desire by the inhabitants to plant parks and shelterbelts of trees to make life more pleasant. Unfortunately, the planted trees, whether indigenous or exotic, may be badly damaged by the polluted air. The most serious effects of toxic gases on trees are usually within a radius of about 10 km (6 mi) from the source, but may extend up to 100 or even 200 km (60–120 mi) away depending upon the type of gases, their concentration, and the wind direction.

The major chemical toxicants that pollute the air are: sulfur dioxide, ozone, fluorides, peroxycal nitrates, ethylene, chlorine, hydrogen chloride, and oxides of nitrogen. Sensitive plants can be injured by sulfur dioxide when its concentration in the air exceeds 0.7 ppm for 1 hour.

Air pollutants damage the leaf tissues through chemical action. The general characteristics that aid in the diagnosis of the injury are premature color changes, premature leaf or flower drop, reduced vigor, or stunted growth. These symptoms are easily confused with those produced by other causal factors. Injury to evergreen trees by pollutants is generally more drastic than injury to deciduous trees because the toxicants or their derivatives can accumulate in leaves of evergreens for from two to several years, whereas deciduous trees renew their foliage each year with leaves free from pollutant material.

Tree species appear to vary considerably in their susceptibility and sensitivity to different atmospheric pollutants, but little is known about the relative degree of tolerance of tree species to the different toxicants. Some species are able to withstand light concentrations of sulphur dioxide and chlorine when planted in industrial areas; among these are *Ailanthus altissima* (Mill.) Swingle, *Elaeagnus angustifolia* L., *Eucalyptus* spp., *Fraxinus* spp., *Juniperus* spp., *Platanus occidentalis* L., *Robinia pseudoacacia* L., and *Ulmus* spp.

When introducing exotic species into an area with badly polluted air, a few trees of each species should be planted and tested until their tolerance has been determined.

Some tree species successfully grown in hot and arid zone groves and parks are:

Acacia cyanophylla Lindl., *A. melanoxylon* R. Br., *A. pycnantha* Benth.†, *A. salicina* Lindl.†,
Brachychiton populneum (Schott) R. Br.,
Callitris glauca R. Br.*,
Casuarina equisetifolia Forst.,
Cedrus atlantica Manetti, *C. deodara* (Roxb.) Loud.,

Celtis australis L.,
Ceratonia siliqua L.,
Cupressus arizonica Greene, *C. sempervirens* L.,
  Dalbergia sissoo Roxb.,
Delonix regia (Bojer) Raf.,
Elaeagnus angustifolia L.*,
Eucalyptus brockwayi C. A. Gardner*†, *E. camaldulensis* Dehnh., *E. dundasi* Maiden*†, *E. gomphocephala* A. DC*, *E. gracilis* F. Muell.*, *E. occidentalis* Endl.*, *E. oleosa* F. Muell.†, *E. salmonophloia* F. Muell.*, *E. salubris* F. Muell.*†, *E. sargenti* Maiden*, *E. spathulata* Hook.*, *E. torquata* J. G. Luehm.*,
Ficus benjamina L.,
Grevillea robusta A. Cunn.,
Jacaranda mimosaefolia D. Don,
Juniperus communis L.,
Melia azedarach L.,
Parkinsonia aculeata L.†,
Pinus brutia Ten., *P. halepensis* Mill.,
Pistacia lentiscus L.,
Prosopis juliflora (Swartz) DC†,
Robinia pseudoacacia L.,
Schinus molle L.†, *S. terebenthifolius* Raddi,
Tamarix aphylla (L.) Karst., *T. gallica* L.*†,
Ulmus pumila L.†,
Zizyphus spina-christi (L.) Willd.

* In saline soils.
† In the more arid zones.

BIBLIOGRAPHY

ANDERSON, P. O. Planting the standard windbreak. Minn. Univ. Agric. Ext. Serv.
  1937   Spec. Bull. 168. St. Paul. 8 p.
ARNEMAN, F. F. Fertilization of forest trees. Adv. Agron. 12:171–195.
  1960
BAGNOLD, R. A. The physics of blown sand and desert dunes. 2nd ed. Methuen,
  1954   London. 265 p.
BALCH, R. E. Forest entomology: IV. Silvicultural control. Pages 193–204 *in* Proc.
  1963   Spec. Field Inst. For. Biol. 1960. Sch. For. N. C. State Coll., Raleigh.
BALDWIN, M., *et al.* Soil conservation, an international study. FAO Agric. Stud. 4.
  1948   Food Agric. Organ. U. N., Washington, D. C. 189 p.
BATES, C. G. The windbreak as a farm asset. U. S. Dep. Agric. Farmers' Bull. 1405
  1944   rev. Washington, D. C. 22 p.
BATES, C. G., and R. G. PIERCE. Forestation of the sand hills of Nebraska and
  1913   Kansas. U. S. Dep. Agric. For. Serv. Bull. 121. Washington, D. C. 49 p.
BENGSTON, G. W. Fertilizer use in forestry: Part I. Materials available and in
  1973   prospect. FAO/IUFRO Int. Symp. For. Fert. Paris 3–7 Dec. 1973. FOR:
            FAO/IUFRO/F/73/25. Food Agric. Organ. U. N., Rome. 21 plus 5 p.
———. Fertilizer use in foresty: Part II. Developments and trends in application
  1973   methods. FAO/IUFRO Int. Symp. For. Fert. Paris 3–7 Dec. 1973. FOR:

FAO/IUFRO/F/73/26. Food Agric. Organ. U. N., Rome. 14 p. plus 13 fig.

BENNETT, H. H. Soil conservation. McGraw-Hill, New York. 993 p.
1939

BHIMAYA, C. P., R. N. KAUL, and B. N. GANGULI. Sand dune rehabilitation in west-
[1962] ern Rajasthan. Proc. World For. Congr. (Seattle 1960) 5(1):358–363.

BOOTH, G. Afforestation of sandy soils in arid zones, with particular reference to the
1968 Republic of Sudan. FAO Seminar on Heathland and Sand-Dune Silviculture, Denmark 23 June–19 July 1968. Food Agric. Organ. U. N., Rome.
9 p.

———. Shelterbelts in arid zones. FAO Seminar on Heathland and Sand-Dune
1968 Silviculture, Denmark 23 June–19 July 1968. Food Agric. Organ. U. N.,
Rome. 4 p.

BOSSHARD, W. C. Irrigation methods in Khartoum greenbelt. Sudan For. Dep. For.
1966 Res. Inst. Pam. 21. Soba, Khartoum, Sudan. 23 p.

BURG, J. VAN DEN, and C. P. VAN GOOR. The influence of fertilizers on tree growth
1973 and their interaction with factors of the site. FAO/IUFRO Int. Symp. For.
Fert. Paris 3–7 Dec. 1973. FOR: FAO/IUFRO/F/73/30. Food Agric.
Organ. U. N., Rome. [12] p.

CABORN, J. M. Shelterbelts and microclimate. Great Britain For. Comm., Bull. 29.
1957 Edinburgh. 135 p.

———. Width and cross-sectional profile in shelterbelts. Int. Union For. Res.
1958 Organ., 12th Congr. Oxford 1956, Papers vol. 1:5–11.

CANO SÁINZ-TRÁPAGA, B. Las dunas de Tardir—el *Eucalyptus gomphocephala* D. C.
1947 Montes 3:430–433.

CHAPMAN, G. W. Afforestation techniques in Cyprus. Unasylva 6:160–165.
1951

COMMONWEALTH FORESTRY REVIEW. Sand dune stabilisation and afforestation in
1969 Libya. Commonw. For. Rev. 48:377–381.

COOK, C. W., R. M. HYDE, and P. L. SIMS. Revegetation guidelines for surface mined
1974 areas. Colo. State Univ., Range Sci. Dep., Sci. Ser. 16. Ft. Collins. 73 p.

COOK, D. I., and D. F. VAN HAVERBEKE. Trees and shrubs for noise abatement.
1971 Nebr. Agric. Exp. Stn. Res. Bull. 246. Lincoln. 77 p.

———. Tree-covered land-forms for noise control. Nebr. Agric. Exp. Stn. Res. Bull.
1974 263. Lincoln. 47 p.

COSTIN, E., A. S. BALEIDI, and M. BAZARA. Establishment of windbreaks and shelter-
1974 belts in arid regions, with special reference to P.D.R. of Yemen. Pages 151–
165 *in* Report on Heathland and Sand Dune Afforestation. FAO/DEN/TF
123. Food Agric. Organ. U. N., Rome.

COSTIN, E., A. S. BALEIDI, M. EZZ, and M. BAZARA. Sand dune fixation and affores-
1974 tation in some semi-desert countries of the Middle East area. Pages 66–78
in Report on Heathland and Sand Dune Afforestation. FAO/DEN/TF 123.
Food Agric. Organ. U. N., Rome.

DEPARTMENT OF FORESTRY, REPUBLIC OF SOUTH AFRICA. The management of man-
1966 made forests and industrial plantations: problems and solutions. Proc. World
For. Congr. (Madrid) 6:2217–2225.

DEY, B. N. Reclamation and fixation of sand dunes and other shifting sands. West
1957 Bengal For. Bull. n.s. 4.

DUFFIELD, J. W. Silviculture need not be ugly. J. For. 68:464–467.
1970

DUGELAY, A. Le role des terrasses dans le contrées méditeranéennes. Rev. For. Fr.
1953 5:469–475.

EARDLEY, C. M. Tree-legumes for fodder. J. Agric. South Aust. 48:342–345.
1945

FAO. Poplar planting on sand dunes. For. Equip. Note A.2 Tec. 61. Rome.
1961 1 p.

———. Report on the FAO study tour on shelterbelts and windbreaks in the U.S.S.R.
1968 Part II. U. N. Dev. Programme TA 2561. Rome. 88 p.

————. Report on the FAO study tour on shelterbelts and windbreaks in the U.S.S.R.
1969   Part I. U. N. Dev. Programme TA 2561. Rome. 133 p.
————. Report to the government of Pakistan on intensive forestry with fast-grow-
1971   ing species in West Pakistan. Based on the work of Silvio May. U. N.
       Dev. Programme. FAO TA 3012. Rome. 80 p.
————. Report on sand dune stabilization in Israel. Based on the work of D. E.
1974   Tsuriell. Danish Funds-in-Trust. FAO/DEN/TF 114. Rome. 21 p.
————. Report on the FAO/DANIDA Inter-Regional Training Centre on Heath-
1974   land and Sand Dune Afforestation, Denmark and Libya 26 Aug.–21 Sept.
       1973. FAO/DEN/TF 123. Food Agric. Organ. U. N., Rome. 239 p.
FEIGENBAUM, S., J. HAGIN, and Y. KAPLAN. Fertilization of Aleppo pine (Pinus hale-
1973   pensis Mill.). FAO/IUFRO Int. Symp. For. Fert. Paris 3–7 Dec. 1973.
       FOR: FAO/IUFRO/F/73/6. Food Agric. Organ. U. N., Rome.   5 + 9 p.
GANGULI, B. N., R. N. KAUL, and K. T. N. NAMBIAR. Preliminary study on a few
1964   top-feed species. Ann. Arid Zone 3:33–37.
GEORGE, E. J. Spacing distances for windbreak trees on the northern Great Plains.
1948   U. S. Dep. Agric., Circ. 770. Washington, D. C. 28 p.
GLOYNE, R. W. Some effects of shelterbelts upon local and micro climate. Forestry
1954   27:85–95.
GOOR, A. Y. Woods and windbreaks in the farm. Hassadeh 23 (5–6).
1943
————. Sand dune fixation in Palestine. Palestine Dep. For. Annu. Rep. Append.
1947   I. Jerusalem. 8 p.
————. The Tiberias special area. Palestine Soil Conserv. Board, Bull. 4. Jeru-
1948   salem. 10 p.
————. Report to the government of India on control of the arid zone of Rajasthan.
1955   [FAO] Rep. 378. T. A. 272/S/10. Proj. IND/FO [Food Agric. Organ.
       U. N.], Rome. 29 p.
————. Informe al gobierno de Chile sobre repoblación forestal y rehabilitación de
1956   la zona arida del norte. FAO Tech. Pap. 500. Food Agric. Organ. U. N.,
       Rome. 29 p.
————. Informe al gobierno del Uruguay sobre cortinas protectoras y rompevientos.
1959   FAO Rep. 1079. Food Agric. Organ. U. N., Rome. 16p.
————. Informe al gobierno de la República Argentina sobre actividades forestales
1961   en las zonas áridas y semiaridas. FAO Rep. 1325. Food Agric. Organ. U. N.,
       Rome. 32 p.
————. Tree planting practices for arid areas. FAO For. Dev. Pap. 6 rev. Rome.
1964   126 p. (Engl., Fr., Span., Turk., Arab. eds., also Greek and Iranian in
       part.)
GRASOVSKY, A. Y. [GOOR, A. Y.] A world tour for the study of soil erosion control
1938   methods. Imp. For. Inst., Inst. Pap. 14. Oxford. 76 p.
HALL, N., et al. The use of trees and shrubs in the dry country of Australia. Aust.
1972   Gov. Publ. Serv., Canberra. xxx + 558 p.
HETH, D. Eucalypt introduction trials (preliminary results). For. Res. Inst. Ilanoth,
1961   Leafl. 17. 8 p.
————. Eucalypt introduction trials in the northern Negev. La-Yaaran 12:158–157
1962   (Engl. Abstr.); 138–142 (Hebrew text).
HILEY, W. E. Craib's thinning prescriptions for conifers in South Africa. Q. J. For.
1948   42:5–19.
————. Conifers: South African methods of cultivation. Faber and Faber, London.
1959   123 p.
IMPERIAL AGRICULTURAL BUREAUX. The use and misuse of shrubs and trees as fodder.
1947   Joint Publ. 10. Imp. Bur. Pastures and Field Crops, Aberystwyth. 231 p.
JAMES, A. L. Stabilizing mine dumps with vegetation. Endeavour 25:154–157.
1966
KAUL, R. N. ed. Afforestation in arid zones. Monogr. Biol. 20. W. Junk N. V. Publ.,
1970   The Hague. 435 p.
KHAN, M. I. R. Irrigated forest plantations of West Pakistan. Proc. World Congr.
[1962] (Seattle 1960) 5(1):366–369.

KITCHINGMAN, G. D. The Punjab irrigated plantations. Emp. For. J. 23:115–121.
1944

KREUTZER, VON K., and H. WEIGER. The influence of ammonium nitrate fertilization
on the quality and the amount of the draining water beyond the root horizon.
FAO/IUFRO Int. Symp. For. Fert. Paris 3–7 Dec. 1973. FOR: FAO/
IUFRO/F/73/12. Food Agric. Organ. U. N., Rome. 5 p.

LALYMENKO, N. K. Puti povyšenija produktivnosti takyrov. [Ways of increasing the
1959 productivity of takyrs.]. Lesn. Khoz. 12(8):32–37.

LAURIE, M. V. The changing face of forestry. Emp. For. Rev. 41:146–152.
1962

———. Tree planting practices in African savannas. FAO For. Dev. Pap. 19. Rome.
1974 185 p.

LAZAREVIČ, I. I., and L. P. KRUTIKOV. Aèrosev v peskah Sredneĭ Azii. [Aerial sow-
1950 ing on the central Asian sands.] Lesn. Khoz. 3(10):34–43.

LEONE, G. Le dune mobili della Tripolitania ed i risultati ottenuti con l'opera di
1924– riboschimento. Riv. Tripolit. 1:385–409.
1925

LOGGINOV, B. I. Principles of field-protective forestation (Osnovy polezashchitnogo
1964 lesorazvedeniya. n.d.). Transl. from Russian by A. Gourevitch. Israel
Program for Scientific Translations, Jerusalem. (OTS 64–11010). 302 p.

LONG, E. J. Sand + oil = trees. Am. For. 70:46–48.
1964

LUNCZ, G. Les plantations routières et leur importance au point de vue forestier.
1942 Silva Orbis 5. Berlin. 267 p.

MAROC MINISTERE AGRICULTURE. L'eucalyptus au Maroc. Rabat.
1960

McCOMB, A. L., and J. K. JACKSON. The role of tree plantations in savanna develop-
1970 ment: technical and economic aspects (with special reference to Nigeria).
Pages 68–83 in FAO Committee on Forest Development in the Tropics.
Rep. Second Sess. Rome 21–24 Oct. 1969. Food Agric. Organ. U. N., Rome.
162 p.

MESSINES, J. Methods for controlling mountain torrents used by the Administration
1951 des Eaux et Forêts in the Alps. Proc. U. N. Sci. Conf. Conserv. Util. Resour.
(Lake Success, 1949) 5:155–161.

———. Sand-dune fixation and afforestation in Libya. Unasylva 6:50–58.
1951

METRO, A. Eucalypts for planting. FAO For. For. Prod. Stud. 11. Rome. 401 p.
1955

MIROV, N. T. Two centuries of afforestation and shelterbelt planting on the Russian
1935 steppes. J. For. 33:971–973.

MONJAUZE, A. Note sur le développement des Eucalyptus dans certains arboretums
1958 de l'Oranie semi-arid froide. Soc. Hist. Nat. Afr. Nord, Bull. 49. p. 143–
160. Algiers.

MUDD, J. B., and T. T. KOZLOWSKI (editors). Responses of plants to air pollution.
1975 Academic Press, New York. 383 p.

MULFORD, F. L. Planting the roadside. U. S. Dep. Agric. Farmers' Bull. 1481. rev.
1938 Washington, D. C. 37 p.

NAEGELI, W. Report to the Government of Israel on shelterlands and windbreaks
1957 Food Agric. Organ. U. N. Expanded Tech. Assist. Programme. FAO Rep.
586. Rome. 27 p.

PAEZ MENA, U. [Some pine species used in dune afforestation at Punta Mogotes.]
1961 [Proc.] 1ᵃ Reun. Reg. Conif. Assoc. For. Argent. B. Aires, p. [139–154].

PAVARI, A. Problèmes intéressant la culture du peuplier dans la région méditer-
1948 ranéenne. FAO Subcommission on Mediterr. For. Prob. FAO/EFC/
MSC/1. Food Agric. Organ. U. N., Rome. 14 p. (Mimeo.).

———. Problèmes de populiculture dans la région méditerranéenne. Pages 75–90
1953 in Proc. Second Sess. Comm. Int. Peuplier, Rome 1953.

PENFOLD, A. R., and J. L. WILLIS. The eucalypts: botany, cultivation, chemistry, and
1961   utilization. Leonard Hill [Books] Ltd., London. Interscience, New York.
       551 p.
PETROV, M. The USSR. Pages 210–233 *in* Afforestation in arid zones, R. N. Kaul
1970   ed. Monogr. Biol. 20. W. Junk N. V. Publ., The Hague.
———. Central Asia. Pages 234–267 *in* Afforestation in arid zones, R. N. Kaul ed.
1970   Monogr. Biol. 20. W. Junk N. V. Publ., The Hague.
POURTET, J. The poplar—its place in the world. Unasylva 5:55–58.
1951
PRAKASH, M., and M. CHOWDHARY. Reclamation of sand dunes in Rajasthan. Indian
1957   For. 83:492–496.
READ, R. A. The Great Plains shelterbelt in 1954. Nebr. Univ. Coll. Agric., Agric.
1958   Exp. Stn. Bull. 441. Lincoln. 125 p.
———. Tree windbreaks for the central Great Plains. U. S. Dep. Agric., Agric.
1964   Handb. 250. Washington, D. C. 68 p.
RICHARDSON, S. D. Forestry in communist China. Johns Hopkins Press, Baltimore,
1966   Md. xvi + 237 p.
ROSENZWEIG, D. Study of difference in effects of forest and other vegetative covers on
1972   water-yield (final report). Israel Minist. Agric., Soil Conserv. Drain. Div.
       Res. Unit Res. Rep. 33. Hakirya Tel Aviv. [136 p.]
SALTIEL, M. Sand dune stabilization for the protection of engineering structures.
1963   Joint Experimental Coastal Groundwater Collectors Project, Tech. Rep. 2.
       TAHAL, Water Planning for Israel Ltd., Tel Aviv. 46 p.
SAPRIZA VERA, C. La erosion y los medios de dominaria. Suelo Argentino 4:306–
1954   311, 324, 326, 374–381, 388.
SCOTT, D. H. Air pollution injury to plant life. Natl. Landscape Assoc., Washington,
1973   D. C. 12 p.
STARK, N. Review of highway planting information appropriate to Nevada. Univ.
1966   Nev. Coll. Agric. Bull. B-7. Reno. 209 p.
SWAN, H. S. D. The fertilization of man-made forests. Doc. FAO World Symposium
1967   on Man-Made Forests and their Industrial Importance. Canberra, Aust. 14–
       24 April 1967. Vol. 1:415–434.
TAMM, C. O. Effects of fertilizers on the environment. FAO/IUFRO Int. Symp.
1973   For. Fert. Paris 3–7 Dec. 1973. FOR: FAO/IUFRO/F/73/17. Food Agric.
       Organ. U. N., Rome. 7 p.
TSURIELL, D. E. Sand dune stabilization in Israel. Israel Minist. Agric., Soil Conserv.
1966   Dep., Tel-Aviv. 19 + 3 p.
———. Sand dune stabilization in Israel. Int. J. Biometeor. 18(2):89–93.
1974
VANSELL, G. H. Nectar and pollen plants of California. Calif. Univ. Coll. Agric.,
1931   Agric. Exp. Stn. Bull. 517. Berkeley. 55 + [5] p.
VICTORIA DEPARTMENT OF FORESTRY. The honey flora of Victoria. Melbourne. 136
1949   p.
WAHEED KHAN, M. A. Results of differential irrigation in a plantation of *Eucalyptus*
1965   *microtheca* during the first year. Sudan For. Dep. For. Res. Inst. Pam. 13.
       Soba, Khartoum, Sudan. 28 p.
WARING, H. D. Early fertilization for maximum production. FAO/IUFRO Int.
1973   Symp. For. Fert. Paris 3–7 Dec. 1973. FOR: FAO/IUFRO/F/73/19.
       Food Agric. Organ. U. N., Rome. 18 + [7] p.
WIDMANN, M. Banquettes et plants Putod. Rev. For. Fr. 4:571–585.
1952
WIMBUSH, S. H. Afforestation of restored tin-mining land in Nigeria. Commonw.
1963   For. Rev. 42:255–262.
YUSSEM FAVRE, R. Cortinas forestales rompevientos (con referencia especial a la
1956   Region Central Pampeana). An. Adm. Nac. Bosques 1956: 31–43. B.
       Aires.
ZEDNIK, F. Waldbau gegen Versteppung und Erosion in Mittelmeerraum. Allg.
1964   Forsztztg. 75 (9/10):93–95.

6

Species for Arid-Zone Afforestation

CHOICE OF SPECIES

The choice of the species to be planted in an area should be made only after careful consideration of their adaptability for growth and their fitness for the purpose of the plantation. Few species are suitable for timber production in arid zones, and some of these withstand drought but will not grow where frosts occur or where the soil is unfavorable. Many attempts to introduce tropical xerophytic plants have failed because they were not adapted to the low temperature of the desert.

Native species growing in the area to be planted and fit for the purpose in view are the safest choice, and every effort should be made to find the strains best adapted for planting. Preferably the seed should be collected within 200 kilometers (125 miles) distance and 500 meters (1,600 ft) altitude of the plantation area. In some places, native species meet all the requirements for selection: ease of obtaining the seed, ease of establishment, immunity to disease or insect attack, fast growth, usefulness, and value of the product. All these qualifications are not easy to find in an exotic species, yet introduction of species into new areas cannot and must not be ruled out. Many areas where afforestation is contemplated have no suitable native trees, or perhaps no native trees at all. Furthermore, the possibility of introducing trees with better characteristics than the native species possess should not be ignored. Desirable exotics should grow fast, have good timber qualities, and be immune to local disease and insect attack.

Introduced species should be used with some caution until their superiority has been demonstrated by trials in the area, or by their performance in other comparable areas with similar climatic and edaphic conditions. Occasionally, too much caution or even patriotic bias is displayed before approving the introduction of a species to an area. In some countries, exotic species are used reluctantly until they have been tried out within the political boundary, yet native species are transferred freely from one end of the country to the other with little consideration for ecologic factors. Transfer from one locality to another should be governed primarily by the similarity of climate and soil in the new area to those within the natural range of the species. Mean and extreme temperatures, season and duration of frosts, annual rainfall, length of dry season, minimum rainfall, and humidity are the most important climatic factors to be compared. Climatic extremes rather than averages are the decisive factors for plant growth. Local climatic records are needed for estimates of potential evapotranspiration in order to determine the degree of aridity of an area and the possibility for success of introduced species.

Graphs showing the water balance in different regions according to the method proposed by Thornthwaite can be used to advantage when contemplating the introduction of trees from one area into another. For example, the graphs for Monterey pine (*Pinus radiata* D. Don) (Fig. 6–1) show the water balance in its native habitat (graphs a & b), in areas in Australia and Spain where it has been successfully introduced (graphs c & d), and for areas in Kenya and Italy where attempts to grow Monterey pine have failed (graphs e & f). The similarity of the graphs where it has been successfully introduced to those of its native range is quite evident. It also seems clear that the graph for Kenya, where it failed, represents a different climatic type than that found in the species native region. Although the graph for Rome where plantings were also unsuccessful, appears similar to those for California, winters are cooler and wetter and summers are hotter and with much more severe water deficits than those of its native habitat. It should also be noted that the high altitude and equatorial position of the Kenya site confound any conclusions that may be drawn from the graph. Furthermore, edaphic factors such as soil moisture, texture, and salinity have not been included nor were physiographic factors and several important climatic factors.

Maps showing large areas of climatically similar environment known as homoclimates are usually of such small scale that they delimit only the overall climate, or macroclimate of a region (See Figs. 1–1 and 1–2). Consequently they do not show local variations, or microclimates, thus ignoring the climates of specific sites. Microclimates may vary in size from tiny fields to entire valleys and mountain slopes. They are chiefly the result of differences in topography and vegetation—including man-made forests and shelterbelts. Microclimates are characterized by uniformity of wind, humidity, and temperature over the site involved.

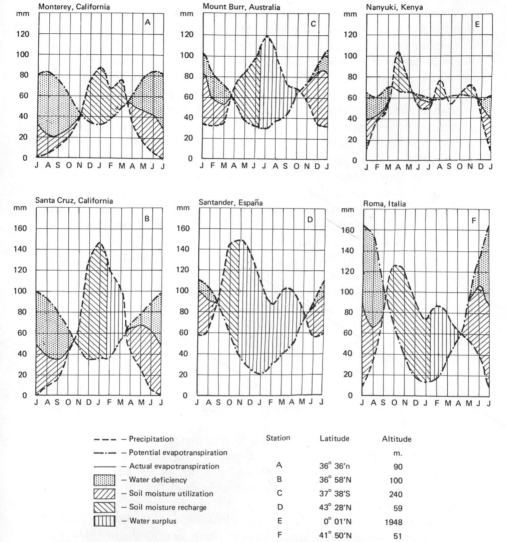

	Station	Latitude	Altitude
− − − − Precipitation			m.
−·− − Potential evapotranspiration			
──── − Actual evapotranspiration	A	36° 36′n	90
▒▒ − Water deficiency	B	36° 58′N	100
▨ − Soil moisture utilization	C	37° 38′S	240
▨ − Soil moisture recharge	D	43° 28′N	59
▥ − Water surplus	E	0° 01′N	1948
	F	41° 50′N	51

Fig. 6–1. March of precipitation and evapotranspiration in six selected stations where Monterey pine (*Pinus radiata* D. Don) (a, b) grows naturally (c, d) has been introduced successfully and (e, f) where introduction failed. (After Golfari 1966, 1967.)

Homoclimatic maps also fail to indicate soil differences, which, together with the microclimate, can have a profound influence on the suitability of a site for planting.

Seasonal precipitation patterns are important determinants of vegetation types. Species native to winter rainfall areas usually will not thrive in summer rainfall areas, but species native to summer rainfall areas are likely to succeed in winter rainfall areas, if other climatic factors are favorable. Pines of the Mediterranean climate, for example *Pinus halepensis* Mill and *P. canariensis* C. Sm., have not succeeded in summer rainfall regimes in the tropics even though they were planted at high altitude where temperatures were cool. Some species, and especially some provenances, show marked differences in response to different photoperiods. When species indigenous to high latitudes are planted in the tropics, they usually react unfavorably to the shorter days.

None of these comparisons and criteria should be regarded as absolute and inviolable so that experimental introductions of exotics are curtailed. In fact, some extremely successful introductions would not have been made if researchers had adhered strictly to a rigid set of rules.

Species suitable for planting in arid zones are classified according to their site requirements in Appendix D.

As a general rule, tree species can be moved from their home to other localities on the same parallel of latitude without adverse effects because of the similarity of climate. Usually hardwood species, except for eucalypts, native to low elevations and high latitudes will not thrive if planted at high elevations in tropical regions. But even if all climatic and edaphic factors have been taken into account when introducing plants to a new environment, success is not assured. Some plants are so exacting in their requirements that a small variation in season or intensity of site factors may cause failure.

Afforestation efforts in arid zones have generally been economically disappointing. This has been due, in part, to the fact that forest trees were planted only on land remaining after all other land users had selected the more productive and accessible land for their enterprises. Nothing was left for afforestation except rocky or dry soils. Utilization of poor land by foresters became a virtue—and a tradition. Perhaps it is for this reason that many people have accepted the idea that afforestation in arid zones is not expected to yield any returns on the capital invested. Great efforts were made to improve the techniques of planting in such zones; better seedlings were grown for the plantations, selected species were used, and the methods of cultivating the soil were improved. Yet, in the end, the usual results were great seedling mortality after planting and slow growth of the few survivors. Cost of potting, transporting, and planting was high, and when all expenses were weighed against the slow growth of the inferior timber produced, the balance showed that planting for wood production was inadvisable.

Plantations were usually on eroded watersheds which, if they remained denuded, were the source of destructive floods. When floods occurred, the agricultural land and houses in the valleys below these slopes were severely damaged or completely buried under sediment. The planting of forest trees was considered essential for the protection of the valleys from flood damage, and the expense of planting the watershed was debited entirely to the protection measures. Little heed was given to the timber production of the area planted.

The protective value of tree plantations on a watershed is not always greater than that of other vegetative cover, such as brush or grass. In fact, it can often be shown that a well-managed grassland will protect a watershed just as effectively as a tree plantation and be more easily established and maintained. It has also been established in many semiarid areas that because grassland has a more favorable water balance than forest, maquis, or chaparral, more usable water will enter the soil and eventually filter down to the valley below. Stream flow normally decreases following afforestation of non-forested land. In South Africa experiments have shown that during the period of vigorous growth, exotic plantations cause significant reduction of stream flow. Over large areas of grassland that have been invaded by shrubs or trees, springs have ceased flow during part of the year, or even permanently. Loss of ground water is due principally to higher transpiration from the much larger and more exposed evaporating surfaces of leaves and stems of woody plants compared to those of grasses and other herbaceous vegetation. In a watershed where the primary concern is water conservation, transpirational losses should be reduced by replacing brush and most trees with grasses. By eradicating brush and converting back to grassland or savanna, springs may be induced to flow again. In dry countries the relative importance of timber production and the water requirements for agriculture should be carefully considered before embarking on afforestation schemes which might possibly affect water supply. In some places forests are considered more important than the agricultural crops that could be grown on the same area. It is important to direct the management of such forests toward restricting excessive transpiratonial losses. Proper silvicultural treatment for each species is necessary to conserve the limited amount of water available in a watershed for agricultural use. Water consumption of forests can be controlled by spacing, arrangement, thinning, pruning, or harvest.

To plant denuded areas successfully, certain fundamental phytogeographical facts must first be ascertained. It is frequently possible to determine the composition, structure, and condition of the original forests from the vestiges of vegetation that have in some manner escaped destruction. This knowledge is a valuable guide in choosing the species to be planted.

Where the native tree and shrub vegetation has completely disappeared—or perhaps where none ever existed, as on the treeless plateaus —a thorough knowledge of climate, soil, and silvical requirements is essential in choosing species for afforestation.

Many tree species in nature are confined to comparatively small areas. It appears that their lack of diffusion to other parts of the world was not because the other areas were unsuitable for their growth, but because natural barriers—physical, climatic, and even biotic—stopped their spread to other localities that might be equally, or perhaps more, suitable for their growth than their present site. Man can overcome such barriers by artificial introduction of a species into new areas. In fact, within this century the limits of the management range of several tree species have been greatly expanded, demonstrating that with proper judgment the introduction of exotics can be successful. For example, *Acacia tortilis* Hayne grows faster in Rajasthan than in its native Dead Sea valley; Monterey pine (*P. radiata* D. Don) does far better in New Zealand, and in many other localities outside its native habitat, than it does within its natural range in California; several species of eucalypts and acacia grow faster in Brazil, California, Portugal, and South Africa than in their natural Australian environment. For many plants, it is apparent that under cultivation the potential environment is often much more extensive than their natural range would lead one to expect.

Some species grow well in areas where they would not be expected to thrive, and may even flourish in areas with soils and climatic conditions quite different from those of their native habitat. Several species that are native to quite cold and humid areas may be planted successfully in much warmer and drier climates. For example, *Pinus brutia* Ten. from Turkey has succeeded in regions that are much warmer than its native habitat, notably in parts of Chile, Argentina, and the Middle East. *Eucalyptus camaldulensis* Dehnh. grows in Australia between 15° and 38° south latitude. It is found usually in valley bottoms that are regularly flooded from 10 to 20 days each year, and which receive an annual rainfall of 300–600 mm (12–24 in) evenly distributed throughout the year. This species is commonly grown outside Australia, well beyond the 15° to 38° south latitude belt, on a great variety of soils not subject to flooding, and where the annual rainfall is less than 200 mm (8 in), with eight to nine rainless months. Its growth rate in many places outside Australia is actually much faster than in its native habitat.

Some species which grow equally well in one area respond quite differently when planted in another area. Over much of southern Africa *Eucalyptus grandis* (Mill.) Maiden and *E. salinga* Sm., which are closely related, grow almost equally, but under the harsh conditions of the Central African plateau important differences in drought hardiness and stem straightness become apparent and the two must be grown on separate sites.

The properties of the wood derived from an exotic plantation often differ significantly from those of the same species in its native habitat due to the changes in environment. Among the most noticeable differences are those of wood density and fiber length.

Sometimes the lack of proper fungi to form mycorrhizae with the roots of introduced trees precludes the establishment or reduces the growth of exotic trees in their new environments. Many pines from southern California, Arizona, and Mexico, for example, have not grown well in the Mediterranean Basin despite the apparent similarity of all site factors in the two areas. Their failure has been attributed to the lack of specific mycorrhizal fungi that inhabit the roots of some North American pines. Seedbeds may be inoculated with the required mycorrhizal fungi by spreading a few handfuls of soil (preferably with rootlets) that have been collected under natural stands of the species to be propagated.

The importance of mycorrhizae for successful tree planting in arid zones is indicated by the presence of mycorrhizae in natural stands of pines and observations of their effect on the vigor and health of pines and oaks in plantations and nursery beds. Local fluctuation in mycorrhizal development in new plantations may be due to variations in residual root material from earlier plantations or natural forests.

Successful establishment of exotics often depends on improvement of several site factors. When *Pinus pinaster* Ait. was first introduced into Australia, seedling growth was poor. Plowing the site and clearing it of competing vegetation improved growth a little; inoculating the soil with the proper mycorrhizal fungus increased growth to nearly "normal"; and, finally, application of phosphates resulted in above average growth of seedlings.

To lessen the risk of bringing in fungal disease or insect pests, it is always advisable, when introducing a new species to an area, to import the seed rather than the live plants or cuttings. Seed can be easily fumigated and freed from pests, but it is difficult to fumigate plants or cuttings without injuring them. Many countries and their political subdivisions have strict quarantine laws that govern the import or export of seeds or other living plant material.

The fact that the new environment does not have the natural enemies of the introduced species is a considerable advantage in afforestation. The fast rate of growth of eucalypts outside Australia is due in large measure to the absence of the native Australian leaf-eating insects. It is claimed that in South Africa almost all insects and fungi which damage plantations are indigenous and have become a problem only since the environmental balance has been upset by large scale afforestation.

When trees are planted for the production of poles or posts, the species selected should have a straight bole and durable wood. If charcoal or firewood is desired, the main considerations are the volume and quality that the species will produce in a given rotation. Where shelterbelts are planted, the object is to protect the soil and crops in nieghboring fields. Consequently, the trees of the belt must attain at least moderate height to obstruct and minimize the damage of desiccating winds. The taller the trees, the greater the distance on the lee side of the belt that will be protected. Often it is possible to select species for planting that will produce two or more benefits. A multiple purpose plantation might be a shelterbelt of trees with flowers that will attract honey bees, charcoal-producing trees whose leaves yield essential oils, or a fuelwood plantation that produces leaves and pods for fodder.

The selection of species adapted to a particular afforestation project requires a definite knowledge of their technical properties, their ecological requirements and geographical distribution in their native habitat, and their behavior and growth when planted as exotics in new environments. The number of trees which have economic value or which are suitable for the different purposes for which they may be chosen for planting in any selected arid-zone site is unfortunately very small, particularly in relation to the vast arid zones of the world and the numerous species from which the selection may be made.

Above all, plantations managers must realize that the object of their work is to serve the people. To do this, much knowledge and understanding are required and at times economic sacrifices may be necessary to reach this goal.

TRIALS FOR INTRODUCTION OF EXOTICS

The procedure adopted in Nigeria, Uganda, and Zambia for the introduction of exotic species has been quite successful and is recommended for use in other arid zones. After the plant material for testing is available from the nursery, the procedure follows three distinct operational steps which are referred to as: elimination, growth, and plantation trials.

The Species Elimination Trial. This trial is designed to eliminate from further consideration those species clearly unsuited to the environment of the new planting area. Each species is planted in small plots which are replicated 3 times in a given site. Standard cultivation and maintenance regimes are followed. Where time and resources permit, plants of identical seed origin and nursery treatment may be tested simultaneously on sites covering a range of climatic conditions. The recommended design is a randomized block with 25 trees per plot using 1.5 or 1.8 m (5 or 6 ft) spacing in a square pattern. Trials are assessed at the end of the fourth year. It is important that the site be kept free of weed growth by regular cultivation so that in all plots the different species will have equal opportunity to respond to soil and climatic conditions.

Species elimination trials in Nigeria have given sufficiently reliable information to eliminate about half the species at a reasonable cost after two years.

The Species Growth Trial. The growth trial provides information on performance, growth rate, stem and crown form, agencies causing injury or death, and crops and benefits to be derived for those species emerging successfully from elimination trials. The standard design is a randomized block with 4 replications of 100 trees per plot. Normal spacing for the species is used in these trials so plot size may vary from about 300 sq m (0.08 A) for 1.8 × 1.8 m (6 × 6 ft) spacing to 900 sq m (0.23 A) for 3 × 3 m (10 ×10 ft) spacing.

Growth trials are established on different soil types and in the different climatic zones of the region and when results are analyzed valuable information on site requirements and best location for plantation trials is obtained. Replication in a standard statistical design is essential at this stage. Grass must be eliminated and insects and diseases controlled in the plots. A single application of a complete fertilizer at the time of planting is recommended.

Species Plantation Trials. These trials are restricted to species which after five years of good growth in the species growth trials are judged suitable for plantation trials. Usually only a few species qualify for this stage. The plots are about 0.4 ha (1 A) in area for a single silvicultural treatment, or from 1.2 to 2.0 ha (3 to 5 A) if more than one silvicultural treatment is to be evaluated. Comparisons of different spacing, fertilization, cultivation, and other silvicultural treatments should be made on trial plots designed for that purpose.

The species which pass this test and which will meet the desired purpose, may then be recommended for regular field planting.

SILVICS OF ARID-ZONE TREE SPECIES

A description of the species most likely to be chosen for planting in different sites and for different purposes follows.

Acacia albida Del.   apple ring acacia

Apple ring acacia is a large, thorny tree up to 18 m (60 ft) in height and 1 m (3.3 ft) in diameter. It occurs in the dry savannas throughout western and northern Africa to Egypt, and in eastern Africa, southward to Rhodesia, Botswana, and the Transvaal. Also present, but rare, in Israel and Lebanon. It grows where the annual rainfall is 300 to 500 mm (12 to 20 in) and the water table is within reach of the taproot; often on the banks of watercourses. It makes its best growth on sandy or silty soils. Often seen in cultivated fields where it is grown for shade and to improve the soil. It comes into leaf at the end of the rainy season and remains green during the hot dry season. This peculiar habit makes if extremely valuable as a shade tree and a producer of fodder for livestock in the dry period.

Apple ring acacia coppices freely and may produce abundant suckers. There are about 11,000 seeds per kilogram (5,000 per lb). Seeds are collected and planted in April. Before planting all seeds with insect holes should be removed and the seeds scarified or soaked for 48 hours in water. Due to the rapid growth of the taproot, seedlings must be raised in pots and root pruned frequently. Two or three seeds are sown in each pot and after a month thinned to one seedling per pot. Seedlings grow slowly and reach the planting height of 10 to 15 cm (4 to 6 in) in 14 to 16 weeks. Apple ring acacia is planted only as single trees in fields and villages, not in closed plantations. Seedlings are planted in pits and must be staked to prevent damage due to their slow height growth during the first three years before the taproot reaches the subsoil water supply. After the roots reach water the tree becomes one of the fastest growing trees in the savanna.

The wood is soft and easy to work. It is used for dugout canoes, furniture, boxes, and fuelwood.

Acacia arabica Willd.   babul

A small to medium-sized evergreen tree, 10–12 m (33–40 ft) in height, native to the dry zones of northeast Africa, Arabia, northwest India, and Pakistan. It grows in association with other acacias, *Tamarix*, and *Prosopis*. The species is usually found on moist river alluvium and black cotton soil, but it also grows on relatively saline soil with adequate moisture. Annual rainfall within its natural range is 100–1,000 mm (4–40 in), with 8 to 10 rainless months a year. Maximum rainfall may be in summer or in winter. The equivalent of 400 mm (16 in) annual rainfall is needed for normal growth; this may be by rain, flood, or irrigation. It can tolerate a maximum air temperature of 50° C (122° F) in the shade, but dies if the temperature falls below −1° C (30° F).

It regenerates freely from seed or cuttings but is a poor producer of coppice and root suckers. It fruits annually, and in some places twice a year. A kilogram contains about 8,000 to 10,000 seeds (3,600–4,500/lb). Seeds are easily stored, require no special technique, and will keep well unsealed under normal room conditions. Germination is normally about 90 per cent. Seed collected from feces after the pods have been eaten by goats and sheep germinate well, but seed collected from trees will not germinate until seedcoat dormancy is overcome. This may be done by pouring boiling water over the seeds just before sowing and allowing them to soak for 48 hours while the water cools. Seeds are usually severely attacked by insects and may require fumigation before storage. Because the seedling develops a long taproot, seeds are usually planted directly in the field rather than in nurseries. The tree grows well in irrigated plantations or cultivated fields. Field plants should be weeded and the soil around them disced for three years after germination. The wood is durable and is used in buildings, carts, agricultural implements, and as fuel. Tannin may be extracted from the bark. Pods and the leaves, which contain 15 per cent crude protein, are eaten by goats, sheep and camels. The tree is occasionally planted for erosion control. It is easily grown and is planted extensively in its native habitat because of the value of its produce and its adaptability to rigorous conditions. Trees over 25 years of age tend to decay. It is recommended for planting in areas where conditions are similar to its native habitat, e.g., in Chile.

Fig. 6–2. *Acacia caven* (Mol.) Molina is a small spiny tree of the semi-arid region of Santiago Province, Chile. (Courtesy Instituto Forestal, Santiago, Chile)

Acacia caven (Mol.) Molina   espino

A small, spiny tree 5–6 m (16–20 ft) tall with an open crown, which grows in the semiarid zones and the open dry-zone forests of Bolivia, central Chile, northern Argentina, Paraguay, and Uruguay. It is found in association with *Schinus molle* L., *Prosopis alba* Griseb., *P. nigra* Hieron., *Schinopsis* spp., *Caesalpinia* spp., and *Gleditsia* spp., and grows on sandy loams in areas with annual rainfall of 100–1,000 mm (4–40 in) and with a winter dry season. The mean annual temperature in its range is about 20° C (68° F), but it can withstand a minimum temperature of −8° C (18° F). It regenerates by coppice, root suckers, and from seed. There are about 10,000 seeds per kg (4,500/lb). Seeds germinate easily. The wood is used as fuel and for posts, and the pods contain tannin.

Acacia cyanophylla Lindl.   blue-leafed wattle

A tall shrub, up to 7 m (23 ft), which is native to southwestern Australia. It grows on sandy loam and on drained and calcareous soils, where the annual rainfall is 300–1,000 mm (12–40 in), with a summer dry season. Within its range the mean temperature is about 15° C (59° F) in winter and 20° C (68° F) in summer. It grows in association with *Eucalyptus gomphocephala* A. DC and *Acacia cyclops* A. Cunn. It grows rapidly and coppices freely. It flowers early and produces seed profusely after the sixth year—about 60,000 seeds per kg (27,000/lb); 80 to 90 per cent of the seeds are sound. After treatment with boiling water, seeds will germinate in 24 hours.

Strongly resistant to drought, it grows well in plantations in areas where the annual rainfall is less than 300 mm (12 in). It may be planted for erosion control in mountains not subject to frost, but only if climatic and edaphic conditions do not permit planting of pines or other similar species. Useful as a windbreak in arid areas and for roadside plantings, this is also one of the best species to use for binding moving sand. It can be planted as naked-rooted, or balled, 1 + 0 seedlings, or even as eight-month-old plants, and is now extensively planted in all countries where the required climatic conditions exist, e.g., Iraq, South Africa, and Mexico.

Acacia cyclops A. Cunn.   cyclops

A shrub, up to 3 m (10 ft) tall, which is found in coastal areas from southern Western Australia to the dry, western part of South Australia. It grows where the annual rainfall ranges from 250–750 mm (10–30 in) and the summers are extremely dry. It needs mild temperatures—winter temperatures that rarely drop to freezing and summer temperatures that seldom exceed 35° C (95° F). Its reproductive characteristics are similar to the preceding species. Cyclops is a very useful species for binding coastal dunes and planting on difficult sites.

Fig. 6–3. *Acacia cyanophylla* Lindl. (blue-leafed wattle) planted at 300 m (1,000 ft) above sea level in the eastern Mediterranean Basin.

Fig. 6–4. Cassie flower [*Acacia farnesiana* (L.) Willd.] planted as a hedge forms an impenetrable barrier.

Acacia farnesiana (L.) Willd. [A. cavenia Bert.]   **cassie flower**

Thorny bush or small tree usually 3–4 m (10–13 ft), rarely 10 m (33 ft) high. It is native from southern Texas through Central America to Chile, and is found on poor soil in areas where the annual rainfall is 400–500 mm (16–20 in). It is not hardy in temperatures below −5° C (23° F). It grows rapidly, and seeds profusely each year—about 10,000 seeds per kg (4,500/lb) with average germination of 70 per cent after treatment with hot water. Seeds may be stored under ordinary room conditions, but are susceptible to insect attack. Wood may be used for fuel and posts. Tannin can be extracted from the bark and fruit. Gum from the trunk can be employed locally in making mucilage, and the leaves are valuable for fodder. An extract for perfumes is distilled from the flowers. Cassie flower has been planted extensively in India, Iraq, and the Mediterranean Basin as a hedge. It is recommended for irrigated and canal plantations and as a hedge to protect irrigated orchards.

Fig. 6–5. *Acacia melanoxylon* R. Br. (blackwood) is planted as an ornamental because of its dense, evergreen crown.

Acacia melanoxylon R. Br.   **blackwood**

An evergreen tree up to 30 m (100 ft) high, but usually 15 m (50 ft) or less, which is native to southeastern Australia, including Tasmania. It grows on a wide range of soils from rich alluvial to sandy podsols, and is found in regions of more than 700 mm (28 in) rainfall. Associated with eucalypts as an understory tree. It is only moderately drought-resistant and requires a climate that is subtropical to mild temperate with a few light frosts. It needs an average annual temperature of 15° C (59° F), with an absolute minimum of −10° C (14° F). Blackwood reproduces easily from seed with good crops yearly—about 70,000 seeds per kg (32,000/lb). Germination of seeds pretreated in boiling water averages 65 per cent. Seeds are easily stored under normal room conditions. It is fast growing, produces a valuable wood with handsome grain which is used for furniture, interior woodwork, and construction of railway carriages, and also is an excellent fuelwood. Blackwood is used in windbreaks and shelterbelts, and is planted extensively in east Africa, South Africa, Uruguay, and the Mediterranean area, and in smaller plantations in most countries with Mediterranean climate.

Acacia nilotica (L.) Del. [*A. arabica* Willd.]

A spiny tree usually 3 to 5 m (10 to 16 ft) high but occasionally up to 9 m (30 ft). Its natural range extends from northern Nigeria and the Lake Chad region eastward to the Nile Valley, eastern Sudan, and Kenya. It grows chiefly in regions that receive 250 to 750 mm (10 to 30 in) annual rainfall, but it is also found in true desert climate on areas subject to annual flooding. It is an important species in the Sudan for establishing plantations on inundation flats. On these sites, ridges 45 to 60 cm (1.5 to 2 ft) high are prepared and seedlings or seeds are planted on top of the ridges. As the flood recedes the plants develop rapidly and the roots penetrate the soil following the receding moisture. Seeding characteristics are similar to those of *A. arabica* Willd. Trees can tolerate some salt in the soil in irrigated plantations. The inner bark contains about 20 percent tannin and is an important source locally of this material. Trees are occasionally tapped for the production of gum arabic. Leaves and pods provide fodder for cattle, goats, sheep, and camels. Various parts of the tree are employed locally for their medicinal properties. The wood is used for fuel, charcoal, sawlogs, sleepers, and building poles. *A nilotica* (L.) Del. is considered by many taxonomists as a race of *A. arabica* Willd. and not a separate species.

Acacia pycnantha Benth.   **golden wattle**

Golden wattle is a much branched shrub or small tree from 3 to 6 m (15 to 30 ft) tall. Stem diameter rarely exceeds 30 cm (12 in). When in flower, the entire plant is a mass of attractive golden yellow blossoms. Native to southern Australia but now acclimatized in many other dry regions of Australia and dry zones in many parts of the world. In its native habitat summers are hot and winters cool and the annual rainfall is 400 to 750 mm (15 to 30 in). Golden wattle is drought resistant but subject to damage by light frosts. A kilogram contains about 54,000 seeds (24,000 per lb) of which approximately 75 percent are viable. Seeds must be pretreated by soaking in hot water to insure prompt germination. Establishment of golden wattle plantations is usually by direct seeding on prepared soil. Its bark is rich in tannin but due to competition from other tannin material little financial incentive exists for tannin production. It is an extremely valuable ornamental because of the profusion of golden flowers. It has been planted as the low, shrubby species in multi-row windbreaks.

Acacia salicina Lindl.   **cooba**

Cooba is a bush or small tree with a spreading crown from 6 to 12 m (20 to 40 ft) high. Due to its pendulous branchlets and drooping foliage it resembles willow (*Salix* sp) in general appearance. The trunk is fairly straight up to one quarter of its height, above that it divides into a number of smaller stems. The natural occurrence of cooba is from the arid zone of South Australia and New South Wales to the humid coastal areas of Queensland. It extends inland to the vicinity of Alice Springs in central Australia. It grows well where the annual rainfall is 375 to 550 mm (15 to 22 in) but can be found where the rainfall is no more than 200 mm (8 in) and in humid climates where rainfall is about 1000 mm (39 in). Cooba grows on a variety of soils from alluvial clay of river bottoms to sandy soils of the uplands. The number of viable seeds per kilogram ranges from 11,000 to 17,000 (5,000 to 7,700 per lb). Seed should be pretreated with hot water to hasten germination. Its weeping habit of growth and silver-gray foliage make it one of the most attractive ornamentals for arid zone planting. It often produces suckers from the roots which increases its value for erosion control plantings. Cooba wood is used principally for fuel.

Acacia senegal Willd.   **gum arabic**

A thorny shrub or tree 3–5 m (10–16 ft) tall, with deep penetrating and wide spreading roots, which is indigenous from northwest India across north Africa to Senegal, and from the Red Sea to Chad. It is found in the Thal desert in Pakistan and India and forms an open park-like stand in the savanna of the Sudan. It grows on poor soil, rocky hills, and sandy tracts, but is also found on black cotton soils, and occurs in mixtures with *Euphorbia*, *Zizyphus*, and other species of

Acacia, depending on the region. No more than a low bush in areas with just over 100 mm (4 in) rainfall, it grows to be a tree 3–5 m (10–16 ft) high in areas with rainfall of 300–500 mm (12–20 in). Tropical to warm temperate climate is best, where the mean annual temperature is between 25° and 27° C (77°–81° F), and where the maximum shade temperature may reach 45° C (113° F). However, some varieties are moderately frost hardy, and survive under the most adverse conditions of prolonged drought. It coppices well and is easily raised from seeds. It seeds abundantly every year, with 11,000–20,000 seeds per kg (5,000–9,000/lb), and 60 per cent germination. Seeds are easily stored under normal room conditions, but may require fumigation to rid them of insects. Trees have a life span of 25 to 30 years. Wood is hard and is used for weavers' shuttles, agricultural implements, and fuel. Most of the best gum arabic is exported from the Sudan and is used in medicine, the manufacture of chewing gum, and the textile industry. The leaves are collected for fodder. In regions with warm to hot summers and low rainfall it is used as a protective cover on dry tracts. It can be direct-seeded with or without pretreatment. In the Sudan, seeds are broadcast on the receding flood waters of the Nile. Because broadcast seeding gave poor results new techniques were developed. The most efficient of these are the "pit" method and the "single furrow" method. In the pit method, holes approximately 30 × 30 × 30 cm (1 × 1 × 1 ft) are dug at intervals of 4 m (13 ft) along the planting line. Holes are then refilled with soil and 3 to 5 seeds are sown in the center of the worked-up soil. In the single furrow method a continuous furrow is made by a plow following the planting line. The furrows are spaced 4 m (13 ft.) part and seeds are sown in the furrows at 4 m intervals. The furrow method is more commonly used than the pit method under current practice.

Acacia tortilis Hayne [*A. raddiana* Savi]   **tortilis tree**

A small thorny tree 4–6 m (13–20 ft) high, native to northeastern African deserts (from Kenya northward), the Near East, and southern Arabia. It grows in savanna formation or as a single tree on the edges of the depressions in which water collects from the hillsides. It is found in association with other acacias and *Haloxylon* spp. in alluvial deposits of sand, flint, or limestone. The tortilis is found in extremely dry climates, with less than 100 mm (4 in) rainfall, and long dry seasons. It can survive where maximum temperature is over 40° C (104° F) and minimum temperature is close to 0° C (32° F). It regenerates from seed and coppice. It yields about 15,000 seeds per kg (6,800/lb); germination is 40 per cent if seeds are not attacked by insects. Seeds are germinated in receptacles after soaking in water for 24 hours. The

Fig. 6–6. Tortilis tree (*Acacia tortilis* Hayne) growing where the annual rainfall is 200 mm (8 in). This extremely drought-hardy species has been found in some areas that receive less than 100 mm (4 in) per year. (Photo M. Shaltiel)

Fig. 6–7. *Acer negundo* L. (boxelder) is commonly planted as an ornamental or shelterbelt tree in semiarid regions.

tree has been planted in Rajasthan under extreme drought conditions and on poor soil, and has grown better than in its native habitat. The wood is used as fuel.

Acer negundo L.   boxelder

A medium to large deciduous tree, up to 20 m (65 ft) tall, native to North America—scattered in the eastern hardwood forests and westward along streams through the Great Plains. It withstands drought and severe cold to −50° C (−58° F), or possibly lower. Good crops of seeds are produced almost yearly with about 18,000 to 30,000 seeds (samaras) per kg (8,000–14,000/lb). Seeds must be cold stratified for storage and germination. Germination is about 50 per cent. Plants from rooted cuttings are not nearly as satisfactory as seedlings. The tree has little value for lumber but is good for fuelwood. Although the sap is not as rich in sugar as some other maples, it can be used for making sugar. It is useful as an ornamental or for roadside planting. Widely introduced into semiarid zones, it has been planted in shelterbelts on the steppes of USSR where the yearly precipitation is about 300 mm (12 in).

Acer syriacum Boiss. & Gaill.   Syrian maple

A small tree, up to 6 m (20 ft) high, and a typical constituent of the Mediterranean scrub in the Near East. It usually grows at medium altitudes on northern slopes and on rocky ground, where rainfall is 600 mm (24 in) or more annually. It produces valuable wood and is used as an ornamental.

Ailanthus altissima (Mill.) Swingle   tree of heaven
[A. glandulosa Desf.]

A large deciduous tree, up to 20 m (65 ft) tall, native to northern China but widely cultivated in many countries. It grows on a variety of soils, from sandy to light clay, and can be planted on eroded soil. Tree of heaven is found in temperate to subtropical climates with low rainfall, 350–600 mm (14–24 in), with 8 dry months. Though it withstands drought and some frost, it may be killed back by severe cold. It is a very fast-growing tree, with an open canopy reaching a height of 15 m (50 ft) or more in 25 years, and a straight trunk for 10–12 m (30–40 ft). Not attacked by insects, it regenerates abundantly from seed and easily from root cuttings, and reproduces profusely from root-suckers. It flowers in early spring, and its fruit ripens in autumn and persists through the winter. After collection, the samaras are air dried and may be sown without further extraction. There are about 27,000 seeds per kg (12,000/lb), and germination of stratified seed is 40–90 per cent. Seed can be stored dry, sealed, cold for two years without

Fig. 6–8.   The tree of heaven [*Ailanthus altissima* (Mill.) Swingle] is known for its ability to resist atmospheric impurities when planted in industrialized areas.

losing viability. In nurseries, seeds are sown in rows; seedlings are ready for field planting as naked-rooted stock after 8 to 10 months. This species is planted mainly as an ornamental tree and for conservation of soil, especially on eroding slopes, where it spreads rapidly by root-suckers. The wood is suitable for cellulose manufacture. It should not be planted on roadsides where its root suckers can invade nearby fields. It has been introduced in many parts of the world and into most arid zones. Because of the disagreeable odor of the male flowers, only female trees should be used in amenity planting.

Albizia lebbek (L.) Benth.   siris
A large deciduous tree of tropical and subtropical climates. Its natural habitat is from the Indian sub-Himalayas to Burma and the Anda-

man Islands. Found in altitudes as high as 1,200 m (4,000 ft), it grows in forests mixed with other trees, but is planted as a garden and avenue tree in the drier parts of India and North Africa. It can grow on a variety of soils where annual rainfall varies from 500 to over 2,000 mm (20–79 in); in its native habitat summers are wet. It is resistant to drought and mild frosts. It grows rapidly on good soils, sometimes reaching a diameter of 40 cm (16 in) in 10 years. Seeds are produced annually in great quantities—about 10,000 seeds per kg (4,500/lb)—and should be collected as soon as they ripen, to prevent loss by insects. Germination is 50 to 90 per cent for seeds pretreated with boiling water. Extracted by first drying the pods in the sun and then beating them lightly, seeds are easily stored and retain their viability for four or five years with little loss when kept in a cloth sack under room conditions. Before sowing in the nursery, seeds should be poured into boiling water and allowed to soak for 24 hours as the water cools. Seeds should be sown in March. Siris can be propagated by cuttings, root-shoot cuttings, or by seeding directly in the field. The area planted should be cleared of competing vegetation by repeated cultivation. The wood is used for furniture and for wheel work. The tree produces a gum similar to that of gum arabic. Leaves are good camel fodder and are considered moderately palatable. Dry leaves contain 30 per cent crude protein. This species has been widely planted in northeast Africa, India, Pakistan, and some countries of South America.

Alnus orientalis Decne.   eastern alder

A medium-sized deciduous tree, native to the eastern Mediterranean region. It grows in wet areas and along rivers at low to medium altitudes. Its fruit is borne in clusters of small, woody catkins which should be collected as soon as ripe and air dried to release the seed. The seed —actually the fruit—is a small, unwinged nutlet yielding about 1 million per kg (450,000/lb). Based on the recommendations for other species of alder, seeds should be stratified in sand at 5° C (41° F) for 60 to 90 days to overcome embryo dormancy. Alder seeds lose their viability rapidly when kept in open containers; dry, sealed, cold storage is therefore suggested. Eastern alder is a useful species for planting on the banks of rivers and water channels. The wood is used for furniture, paneling, and floor blocks.

Araucaria heterophylla (Salisb.) Franco [*A. excelsa* R. Br.]
                                                  Norfolk Island pine

A large, evergreen conifer that may attain a height of 60 m (200 ft) and a diameter of 3 m (10 ft). Its natural range is confined to Norfolk Island but the species is naturalized in northeastern Australia and is widely planted as an ornamental in mild-temperate to tropical cli-

Fig. 6–9. Norfolk Island pine (*Araucaria heterophylla* (Salisb.) Franco Christmas tree plantation in Hawaii. (Photo D. Fullaway)

mates. Found up to 300 m (1,000 ft) asl, it grows well on most soils where the annual rainfall exceeds 600 mm (24 in). It is sensitive to frost and drought and cannot stand intense sunlight; it should be shaded until 2 m (6.5 ft) high. It is fast-growing and regenerates well from fresh seed. Seeds are easily extracted by breaking the large cone. Between 1,300 and 2,000 seeds per kg (600–900/lb) are produced. Seeds should be treated with a fungicide and either planted immediately or stratified. Seed is difficult to store; cold storage in sacks or dry sand is recommended. The wood is used for lumber and in carpentry. The tree is planted extensively as an ornamental in gardens in semiarid zones, and is much in demand as a Christmas tree.

Arbutus andrachne L.　　　　　　　　　　　　　　　strawberry tree

A quite common evergreen shrub or small tree from 3 to 9 m (10–30 ft) tall. It is found in Greece and the eastern Mediterranean maquis on a variety of soils, but grows best on well-drained soils and generally requires shade; it is not frost-hardy. It bears attractive red friut that yields about 500,000 clean seeds per kg (230,000/lb). To hasten ger-

Fig. 6–10. *Arbutus andrachne* L. (strawberry tree) is noted for its attractive red fruit.

mination, soak seeds 5–6 days in warm water or, based on recommendations for other species, stratify at 5° C (41° F) for 90 days. Although the dried berries can be stored for one or two years at room temperature, only clean seeds should be stored for longer periods. Dry, cold, sealed storage is recommended. The wood is used for furniture and the tree is valuable to beekeepers.

Argania sideroxylon Roem. & Schult. [A. spinosa Skeels.]   **argan tree**
    A small to medium-sized spreading tree, up to 10 m (33 ft) tall, native to the arid Atlantic coastal hills of south Morocco and southward to the edge of the Sahara. It grows on poor soil and between rocks, but is not found on sands. It forms open stands where the annual rainfall is between 100 and 200 mm (4–8 in) and the summers are nearly rainless. The tree grows up to 1,500 m (5,000 ft) asl. It cannot withstand cold but does resist extreme heat and drought. It regenerates well from seed and coppice, and seeds abundantly, with about 500 seeds per kg (230/lb). Average germination is about 50 per cent; it is planted only as balled stock. It is of great importance to local inhabitants because

Fig. 6–11. *Argania sideroxylon* Roem. & Schult. (argan tree) in Morocco. The fruit is the source of argan oil used locally in cooking. (Photo G. Giordano; courtesy American Geographical Society)

an oil squeezed from the fruit is used as a substitute for olive oil. Its wood is heavy and is used in construction and carpentry and for charcoal; its fruit (nuts of argan) and foliage are eaten by cattle and goats. Goats may often be seen climbing in the trees to browse. The tree has not been planted outside Morocco, except in arboretums. In its native habitat it is severely infested by the Mediterranean fruit fly.

Aspidosperma quebracho-blanco **Schlecht.**   **white quebracho**
A very slow-growing, evergreen tree with a short, clear bole and a small crown with drooping (weeping) branches; up to 30 m (100 ft) tall. It is drought-resistant because of its very deep taproot which may penetrate to 16 m (53 ft). The surface roots do not interfere with the establishment of grass which may grow right up to the trunk. The tree is native to northern Argentina, Bolivia, and Paraguay and grows in association with quebracho colorado (*Schinopsis lorentzii* Engelm.) and various species of *Prosopis, Caesalpinia, Acacia, Zizyphus,* and *Bulnesia*. It is found on sandy soil, usually in flat country, where rainfall is normally 300–900 mm (12–35 in), but may be as little as 200 mm (8 in). It requires average temperatures of 15° C (59° F) in winter and 25° C (77° F) in summer. The fruit matures in December, or in

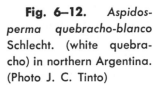

Fig. 6–12. *Aspidosperma quebracho-blanco* Schlecht. (white quebracho) in northern Argentina. (Photo J. C. Tinto)

the rainy season of the region in which the tree grows. In good seed years, a tree may produce 300 to 400 capsules, each containing approximately 30 samara-like seeds; average production is about 4,000 seeds per kg (1,800/lb). Seeds remain viable for 6 to 12 months, and are wind disseminated. In favorable sites, when the rain wets the soil, the seeds germinate and the strong taproot of the seedling follows the infiltrating rain water deep into the soil. Few tests of artificial regeneration have been made because of the extremely slow growth of this species. Only a few small plantations (chiefly in northern Argentina) have been established. The wood, which is yellow, hard, and heavy, is used for building construction, firewood, and after preservative treatment for railway sleepers, posts, and poles.

Azadirachta indica A. Juss.   neem

An evergreen tree, usually from 10 to 15 m (30–50 ft) high, with a fairly dense, large, rounded crown. Native to the dry regions of the Irrawaddi valley of Burma and the Siwalik hills of India, this tree grows on a variety of soils—clay, sand, or black cotton soil. It occurs in dry, subtropical climate with from 400 to 1,100 mm (16–44 in) of rainfall. Neem coppices well, produces root suckers, and is also propagated by seed. About 4,000 seeds per kg (1,800/lb) are produced, and the average germination is 75 per cent. Seed is extracted from the fruit by allowing the pulp to rot away. Seeds must be sown immediately because they lose their viability a few weeks after they ripen. Neem has been planted in dry areas of India and Africa, mainly as a garden or roadside tree. It does well when given some irrigation. Its wood is hard and is used for furniture.

Balanites aegyptiaca (L.) Del.   **desert date, heglig tree**

Desert date is a thorny bush or small tree usually from 5 to 7 m (15 to 23 ft) tall but occasionally reaching 10 m (33 ft). An evergreen tree, although it drops part of its leaves during the dry season. It is indigenous to the savannas and drier regions of northern Africa from the Atlantic coast to the Red Sea region and southward to Tanzania and northern Rhodesia in areas with 250 to 800 mm (10 to 32 in) of rain per year. In the drier areas it is confined to sites with available ground water such as river banks. Desert date grows mainly on dark clay soils, but can be found on a great variety of other soils. However, on sandy soils growth is poor and only scattered trees occur. It is usually associated with several species of *Acacia,* but pure stands can be found, especially where other species have been cut for firewood or to clear land for cultivation and the desert date has been left because of the value of its fruit. It has a wide-spreading, deep root system with a tap root that may penetrate to a depth of several meters. Little work has been done on artificial regeneration, but a few trials indicate that desert date can be established by direct seeding. Cut trees coppice readily.

Desert date is grown mainly for its fruit which ripens from August to December depending on the local climate. The fruit is a yellowish drupe about 2.5 to 5.0 cm (1 to 2 in) long with a sticky, edible pulp covering a large pit enclosing an oily seed. The pulp contains up to 40 percent sugar and is collected and dried by nomadic tribes as a reserve food to be used when other food is scarce. There are from 70 to 100 whole fruits per kilogram (30 to 40 per lb). Fruit should be picked from the tree as soon as it ripens and not allowed to drop to the ground where they are often attacked by a borer. An emulsion made from the fruit is lethal to the snails which are the intermediary host of *Bilharzia* and to the water flea that carries the Guinea-worm disease. Since the fruit is not toxic to man or domestic animals, wells and water supplies can be safely treated.

Poles cut from the trees are used locally in building houses. It also produces a good quality firewood. The wood is fine-grained and durable and easy to work. It can be used in turnery but problems are encountered with some trees due to the fluted stem and ingrown bark. Leaves are used as fodder and a saponin in the roots, bark, wood chips, and fruit provides a soap for washing clothes.

Bauhinia purpurea L.   **bauhinia**

A small, deciduous tree from 4 to 6 m (13–20 ft) high, indigenous to India, Burma, and south China. It grows in a subtropical climate on sandy soils, and will grow rapidly under favorable conditions. Its profuse flowers vary from a rich purple to white, and its fruit matures in January or March. Seeds germinate readily and retain viability well in storage; germination percentage is high. Seeds are sown in the nursery during April and May in India and can be transplanted during the first rains. Bauhinia is planted as an ornamental in parks and gardens in many semiarid-zone countries. The wood is moderately hard but of little or no commercial value. The leaves are given to cattle as fodder. Various parts of the plant are used medicinally; however, the bark of the root is poisonous, even in small quantities.

Boswellia serrata Roxb.   frankincense

A small, deciduous tree, up to 5 m (16 ft) tall, native to northeastern Africa and India. Drought-resistant, it grows in areas with about 150–200 mm (6–8 in) rainfall and with 7 or 8 dry months, and is found on thin, poor soils. Natural seedlings frequently establish themselves in cracks of large boulders. The tree reproduces by seed, but artificial reproduction is usually by cuttings which root easily. Trees are tapped in India to obtain frankincense, a gum resin used in medicines, incense, and perfumes. The wood is soft and spongy and while not used for lumber, it can be made into paper of good quality. It is now being planted in India for pulpwood. The leaves are eaten by goats and camels.

The closely related species, *B. carterii* Birdw., which grows in northeastern Africa and Arabia, is one of the leading species tapped for frankincense. The production of frankincense could be increased by planting.

Brachychiton populneum (Schott) R. Br.   kurrajong

A smooth-barked, evergreen tree of eastern Australia; attains a height of about 15 m (50 ft). It usually grows on sandy soil of limestone formations and is not found on acid soil. Found in a warm, dry climate with minimum rainfall of about 250 mm (10 in) and an eight-month dry season, it cannot stand frost. This is a fast-growing tree with a stem that is conspicuously swollen near the ground. Seeds are borne in follicles, with about 9,900 per kg (4,500/lb). Kurrajong may be grown in beds, but is usually propagated as potted stock. Its leaves and branches are useful as fodder in drought years. It will stand lopping, and is planted mainly as an ornamental for roadsides and homesteads in arid zones.

Bulnesia retamo Griseb.   retamo

A tree from 6 to 8 m (20–26 ft) tall, native to northern Argentina. It occurs on sandy, mainly alluvial, soils up to an elevation of 300 m (1,000 ft) asl, in areas of 100–300 mm (4–12 in) rainfall. Its growth is very slow. The tree attains its maximum height in the higher rainfall areas and is only a bush in the drier parts of its range. It regenerates from seed and cuttings. There are approximately 45,000 seeds (actually

Fig. 6–13. *Brachychiton populneum* (Schott) R. Br. (kurrajong) is notorious because of the damage its roots cause to paved surfaces.

samaras) per kg (20,000/lb). Seeds lose their viability rapidly and are difficult to store. The species is grown in beds in the nursery. Its wood is used in carpentry, but it is mainly valued for vine supports because it is extremely durable (it remains sound for 15 to 20 years in the ground without preservative treatment). Since this species is very resistant to drought and cold, it is used in extremely arid zones for soil conservation along gullies. Its branches are covered with a layer of vegetable lard which is thickest in the more arid zones and becomes thinner as the rainfall increases. The lard is extracted commercially.

Calligonum comosum L'Herit.   calligonum
A tall, nearly leafless shrub or small tree common in North African and Near Eastern deserts. It is mostly confined to dunes where the annual rainfall is from 50 to 175 mm (2–7 in). Its fruit, an achene covered with bristles, produces a burr-like sphere about 1.3 cm (0.5 in) in diameter that is easily rolled by the wind over the sands. The fruit ripens from late spring to early summer; the mature fruit drops almost immediately. Seeds (i.e., the fruit) may be gathered from the ground

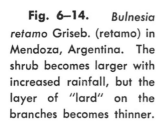

Fig. 6–14. *Bulnesia retamo* Griseb. (retamo) in Mendoza, Argentina. The shrub becomes larger with increased rainfall, but the layer of "lard" on the branches becomes thinner.

Fig. 6–15. *Bulnesia retamo* Griseb. (retamo). In the more arid zones the shrubs are small, but the layer of "lard" on the branches is thick.

or stripped or shaken from the bushes onto canvas. To dry them, they are spread on the sand in a layer about 10 cm (4 in) deep which should be stirred from time to time. There are about 30,000 fruits per kg (13,600/lb). Germination is inhibited by light. Seeds should be sown on sand and covered with a sand mulch 2 cm (0.8 in) deep; uncovered seeds will not germinate. The species is a valuable sand binder on inland dunes. A closely related species occurs in Pakistan.

Fig. 6–16. White cypress pine (*Callitris glauca* R. Br.) on sandy soil near sea level in an area that receives 400 mm (16 in) of rain a year.

Callitris glauca R. Br.   white cypress pine

An evergreen conifer; normally 20 m (65 ft) tall, but in the dry plains may be no more than 6 m (20 ft). A native of Australia, principally of New South Wales and Queensland, it also occurs in the other states on the continent. Usually found on good, sandy loam, it also grows on poor, sandy soils. Climate of its habitat is warm-temperate to subtropical with 150–650 mm (6–26 in) rainfall, and temperatures that generally range between 10° and 30° C (50°–86° F), but it can withstand light frost. This species grows slowly, and produces some seed every year; it also reproduces by coppice. Its timber is resistant to termite attacks and decay, and is used for poles and posts. The wood is used for carpentry and construction. It can be planted in hot, arid zones and is suitable for shelterbelts.

Caragana arborescens Lam.   pea tree

A deciduous, spiny shrub or small tree, up to 5 m (16 ft) high, indigenous to Siberia and Manchuria. Usually it produces yellow flowers,
although some varieties have white or pink flowers. It grows in almost
any soil, but is best adapted to sandy soil, and can be successfully
grown where the precipitation is no more than 350 mm (14 in) per
year and winter temperatures drop to −40° C (−40° F). To prevent
loss of seed, pods should be collected as soon as ripe and opened by
air-drying. Seeds may be extracted by lightly threshing and can be
cleaned by sieving. About 28,000 to 48,000 seeds per kg (13,000–22,000/
lb) are produced. Seeds may be planted either in autumn or spring, but
should be soaked two or three days in tepid water before sowing.
Seeds may be kept for short periods under ordinary room conditions,
or for longer periods in dry, sealed, cold storage. The pea tree can
also be propagated by root cuttings. Commonly planted as a hedge,
it is useful in low shelterbelts and for erosion control.

Cassia siamea Lam.   cassia

A small, fast-growing tree that attains a height of 6 m (20 ft). Probably native to Malaya, cassia is commonly planted as an ornamental in
hot, arid areas, especially in Burma, Ceylon, and India, and is found up
to 600 m (2,000 ft) asl. It grows on well-drained, sandy soils and
occurs naturally in a tropical climate with 1,000 to 1,500 mm (40–60 in)
annual rainfall and 6 months drought, but is adaptable to as little as
500 mm (20 in). It withstands drought but not cold. Cassia seeds
yearly with about 30,000 to 35,000 seeds per kg (14,000–16,000/lb) and
germination of 75–80 per cent. Dry seed can be stored for several
years. Before planting, seed should be scarified by soaking in concentrated sulphuric acid for about 20 minutes, or covered with boiling
water and allowed to soak for 24 hours as the water cools. It reproduces by root suckers. The wood is resistant to termites and is used for
poles and posts and also for fuel. Leaves are fed to livestock. It is
planted mainly as an ornamental tree in gardens and on roadsides in
arid and semiarid areas, and is recommended for windbreaks, irrigated
plantations, and canal plantings. It has been widely planted in Africa
from Somalia to northern Nigeria where it has become naturalized in
many areas.

Casuarina cunninghamiana Miquel   river oak

An evergreen hardwood tree resembling pine, ranging in height from
12 to 30 m (40–100 ft), and native to northern and eastern Australia
and New Caledonia. It grows along the seacoast, as a gallery forest
along river fronts, and on silt loams, sands, and shingle terraces of old
river courses. It is found up to 1,000 m (3,300 ft) altitude. Its native

Fig. 6–17. Twelve-year-old river oak (*Casuarina cunninghamiana* Miquel) growing on sandy soil at sea level under about 500 mm (20 in) rainfall per year.

climate is temperate to tropical, with mean annual temperatures ranging from 13° to 27° C (55°–81° F); some stands, are subject to 50 or 60 frosts per year. Annual rainfall is from 500 to 1,500 mm (20–60 in); however, because of riverain site, roots have access to ground-water. "Cones" are dried in the sun for seed extraction. Seed number is about 500,000 to 1,650,000 seeds per kg (230,000–750,000/lb) and germination is up to 75 per cent. Seeds may be stored, sealed and cold, for two years. River oak is not as drought-resistant as *C. equisetifolia* Forst., but the wood is more valuable. It has been grown in most semi-arid zones as a windbreak. It produces excellent fuelwood, and the foliage is useful as emergency fodder during drought.

Casuarina equisetifolia Forst.   **casuarina, she-oak**

    A large, evergreen hardwood, up to 35 m (115 ft) high, producing a straight bole. Its natural range extends from Burma, India, Malaysia,

Fig. 6–18. *Casuarina equisetifolia* Forst. (she-oak). A 15-year-old planta-tion in an area of 500 mm (20 in) annual rainfall. (Photo M. Shaltiel)

and Indonesia into northern and eastern Australia. It grows on sandy soils and tolerates calcareous and slightly saline soils but does not grow well on clay and is very intolerant of shade. It is essentially a littoral species that grows best in pure stands near the seashore, but it can be found inland up to 1,500 m (4,900 ft) asl. In its natural habitat rainfall is from 700 to 2,000 mm (28–80 in) annually, with winter rain and a dry season of 6–8 rainless months, and the mean annual temperature is 20° C (68° F). It has been planted successfully in areas with 300 to 400 mm (12–16 in) of rain. It grows rapidly, and in favorable sites attains a height of 20 m (66 ft) in 10 years. Casuarina regenerates from both coppice and seed and produces good seed crops almost every year. "Cones" are dried in the sun for seed extraction. Seeds are small; about 700,000 per kg (320,000/lb) are produced, with germination of about 70 per cent. Seeds dried to a moisture content of 6 to 16 per cent retain viability for at least two years when stored at −7° or 3° C (20° or 38° F). Root nodules harbor nitrogen-fixing bacteria. When seeds are planted outside their natural range, the soil should be inocu-lated with crushed nodules from natural stands. This species is widely planted on all continents in favorable climatic regions for windbreaks, roadside and ornamental trees, swamp reclamation, soil conservation, and dune fixation. The wood is extremely hard, likely to split and twist. It is used for posts and poles and said to be one of the best fuelwoods.

Fig. 6–19. Atlas cedar, *Cedrus atlantica* Manetti, in the state forest at Sgag, Algeries. (Courtesy J. A. Urbanovski)

Cedrus atlantica Manetti   Atlas cedar

An evergreen conifer, up to 40 m (130 ft) in height. Its natural habitat is the mountains of Morocco and Algeria, where it grows between 1,000 and 2,500 m (3,300–8,200 ft) altitude. It regenerates well under *Quercus ilex* L. and *Q. pubescens* Willd. and eventually outgrows them and remains as a pure stand. The species occurs on deep, moist, permeable, sandy or stony soils and often on limestone or sandstone formations. Its habitat is in semiarid zones with 600–1,600 mm (24–64 in) rainfall, but it does well in areas with 700 mm (28 in) and grows in areas with only 500 mm (20 in) rainfall and with eight dry months. It can withstand temperatures to −15° C (5° F). It regenerates well from seed if conditions are favorable. Good seed crops are produced about every two to four years; cones are collected in the autumn, soaked in warm water two days, sun dried, and broken apart to release seed.

There are about 14,000 seeds per kg (6,300/lb), with 50 per cent germination. Seeds are oily and difficult to store; they generally lose their viability after two years, even if well stored. They are sown in receptacles in the nursery because the seedlings develop strong taproots. One- or two-year-old seedlings, or 1 + 1 transplants, are planted out. Atlas cedar is commonly planted as an ornamental. The wood is durable and is used in carpentry; it usually has a scent, but the odor is not universally liked. It has been planted in most semiarid areas of the world as a park and garden tree because it is cold- and drought-resistant and indifferent to soil quality, and also because of its beauty.

Cedrus brevifolia (Hook.f.) Henry   Cyprus cedar

Shrubby, evergreen conifer, up to 12 m (40 ft) in height, native to Cyprus. It grows at altitudes of 900–1,400 m (3,000–4,600 ft) asl. In its natural habitat, it receives about 900 mm (36 in) rainfall with nine dry months annually. It often grows on poor soil. It is frost- and drought-resistant, and is used in semiarid afforestation. Seeding, regeneration, nursery and plantation practices, and use of wood are the same as for *C. atlantica* Manetti.

Cedrus deodara (Roxb.) Loud.   deodar cedar

An evergreen conifer, up to 50 m (165 ft) tall. Its natural habitat is the western Himalayas (Afghanistan to Garhwal) at elevations of 1,200–3,000 m (4,000–10,000 ft). It grows on almost any soil except firm and badly drained; on poor, shallow soil its growth is stunted. It is found in summer or winter rainfall zones with as little as 500 mm (20 in) per year and withstands low temperatures to −12° C (10° F). About 8,000 seeds per kg (3,600/lb) are produced. Seeding habits, nursery and plantation practices, and use of wood are the same as for *C. atlantica* Manetti.

Cedrus libani A. Rich.   cedar of Lebanon

An evergreen conifer, from 25 to 40 m (80–130 ft) tall, indigenous to the Lebanon mountains and the Taurus and Anti-Taurus ranges of Turkey, at an altitude of 1,000–3,000 m (3,300–10,000 ft). Mediterranean climate, with 1,000 to 1,500 mm (40–60 in) precipitation and prolonged summer drought is its habitat, but it can withstand severe frost [arboretum trees as low as −20° C (−4° F) in Massachusetts]. It forms pure stands or is mixed with *Abies cilicica* Carr., oaks, and *Juniperus* spp., and occurs mostly on limestone. Yield is about 11,000 seeds per kg (5,000/lb). Seeding habits, regeneration, nursery and plantation practices, and wood uses are the same as for *C. atlantica* Manetti. Planted mainly as an ornamental, it is also suitable for afforestation in the western Mediterranean region.

Fig. 6–20. Cedar of Lebanon (*Cedrus libani* A. Rich.). A grove of ancient trees near Becharré. The stone wall was built in the 19th century to protect the trees from destruction by goats. (Photo V. U. Contino; courtesy FAO)

Celtis australis L.   **European hackberry, nettle tree**

A tall deciduous tree, up to 20 m (65 ft) high, with straight bole and often without branches for 12 to 15 m (40–50 ft). Native to most of the Mediterranean countries, it is found also in Iran, the Caucasus, and in the Himalayas as far east as Nepal. It grows on mountains up to 2,400 m (8,000 ft) asl, but usually below 1,500 m (5,000 ft). Occasionally found in swampy sites, it is more typical on dry sites, and occurs on clays and loams. It requires rainfall of 500–1,200 mm (20–48 in). The species regenerates from seed, with about 4,500 seeds per kg (2,000/lb), which when fresh are covered with a sweetish edible pulp. Pulp should be removed by macerating in water. Seed should be stored cold in sealed containers, and should be cold stratified before germination. The wood is tough, strong, flexible, and rot-resistant and is used in carpentry, especially for oars, tool handles, and agricultural tools. It is pollarded for fodder in arid parts of the range, and is planted as an ornamental.

A related species, *C. tournefortii* Lam., is also found in Asia Minor and Iraq.

Fig. 6–21. *Celtis australis* L. the European hackberry or nettle tree. A tall deciduous tree native to the Mediterranean countries, Ethiopia, the Caucasus, India, and Nepal.

Celtis occidentalis L.   **hackberry**

A medium-sized, deciduous tree, usually 9–15 m (30–50 ft) tall, but occasionally over 30 m (100 ft). It is native to the north-central and northeastern U. S. and extreme south-central and southeastern Canada. It grows on a variety of soils and sites, though in the Great Plains it is principally a bottomland tree. It is frequently found on limestone soils. In western Nebraska, it grows on north aspects in the sandhills. Sites with a permanently high watertable are unfavourable. It grows in a cold, dry to moist continental climate with precipitation from 360 to 1,500 mm (15–60 in), and can withstand temperatures from 40° to −40° C (104° to −40° F). Its drought resistance equals that of boxelder and black locust. Good seed crops are produced almost yearly, and seeds can be picked from the tree and depulped by macerating in water and then rubbing over screening. From 7,000 to 11,000 seeds per kg (3,000–5,000/lb) are produced. Seeds should be stratified for two to three months at 5° C (41° F) to overcome embryo dormancy. Germi-

Fig. 6–22. The hackberry (*Celtis occidentalis* L.) is frost-hardy and drought-resistant. This species has been commonly planted as an ornamental and windbreak tree in the Great Plains, United States.

nation may also be improved by scarifying seed for 15 to 20 minutes in concentrated sulphuric acid before stratification. Germination is usually between 30 and 70 per cent. The wood is heavy but rather soft and weak and is not often cut for lumber. Hackberry is commonly planted in dry, cold regions as an ornamental and a windbreak tree.

Ceratonia siliqua L.   carob
A small, crooked, branching evergreen tree, up to 8 m (26 ft) tall, native to the Mediterranean Basin and naturalized in northern India. It grows from sea level to about 1,000 m (3,000 ft) asl, and is found on calcareous soil, sand dunes, and Terra Rossa soils. Typical in semi-arid climatic conditions, it grows in open stands in association with

scrub oak and other Mediterranean maquis species. Slow-growing, this tree is not often considered a forest tree but is planted for the pods it bears every second year. About 4,000–5,000 seeds per kg (1,800–2,300/lb) are produced, with 80 per cent germination. Seeds retain viability for five years or more. Before germination, they must be pretreated in concentrated sulphuric acid for one or two hours, then soaked in water for 48 hours. Direct sowing without transplanting is said to produce superior stock. The pods have a high nutritive value for cattle.

Fig. 6–23. *Ceratonia siliqua* L. (carob.) A 10-year-old plantation in an area receiving 500 mm (20 in) of rain per year. (Photo M. Shaltiel)

Carob is planted about 100 trees to the hectare (40/acre) and must be well cultivated. When it is planted for its pods, care should be taken to grow at least 5 per cent male trees for pollination. Such trees should be grafted with known high-producing varieties. A large tree may bear up to 1,000 kg (2,200 lb) of pods in a good seed year.

Cercis siliquastrum L.   Judas tree, redbud

A small or medium-sized deciduous tree, up to 9 m (30 ft) in height, native to the eastern Mediterranean region. It grows with other broad-leaved trees where the rainfall is over 600 mm (24 in). Seed pods may be handpicked from the tree. There are about 30,000 to 60,000 seeds per kg (13,500–27,000/lb). Based on recommendations for related species, the seeds should be scarified by soaking in concentrated sulphuric acid for 20 to 30 minutes and stratified in moist sand for about 60 days at 5° C (41° F). Germination should exceed 70 per cent. Seeds may be kept for a few months under room conditions or kept in dry, cold, and sealed storage for longer periods. This species is widely planted along roads and as an ornamental because of the profusion of flowers that appear before the leaves in early spring. The wood is used in turnery and for fuel.

Conocarpus lancifolius Engl.   damas

An evergreen tree up to 20 m (65 ft) in height and 60 cm (24 in) in diameter. Natural stands are found beside intermittent (usually dry) watercourses of northern Somalia and in the Arabian Peninsula. Some of the streams have fresh water, but most are salty and sulphurous. The desert climate of this region is one of the harshest on earth. Rainfall varies from 75 mm (3 in) near the coast of the Gulf of Aden to 400 mm (16 in) near the top of the escarpment. During the summer the dry, hot air is landen with sand carried by a southwest gale. The maximum summer temperature in this area has reached 50° C (122° F). Winter temperatures are moderate and without frost. Conocarpus grows from sea level up to about 1000 m (3280 ft) a.s.l. It does well on deep soils ranging from clays to loams but has difficulty on shallow soils. It has few woody associates, the principal one being Zizyphus sp. It seeds profusely at an early age and regenerates easily on alluvium after spring or autumn floods. Seeds are scale-like and light, about 1,700,000 per kg (773,000 per lb). Germination is about 25 percent in the nursery. Usually 5 to 7 seeds are sown in each polyethylene bag; these germinate in 3 to 5 days and after a few days all but the most vigorous seedlings are removed. Newly germinated seedlings are highly susceptible to damping-off making pretreatment of seeds and the rooting medium essential. Shading is not necessary. Seedlings reach a height of about 45 cm (18 in) by the end of the year and are then suitable for field planting. Soil of the planting site should be carefully prepared to reduce competition and any subsurface layers that might interfere with root growth should be broken up so the roots can reach moist soil. Spacing between trees varies from 4.5 to 6 m (15 to 20 ft). Weeding and watering are essential after planting to insure establishment. Trees may reach a height of 20 m (65 ft) in 8 years provided that they are irrigated or the roots reach moist soil. The annual yield of one irrigated plantation was approximately 21 cu m per hectare (300 cu ft per acre). Without irrigation or ready access to soil moisture it grows much slower and on some sites may not reach usable size in a reasonable time. Trees planted in the Sudan usually form a single, straight, round stem whereas in its natural habitat it is a much branched tree.

It is a drought resistant species, at least in young stands, and is one of the more promising species for trial in arid areas. The wood is light colored and strong and is used for poles in house construction and in carpentry. At one time its chief use was for building dhows, the Arabian sailing ship; it is still favored for use as ship knees. The wood yields an excellent charcoal. Leaves and branches may be used as fodder and it is a very good shade and roadside tree. It is recommended for a variety of soil types including saline soils under irrigation.

Crataegus azarolus L.   **common hawthorn**

A slow-growing shrub or small tree, up to 8 m (25 ft) in height, with branches armed with thorns. Native to the Near Eastern scrub forests from sea level to 2,000 m (6,500 ft) asl, it grows on heavy soils in areas of from 300 to 1,000 mm (12–40 in) rainfall. It is extremely hardy, withstands drought, heat, and frost, and has edible fruit. It seeds yearly, with about 1,300 seeds per kg (600/lb), and reproduces by coppice. The recommended germination pretreatment for fresh *Crataegus* seed is stratification in peat for several weeks at 20° to 27° C (68° to 81° F), followed by 75 to 90 days at 5° C (41° F). The species is planted in gardens and for windbreaks and hedges. Other species of hawthorn are valued for their resistance to drought and wind.

Fig. 6–24. *Cupressus arizonica* Greene (Arizona cypress) planted in the Mediterranean region 400 m (1,300 ft) above sea level where the annual rainfall is 700 mm (28 in).

Cupressus arizonica **Greene**   **Arizona cypress**

A fast-growing, medium-sized, evergreen conifer, up to 20 m (65 ft) high, with a conical crown and usually with heavy branches. It is native to the mountains of Arizona and New Mexico. The best trees grow on moist gravelly soil, but the species is also found on dry, sterile, rocky, mountain slopes. It is found naturally in arid and semiarid climates with rainfall of 250–500 mm (10–20 in) and a mean annual temperature of 15° to 20° C (59°–68° F). It is resistant to drought and light frost, but is killed by severe cold. In its native habitat, it grows in pure stands at elevations of 1,500–2,000 m (5,000–6,500 ft) asl, but it can be successfully planted down to sea level. The tree reproduces from seed; from 60,000 to 100,000 seeds per kg (27,000–45,000/lb) are produced, with low germination (20–30 per cent). Its cones often remain closed and persist on the tree several years after ripening. They can be opened by drying in the sun. Cold stratification may improve germination of some lots. Seed keeps well for several years in cold, sealed storage. Glaucous foliage makes the species useful as an ornamental tree. Effective as a windbreak and for erosion control because of its fast initial growth, it has been planted widely in Argentina, Mexico, the Mediterranean Basin, and Australia. Its timber is very knotty but has been used for construction, posts, and fuelwood.

Cupressus lusitanica **Mill.**   **Mexican cypress**

An evergreen, coniferous tree, up to 30 m (100 ft) tall. It grows in Mexico, Guatemala, El Salvador, and Honduras between 1,300 and 3,300 m (4,300–10,800 ft) asl, and has been naturalized in Portugal and planted in Ethiopia, Kenya, South Africa, Australia, and Central and South America. The species grows on moist slopes and near streams. Climate of its natural habitat is mild to warm subhumid and humid, and it is only moderately drought-resistant. Cones may be opened by drying in the sun. It produces seed nearly every year, with 220,000–400,000 seeds per kg (100,000–180,000/lb). Germination is low to moderate and may be hastened by cold stratification. Seed should be stored in sealed containers at 5° C (41° F). Close spacing— 2 × 2 m (6.5 × 6.5 ft)—in plantations is recommended because of the tendency of the crowns to spread. The wood, which has a spicy, sometimes unpleasant odor, is very durable and is used for poles, posts, and general carpentry. The tree is commonly grown in shelterbelts. (Nomenclature of this species and its varieties is very confused, consequently the information on this species applies in part to *C. lusitanica* var. *benthamii* (Endl.) Carr. and perhaps to other varieties.)

Fig. 6–25. Mexican cypress (*Cupressus lusitanica* Mill.) 22 years old in a plantation near Guatemala City. (Photo L. R. Holdridge; courtesy American Geographical Society)

Cupressus macrocarpa Hartw.   **Monterey cypress**

A medium-sized, evergreen conifer, up to 20 m (65 ft) high, restricted in its natural range to the shores of Monterey Bay and Carmel Bay on the central California coast. It occurs on rocky sea cliffs on clay loam soil and occasionally is mixed with *Pinus radiata* D. Don. The climate is mild—temperatures seldom drop to freezing or exceed 32° C (90° F). Annual rainfall is 400–500 mm (16–20 in), but strong, moist sea winds keep the air humid during most of the year. A prolific annual seeder, the tree produces about 150,000 seeds per kg (68,000/lb)

Fig. 6–26. *Cupressus macrocarpa* Hartw. (Monterey cypress) has been successfully planted in the eastern Mediterranean region in areas receiving 600 mm (24 in) rainfall yearly.

with germination of about 20 per cent. Cold stratification may improve germination slightly. Seeds keep well in cold, sealed storage. This tree produces a fine-grained durable wood and it has been extensively planted in arid zones, mainly as an ornamental or windbreak, but occasionally mixed with other cypresses and pines in afforestation.

Cupressus sempervirens L.   **Italian cypress**

An evergreen, coniferous tree, up to 25 m (80 ft) high, native to the Mediterranean region—Greece, Turkey, Jordan, eastern Mediterranean islands, and Cyrenaica—and also found in Morocco. Found from sea level to 1,800 m (5,900 ft), it grows in a Mediterranean climate with 300–1,400 mm (12–56 in) annual rainfall. The mean annual temperature is over 10° C (50° F) and the minimum is −15° C (5° F). It is found on a great variety of soils and often on limestone outcrops, and is strongly wind- and drought-resistant. It develops a deep and extensive root system and forms dense stands except under semiarid condi-

Fig. 6–27. Horizontal cypress [*Cupressus semper-virens* var. *horizontalis* (Mill.) Loud.] may be recognized by its spreading branches.

Fig. 6–28. A narrow, fastigiate crown identifies *Cupressus sempervirens* var. *pyramidalis* Nyman (pyramidal cypress).

tions, where rather open stands occur. The species reproduces by coppice and usually is propagated by cuttings or seed. It produces good seed crops almost annually, with about 100,000–160,000 seeds per kg (45,000–73,000/lb). Cones may be opened by drying in the sun. Average germination is 30–40 per cent. Stratification for two to three months may hasten germination. Seeds keep well in cold, sealed storage.

The common variety with spreading branches, *C. sempervirens* var. *horizontalis* (Mill.) Loud., is recommended for planting in mountainous areas with at least 400 mm (16 in) rainfall. This is the preferred variety for windbreaks.

The cultivated variety with fastigiate branches, *C. sempervirens* var. *pyramidalis* Nyman, is an ornamental tree commonly planted in cemeteries. It is a characteristic tree of the landscape in many Mediterranean countries.

A strain that grows in Morocco is very drought- and frost-resistant.[1]

Cypress wood is used for carpentry, window and door frames, clothes chests, rustic furniture, poles, and posts. Its valuable wood, quick growth, and modest site requirements make it one of the most important trees for planting in semiarid areas, often in mixture with pines. It is planted in nearly all semiarid zones and, with irrigation, in many places in the arid zones.

Dalbergia sissoo Roxb.   sissoo, shisham

A large, deciduous, leguminous tree, up to 30 m (100 ft) high, indigenous from the Indus to Assam, and in the Himalayas. It occurs from lowlands to over 1,000 m (3,300 ft) asl, and is especially common along river banks. It grows in association with *Acacia catechu* Willd. on sandy alluvial flats, sandy or stony stream beds, or on cotton soils, if they are well drained and not too heavy and compact. Rainfall within its natural habitat varies from 500 to 2,000 mm (20–80 in), most of which falls during the summer monsoon from June to September. Temperatures range from just below freezing to nearly 50° C (122° F). Sissoo is a fast-growing tree. It reproduces vigorously by root suckers; production of suckers may be stimulated by trenching between plantation rows and cutting the surface lateral roots. The suckers that arise should be completely severed from the parent tree in one or two years. The tree is artificially propagated by seed, shoot cuttings, or root-shoot cuttings ("stumps"). Pods ripen from the end of December to February. They should be collected from the tree and not picked up from the ground. The first pods that fall when the tree is lightly shaken should be rejected. Ripe pods are black and should be dried in the

---

[1] Named *C. atlantica* by Gaussen, but not recognized as a species by Den Ouden and Boom in their Manual of Cultivated Conifers, 1965.

Fig. 6–29. Twelve-year-old plantation of shisham (*Dalbergia sissoo* Roxb.). (Photo M. Shaltiel)

sun after collection. About 45,000 to 55,000 clean seeds per kg (20,000–25,000/lb) are produced. However, it is difficult to extract seed from pods, so the pods are usually broken and pieces containing one or two seeds are sown. The broken pods should be soaked in water for at least 24 hours before sowing. Germination of fresh seed averages about 80 per cent. Seeds are easily stored for a year or more, but should be kept in tins to prevent rodent damage. Seeds are sown in the nursery in the spring, and seedlings are lifted and transplanted for root-shoot cuttings in their second season. Direct seeding is much less successful than stump planting, but if it is to be used the seeds should be soaked in water for 48 hours before planting. The soil should be thoroughly prepared before direct seeding and should contain enough moisture for germination. Sissoo should not be grown in pure plantations because of its susceptibility to damage by porcupines and some browsing animals. Plantations must be cultivated and weeded frequently. If sissoo is planted with *Morus*, it is likely to be crowded out in a few years by the new mulberry seedlings that establish within the stand. It is used in irrigated plantations in the Punjab outside its natural range. The wood is strong and durable with a nearly black, figured heartwood that is much used for veneers, carpentry, and fuel. Sissoo is commonly planted as an ornamental along roads and in gardens. It has been introduced into South America and the Middle East.

Delonix regia (Bojer) Raf.   flamboyant, poinciana

A flowering tree of Madagascar, from 12 to 15 m (40–50 ft) tall, that grows well on sandy loams in frostless countries. It has a spreading and picturesque crown with large, deciduous, feathery leaves and bright, scarlet flowers. Its pods are 30–60 cm (12–24 in) long and persist on the tree during the leafless period. It produces seeds annually, with about 2,200 seeds per kg (1,000/lb), and is easily propagated in nursery beds from seeds that have been soaked for three hours in concentrated sulphuric acid. Seedlings can be transplanted without difficulty. The tree is planted extensively in gardens, parks, and along roads and streets in semiarid zones, but it is somewhat objectionable because of its persistent pods and superficial root system and also because of the nests and tunnels of termites which frequently attack it. The wood is weak and soft and of little use except as fuel.

Elaeagnus angustifolia L.   Russian-olive

A small, spiny, deciduous tree, 4–6 m (12–20 ft) high at maturity, that is native from southern Europe to the western Himalayas. Asso-

Fig. 6–30. Russian-olive (*Elaeagnus angustifolia* L.) has been extensively planted as an ornamental and windbreak tree in cold, dry regions.

ciated in some places with species of *Salix, Populus,* and *Tamarix,* it usually grows on sandy soil, but can be found on almost any well-drained soil and can be planted on alkaline and saline soils. Trees in cultivation have withstood temperatures above 40° C (104° F) and below −40° C (−40° F). Very fast-growing, its growth often exceeds a meter per year for the first few years after planting. It seeds yearly with about 11,000 clean seeds per kg (5,000/lb). Stratification at 5° C (41° F) for 90 days is recommended to overcome slight embryo dormancy of some seed lots. Only clean seeds should be stratified. Average germination is 50–60 per cent. Clean seeds retain their viability for several years in dry, sealed, cold storage. The tree coppices and can be grown from cuttings. Its fruit is a one-seeded drupe, and the sweet, dry pulp of some varieties is edible. Planted extensively as an ornamental and windbreak tree on open, windswept, cold plains; it is also an excellent species for wildlife plantings. It is not a timber tree because of its branching habit and the crook of its stem.

Eucalyptus spp.   the eucalypts
See Chapter 5, Species Suitable for Forest-Tree Orchards.

Eucalyptus brockwayi C. A. Gardn.   Dundas mahogany
Natural stands of Dundas mahogany are restricted to a small area in the vicinity of Norseman, Western Australia. It is a fine, dry country eucalypt that attains a mature height of 15 to 25 m (50 to 82 ft) in a locality where the annual rainfall is from 250 to 325 mm (10 to 13 in). Widely spaced plantings on deep sandy loam near Broken Hill in eastern Australia have succeeded under an annual rainfall of only 225 mm (9 in), which is considered to be the minimum amount necessary for satisfactory growth. It can withstand light frost without damage. Viable seeds average about 350,000 per kg (160,000 per lb) and germinate readily without pretreatment. Dundas mahogany is relatively fast growing, reaching a height of 6 m (20 ft) in 6 to 8 years. Its crown is of medium size and rather open at maturity. It is recommended chiefly as an ornamental and shade tree for parks, groves, and roadsides. It may be used in mixture with other species in multi-row windbreaks. The wood is tough and straight grained and trees are cut for sawlogs and firewood. It is also used for poles and posts although it is not resistant to termites.

Eucalyptus camaldulensis Dehnh.   river red gum
A tall, evergreen tree, reaching a height of 40 m (130 ft) and a diameter of 2 m (6.5 ft). It is the most widely distributed of all Australian eucalypts and occurs in all states except Tasmania. Found up to 600 m (2,000 ft) altitude along rivers and streams, and at the edge of shallow depressions, it grows in pure, dense stands or in open, park-like forests. The species also occurs in association with various other euca-

Fig. 6–31. *Eucalyptus camaldulensis* Dehnh. (river red gum) in the 250–500 mm (10–20 in) rainfall zone of Victoria. This species is typically found along watercourses and around the edges of shallow depressions that are occasionally filled during the winter. (Photo W. G. D. Middleton; courtesy Forests Commission, Victoria, Australia)

lypts; among its more common associates are *E. melliodora* A. Cunn., *E. microcarpa* Maiden, and *E. ovata* Labill. Though it occurs on many different soils, its best growth is on deep, silty soils with a clay subsoil about one meter below the surface. In its native habitat it does not grow on soils containing lime or soluble salts. Rainfall in regions where it is grown ranges from 200 to 600 mm (8–24 in), with up to eight dry months. It also may be found on flood plains, where it is subject to one or more annual floods that may inundate the area for as long as 40 days. It is hardy down to −5° C (23° F), but cannot withstand salt spray. Fast-growing in favorable sites, it produces good seed crops every one or two years. Capsule-laden branches are cut or pulled from the tree. Capsules are air dried or sun dried for seed extraction; sieving removes leaves and sticks. Seed of this species is too small for efficient chaff removal. From 200,000 to over 1,000,000 seeds per kg (90,000–450,000/lb) are produced, depending on the provenance. Average germination is 90 per cent for fully ripened seeds. Pretreatment is unnecessary. Seeds are long-lived in dry, sealed, cold storage. Seedlings are usually grown in receptacles in the nursery. Fields should be planted 3 × 3 or 3 × 4 m (10 × 10 or 10 × 13 ft) and intensively cultivated. The tree coppices well for six or more rotations. It is too often planted on calcareous soils, where it becomes chlorotic. If "active lime" is prominent in the soil, even trees that grew successfully in the first rotation are likely to die after coppicing. This species has been extensively planted with great success in many semiarid zones of the world and successfully planted in irrigated plantations in some arid zones. It produces 10–25 m³/ha/yr (140–350 ft³/acre/yr). The wood is difficult to season, but is very durable and resistant to insect attacks and is used mainly for posts, poles, piles, sleepers, and fuel. It is also used in the cellulose industry for textile pulp, and to some extent for paper pulp by mixing with better pulps. The species is commonly planted along roadsides, in shelterbelts, and in farm wood lots and is of importance as a honey and pollen producer. It is recommended for all semiarid zones and for arid zones with at least 200 mm (8 in) rainfall. Its roots cover a large area and, therefore, it should not be planted in or near fields with crops, in vegetable gardens, or near orchards. The provenance of the seed is important in selecting drought-resistant plants, and several strains and hybrids are known.

Eucalyptus dundasi Maiden   **Dundas blackbutt**

Dundas blackbutt is a small tree from 9 to 18 m (30 to 60 ft) high at maturity. Its native habitat is limited to a small area in the semiarid zone near Norseman, Western Australia where the annual rainfall is 250 to 350 mm (10 to 13 in). Winter temperatures are moderate although an occasional light frost may occur. It has been grown without irrigation under about 225 mm (9 in) annual rainfall in western New South Wales. It is often found on gravelly loams or alluvial soils in the drier parts of its natural range. The average number of viable seeds per kilogram is about 390,000 (177,000 per lb). Pretreatment of the seed before germination is not needed. It has a dense crown and is a useful ornamental and shade tree in extremely dry areas with uniform or winter maximum rainfall. It is also used for fence posts, mine timbers, and firewood. It is tolerant to salt in the soil.

Eucalyptus gomphocephala A. DC   **tuart**

A tall, evergreen tree, up to 42 m (130 ft) in height, usually with poor bole form. Native to Western Australia, it is found in a narrow belt, often only 1.5 k (1 mile) wide, behind the coastal dunes. Its chief associates are other eucalypts, and it grows on sandy loams overlying limestone. It requires a mild climate, usually with frost-free winters [minimum temperature of −1° C (30° F)] and moderate summers, and an annual rainfall of 700–1,000 mm (28–40 in), with six dry months. Tuart is windfirm and drought-resistant. The interval between seed years exceeds three years. Seed extraction is the same as that described for *E. camaldulensis* Dehnh. From 100,000 to 200,000 fertile seeds per kg (45,000–90,000/lb) are produced. Germination usually exceeds 50 per cent, and seeds germinate quickly without pretreatment. Its timber, one of the heaviest, strongest, and most durable (except for termite attacks) produced in Australia, is used for sleepers and construction of railway carriages and contains tannin. The tree is frequently used in afforestation in arid zones, especially in the southern Mediterranean Basin. Unfortunately it is too often planted in zones with less than 250 mm (10 in) rainfall, where it fails in a few years. It can be planted as forests and shelterbelts in soils with some lime content, and along sea shores. Although it is more tolerant to salt-laden wind from the sea than *E. camaldulensis* Dehnh., the leaves will be severely damaged; it should not, therefore, be planted on sites directly exposed to such winds. It is a good producer of honey.

Eucalyptus gracilis F. Muell.   yorrell

Yorrell is a small tree from 8 to 12 m (25 to 60 ft) high. Its native habitat is the dry zone from central Western Australia eastward to western Victoria and southwestern New South Wales. Annual rainfall within its natural range is 250 to 450 mm (10 to 18 in). Summer temperatures are moderate to hot and winter temperatures moderate to cool with an occasional frost. Yorrell grows best on sandy soil and is fairly tolerant of salt. There are about 560,000 viable seeds per kilogram (255,000 per lb). Before sowing the seed should be scarified by tumbling in a drum with an abrasive lining. Yorrell is recommended for planting as a shade tree or in windbreaks where the annual rainfall is as low as 275 mm (11 in). The wood is hard and durable but it is subject to termite attacks so it is not recommended for use in the ground.

Eucalyptus leucoxylon F. Muell.   white ironbark

An evergreen tree, up to 25 m (80 ft) high, found in Victoria, South Australia, and New South Wales on hills from 100 to 450 m (330–1,500 ft) asl. It grows in open forests with *E. sideroxylon* A. Cunn., *E. melliodora* A. Cunn., and several other eucalypts. Found on heavy alluvial soils, stiff clays, and sandy loams, it tolerates soil alkalinity. It grows in a mild, dry climate with 400–700 mm (15–28 in) rainfall occurring mainly in the winter. It withstands hot, dry winds and long periods of drought, and summer temperatures may exceed 40° C (104° F); 5–20 frosty days may occur in winter. The tree coppices well and produces some seed yearly; about 200,000 seeds per kg (90,000/lb) with 25 per cent germination. Its wood is hard and heavy, and is used for sleepers, hewn timbers, and firewood. It can be planted in shelterbelts and plantations, and it produces honey of good quality.

Fig. 6–32. A plantation of tuart (*Eucalyptus gomphocephala* A. DC) in the eastern Mediterranean region at 300 m (1,000 ft) above sea level in the 600 mm (24 in) rainfall zone.

Fig. 6–33. White ironbark (*Eucalyptus leucoxylon* F. Muell.) growing in association with *Callitris* (large tree at right), casuarina (small trees with dense crowns to left), and acacia (foreground). (Photo W. G. D. Middleton; courtesy Forests Commission, Victoria, Australia)

Fig. 6–34. *Eucalyptus melliodora* A. Cunn. (yellow box) growing in association with *E. leucoxylon* F. Muell. and *E. hemiphloia* F. Muell. in the 500 mm (20 in) rainfall belt of Victoria. (Photo W. G. D. Middleton; courtesy Forests Commission, Victoria, Australia)

Eucalyptus melliodora A. Cunn.   yellow box

An evergreen tree, up to 25 m (80 ft) tall, with a spreading crown and pendant twigs. Native to Victoria, New South Wales, and Queensland, it is found mainly between 150 and 600 m (500–2,000 ft) asl, but reaches nearly 1,200 m (4,000 ft) on the northern tablelands of New South Wales. It grows in open park-like stands in association with *E. blakelyi* Maiden and other eucalypts and is found on sandy loam and heavy alluvial soils, but not on poor sands. Yellow box can grow on soils with some lime content. Annual rainfall in its natural habitat is from 350 to 900 mm (14–35 in), with eight to nine dry months. It withstands drought and some frost [to −5° C (23° F)]. It is easily propagated from seed. Good seed crops are produced every two years, with about 165,000 seeds per kg (75,000/lb). The wood is hard and heavy and is used for firewood and posts. Yellow box is planted mainly as a roadside tree and for sheltering cattle; occasionally the leaves are used for fodder. It is one of the most valuable eucalypts for honey.

Eucalyptus microtheca F. Muell. [*E. coolabah* Blakeley & Jacobs]
                                                        flooded box, coolibah

Flooded box is native to the semiarid zones of northern Western Australia, Northern Territory, Queensland, and northwestern New South

Wales. It is able to grow on sites where the annual rainfall is as low as 200 mm (8 in), but it is more commonly found where the rainfall is from 250 to 625 mm (10 to 25 in) per year. Due to variations in site, it ranges in habit from a small, scraggly tree a few meters high to a fairly well-formed tree up to 20 m (65 ft) tall. It grows along streams or in areas subject to seasonal flooding, often occurring in pure stands. It can withstand an occasional light frost without damage. Flooded box reproduces by coppice or seeds. There are about 560,000 viable seeds per kilogram (256,000 per lb). Seeds must be exposed to light during germination. In the nursery, the seeds are sown directly into polypots. In about six months after sowing the seedlings will be 40 cm (16 in) tall and ready for field planting. On suitable sites with irrigation, height growth is rapid and may reach 2.5 to 3 m (8 to 10 ft) per year. Flooded box has been introduced into Iraq and the Sudan where it is grown on an 8-year rotation. It has grown well in Tanzania on black cotton soils subject to alternate flooding and drying.

Flooded box is a good tree for shelterbelt planting; it is windfirm and almost free from insect and fungal pests. It produces one of the strongest and hardest timbers in the world. The wood is difficult to work because of its interlocked grain. The wood is resistant to decay and termites. In dry areas poor stem form limits its use mainly to firewood, charcoal production, and fence posts.

Eucalyptus occidentalis Endl.   swamp yate

An evergreen tree, up to 25 m (80 ft) high, native to Western Australia. It grows in association with *E. astringens* Maiden on wet, clayey, alluvial peats, on sandy soils near swamps, and even on slightly alkaline or salty soils. Rainfall in its natural range is 300–550 mm (12–22 in), and it can stand light frost. It withstands extreme drought in plantations, even though its native habitat is marshland. Its growth is slow. About 350,000 live seeds per kg (160,000/lb) are produced. The wood contains 15–25 per cent tannin and is used in construction. Planting is mainly on dry, slightly saline sites.

Eucalyptus oleosa F. Muell.   giant mallee

An evergreen shrub or small tree, from 1 to 10 m (3–33 ft) tall. It grows in association with *E. brockwayi* C. A. Gardner in the interior of Australia where the annual rainfall is from 200 to 300 mm (8–12 in) and the minimum temperature is about 15° C (59° F). Found on Gray and Brown calcareous soils and sandy loam, it coppices freely. About 150,000 to 300,000 seeds per kg (70,000–140,000/lb) are produced; it is reported to produce about 44,000 seedlings per kg (20,000 seedlings/lb). The wood is brown, hard, and durable, and is suitable for fuel. Leaves yield essential oil. The aborigines obtain water from the roots of this

Fig. 6–35. *Eucalyptus oleosa* F. Muell. (giant mallee) on calcareous soil in the 250–350 mm (10–14 in) rainfall area of Victoria. (Photo W. G. D. Middleton; courtesy Forests Commission, Victoria, Australia)

and other mallees. At least eight varieties of this species have been named.

Eucalyptus rudis Endl.   moitch

An evergreen tree, up to 15 m (50 ft) high, usually with a short, stout bole. It is native to Western Australia. Annual rainfall of its habitat is about 900 mm (35 in), coming mainly in winter. It can withstand some frost. Its requirements and potential uses are similar to those of *E. camaldulensis* Dehnh. It does well in brackish swamps and grows on slightly alkaline soils.

Eucalyptus salmonophloia F. Muell.   salmon gum

Salmon gum is one of the best eucalypts for dry regions. It can reach a height of 12 to 24 m (40 to 80 ft) in areas where the rainfall is as low as 250 mm (9 in) per year. Its native habitat is the dry zone of Western Australia from Kalgoorlie westward to about 100 miles east of Perth. Annual rainfall in this area is 200 to 500 mm (8 to 20 in), summers are hot, and winters moderately cool with an occasional light frost. Its best growth is on red clay loams, but it also grows satisfactorily on soils ranging from sandy loams to fairly heavy clay loams. It can be grown on slightly saline soils. The average number of viable seeds per kilogram is about 530,000 (240,000 per lb). Seeds germinate well without pretreatment.

Fig. 6–36. *Eucalyptus rudis* Endl. (moitch). A large, much-branched tree. (Courtesy Forestry and Timber Bureau, Australia)

Salmon gum is a handsome tree for shade and ornamental plantings in parks and along roadsides. It is also a useful tree for multi-row windbreaks. It can be recommended for planting in areas where the annual rainfall is as low as 300 mm (12 in). The wood is dense, straight-grained, very strong, and durable, but susceptible to termite attack. It can be sawn for construction lumber or used for mine timbers.

Eucalyptus salubris F. Muell.   gimlet

Gimlet is a medium sized tree 12 to 20 m (40 to 65 ft) in height with a moderately dense crown. Its common name refers to its spirally twisted trunk which is especially noticeable in young trees. Its natural and climatic requirements are approximately the same as those of *E. salmonophloia* F. Muell. with which it is generally associated. The presence of gimlet is considered to be an indication of good loamy soils. It can tolerate small amounts of salt in the soil. There are approximately 260,000 viable seeds per kilogram (118,000 per lb). Pretreatment of the seed is not necessary.

Gimlet is suitable for ornamental plantings or for use in multi-row windbreaks in areas where the rainfall is as low as 250 mm (10 in). The wood is heavy, strong, straight-grained, and durable, but is subject to termite attacks. Its principal uses have been for poles, posts, mine timbers, and firewood.

Eucalyptus sargenti Maiden   Salt River mallet

Salt River mallet is an attractive, somewhat bushy, small tree from 8 to 12 m (25 to 35 ft) tall. It has a very restricted distribution in the dry zone of southwestern Western Australia around the Salt River near Lake Mears. Annual rainfall in this area is from 300 to 450 mm (13 to 18 in) with a marked winter maximum. Summers are hot and winters moderately cool with an occasional light frost. Salt River mallet is one of the most salt tolerant eucalypts. Where the salinity of some soils has increased in recent years killing the native trees, Salt River mallet has survived the longest. Its salt resistance makes it an extremely valuable tree for planting on saline soils outside its native habitat. The average number of viable seeds per kilogram is about 211,000 (96,000 per lb). The seeds do not require pretreatment before sowing.

Salt River mallet is one of the hardiest eucalypts of the dry country of Western Australia. Its principal value is for ornamental, roadside, and shade tree plantings. Given ample spacing, it has been successfully planted outside its natural range in areas with average annual rainfall as low as 225 mm (9 in) per year. However, it is not recommended for shelterbelt planting in areas with less than 375 mm (15 in) of rain per year.

Eucalyptus sideroxylon A. Cunn.   red flowering ironbark

An evergreen tree, up to 18 m (60 ft) high in dry areas but reaching 30 m (100 ft) in high-rainfall areas. A native of Victoria, Queensland, and New South Wales, at times it forms pure stands but usually occurs in association with other eucalypts such as *E. leucoxylon* F. Muell. and *E. microcarpa* Maiden. It grows from sea level to 500 m (1,650 ft) asl

Fig. 6–37. Red flowering ironbark (*Eucalyptus sideroxylon* A. Cunn.) in the 460–560 mm (18–22 in) rainfall area of Victoria. This species is usually found on hard-setting loam soils with a yellow clay subsoil of acid reaction. (Photo W. G. D. Middleton; courtesy Forests Commission, Victoria, Australia)

on poor shallow sands, gravels, or clay and is drought-resistant. The climate of its habitat is temperate to subtropical; rainfall is 350–600 mm (14–24 in) with seven to nine dry months. The tree withstands hot summers [maximum over 36° C (97° F)] and considerable frost [−10° C (14° F)], and resists hot winds. It seeds abundantly every year. Its fruits may be air dried or sun dried for seed extraction. Seed is cleaned by sieving, and there are about 100,000–200,000 seeds per kg (45,000–90,000/lb). Seed pretreatment is not needed. Germination of fully ripened seeds is 90 per cent, but seed quality is often low. Good seed keeps well for at least a year in dry storage. Seed provenance is very important; drought-resistant strains are found in low-rainfall areas of Victoria. The tree coppices well. The wood is hard, durable, and heavy and is used for sleepers and fence posts. The bark contains tannin. It is a fair producer of honey. The tree has been planted extensively in many arid and semiarid areas of the world with success. It is planted in areas of low rainfall, poor calcareous soils, and some frost. The increment may be as high as 9 m³/ha/year (196 ft³/acre/yr.) It is also planted as an ornamental for its crimson flowers.

Eucalyptus spathulata Hook.   swamp mallet

Swamp mallet is a shrubby mallee with a very restricted natural range in the semiarid region of southwestern Western Australia. Rainfall in this area is about 300 to 400 mm (12 to 15 in) per year, summers are hot, and winters moderately cool with an occasional light frost. It grows on medium to heavy loams on lakeside flats. Trees planted in arid areas usually have one short main stem near the ground and profuse branching above. This shrubby habit together with its small leaves makes it a desirable species for planting where a moderately open wind screen is wanted. Trees growing naturally are rarely over 6 m (20 ft) tall, but when planted on good soils in areas receiving over 400 mm (15 in) of rain a year, it may reach a height of 10 m (33 ft). A kilogram contains about 420,000 (191,000 per lb) viable seeds. Pretreatment of seed before sowing is not necessary.

Swamp mallet is recommended mainly for ornamental and roadside plantings and for use in low shelterbelts.

Eucalyptus tereticornis Sm.   forest red gum

A tall, evergreen tree, with a stout trunk up to 45 m (146 ft) high. Native to parts of New Guinea and the eastern coast of Victoria, New South Wales, and Queensland, it occurs on fairly deep, moist, sandy loams, and gravels of alluvial plains subject to some flooding, but not on acid soils. It grows in areas of warm temperate to subtropical climate with 500–1,500 mm (20–60 in) rainfall, and withstands frost [−5° C (23° F)]. The species occurs from sea level to over 1,000 m (3,300 ft) asl. It coppices well and seeds yearly. Seed extraction, pretreatment, and storage are the same as for *E. camaldulensis* Dehnh. About 200,000 seeds per kg (140,000/lb) are produced. Germination is 90 per cent. The wood has interlocked grain and is hard, heavy, and durable; it is used for mine props and posts. The species is frequently planted in afforestation in arid regions with calcareous soils and has many of the same qualities of growth and texture as *E. camaldulensis* Dehnh.

Eucalyptus torquata Luehm.   coral-flowered gum

Coral-flowered gum is a small tree usually from 6 to 9 m (20 to 25 ft) in height with a short trunk and a broad, dense crown. Its native habitat is in a small area south of Kalgoorlie, Western Australia where the rainfall is 200 to 250 mm (8 to 11 in) per year, summers are hot, and winters moderately cool with an occasional light frost. It is often found on moderately heavy, stony soils, but grows well when planted on well-drained loams or sandy soils in areas receiving up to 500 mm (20 in) of rain per year. It is tolerant to saline soils. It has grown well without

Fig. 6–38. *Eucalyptus tereticornis* Sm. (forest red gum). A species that has been widely planted throughout the world in tropical to cool-temperate climates. (Courtesy Forestry and Timber Bureau, Australia)

watering when planted outside its natural range in an area receiving about 225 mm (9 in) of rain per year. A kilogram contains about 90,000 viable seeds (41,000 per lb.). Seeds do not require pretreatment before sowing.

Its masses of coral-pink flowers make it one of the most desirable and beautiful of ornamental trees for parks, roadsides, and gardens in hot dry climates. Occasionally it produces a good crop of light amber honey.

Euphorbia tirucalli L.   milk-bush

An unarmed, succulent shrub or small tree, up to 15 m (50 ft) tall. Without true leaves, the "foliage" consists of a mass of thin, green branchlets. It grows in the semidesert of tropical Africa where the annual rainfall is less than 700 mm (28 in) and usually is found where ground water is available. Milk-bush can survive in the driest country where its fresh green appearance is a welcome change in an otherwise barren and monotonous landscape. It occurs in India where it has become naturalized. Though it is not frost-hardy, it can be planted in Africa up to 1,500 m (5,000 ft) asl. It is propagated only by the use of branch cuttings which should be set in the ground late in the dry season, just before the rains begin. Milk-bush is very useful as a hedge or low windbreak, and large trees yield some fuelwood. It is unpleasant to handle because the milky sap will cause extreme irritation if it gets into the eyes. It may also harbor rodents which burrow among its roots. Despite these disadvantages, it is a very useful species for windbreaks in dry, open country because it does not compete with adjacent crops.

Ficus sycomorus L.   sycamore

A medium to large, deciduous tree, up to 12 m (40 ft) high, with a wide, spreading crown. Native to the Sudan and Egypt, it is often found in groves near villages in the Near East. The fruit is edible, although it is smaller and less flavorful than the cultivated fig (*Ficus carica* L.). The tree is propagated by hardwood cuttings. It is suitable for roadside planting in dry, hot areas where the rainfall exceeds 200 mm (8 in) annually.

Fig. 6–39. *Ficus sycomorus* L. (sycamore) is frequently found in groves close to villages in the Near East.

Fraxinus syriaca Boiss.   Syrian ash

A medium-sized, deciduous tree, native from Syria to Kurdistan. It grows near springs or perennial watercourses on a variety of soils. The fruit should be gathered when ripe and either sown immediately or stratified. This is a valuable tree for planting along roadsides or water channels because of its fast growth and its fine timber.

Other species of ash, indigenous to parts of the Near East, have similar site requirements.

Gleditsia triacanthos L. honeylocust

A large, thorny, deciduous tree, up to 30 m (100 ft) high, native to east-central United States from Nebraska to Texas and eastward to Alabama and western Pennsylvania. Commonly planted outside its natural range, the tree is usually found on moist, alluvial flood plains

Fig. 6–40. *Gleditsia triacanthos* L. (honeylocust) derives its specific name from the branched spines borne in profusion on the trunk and branches. An unarmed variety is planted as an ornamental.

and limestone soils. It grows poorly on gravel or heavy clay. It has a high tolerance of alkalinity and some tolerance of salinity. Its natural range is mostly within a cold, temperate, continental climate with rainfall usually 500–1,000 mm (20–40 in) and temperatures from 40° to −40° C (104° to −40° F). It grows well in semiarid zones and reproduces by coppice. Good seed crops are produced at one- to two-year intervals. Pods are easily gathered from the ground or picked from the tree. Seeds are extracted by breaking the pods. About 4,000–9,000 seeds per kg (1,800–4,100/lb) are produced, and germination of fresh, pretreated seeds is over 75 per cent. To overcome seedcoat dormancy, seeds must be pretreated with concentrated sulphuric acid for one hour, or covered with boiling water which is then allowed to cool. Seeds may be stored for one or two years under ordinary room conditions. The viability of seeds is preserved for many years in dry, sealed, cold storage. Seeds should be fumigated before storage to prevent insect damage. The tree grows well in the Mediterranean Basin, Argentina, and Australia. The thornless variety is used as an ornamental. It is planted for erosion control, hedges, and shelterbelts on dry sites. Honeylocust may suffer some breakage in crowns during high winds. The wood is heavy, strong, and durable and is used for posts, sleepers, fuel, and lumber. The pods are eaten by cattle and wildlife.

Grevillea robusta A. Cunn.   silky oak

A large, evergreen, hardwood tree, up to 35 m (115 ft) high, native to New South Wales and Queensland. It grows best on sandy loam and other sandy soils. The annual rainfall in its natural habitat is from 700 to over 1,500 mm (28 to over 60 in), most of which falls during the

Fig. 6–41. *Grevillea robusta* A. Cunn. (silky oak) planted in a region receiving 500 mm (20 in) rainfall annually. (Photo M. Shaltiel)

summer, but it has been introduced into many areas with annual rain-fall of only 400–600 mm (16–24 in), and with six to eight dry months. It can withstand occasional light frost, but needs protection when young. Fast-growing, it reaches a height of 20 m (66 ft) in 15 to 20 years in sites with favourable soil and climate. About 80,000 to 100,000 seeds per kg (36,000–45,000/lb) are produced, and germination of fresh seed is 60–80 per cent. Seeds remain viable for only a few months after collection under ordinary storage conditions, but seeds dried to six per cent moisture content and stored at −7° or 3° C (20° or 38° F) are reported to keep well for two years. The wood is strong, hard, moder-ately durable, light-colored, and has a silky texture. It is used in cabinet work, furniture, and turnery, and for packing cases. This species is widely planted in semiarid zones in beekeeping areas and as an ornamental and roadside tree. It is also grown as a shade tree in tea and coffee plantations in Kenya, and in open grazing areas as a shade tree for cattle.

Haloxylon ammodendron Bunge [*H. persicum* Bunge]   saxaul

A tall shrub or small gnarled tree, up to 6 m (20 ft) high, native to Arabia, Iraq, Afghanistan, Turkestan, and Central Asia. It is usually found on sandy soils and dunes in areas of 100 mm (4 in) rainfall. A halophytic, desert tree, it cannot withstand low temperatures or high atmospheric humidity. Seeds (actually the winged fruits) are extremely small and light and do not keep well in storage; therefore they must be sown while still fresh. From 200,000 to 500,000 seeds per kg (91,000–227,000/lb) are produced. The species is useful as camel fodder, fuel, and for charcoal, and is suitable for binding inland dunes. Easy to establish, it develops a very deep and spreading root system.

A related species, *H. aphyllum* Minkw., can withstand cold and has been extensively sown in Soviet central Asia and Mongolia to fix dunes. Fixation of dunes in this area is necessary to increase the grazing capacity, to improve the scenery, and to protect railways, highways, industrial units, and oil installations from blowing sand. Seed is broad-cast from the ground or air over large areas while the soil is still wet after rain or snow melt. To prevent the seed from blowing away, dry brush barriers are erected in an open grid pattern. Although this is an expensive operation, it is widely used. Container plants are recom-mended for deep moving dunes. In Iran both seeds and container stock are planted to insure complete cover. This species is used principally for camel fodder and fuel.

Haloxylon articulatum (Cav.) Bunge   haloxylon

A tall shrub or small tree, 4–6 m (13–20 ft) high, with scale-like leaves, native to the eastern Mediterranean Basin, Arabia, and Iraq.

It usually is found on sandy soils and dunes in areas of about 100 mm (4 in) rainfall. Strictly a desert plant, it cannot withstand high atmospheric humidity. Seed (actually the winged fruit) is small and light and must be sown as soon as ripe because it quickly loses its viability in storage. Since it develops a very deep and spreading root system, the tree is suitable for binding inland dunes, but it is difficult to establish unless conditions are very favourable. It is also useful as camel fodder, fuel, and for charcoal.

Jacaranda mimosaefolia D. Don   jacaranda

A deciduous tree with a spreading crown, up to 15 m (50 ft) in height, native to Brazil, Bolivia, and northwestern Argentina. It is found on sandy loam soil. Its leaves are large and feathery and its flowers are various shades of blue, depending on the variety. About 66,000 seeds per kg (30,000/lb) are produced; however, it is usually propagated by cuttings of half-ripened wood. Considered by many to be one of the best flowering trees for subtropical regions, jacaranda has been extensively planted as an ornamental and avenue tree in many arid-zone countries. The wood has no commercial value.

Juglans regia L.   Persian walnut

A tall, deciduous tree, up to 27 m (90 ft) high, native to eastern Europe and southern Asia to northern Burma and found up to 3,300 m (11,000 ft) asl in the Himalayas. Extensively cultivated for its wood and edible nuts, it is planted in relatively moist areas in the semiarid zone with 600–800 mm (24–32 in) rainfall annually and dry summers. It grows best on deep fertile soils and should not be planted on heavy, badly-drained soil. It is regenerated by seeding, producing about 60–110 seeds per kg (27–50/lb). After collecting the seeds, remove the husks and stratify the seeds in moist sand at 5° C (41° F), or put them in a pit, cover them with dry earth, and leave them until time for spring planting. Seeds that have been properly handled should have a 70 per cent germination. The tree may be direct-seeded in autumn or early spring by dibbling or sowing in shallow trenches. Spacing distance should be 3–6 m (10–20 ft). Newly seeded areas should be protected by covering with thorny brush. Walnut does not grow well in exposed windy sites.

Juniperus communis L.   common juniper

A shrub or small, evergreen, coniferous tree, up to 12 m (40 ft) high, circumpolar in the Northern Hemisphere. The shrubby form is found from sea level to 4,000 m (13,000 ft) and grows in exposed sites and on dry, rocky slopes. Precipitation in its natural habitat is 350–750 mm (14–30 in), and temperatures range from 40° to −50° C (104° to −58° F). Seeds are borne in one- to three-seeded, berry-like cones, which require three years to mature. There are about 100,000 seeds per kg

(45,000/lb). Extraction, pretreatment, and storage are the same as for *J. scopulorum* Sarg. The wood is used for fuel. Oil from the wood and leaves is used in the manufacture of perfumes and medicines. The shrubby form is commonly planted as an ornamental and should be useful in control of gully erosion.

Juniperus excelsa Bieb.   Greek juniper
A tree, up to 20 m (66 ft) high, native to the mountains of the Balkans and Asia Minor, at altitudes from 1,300 to 2,100 m (4,300–6,900 ft) asl. The species often grows in pure stands, although locally it can be mixed with other junipers. Seeding habits and seed characteristics are similar to *Juniperus scopulorum* Sarg. Its wood is durable and suitable for turnery and railway sleepers. The tree can be planted on arid rocky slopes.

Juniperus scopulorum Sarg.   Rocky Mountain juniper
An evergreen, coniferous tree, up to 15 m (50 ft) high but usually only 6–8 m (20–26 ft). It is found in the dry zone of the Rocky Mountains

Fig. 6–42. *Juniperus scopulorum* Sarg. (Rocky Mountain juniper) in northern Colorado. A species of dry, exposed, rocky slopes.

and adjacent highlands from New Mexico to western North Dakota, westward to British Columbia, Nevada, and Arizona. It occurs on dry, rocky slopes and on sands and gravels of ravines, but achieves its best growth on soils that are calcareous and somewhat alkaline. It is commonly associated with *Pinus ponderosa* Laws. and *Pseudotsuga menziesii* (Mirb.) Franco. Precipitation in its natural habitat varies from 300 to 650 mm (12–26 in), and extreme temperatures are 38° and −37° C (100° and −35° F), but the tree grows best where the minimum is above −20° C (−4° F). Large seed crops occur at two- to five-year intervals. Seed is extracted by macerating the berry-like cones in water to which 1 teaspoonful of lye is added for every 4 liters (1 gal) to break down the resin. There are about 36,000–80,000 seeds per kg (16,300–36,300/lb). Seeds are spread by birds and mammals. Seeds must "after-ripen" for 14 to 16 months before germination. Pretreatment is needed to overcome embryo and seed-coat dormancy: cold stratification at 5° C (41° F) for 60 days followed by 30 days of warm stratification at room temperature [15° to 20° C (59° to 68° F)] after which the seeds are returned to cold stratification for the remainder of the treatment period. Soaking the seeds in concentrated sulphuric acid for one half hour before stratifying may be beneficial. Seeds are easily stored—dry, sealed, cold storage is recommended for prolonged periods. The wood is durable and is used for posts. Some wood is used for fuel, pencils, and lumber. The tree is very valuable in erosion control and shelterbelt plantings and is a desirable species for wildlife food and cover.

Juniperus virginiana L.   eastern redcedar

A small, evergreen, coniferous tree, usually about 10–15 m (33–50 ft) high, native to the United States east of the 100th meridian. It grows on a variety of soils from loams to dry, thin, rocky soils and frequently on limestone outcrops. It can tolerate soil alkalinity up to pH 8. Precipitation within its natural habitat varies from 500 to 1,000 mm (20–40 in) and temperatures range from 40° to −50° C (104° to −58° F). There are about 90,000 seeds per kg (41,000/lb). Extraction, pretreatment and storage are the same as for *J. scopulorum* Sarg. The wood is used for furniture, chests, paneling, pencils, and fence posts. These trees are commonly planted as ornamentals and in windbreaks.

Khaya senegalensis (Desr.) A. Juss.   dry-zone mahogany

A fairly large deciduous tree up to 30 m (100 ft) tall and 1 m (3.3 ft) d.b.h. with a wide-spreading crown. Native to the savanna south of the Sahara from Senegal and Gambia eastwards to Sudan and Uganda; often as a gallery forest along streams. Rainfall in its natural range is about 575 to 1,000 mm (23 to 40 in) per year. Can withstand long periods of drought if subsoil moisture is available. Natural reproduction is mainly by suckers. It produces seeds at an early age and may produce two crops per year. Collection time varies depending on the locality. There are about 3,800 to 6,000 seeds per kilogram (1,500 to 2,700 per lb). Germinates well, up to 90 percent, without pretreatment in 10 to 20 days after sowing. Seedlings require shade for a short time after germination, but shade must soon be removed to promote rapid growth. When grown in plantations this species is especially susceptible to attacks by the shoot borer (*Hypsispila* sp.) which results in a deformed tree of no timber value.

The wood is moderately hard and heavy and difficult to work. This species was the first of the African mahoganies to be exported for cabinet work and furniture manufacture. Recommended for planting as an avenue tree where irrigation is available. Branches are heavily lopped in some areas for cattle and camel fodder.

Laretia compacta Reiche [*L. acaulis* Gill. and Hook.]   yareta, llareta

A shrub, up to 2 m (6.5 ft) high and 2–3 m (6.5–10 ft) in diameter, resembling a large, green, stemless mushroom. Native to the high

Fig. 6–43. *Laretia compacta* Reiche (yareta) is a shrub up to 2 m (6.6 ft) high resembling a green, stemless mushroom. Specimen shown growing on the lower slopes of Mt. Licancábur, Chile near the Bolivian border.

Andes of Peru and northern Chile, it is found between 2,000 and 5,000 m (6,500–16,400 ft) asl. It grows in the protection of rocks and in the open on poor soils, and is found where the precipitation is less than 200 mm (8 in) per year. It does not grow in a forest formation but rather in the transition zone of grass and brush between two deserts. The branches, which are covered with resin that nearly cements them to each other, are used extensively as fuel.

Laurus nobilis L.   Greek laurel, bay

A tall, evergreen shrub, or rarely a small tree, up to 15 m (50 ft) high, native to most of the Mediterranean countries, at altitudes up to 1,000 m (3,300 ft). Confined to areas of 600 to 1,000 mm (24–40 in) rainfall, it grows in shady ravines or on northern slopes and requires a considerable amount of soil moisture. Usually it is reproduced by cuttings, which are set in sharp sand and covered with glass jars until they root. It is useful as an ornamental tree and for hedges.

Fig. 6–44. Chinaberry (*Melia azedarach* L.) is frequently planted as a roadside tree.

Melia azedarach L.   Chinaberry, Indian lilac

A deciduous tree, up to 15 m (50 ft) high, with a short bole and spreading crown, bearing handsome flowers, foliage, and fruit. It is thought to be indigenous to Baluchistan and Kashmir, but has been cultivated and naturalized in most subtropical and tropical countries. It occurs up to 2,500 m (8,200 ft) in the Himalayas and is found on a wide range of soils, but the best trees are on well-drained alluvial soils. The species grows in subtropical and temperate-warm climates receiving 400–1,000 mm (16–40 in) precipitation and having a mean annual temperature of 18° C (64° F). It is quite resistant to drought, and the older trees resist frost. It has very rapid growth and produces abundant seed crops nearly every year. Fruit should be collected in the early autumn or winter after leaf fall. The entire fruit may be planted or the pulp removed from the pit by macerating. From 1,400 to 2,500 fruits or 4,000 to 13,000 pits per kg (650–1,110 fruits or 1,800–6,000 pits per lb) are produced. Pits contain from 1 to 5 seeds which are not extracted. One fruit, or a single pit, may produce 1 to 5 seedlings; the average is 2 per pit. Average germination is about 65 per cent. Seeds should be soaked in water for a few days to hasten germination. Seed retains viability for one year under room conditions, and for several years in sealed, cold storage. The tree reproduces by root suckers and is an outstanding ornamental, but the crowns may be broken by high winds. The wood is soft with a red heartwood and is used for furniture, cigar boxes, and fuel. The pits are used for beads, and the leaves for goat fodder. It is planted in parks, along roads, and as a shelter tree for cattle.

Morus alba L.   white mulberry

A deciduous tree, usually 6–9 m (20–30 ft) tall, but occasionally over 15 m (50 ft), with a straight, cylindrical bole to 3 m (10 ft). Probably native to China, it is also widely distributed in Asia and southern Europe. It grows on sandy to heavy clay loams and even on gravelly and rocky soil, but not on strongly alkaline soil. It is resistant to drought and frost, but is short-lived. It reproduces by coppice and seed. Fruit is collected by shaking or stripping it from the tree. Seeds are extracted by flailing the dry fruit with sticks, or by macerating the fresh fruit in water and rubbing on a screen to release the seeds. There are about 250,000–700,000 seeds per kg (114,000–318,000/lb). Embryo dormancy can be broken by stratification in moist sand for 60 days at 5° C (41° F). Germination of treated seeds is about 70 per cent. For overwinter storage, seed may be stratified in fine, *dry* sand or ashes at 5° C; for longer periods, dry, sealed, cold storage is recommended. The species may also be propagated by branch cuttings and root-shoot cuttings. It is planted with *Dalbergia sissoo* Roxb. in irrigated plantations. The

Fig. 6–45. White mulberry (*Morus alba* L.) is cultivated for its edible fruit.

tree is cultivated for its edible fruit, for the rearing of silkworms, and as an ornamental. It does well under irrigation. The wood is used in cabinet work, musical instruments, and for charcoal.

Morus nigra L.   black mulberry

A small to medium-sized, deciduous tree, 6–9 m (20–30 ft) high, native to western Asia. It is similar to *Morus alba* L. in most characteristics. It cannot withstand severe cold, and is easily propagated from cuttings. The wood is used for furniture. Black mulberry is cultivated in Europe and elsewhere for its edible fruit. The tree is also planted as an ornamental and for its leaves in rearing silkworms.

Parkia clappertoniana Keay   West African locust

A deciduous tree up to 18 m (60 ft) high and over 1 m (3.3 ft) d.b.h. Found in the savanna from Ghana to Sudan mainly along stream courses. Also in the woodland of the "derived savanna" of West Africa that was artificially created when land was cleared for farming. This species is considered to be one of the most valuable of farm trees and is found on most of the farms in northern Nigeria. Grows on sandy soils. Best growth is where the annual rainfall exceeds 650 mm (25 in). Grows well from seed and transplants easily.

The wood is used mainly for fuel and a few minor local products. The seeds and a yellow mealy material around the seeds are used for food. The leaves are rich in nitrogen and are used in some places for fertilizer. It makes a good avenue tree in the drier regions.

Parkinsonia aculeata L.   **horsebean**

A small, evergreen, spiny tree, from 4 to 5 m (13–16 ft) in height. Its compound leaves are much reduced to "streamers" with tiny leaflets. Found from Texas through Central America and along the coast to Peru and Argentina, it grows in association with *Zizyphus* spp. and *Cordia* spp., forming an open community on dry gravelly or sandy river beds and alluvial fans. Dry tropical or subtropical climate is best, for it stands extremely dry conditions: rainfall from 200 to 350 mm (8–14 in), with nine dry months. It can also stand slight frost. The tree grows fast if irrigated, and seeds yearly. Seeds are extracted from pods by trampling or flailing. About 12,000 seeds per kg (5,500/lb) are produced; germination of pretreated seed is 85–90 per cent. Seeds should be soaked in water for from three to four days or scarified and soaked in warm water [38° C (100° F)] for one day. Horsebean is planted extensively as an ornamental in extremely dry areas, where very few other species can survive. It is used in soil fixation and erosion control.

Fig. 6–46. *Parkinsonia aculeata* L. (horsebean) planted in the eastern Mediterranean region with under 300 mm (12 in) yearly rainfall.

Peumus boldus Molina [*Boldea boldus* (Molina) Looser]   **boldo**

A small, straight-stemmed, evergreen tree, up to 8 m (26 ft) high. It grows in central Chile in a Mediterranean climate and coppices vigorously. The wood is extremely hard and is used for making many kinds of implements and tool handles. The charcoal is prized by smiths. Bark extracts are used for tanning and dyeing leather. Bark fiber is used for making ropes. Tea from the leaves is said to aid digestion. It is planted as an ornamental.

Fig. 6–47. Blue spruce (*Picea pungens* Engelm.) along a mountain stream in northern Colorado.

Picea pungens Engelm.   **blue spruce**

A handsome, coniferous evergreen, up to 50 m (165 ft) tall, found in the Rocky Mountains from Montana and Idaho to Arizona and New Mexico. It occurs singly or in small groves on moist soils, usually along stream courses, from 1,800 to 3,000 m (5,900–9,800 ft) asl. Commonly associated species are *Pinus ponderosa* Laws., *Pseudotsuga menziesii* (Mirb.) Franco, *Juniperus scopulorum* Sarg., and *Populus* spp. Blue spruce grows in cold mountain climate with 500–750 mm (22–30 in) precipitation. It has slow growth, but will grow on the driest site of any spruce and can withstand severe cold [−40° C (−40° F)]. A good seed crop is produced every two to three years, with about 200,000 seeds per kg (91,000/lb) and germination usually over 50 per cent. Stratification for 30–90 days at 5° C (41° F) is recommended to break dormancy of some seed. Commonly planted throughout the North Temperate Zone as an ornamental, it also is used for windbreaks in cold dry regions. It is very windfirm.

Pinus spp.   the pines
See also Chapter 5, Species Suitable for Forest-Tree Orchards.

Pinus brutia Ten.   brutia pine
A medium- to large-sized, evergreen, coniferous tree, from 20 to 30 m (65–100 ft) high. It is a species of northeastern Mediterranean countries, principally Turkey and Cyprus, but is also found in Crete, Greece, Syria, Lebanon, and Iraq, with varieties in Crimea and Transcaucasia. Commonly planted in Iran and Afghanistan. It grows on limestone and sandstone and almost every soil, except compact clays. It occurs from sea level to 1,400 m (4,600 ft) asl, with rainfall from 300 to 900 mm (12–35 in). It is very drought-resistant, and withstands hot climates and long rainless summers. It also withstands frost well. This pine is found in association with *P. halepensis* Mill., *P. nigra* Arnold, *Cupressus* spp., *Cedrus libani* A. Rich., *Abies cilicica* Carr., *Quercus* spp., *Juniperus* spp., and others of the scrub vegetation type, including *Erica, Arbutus,* and *Cistus.* Closely related to *P. halepensis* Mill., it generally has straighter form, especially in good climate and soil. Its form may also be affected by elevation. On the Taurus in Turkey it has good form between 400 and 700 m (1,300–2,300 ft) asl, but has poor form below and above this belt. It roots are deep; thus, it is often planted in poor, severely eroded soil. It reproduces well on mineral soil in its native habitat, if not grazed or otherwise disturbed. Natural reproduction is good. Large seed crops are produced nearly every year with germination usually about 75–80 per cent and about 17,000–25,000 seeds per kg (7,700–11,000/lb). Seeds are sown in nurseries in autumn or early spring. Usually no pretreatment is needed. Seeds in dry, sealed, cold storage remain viable for many years. The wood is used for general construction, poles, and boxes. The tree is tapped for resin production and is planted extensively in countries with Mediterranean climate. A quick-growing species, under favourable climatic and soil conditions, its growth may exceed 6 m³/ha/year (86 ft³/acre/yr).

Pinus canariensis C. Sm.   Canary Island pine
A large, coniferous, evergreen tree, up to 30 m (100 ft) high. Its natural range is limited to the Canary Islands where it grows on volcanic soils and deep, well-drained sandy or clayey loam soils over sandstone and granite. It requires a subtropical to warm-temperate climate, with annual rainfall of 400–650 mm (16–26 in) falling mostly during

Fig. 6–48. *Pinus brutia* Ten. (brutia pine) in the Taurus Mountains of Turkey at 600 m (2,000 ft) altitude. (Photo T. Beşkok)

Fig. 6–49. An open stand of brutia pine (*P. brutia* Ten.) in the Turkestan Mountains of northern Iraq.

Fig. 6–50. A 25-year-old plantation of Canary Island pine (*Pinus canariensis* C. Sm.) where the annual rainfall is 500 mm (20 in).

winter, and seven to eight dry months. In its native habitat it grows in an almost permanent mist, and the rhythm of growth is directly linked with the humidity of the air. When transplanted to drier areas, the stomata close when the humidity is low; its growth then depends on the frequency and duration of rains that increase humidity. The lowest temperature in its habitat is −8° C (19° F). It is a fast-growing tree; in favorable sites it gains up to 1.5 meters (5 ft) in height per year. Good seed years occur at two- to four-year intervals, with about 10,000–13,000 seeds per kg (4,500–6,000/lb) and germination of 40–60 per cent. Pretreatment is not required, and seeds keep well in dry storage. It is one of the few pines that coppices, but it does not coppice well. The wood is strong and is used in construction. The tree may be tapped for resin. Since it withstands drought, it is planted extensively in semiarid zones; it is also used in afforestation and as an ornamental. If the processionary caterpillar (*Thaumetopoea wilkinsonii* Tams) occurs in the area, the trees will be severely attacked.

Pinus cembroides Zucc. **Mexican nut pine**

A slow-growing, somewhat bushy, evergreen tree, up to 5–15 m (16–50 ft) in height. It grows from Arizona and Texas southward in highlands of Central Mexico to the latitude of Mexico City. It occurs on hot, dry, rocky, mountain slopes 1,600–2,600 (5,200–8,500 ft) asl, and in open stands in association with scrub oaks and junipers. Precipitation is from 350 to 600 mm (14–24 in), practically all of which occurs during the summer months. The tree withstands long periods of drought and severe cold. Good seed crops are irregular at intervals of two or more years. There are about 2,500 seeds per kg (1,100/lb) with an average germination of 60 per cent. Stratification is recommended for faster and more uniform germination. Seeds should be stored cold and dry in sealed containers. The species is planted under arid conditions as an ornamental and for its edible seeds.

Fig. 6–51. A typical open stand of pinyon (*Pinus edulis* Engelm.) in northern Colorado.

Pinus edulis Engelm. (pinyon) is a closely related woodland species of Utah, Colorado, Arizona, and New Mexico. In the northern part of its range, it is frequently subjected to winter temperatures below −23° C (−10° F). Seeds are edible, with about 4,000 per kg (1,800/lb).

Germination is about 50 per cent. Stratification at 5° C (41° F) is rec-ommended to hasten germination. Pinyon is commonly planted as an ornamental.

Pinus flexilis James   limber pine

A small, evergreen, coniferous tree, usually not over 15 m (50 ft) tall. It grows in the Rocky Mountains of the United States and southern

Fig. 6–52. *Pinus flexilis* James (limber pine) on boulder clay of a glacial moraine at 2,700 m (9,000 ft) altitude in the Rocky Mountains of northern Colorado.

Canada, and westward, in the mountains, to the Sierra Nevada of Cali-fornia. Its altitudinal range is 1,200–3,500 m (4,000–11,500 ft), and it grows on dry, shallow, rocky, or gravelly soils, frequently along the crests of ridges but uncommonly on heavy, moist clays. Precipitation in its natural habitat is 500–1,000 mm (20–40 in), and the temperature ranges from 30° to −40° C (90° to −40° F). Good seed crops occur at intervals of three or more years. Cones and seeds are often attacked by insects. There are about 7,300–13,000 seeds per kg (3,300–6,000/lb). Seeds have embryo, and possibly seedcoat, dormancy. Seeds should be stratified in moist sand or peat at 5° C (41° F) for 30 to 90 days. Scari-fication with concentrated sulphuric acid for 20 to 30 minutes before stratification is often beneficial. Germination of untreated seeds is usu-

Fig. 6–53. A natural stand of Aleppo pine (*Pinus halepensis* Mill.) in the 500 mm (20 in) rainfall zone 300 m (1,000 ft) above sea level. (Photo M. Zohary)

Fig. 6–54. A 20-year-old plantation of Aleppo pine (P. *halepensis* Mill.) in a 400 mm (16 in) rainfall area, Israel. (Photo M. Shaltiel)

ally low, whereas 80–90 per cent of treated seeds may germinate. Dry, sealed, cold storage is recommended. The wood is seldom used. The tree is planted as an ornamental and occasionally in shelterbelts and for erosion control.

Pinus halepensis Mill.   Aleppo pine

An evergreen tree, up to 25 m (80 ft) high but usually under 18 m (60 ft), widely distributed in the Mediterranean Basin from Spain and Morocco to Greece, Libya, and Jordan. It is not exacting in soil requirements and usually is found on shallow limestone soil, and also on sandstone and other formations. It is very drought-resistant and grows in areas of Mediterranean climate with 250–800 mm (10–32 in) rainfall and seven or eight rainless months. It withstands frost, with an absolute minimum temperature of −10° C (14° F), and is found from sea level to 2,000 m (6,500 ft) asl. A tree of good form and rapid growth where soil and climatic conditions are optimum, it grows in association with *Pinus pinaster* Ait., *P. pinea* L., *P. brutia* Ten., and species of *Cupressus, Cedrus, Quercus, Juniperus, Erica, Arbutus, Cistus, Pistacia, Rhus, Smilex,* and *Genista*. It regenerates freely after fires and on mineral soils. Young natural seedlings suffer from drought, and mortality is great in the first summer after germination. Good seed crops occur almost yearly. Cones should be dried in the sun or in a cone kiln for extraction. There are 30,000–60,000 seeds per kg (14,000–27,000/lb) and germination is 50–90 per cent. Pretreatment is unnecessary, but temperatures over 25° C (77° F) during germination induce dormancy. Seeds should retain viability up to ten years if kept in dry, sealed, cold storage. Seeds are sown in the nursery in autumn or early spring. It can be transplanted in beds or receptacles six weeks after germination. The wood is coarse and resinous and is used for general construction purposes, as well as for packing cases and posts. In Algeria it is tapped for resin. Aleppo pine is planted widely in the Mediterranean Basin and as an exotic in Chile, Argentina, Uruguay, Australia, and South Africa. The tree is used in plantations, for soil conservation, and dune fixation.

Pinus leiophylla var. *chihuahuana* (Engelm.) Shaw   Chihuahua pine

An evergreen tree, 15–25 m (50–80 ft) high, occurring from central Arizona in the United States southward through the highlands of west-central Mexico to Jalisco. Found between about 2,000–2,400 m (6,500–8,000 ft) asl, it grows best on deep, sandy, and stony soils derived from sandstone and in a cold-temperate climate where severe frosts occur. Precipitation required is 450–750 mm (18–30 in). The tree produces vigorous sprouts after logging. There are good seed crops about every other year, but cones often remain closed and persist on the tree for many years. About 70,000–88,000 seeds per kg (32,000–40,000/lb) are produced. Dry, cold, sealed storage is recommended. The wood is used for carpentry, sleepers, and fuel. Since it is drought- and cold-resistant, the tree could be tried in the higher dry areas in Turkey, Iran, and parts of India.

Pinus nigra Arnold [*P. laricio* Poir.]   black pine, Corsican pine

An evergreen tree, up to 40 m (130 ft) high. Taxonomically this species is very complex; the following description covers several regional varieties, chiefly Corsican pine (*P. laricio* Poir.). It is widely distributed in southern Europe from Spain to Austria, throughout the Balkan Peninsula and Asia Minor, and in the Caucasus, Crimea, Morocco, and Algeria. It is found generally on mountains, up to 2,000 m (6,500 ft) asl, and often on poor calcareous or sandy soils. It needs deep, but not necessarily fertile, soil. The species occurs in a cool to cold-temperate climate. The northern varieties are very frost-hardy down to −30° C (−22° F), and the southern varieties to −7° C (19° F) with 600 to 1,000 mm (24–40 in) of precipitation. On good sites, the variety found in southern Italy, Greece, and Turkey is a fast-growing, straight, and beautiful tree. All varieties are deep-rooted. Seed provenance is of great importance. Good seed production occurs every three to four years. Cones are opened by drying them in the sun or in a cone kiln. The southeastern European variety has 60,000 to 70,000 seeds per kg (27,000–32,000/lb). Germination is 70–80 per cent. Pretreatment is not needed but cold stratification will hasten germination. The wood is hard and strong and is used for general construction. The trees are occasionally tapped for resin. They are planted extensively in cold semiarid zones and used in windbreaks and for erosion control and dune fixation.

Pinus pinaster Ait. [*P. maritima* Poir.]   maritime pine

An evergreen tree, up to 30 m (100 ft) high, native to the western Mediterranean from France and Portugal to western Italy, and from Morocco to western Tunisia. It grows on a wide range of soils, but its best growth is on well-drained sandy soils. It occurs from sea level to over 1,000 m (3,300 ft) in Italy and is found up to 2,000 m (6,500 ft) in Morocco. There are several different races adapted to different soils and climates (see Chapter 2, pp. 58–63). For fast growth, this pine needs permeable, loose, well-aerated soil. Some races avoid lime, but others grow on limey soil. Some races are adapted to hot summers and others are hardy to frost. It grows in a mild temperate climate, with precipitation of 400–1,200 mm (16–48 in) a year with dry summers. Generally it is unsuited to regions with high summer rainfall.

Fig. 6–55. A stand of maritime pine (*Pinus pinaster* Ait.) in central Portugal. (Photo V. Natividade)

Good seed production occurs at one- to three-year intervals. Cones are opened by drying in the sun or in a cone kiln. There are about 14,000–26,000 seeds per kg (6,400–12,000/lb). Germination averages 65–70 per cent. Pretreatment is not required, but the germination period can be shortened by cold stratification. Cold, dry, sealed storage is recommended. Maritime pine is tapped for resin, and its wood is used for carpentry, poles, and sleepers. It is widely used in the afforestation of coastal dunes. Under intensive cultivation and on short rotation it is used for production of pulp. It is planted in most semiarid regions.

Pinus pinea L.   **stone pine, umbrella pine**

A large, evergreen tree, up to 24 m (80 ft) high, with a distinctive umbrella-shaped crown, native to the northern Mediterranean region, from Portugal to eastern Turkey. Widely cultivated, it probably was introduced to Lebanon in the sixteenth century to prevent the coastal

Fig. 6–56. The umbrella pine (*Pinus pinea* L.) on eroded white marl in the Baruk valley near 'Ain Zehalta, Lebanon. (Photo H. F. Mooney; courtesy American Geographical Society)

dunes from encroaching on Beirut. No definite genetic races have been reported. It grows on a wide range of soils; best growth is on fixed dunes and sandy loams. Stone pine is not found on calcareous soils. It requires a Mediterranean climate with 400 to 800 mm (16–31 in) annual rainfall. It can withstand light frost and moderate drought. Stone pine is windfirm, but suffers when exposed to strong maritime winds; if planted near the sea, it should have the protection of a narrow belt of trees that are tolerant to salt spray. It develops a deep root system and is therefore suitable for planting on steep slopes, in soil protection plantations, and on dunes in the early stages of fixation.

Trees start producing cones when 15 to 20 years old. Good production continues until about age 50 after which production declines and it almost ceases at about age 80. Heavy seed crops occur every 3 to 4 years. Average seed production is 120 to 160 kg/ha/yr (100–140 lb/A/yr). Cones are collected in the autumn and winter. Cones can be opened by sun-drying, but they must be vigorously tumbled to extract the seeds. There are about 1,000 to 1,540 seeds per kg (495–720/lb). Germination ranges from 25 to 75 percent. No pretreatment of the seeds is necessary before sowing, but germination is hastened by soaking for one or two days in cold water. Temperatures over 25° C (77° F) during germination induce dormancy.

Seeds·are sown in the spring or late autumn either directly in the field or in the nursery; usually in polybags. Direct seeding in the field is by sowing 3 or 4 seeds in a seed spot; this requires 40 to 50 kg per hectar (36–45 lb/A). Seeds are covered with 2 to 3 cm (0.8–1.2 in) of soil, if sown in agricultural land, and with 4 to 5 cm (1.6–2.0 in), if sown in partly stabilized sand. If the sands are not stablized, or if there are many birds in the area, only seedlings are used. One-year-old seedlings are suitable for agricultural land and 2+0 seedlings are planted in sand. Container grown seedlings are used in dry areas, but naked-rooted plants may also be used in the more humid sites. Seedlings develop long roots which should be pruned to fit the depth of the planting holes. Planting holes are dug 15 to 20 cm (6–8 in) deep and 50 to 100 cm (20–39 in) apart on relatively flat sites; on slopes seedlings are planted at the same interval in contour strips 2 to 3 m (6.6–9.8 ft) apart. Young plantations have 2,500 to 3,000 seedlings per hectare (1,000–1,200/A). For best growth plantations should be cultivated to remove competing vegetation. The first thinning is made when the trees are 15 years old, leaving 600 to 700 trees per hectare (240–280/A); the second and last thinning is made when the plantation is 30 to 40 years old, leaving about 300 trees per hectare (120/A). The final cut is made between 80 and 100 years. The average increment is 2 cu m/ha/yr (30 cu ft/A/yr). Growth virtually ceases after 100 years. Natural regeneration is not common, yet in favorable sites in Sicily and Calabria, Italy, and in other areas where the cones are not collected for their seed and where the area is clear of competing vegetation, a profusion of seedlings may occur.

Stone pine is planted for dune fixation, in windbreaks, and extensively as an ornamental in gardens and parks. This is the famous "umbrella tree" of Italy. It can be transplanted to roadsides as a large tree, 15 to 20 m (50–65 ft) in height. Its timber is used for posts, poles, mine props, and for pulp manufacture. Trees are occasionally tapped for resin. The seed are edible and a dye is extracted from the bark to color fishing nets.

Pinus ponderosa Laws.　　　　　　　　　　　　　**ponderosa pine**

A large, evergreen tree, up to 60 m (200 ft) high, but usually under 30 m (100 ft) in dry regions. Indigenous to western North America from southern British Columbia to central Mexico, it is found in the United States in all states west of the Great Plains. In the north, it occurs about 400 m (1,300 ft) asl, and in the south, up to 2,700 m (9,000 ft). It grows on a variety of soils from sandy soils in Nebraska to clay loam, and it tolerates a wide range in pH of soil solution—from pH 4.9 to 9.1, depending on locality and depth below the surface. It requires rainfall of 250–1,500 mm (10–60 in), but is resistant to drought and frost, even to −40° C (−40° F) in some places. This pine may occur in an open pure stand or mixed with *Pseudotsuga menziesii*

Fig. 6–57. *Pinus ponderosa* Laws. (ponderosa pine). Large, old trees on a dry, south aspect in the Rocky Mountains of northern Colorado.

(Mirb.) Franco, *Abies* spp., *Larix* spp., *Juniperus* spp., and other pines. Typically the forest floor is covered with grass and bushes, such as *Purshia tridentata* (Pursh) DC. Good seed crops are produced at irregular intervals from two to ten years. Cones may be sun-dried or kiln-dried and tumbled for extraction. There are 15,000–50,000 seeds per kg (6,800–23,000/lb). Germination usually is from 50 to 90 per cent. Pretreatment is not needed but germination may be hastened by cold stratification. In dry, sealed, cold storage, seeds remain viable for over ten years. The wood is used for construction, carpentry, posts, and mine props. This is probably the most successful species in shelterbelt plantings on sand hills and dunes in the Great Plains of western United States. If planted in favourable sites and under intensive cultivation, it will produce as much as 15 m³/ha/year (210 ft³/acre/yr). Ponderosa pine has been planted in South America with success, but plantations in Europe and the Mediterranean Basin have not been encouraging, and the poor results have, at times, been attributed to lack of proper mycorrhizae.

Pinus radiata D. Don [P. insignis Dougl.]   Monterey pine, insignis pine
An evergreen tree, up to 40 m (130 ft) high. Its natural range is limited to three localities on the central coast of California near Monterey Bay where it grows from sea level to about 300 m (1,000 ft) asl. A variety that grows up to 1,200 m (3,900 ft) is found 800 kilometers (500 miles) to the south on the Mexican island of Guadalupe. It occurs in almost pure stands, but occasionally it is found with *Cupressus macrocarpa* Hartw. In California, it grows on permeable, strongly acid, coarse to fine, sandy loams. It has been planted, however, on a variety of soils outside its native habitat with great success. It grows in a climate of the Mediterranean type with average rainfall of 400–500 mm (16–20 in), but with high humidity and frequent summer fogs, and no snowfall. It does not withstand extreme drought, dry air, or heavy frost, and the lowest temperature in its natural habitat is about −10° C (14° F). Good seed crops occur almost every year. Cones may be opened by sun-drying or kiln-drying. The few serotinous cones produced should be dipped in boiling water to loosen their scales. There are 26,000–46,000 seeds per kg (12,000–21,000/lb). Average germination is 60 per cent. Pretreatment is not required but germination can be hastened by stratification at 5° C (41° F) for 30 days. Plantations in Australia, New Zealand, and South Africa under intensive cultivation on the more favourable sites may have an annual increment of over 20 m³/ha/yr (280 ft³/acre/yr). In semiarid zones, the tree is planted only in the more humid areas and on deep soils. The wood is used for crates, construction, and pulpwood.

Pistacia atlantica Desf.   desert pistachio
A deciduous, hardwood tree, up to 20 m (65 ft) high, widely distributed from Morocco in North Africa to Central Asia in steppes and at the edges of the deserts, up to 2,000 m (6,500 ft) asl. It grows in open stands, and on the more favourable sites it is found with Mediterranean trees such as oak. It is usually the first tree encountered when one comes out of the desert. It grows on clay and alluvial soils and occasionally on calcareous soils in subtropical or Mediterranean climate, with rainfall of 155 to 250 mm (6–10 in). It withstands heat, drought, and winter cold. A slow-growing tree, it seeds almost yearly, with 8,000 dry fruits per kg (3,600/lb). Seeds must be extracted from the fruit pulp by soaking for about 16 hours in water to which about 4–5 gm lye has been added per liter (2–3 oz/gal). Seeds are rubbed on a screen to remove the pulp and are sown immediately or dried and stored. However, seeds do not keep well in storage. Germination percentage is low. The wood is used as fuel. The small seeds are

Fig. 6–58. Desert pistachio (*Pistacia atlantica* Desf.) growing on rocky limestone at 100 m (300 ft) above sea level where the annual rainfall is about 400 mm (16 in).

eaten only by the local inhabitants. However, the tree is often used as the stock on which the commercial pistachio (*Pistacia vera* L.) is grafted. Several other species of pistachio are found on the borders of the deserts. These are planted only in extremely dry areas.

Pithecellobium dulce (Roxb.) Benth.   **blackbead. guamuchil**
Blackbead is a medium-sized tree 9 to 15 m (30 to 50 ft) in height with broad crown and short bole, or shrubby with crooked trunk and branches. Trees retain old leaves until new ones appear. Twigs are usually spiny. The natural range of blackbead is from Mexico through Central America to Colombia and Venezuela. Naturalized in many tropical regions. Grows on waste land and most soils including poor sands. Can also be found on wet soils with brackish or salt water. Extremely drought resistant; in low rainfall areas it develops an extensive surface root system. In favorable soils and climate it may reach a height of 10 meters (35 ft) in five or six years.

Blackbead can be reproduced readily by coppicing. Produces seed at an early age. Ripe pods should be air dried and then beaten to release the seeds. There are about 5,000 to 8,000 seeds per kilogram (2,000 to 4,000 per lb). Pretreatment before germination is not needed. Germination is about 60 percent. Seed may be stored for about 6 months, if treated with an insecticide.

Recommended for planting on sands. Has been planted as an ornamental and shade tree in dry areas of India, Pakistan, Yemen, Arabia, and East Africa.

Platanus orientalis L.   **oriental plane**

A large, deciduous, hardwood tree, commonly up to 25 m (80 ft) high, indigenous to the eastern Mediterranean region, and growing exclusively along permanent watercourses where soil varies from silts to gravels. It is widely cultivated as an ornamental and can withstand severe frost. About 176,000 to 352,000 seeds (achenes) per kg (80,000–160,000/lb) are produced. Stratification at 5° C (41° F) is recommended for seed collected in autumn. Germination often is under 50 per cent. The tree produces valuable wood used chiefly for veneer, furniture, boxes, and decorative work. It is a very useful species for planting along watercourses.

Fig. 6–59. A 12-year-old plantation of oriental plane *(Platanus orientalis L.)* on Rendzina soil at 300 m (980 ft) above sea level in an area that receives 600 mm (24 in) of rain a year.

Populus spp.   **the poplars**

See Chapter 5, Species Suitable for Forest-Tree Orchards.

There are about 35 species of poplar and numerous natural hybrids distributed throughout the Northern Hemisphere outside the tropics. They may be divided into six different groups, of which the more important are the so-called black and white poplars, the aspens, and the large-leaved cottonwoods. Hybrids between Old and New World species are grouped under the collective name × *P. euramericana* (Dode) Guinier. Poplars are fast-growing trees, occurring on moist sites, most commonly on alluvial land along the banks of rivers and streams. A few also occur in mixed forests on drier sites. *Populus alba* L. (white poplar) and *Populus nigra* L. (black poplar) are native to Europe, North Africa, and western Asia. *Populus euphratica* Oliv. (Euphrates poplar) is native to northern Africa and part of Asia, up to the Uzbek region in the USSR; it grows on riverbeds, and may be useful for erosion control. The poplars and cottonwoods can be easily established by branch cuttings. Their fast growth makes them very valuable for planting along rivers and water channels, and along roadsides, and in shelterbelts where sufficient moisture is available throughout the year. Poplars are such prolific seed producers that the female trees are generally not planted because of the nuisance created by the cotton. Poplars and aspens are not commonly reared from seed, but, if seed reproduction is desired, the capsules should be picked from the trees just as they begin to open. Seed may be separated from the cotton by rubbing over a fine mesh screen. Germination is quick and usually over 90 per cent. Seed quickly loses its viability under room conditions, but may be kept several years in sealed containers at −22° C (−8° F). Poplars, remarkable for their vigor and the shape of their boles, may be found throughout the arid zone. Experiments with newly developed hybrids are worthwhile. The wood is light and soft and very valuable for various uses including veneers, wood wool (excelsior), packing cases, fruit boxes, matches, and pulp.

Prosopis alba Griseb.   **algarrobo blanco**

A small, deciduous tree, up to 15 m (50 ft) tall, with a trunk to 70 cm (28 in) in diameter and a short bole with many branches. It grows in the arid zones of northern Argentina, Paraguay, and Bolivia and is associated with other species of *Prosopis* (especially *P. nigra* Hieron. and *P. algarobilla* Griseb.), *Schinus molle* L., and *Acacia caven* (Mol.) Molina. It grows best on permeable sands but is found at times on clays, clayey sands, and even on saline soils. Very drought-resistant, it grows in dry climatic areas with 250–500 mm (10–20 in) rainfall, and an average winter temperature of 15° C (59° F); it is not frost-hardy. Seeds are produced yearly, with about 10,500 seeds per kg (4,700/lb). The tree is seeded directly in the field. Ten-year-old plantations in Argentina, spaced 2 × 2 meters (6.5 ft) on a fair site, produced 7 m³/ha/year (100 ft³/acre/yr). The wood is difficult to work. The sapwood is yellowish, and the heartwood dark brown. It is used for flooring, wine casks, shoes lasts, and paving blocks. The pods are eaten by cattle. A valuable tree for windbreaks and roadside planting, it is also useful as a fodder and timber tree in afforestation on dry and saline soils. The fruit is milled into flour from which cakes are prepared for human consumption.

Prosopis algarobilla Griseb.   ñandubay

A deciduous tree, up to 10 m (30 ft) high, with a large, spreading crown. Found in Uruguay and northeastern Argentina it grows on a variety of soils and can endure some salinity. It occurs in a subhumid climate with about 1,000 mm (40 in) of rain per year, and a mean annual temperature of 15° to 17° C (59° to 63° F). It is associated with *P. alba* Griseb., *Schinus molle* L., and *Aspidosperma quebracho-blanco* Schlecht. The tree coppices well and reproduces by seed. Collection, extraction, germination, and storage techniques for seeds are similar to those for *P. juliflora* (Swartz) DC. The wood is of little value for fuel, but makes a good charcoal; it is also used for posts and marine piles. The pods and foliage are eaten by goats and cattle. Because the pods reminded the Spanish settlers of the pods of carob (*Ceratonia siliqua* L.) of the Mediterranean region, they called this tree *al carrob* (the Arabic name of carob); hence its early name, "algarrobo."

Prosopis juliflora (Swartz) DC   mesquite

A thorny, deciduous, large-crowned, and deep-rooted bush or tree, up to 10 m (30 ft) tall, depending on the variety and site. An extremely variable species, its varieties are often given different botanical and local names. It is a native of southwestern United States, Mexico, Venezuela, and Colombia, and some varieties are found as far south as the Great Chaco. Mesquite grows on a variety of soils and does well on sandy soils. It grows in a very warm, dry climate and is highly drought-resistant. Rainfall required is from 150 to 600 mm (6–24 in) annually. Some of the varieties are not frost-hardy; therefore, choice of provenance is of great importance. Fast-growing, it reproduces by coppice, root suckers, and seeds. Seeds may be collected from the ground or the tree. Weevils often damage much of the seed crop. Consequently pods must be collected when they reach full size but are still green, and fumigated before storage to reduce weevil damage. About 20,000 to 35,000 seeds per kg (9,000–16,000/lb) are produced.

Seedcoat dormancy may be overcome by soaking the seeds in concentrated sulphuric acid for 20 minutes, or by covering them with boiling water and allowing them to soak for 24 hours as the water cools. Germination of pretreated seeds is 80–90 per cent. Seeds keep well in ordinary storage. Sown in receptacles, or in rows in the nursery in spring, they may be field-planted the next spring. Some varieties produce firewood and posts. The palatability of the leaves is considered fair; the pods are eaten by goats. Pods may also be ground to flour for human consumption. The flowers of one variety produce nectar of good quality for honey. Considered a weed tree in some countries, within the last two centuries mesquite has invaded large areas of grazing land in the southwestern United States; control is being attempted by mechanical and chemical means. The tree has been widely planted in many arid zones of the world. It was introduced into India over a hundred years ago and planted mainly for the fixation of dunes, but also for fuel and, in very arid zones, for "greening" the landscape.

Fig. 6–60. *Prosopis spicigera* L. in Rajasthan, India. Many of the branches have been pollarded for fodder. (Courtesy R. N. Kaul)

Prosopis spicigera L.   jhand, spicigera

A thorny tree, 8–10 m (26–33 ft) high, with an open crown. It is leafless for a short period before flowering. Native from the semiarid zones of Rajasthan in India and the Sind in Pakistan to southern India, and extending westward to Iran, it grows on alluvial and sandy tracts, in zones of 100–600 mm (4–24 in) rainfall annually, with a long dry season. Its absolute maximum temperature is 52° C (126° F); hardy to frost. It grows in association with *Acacia arabica* Willd., *Tecoma undulata* G. Don, *Tamarix* spp., and *Populus euphratica* Oliv. Spicigera coppices well, reproduces freely by root suckers, and establishes well from seed. Pods are collected from trees or from the ground. They are dried and broken apart to release the seeds. From 13,000 to 28,000 seeds per kg (6,000–13,000/lb) are produced. Pretreatment other than soaking in water is not needed; germination is 40–60 per cent. Direct sowing with irrigation is successful. The wood is hard but not durable and is used for fuel and agricultural implements. Pods, leaves, and young branches contain 20 per cent crude protein and are used as fodder. Palatability is rated as good. The tree pollards well; pollarding rotation is practiced in Rajasthan to supply fodder in dry years. Pollarding does not adversely affect growth if the right period of rest is given between toppings. The tree is very important for afforestation and fodder production in arid and semiarid zones, where it can survive even under extremely dry conditions. Because of its long taproot [over 35 m (115 ft)] it does not compete for moisture with crop plants, and they may be grown right up to the trunk of the tree. It is strongly recommended for trial in areas with ecological conditions similar to its native habitat.

Prosopis tamarugo F. Phil. [*P. chilensis* (Molina) Stuntz]   tamarugo

A small, deciduous, open-crowned tree, 8–12 m (26–40 ft) in height, native to the northern Chilean plateau up to 1,000 m (3,300 ft) asl. Sometimes it is associated with other species of *Prosopis,* but usually it grows in a pure, open stand. It is found on salt flats with a water-table about 1–2 m (3.3–6.5 ft) from the surface, because its roots can absorb this water. During the rainy season these flats turn into salty marshes, and in the dry season the water evaporates leaving a crust of crystal salts. Indians used to scrape away the salty upper layer, forming long beds known as "canchones," and grow vegetables and cereals which cannot endure salinity. The climate of its habitat is very dry; annual rainfall is 100–200 mm (4–8 in). The tree tolerates temperatures as low as −9° C and as high as 36° C (15° to 97° F). It coppices easily and regenerates from seed. Seeding characteristics are similar to *P. juliflora* (Swartz) DC. The wood is used as fuel and in the nitrate

Fig. 6–61. *Prosopis tamarugo* F. Phil. A 16-year-old plantation in North Chile. (Courtesy M. Yudelevich, Chile)

mines. Pods and young leaves are eaten by cattle. In northern Chile trees planted 10 × 10 m (33 × 33 ft) usually produce 2–3 kg (4.4–6.6 lb) of pods per square meter (1.2 sq yd) of crown cover. The average 30-year-old tree bears 200 to 300 kg (440 to 660 lb) of pods. This species should be tried experimentally in cold, salty marshes.

Quercus spp.   the oaks

Many species of oak grow in the arid and semiarid zones. All are slow-growing and most are stunted, generally never exceeding 10 m (33 ft) in height. They are characterized by a widespread crown, short crooked bole, and a strong taproot. Most species of oak produce abundant seed crops at one- to three-year intervals. Initially seed is of high quality, but it must be collected and sown, or else properly stored, immediately because it is soon killed by desiccation if exposed to air. Seed is usually stored by cold stratification, which also provides the necessary conditions for breaking dormancy and after-ripening. Acorns may also be stored for a year, or perhaps two, in sand in sealed containers at 5° C (41° F). Acorns stored in this way should be fumigated with carbon disulphide to prevent damage by weevils. Germination is usually over 50 per cent. The wood of oak is used as fuel and for charcoal, posts, and small agricultural implements. The five species described below are probably the most important for arid-zone afforestation.

Fig. 6–62. A large specimen of *Quercus aegilops* L., valonia oak, growing under 600 mm (24 in) annual rainfall at 100 m (330 ft) above sea level.

Quercus aegilops L.   **valonia oak**

A medium-sized, deciduous tree, up to 20 m (66 ft) tall, with a spreading crown. Native to the eastern Mediterranean region, Kurdistan, and Turkey, it grows from sea level to 1,000 m (3,300 ft) asl, commonly on the plains and low hills. It is found on all kinds of soils, but grows best on loam in a dry climate with as little as 400 mm (16 in) rain per year. Stands vary from dense to open and park-like; it occurs pure or mixed with other oaks. Valonia oak is a very important species because of the large amount of high quality tannin contained in the acorn cups, especially in the beards.

Quercus coccifera L.   **kermes oak**

A very widely distributed evergreen hardwood, found from the western Mediterranean region to Asia Minor. It grows in an open scrub forest, often only as a bush because of browsing. It is the typical tree on red, mountainous soil (Terra Rossa) where rainfall exceeds 400 mm (16 in). It occurs up to 1,500 m (4,900 ft) asl. Kermes oak is the host of the kermes insects which, when collected and processed, yield a scarlet dye famous since medieval times. The wood is used for fuel and charcoal.

Fig. 6–63. Kermes oak (*Quercus coccifera* L.) and *Pistacia* spp. Degraded vegetation on the Carmel. (Photo M. Zohary)

Quercus douglasii Hook. & Arn.   California blue oak

A deciduous tree, usually from 15 to 18 m (50–60 ft) high; rarely to 30 m (100 ft). Its natural range is restricted to California where it is found on dry loams and gravels of the inner coastal ranges and the foothills of the Sierra Nevada. It occurs mixed with other oaks and *Pinus sabiniana* Dougl. It grows in a Mediterranean climate with about 250–600 mm (10–24 in) of precipitation annually and temperatures ranging from 45° to −15° C (113° to 5° F). A prolific seed producer, its natural germination is abundant except where seed is destroyed by grazing animals or cultivation. There are about 400 seeds per kg (180/lb). Pretreatment of seeds is unnecessary. Its wood is used for fuel. Natural stands are extremely important for watershed protection and soil stabilization.

Quercus macrocarpa Michx.   bur oak

A large, deciduous tree, up to 50 m (165 ft) tall, but usually 15–25 m (50–80 ft) in dry regions. Its natural range extends from New Brunswick west to southeastern Saskatchewan in Canada, and southwest to central Texas. In the prairies of midwestern United States, bur oak grows on dry, usually calcareous soils, sands, gravels, loess, and heavy claypan soils and is often found on exposed south and west aspects. It grows on river bluffs and bottoms in the Great Plains and is very drought-resistant. Generally, it is found in a continental climate with

Fig. 6–64. California blue oak (*Quercus douglasii* Hook. and Arn.) and Digger pine (*Pinus sabiniana* Dougl.) on the lower western slope of the Sierra Nevada, California.

annual precipitation of 380–1,200 mm (15–48 in) and temperatures of 40° to −40° C (104° to −40° F). It is a vigorous sprouter when young. Good seed crops are produced every two or three years. Seeds germinate in autumn soon after seed fall. There are about 100–300 seeds per kg (45–135/lb). The wood is used for lumber, tight cooperage, furniture, sleepers, and fuel. The tree is planted as an ornamental and in shelterbelts. Its acorns are valuable for game food.

Quercus suber L.   **cork oak**

A broad-crowned, evergreen tree, up to 15 m (50 ft) high, with a branchless trunk for 4–6 m (13–20 ft). Native to the western Mediterranean from Portugal to Italy and from Morocco to Tunisia, it grows from sea level to 1,500 m (4,900 ft) asl. Its best growth is on well-drained sands, and it does not tolerate calcareous soils, nor excessive clay or salt. Mediterranean climate is required, with rainfall of 500–800 mm (20–32 in). It is not frost-hardy, nor very adaptable to conditions other than those of its native habitat. It produces good seed crops every two to four years with 110–200 seeds per kg (50–90/lb) and about 70 per cent germination. Its main product is cork. To produce cork, the thick bark is stripped (without harm to the tree) from the trunk and larger branches at intervals of 9 to 18 years. Its acorns are valuable for fodder, especially for pigs. It yields a good wood for

Fig. 6–65. The wide-spreading crown of this bur oak (*Quercus macro-carpa* Michx.) is characteristic of most open-grown oaks.

Fig. 6–66. *Quercus suber* L. (cork oak). Cork (the outer bark) has been harvested from the trunk and lower branches of these trees in central Portugal. (Photo V. Natividade)

fuel and charcoal production, cork oak has been planted outside its range in the Caucasus, on the Caspian shores, and in California, with limited success.

Quillaja saponaria Molina   soapbark

A glabrous, evergreen tree, 10–12 m (33–40 ft) high, found in the semiarid zone of Chile where the annual rainfall is about 350 mm (14 in) and the summers are dry. It grows at both low and high altitudes and can withstand some frost. It coppices well and reproduces by seed with about 140,000 seeds per kg (64,000/lb). The bark contains the alkaloid saponin from which a soap is prepared for washing wool and silk; it is also used as a shampoo.

Rhus coriaria L.   elm-leafed sumach

A deciduous shrub or low tree, up to 6 m (20 ft) high, native from the Near East to Kurdistan. It is found on a variety of soils and at

Fig. 6–67. *Rhus coriaria* L. (elm-leafed sumach) yields a high quality tannin in commercial quantities.

elevations from sea level to over 1,000 m (3,300 ft). Rainfall in its native habitat varies from 400 to 800 mm (10–32 in). It can withstand some frost. It reproduces by root suckers and, therefore, is much used in erosion control for the roots spread well on dry, eroded soil. The tree can be propagated by root cuttings. Good seed crops are produced yearly with about 30,000 seeds per kg (14,000/lb). Pulp can be removed by rubbing the fruit on a screen. Sound seeds sink in water and may be separated from empty seeds by flotation. Based on recommendations for other species of *Rhus,* seeds should be soaked in concentrated sulphuric acid for one to two hours and then stratified for 60 days at 5° C (41° F). Clean seeds should keep well for at least two years in dry, sealed, cold storage. Elm-leafed sumach yields a high-quality tannin in commercial quantities. It has been introduced into several countries for erosion control and frequently escapes from cultivation.

Robinia pseudoacacia L.   **false acacia, black locust**
    A medium-sized, spiny, deciduous tree, 12–30 cm (40–100 ft) tall, with a straight bole. In some strains spines are small or absent. Native to the Appalachian and Ozark Mountains of southeastern and central United States, it is found up to 1,000 m (3,300 ft) asl. It grows

Fig. 6–68. A young black locust (*Robinia pseudoacacia* L.). Grove of older black locust trees in background.

on a variety of soils: limestone soils are particularly favourable, but it will tolerate acid soils; compact, plastic soils are unfavourable. It succeeds well on eroded slopes. Precipitation in its native habitat is over 1,000 mm (40 in) per year, but it has been successfully planted where the rainfall is only 300–400 mm (12–16 in), and it can withstand temperatures down to −40° C (−40° F). It is a prolific producer of root suckers. Good seed crops are produced nearly every year with 32,000–70,000 seeds per kg (14,500–32,000/lb). Pretreatment is needed to break seedcoat dormancy; immerse in concentrated sulphuric acid for 20–60 minutes, wash thoroughly in cold water, and sow. Germination of pretreated seed is about 70 per cent. Treated and untreated seeds retain their viability well under room conditions, but for prolonged periods dry, sealed, cold storage is recommended. The wood is very heavy and extremely durable and is used for posts, in turnery, and for fuel. Black locust is commonly planted on roadsides as an ornamental and for erosion control. Because of the nitrifying bacteria in nodules on its roots, it is especially effective in improving the fertility of eroded soils. It has also grown quite well when planted on spoil banks created by mining. Its leaves are used as fodder. It is now grown in most semiarid zones. In the United States, the saplings are often heavily damaged by the locust borer, *Megacyllene robiniae* (Forst.).

Salix spp.   **the willows**

There are about 300 species of willow. The botanical definition of many of them is somewhat confused because of hybridization. Willows are common along permanent watercourses in most arid zones. The various species range in size and habit from many-stemmed shrubs to large trees. They coppice freely and are easily established by cuttings. In favourable sites with ample soil moisture, they are very fast-growing. They can withstand periodic inundation, and some species grow in saline soil. The seeds are similar to those of *Populus* but are much smaller and more difficult to handle. Seeds are rarely used in afforestation. The wood is used for boxes and in turnery, and the branches of some species for basketwork. Leaves are sometimes fed to cattle. Because of their mat-like roots, willows are very effective in preventing erosion when planted along river banks and water channels.

Salix humboldtiana Willd.   **Humboldt's willow**

A small to medium-sized, deciduous tree, up to 18 m (60 ft) high. This variety has a narrow fastigiate crown, and from a distance resembles Lombardy poplar. It is native from central Mexico south to Chile and Argentina (to 45° S. latitude) and grows along watercourses in subhumid and semiarid zones in association with acacias, *Schinus molle* L., *Prosopis juliflora* (Swartz) DC, and *Caesalpinia spinosa*

Fig. 6–69. *Salix humboldtiana* Willd. (Humboldt's willow) near the Rio Pescado, Salta, Argentina. (Photo D. Cozzo)

(Molina) OK. It is found up to 3,500 m (11,500 ft) in Bolivia. It grows in moist, well-drained, sandy soils and withstands periodic inundation. The tree coppices well and is easily propagated by twig cuttings. The wood is used for fruit cases, turnery, toys, and ordinary carpentry. A valuable species for planting along streams, it is also commonly planted as an ornamental.

Salix viminalis L.   basket willow

A tall, deciduous shrub or small tree, 1.5–6 m (5–20 ft) high, distributed from Europe to India and the Amur River Region of eastern Asia. It grows to 2,700 m (8,900 ft) asl in the Himalayas and is widely planted and naturalized beyond its natural range. It is frost-hardy and is cultivated in Patagonia and Tierra del Fuego. This species is most preferred for basketweaving because of its long slender stems. It is coppiced or pollarded on an annual rotation to produce basket wands and also is used for low windbreaks.

Salvadora persica L.   salvadora

A large, evergreen shrub or small tree, up to 12 m (40 ft) high, with drooping branches. Found in the hot, arid zones of India, Ceylon, West Pakistan, the Red Sea region, Egypt, and Ethiopia to Senegal, it occurs near the seashore, along rivers, in wadis where the ground-water is near the surface, and frequently in salt marshes and saline soils. Annual rainfall required is from under 50 mm (2 in) to about 500 mm (20 in). It coppices well and is also propagated by seed. The wood is soft and little used. Toothbrushes are made locally from the twigs. Seeds yield a high percentage of fat suitable for candles and salt may be extracted from the branches and leaves. Leaves, when incorporated into the soil, reduce the alkalinity. The tree is browsed by cattle and goats and is useful as a shade and fodder tree in extremely arid zones.

Schinopsis lorentzii Engelm.
red quebracho, quebracho colorado santiagueño

A medium-sized, deciduous tree, up to 23 m (75 ft), usually with a short bole and a much-branched crown. It is native to the dry Chaco of northern Argentina, southern Bolivia, and Paraguay. It occurs in open forests in dry and semiarid localities that receive 400–600 mm (16–24 in) rain per year and have a mean annual temperature of 23° C (73° F). It grows on loams and sandy soils in association with *Aspidosperma quebracho-blanco* Schlecht., *Prosopis alba* Griseb., and *P. nigra* Hieron., but is not found on saline soils. It seeds prolifically, with about 8,000 seeds per kg (3,600/lb), and reproduces well in its native habitat when grazing is controlled. The wood is extremely hard, heavy, and durable and is used for building, carpentry, railway sleepers, and posts. The heartwood is rich in tannin. Many persons

Fig. 6–70. Two trees (without leaves) of *Schinopsis lorentzii* Engelm. (quebracho colorado santiagueño) in the semiarid zone of Santiago del Estero, Argentina. (Photo D. Cozzo)

suffer from a skin rash after they come in contact with the leaves, branches, or sawdust, or even pass close to the foliage. Valuable for afforestation and as a timber and tannin-producing tree in semiarid zones, the species has been planted in central Argentina.

Schinus molle L.   **aguaribay, terebinto, pepper tree**

An evergreen shrub or tree; no more than a bush in dry areas, but on favourable sites attaining a height of 20 m (66 ft). In Argentina some varieties have straight boles up to 10 m (33 ft). Native to Peru, northern Argentina, and Bolivia, it grows in dry regions of the Andes 2,000–3,500 m (6,600–11,500 ft) asl. It usually is found on sandy soils and beds of seasonally dry streams where climate is warm-temperate to subtropical. It withstands severe drought and heat, growing in regions with less than 500 mm (20 in) rainfall and from six to eight rainless months, and a mean annual temperature of 15° C (59° F). Young trees are frost-tender but older trees can withstand frost. It is grown in Argentina in places where the temperature drops to −10° C (14° F). In its native habitat, it grows in association with *Prosopis alba* Griseb., *P. juliflora* (Swartz) DC, *P. nigra* Hieron., *Caesalpinia spinosa* (Molina) OK, *Acacia* spp., *Aspidosperma quebracho-blanco* Schlecht., *Schinopsis* spp., and *Salix humboldtiana* Willd. It regenerates from seed with 35,000–65,000 seeds per kg (16,000–30,000/lb) and over 50 per cent viability. Seed keeps well for a short time in dry storage at room conditions. Time of seeding in nurseries in Argentina and Chile is July

Fig. 6–71. The pepper tree (*Schinus molle* L.) is planted extensively in arid and semiarid zones throughout the world.

to September; in the Northern Hemisphere, it is March to April. The wood is not used except for firewood, but it yields a "resin" used medicinally. The species is planted extensively in arid and semiarid zones all over the world as an ornamental in gardens, as a roadside tree, for windbreaks, and as shelter for cattle. Its clusters of seed, covered with a red, soft shell, add to its beauty and may be ground and used as pepper. Since it is subject to black scale, it is a menace to citrus orchards.

Sophora japonica L. [Styphnolobium japonicum (L.) Schott]   pagoda tree
    A deciduous tree, up to 24 m (79 ft) high, indigenous to China. It grows in areas with from less than 500 mm to over 1,000 mm (20–40 in) rainfall and winters that are usually very dry. It withstands temperatures to −20° C (−4° F). Seeds pods may be picked from the trees in autumn or winter. There are 8,000–14,000 seeds per kg (3,600–6,500/lb). Pretreatment is necessary to overcome seedcoat dormancy: cover with boiling water and allow to soak until cool. Seeds may be stored for a few months under ordinary room conditions, but dry, cold, sealed storage is recommended for long periods. The wood is tough and durable and is used in general carpentry. A yellow dye can be obtained from the fruit. The pagoda tree is planted in Mediterranean countries as an ornamental, especially as a roadside tree.

Fig. 6–72. *Tamarix aphylla* (L.) Karst. is an exergreen tree up to 15 m (50 ft) tall. Native to North Africa, the Middle East, and northwestern India.

***Tamarix aphylla* (L.) Karst. [*T. articulata* Vahl]**   **athel tamarisk**

An evergreen tree, up to 15 m (50 ft) tall; often crooked, but some varieties have a straight bole 6–8 m (20–26 ft) high. Native to the arid parts of North Africa and Asia, from Arabia to N.W. India, it grows in steppes and deserts, usually on sandy and sandy loam soils, but also on almost every soil, including saline soils and alluvial flats with high watertables. It occurs where the rainfall is only 100–220 mm (4–8 in) per year; however, in such places it grows better under irrigation. It is extremely resistant to salt and drought and is fast-growing under favorable conditions. Seeds are very tiny and are not often used in artificial regeneration. The tree is easy to establish by cuttings during spring using mature wood of the past season. It coppices freely, but it does not produce root suckers. Galls are collected and marketed for their high tannin content. The wood is white, hard, and durable and

Fig. 6–73.   A windbreak of athel tamarisk (*T. aphylla* (L.) Karst.).

is used for plows, wheels, firewood, and furniture. The tree is most useful for planting in arid or semiarid regions, especially along road-sides, as windbreaks, for erosion control, and for dune fixation by deep planting without stabilizing grasses.

Tamarix gallica L.   French tamarisk

An evergreen, or sub-evergreen, shrub or small tree, 6–9 m (20–30 ft) tall, native to Portugal, northern Africa, the Nile Valley, and east to India, Burma, and China. It ascends to 3,300 m (10,800 ft) asl in Tibet. It grows in deep sandy soil with ground-water, and tolerates salt spray. Seeds that are deposited on alluvial lands during floods germinate after the waters recede and cover the new lands with a dense forest. It is readily propagated by cuttings. The wood is used as fuel. It is com-monly planted as an ornamental because of its showy purple flowers.

Other species of *Tamarix* are more specialized in their soil require-ments, growing on sand, or in dry, desert watercourses where they often are periodically inundated, or on saline soils. Many are merely tall shrubs and never attain tree height; however, some may be quite useful in special situations.

Taxodium distichum (L.) Rich.   baldcypress

A fast-growing, deciduous conifer, up to 40 m (130 ft) high, native to the coastal plain of southeastern United States from Delaware to Texas and the Mississippi River Valley to southern Illinois. It grows

Fig. 6–74. *Tamarix gallica* L. (French tamarisk) in the Dead Sea valley. (Photo M. Zohary)

Fig. 6–75. *Taxodium distichum* (L.) Rich. (baldcypress) in the Okefenokee Swamp, Florida. Planted in many warm, semiarid regions where ample groundwater is available. (Photo M. Braden)

in deep- to shallow-water swamps and on moist banks of streams and is found on mucks, clays, or fine sands. It cannot grow on poor, dry, sandy soils. Its climate is usually warm and humid, but it can tolerate extremely high (40° C or 104° F) and low (−25° C or −13° F) temperatures and can withstand short periods of drought when the swamps dry. It sprouts well from stumps up to 60 years and seeds almost yearly with 10,000–20,000 seeds per kg (4,500–9,000/lb) and germination of about 40 per cent. Seeds should be stratified at 5° C (41° F) for 30 to 60 days to break embryo dormancy. Cold stratification will also serve for winter storage. Dry, sealed, cold storage has been suggested for longer periods. The wood is moderately hard and heavy and very durable, and is used for construction, water tanks, bridge timbers, and sleepers. The tree can be planted successfully in many warm, semiarid countries where ample ground-water is available.

Tecoma undulata G. Don   tecoma

A nearly evergreen shrub or tree, up to 12 m (40 ft) high, native to the driest regions of India, West Pakistan, and Arabia. Found up to 1,300 m (4,300 ft) asl, it coppices well and is easily propagated by seeds and cuttings. It is drought- and fire-resistant but not frost-hardy. The leaves are browsed by cattle and goats. The wood is tough, strong, durable, and polishes well; it is used for furniture, carving, and agricultural implements. This is an interesting species for ornamental plantings and for afforesting dry lands.

Tetraclinis articulata (Vahl) Mast.   alerce

A small, evergreen conifer, up to 15 m (50 ft) high, but usually only 5–6 m (16–20 ft). Native to Malta and coastal regions of Tunisia, Algeria, and Morocco, it occurs from sea level to 1,800 m (5,900 ft). It grows best on calcareous soils, but is found on a variety of soils including deep sands of stabilized dunes; it is usually associated with *Pinus halepensis* Mill., *Olea europaea* L., *Ceratonia siliqua* L., *Quercus calliprinos* Webb, *Pistacia lentiscus* L., and *Cistus* spp. Mediterranean climate is required, with rainfall from 250 to 700 mm (10–28 in), and hot summer and mild winter temperatures. The tree grows slowly and coppices freely after cutting or burning. Good seed crops are produced nearly every year with about 100,000 seeds per kg (45,000/lb) and germination is usually less than 50 percent. Seeds keep well in dry, cold, sealed storage. It produces abundant natural regeneration even where planted as an exotic. It is recommended for planting on eroded areas. The wood is very durable and is used for furniture, posts, and fuel.

Although not too windfirm, it is a useful tree for planting on poor, eroded soil and along roadsides in arid and semiarid areas.

Ulmus americana L.   American elm

A large, deciduous tree may exceed 30 m (100 ft) in height on favourable sites, but in dry regions is usually less than 12 m (40 ft). It is native to the eastern half of the United States and southern Canada, and grows as far west as central Saskatchewan and central Texas. It achieves its best growth on well-drained loams of river beds but is found on nearly every kind of soil from coarse sands to clays. It will

Fig. 6–76. American elm (*Ulmus americana* L.) was one of the most commonly planted ornamental trees in the eastern United States, but in many localities it has been eliminated by the Dutch elm disease.

grow on alkaline soils where the pH is slightly over 8.0. Climate within its natural range varies from semiarid to humid with precipitation from 380 to about 1,500 mm (15–60 in). Annual temperatures range from 40° to −40° C (104° to −40° F). The tree flowers and fruits in the spring and produces good crops almost annually. The fruit is a circular, wafer-like samara containing a single seed. The entire samara constitutes the "seed" used in afforestation. There are from 100,000 to 200,000 such "seeds" per kg (45,000–91,000/lb). Germination is usually over 50 per cent. Seeds frequently have embryo dormancy which may be broken by stratification in sand at 5° C (41° F) for 60 days. Seeds keep well for five or more years in dry, sealed, cold storage. The wood is used in furniture, especially where the piece must be formed by steam bending; it is also used in slack cooperage, crates, and for fuel. It is planted as a windbreak tree in the Great Plains. American elm was the favorite hardwood ornamental in midwestern and eastern North America before millions of trees were killed by the Dutch elm disease and phloem necrosis.

Ulmus pumila L.   **Siberian elm**

A small to medium-sized deciduous tree, up to 10 m (33 ft) high, native to the area from Turkestan to Lake Baikal and China. It grows

Fig. 6–77. Siberian elm (*Ulmus pumila* L.) is a fast-growing tree that is adapted to cold, dry regions.

in continental climate, with precipitation in several places under 380 mm (15 in). It can resist temperatures from 40° to −40° C (104° to −40° F). The fruit is a circular, double-winged samara that ripens in spring. Commercial "seed" is the whole, ripened samara. There are 100,000–200,000 seeds per kg (450,000–91,000/lb), with germination usually over 50 per cent. Seed may be kept for up to four years in dry, sealed, cold storage. The tree has very fast growth. It is useful for planting along roadsides and as an ornamental and is extensively used as windbreak in cold, open, windswept fields.

Chinese elm (*U. parvifolia* Jacq.) is a closely related species from China, Korea, and Japan that matures its seed in autumn. Its uses are similar to those of Siberian elm, but it is not quite so frost-hardy.

Zizyphus jujuba Lam.   **jujube, ber tree**

A spiny, deciduous or sub-evergreen shrub or tree, up to 25 m (80 ft) tall, valued for its edible fruit. It has an open crown and short bole and is indigenous or naturalized from Burma and India in Asia to North Africa and southern Europe. Found from sea level to over 1,300 m (4,300 ft) in the Himalayas, it grows best on sandy or alluvial soils, but it is found on most soils, including moderately saline. It is not favoured by heavy clays. Though it is drought-resistant it cannot withstand severe cold. Rainfall is from 125 to over 2,000 mm (5–80 in), and temperatures are from 48° to −6° C (118° to 21° F). Fast-growing in good sites. Jujube coppices and pollards well. It reproduces by root suckers and by seed. Good fruit crops are produced annually. The fruit is a fleshy drupe, which should be picked from the tree and depulped by soaking in water and rubbing on a rough surface. There are about 1,200–2,500 seeds per kg (550–1,100/lb). Seeds have two embryos and therefore often produce 2 seedlings per seed. Germination pretreatment is to scarify in concentrated sulphuric acid for two to six hours, then stratify at 5° C (41° F) for 60–90 days. There is about 50 per cent germination. Dry, sealed, cold storage is recommended for seeds. The wood is used for fuel, agricultural implements, and charcoal; the branches and leaves are useful as fodder for cattle. Select varieties are grown for fruit production. This is a useful shelterbelt species for arid zones, especially as a sand binder. It is widely planted and naturalized in many arid-zone countries.

Zizyphus spina-christi (L.) Willd.   **Christ thorn**

A thorny, medium-sized tree, up to 5 m (16 ft) high, that attains a very great age. Native to northern Africa and widespread in parts of

Fig. 6–78. In dry regions the Christ thorn [*Zizyphus spina-christi* (L.) Willd.] develops an extremely deep taproot.

the Near East, it grows in desert areas with about 100 mm (4 in) rainfall annually, but usually is found in wadis where ground-water is available. It extends into semiarid areas with much greater rainfall, especially on alluvial plains with deep soil. In steppes, it may form an open forest. It develops an extremely deep taproot and has extraordinary regenerative power. Strongly resistant to heat and drought; but can withstand only slight frost. Its reproduction characteristics are similar to those of. *Z. jujuba* Lam. It is useful for erosion control plantings in arid areas.

Several other species of *Zizyphus* which may prove useful in afforestation are also found in North Africa and the Near East.

BIBLIOGRAPHY

Acosta Solis, M. Algunas consideraciones ecológicas sobre la introducción y aclima-
     1949   tación de especies forestales exóticas a los países andinas. Ecuador Dep.
                 For. Publ. 4. Quito. 8 p.
     ———. La forestación artificial en el Ecuador Central. Inst. Ecuatoriano Cienc.
     1954   Nat. Contrib. 24. [Editora Quito]. 85 p.
Alemparte, R., and C. Mathews. Plan de forestación de las provincias del norte.
     1947   Agric. del Norte 31(8):206–210. Chile.

ANDERSON, R. H. The trees of New South Wales. 3rd ed. A. H. Pettifer, Gov.
1956 Printer, Sydney. 471 p.

ARGENTINE REPUBLIC, DIRECCIÓN DE INVESTIGACIONES FORESTALES. Arboles forestales
1961 argentinos. 2nd ed. Buenos Aires.

AUDAS, J. W. Native trees of Australia. New and enlarged ed. Whitcombe and
[1952] Tombs, [Melbourne]. 396 p.

AUSTRALIA, FORESTRY AND TIMBER BUREAU. Forest trees of Australia. Commonw.
1957 Australia, Canberra. 230 p.

BAILEY, L. H. The standard cyclopedia of horticulture. 3 vols. Macmillan, New
1942 York. 3639 p.

BENSON, L., and R. A. DARROW. A manual of southwestern desert trees and shrubs.
1944 Univ. Ariz. Biol. Sci. Bull. 6. Tucson. 411 p.

BLATTER, E., and W. S. MILLARD. Some beautiful Indian trees. 2nd ed. rev. by
[1954] W. T. Stearn. Nat. Hist. Soc. Bombay. 165 p.

BOSSHARD, W. C. Tree species for the arid zone of the Sudan. Sudan For. Dep. For.
1966 Res. Inst. and U. N. Dev. Programme For. Res. Educ. Proj. Pam. 33. Soba,
Khartoum, Sudan. 33 p.

BOSSHARD, W. C., and G. B. VON WENDORFF. Conocarpus lancifolius Engl. and its
1966 possibilities in the Sudan. Sudan For. Dep. For. Res. Inst. and U. N. Dev.
Programme For. Res. Educ. Proj. Pam. 18. Soba, Khartoum, Sudan. 28 p.

BOYCE, J. S. Introduction of exotic trees: dangers from disease and insect pests.
1954 Unasylva 8:8–14.

BRANDIS, D. Indian trees: an account of trees, shrubs, woody climbers, bamboos and
1907 palms indigenous or commonly cultivated in the British Indian Empire.
Archibald Constable, London. 767 p.

BREITENBACH, F. VON. Exotic trees in Ethiopia. Ethiopian For. Rev. 1961 (2):19–
1961 39.

BROCKWAY, G. E. Forests of the arid gold fields region of Western Australia. Emp.
1941 For. J. 20:16–24.

CARMANTRAND, R. DE. Le pin d'Alep dans la région mediterranéenne. Rev. Eaux
1940 For. 78:223–237.

CHALLOT, J. P. L'arganier (Argania spinosa). Rev. Bois Appl. 4 (7/8):7–12.
1949

CHAMPION, H. G., and N. V. BRASNETT. Choice of tree species. FAO For. Dev. Pap.
1958 13. Rome. 307 p.

CHAPMAN, E. F. Cyprus trees and shrubs. Gov. Print. Off., Nicosia. 88 p.
1949

DALLIMORE, W. The cypresses. Emp. For. Rev. 10:37–47.
1931

DESTREMAN, D. Z., and B. LEPOUTRE. La determination de facteur climatiques
1972 limitant la croissance chez quelques essances de climat méditerranéen. Proc.
World For. Congr. 7th Buenos Aires 1972. In press.

DJAZIRI, A. Etude stationnelle du pin pignon en Italie. U. N. Dev. Programme and
1971 Repub. Tunisienne Minist. Agric. Inst. Natl. Rech. For. Variété Sci. No. 9.
80 + [20] p.

EGLER, F. E. Arid southeast Oahu vegetation, Hawaii. Ecol. Monogr. 17:385–435.
1947

EMBERGER, L. Les arbres du Maroc et comment les reconnaitre. Larose, Paris. 317
1938 p.

FAO. Fuelwood plantations in India. FAO For. Occ. Pap. 5. Rome. 73 p.
1958

———. Poplars in forestry and land use. FAO For. For. Prod. Stud. 12. Rome.
1958 511 p.

FERGUSON, K. V. M. Tree planting guide: with particular reference to selection and
1957 planting of trees on farms in Victoria. Victoria, Aust. For. Comm. Misc.
Publ. 5. W. M. Houston, Gov. Printer, Melbourne. 56 p.

FLINTA, C. M. Practicas de plantación forestal en America Latina. FAO For. Dev.
1960 Pap. 15. Rome. 499 p.

FOWELLS, H. A.   Silvics of forest trees of the United States. U. S. Dep. Agric., Agric.
1965   Handb. 271. Washington, D. C. 762 p.

FULLAWAY, D. T.   Norfolk Island pine culture: collecting and storing seed, propagat-
1972   ing, growing, harvesting, marketing. Univ. Hawaii, Coop. Ext. Serv. Circ.
453. Honolulu. 16 p.

GANGULI, B. N., R. N. KAUL, and K. T. N. NAMBIAR.   Preliminary studies of a few
1964   top-feed species. Ann. Arid Zone 3:33–37.

GINDEL, I.   Ricerche sui semi di specie forestali indigene ed introdotte in Palestina.
1947   Primi risultati. Ist. Selvicoltura Univ. Firenze. Firenze, Italy. 48 p.

GOLFARI, L.   El balance hídrico de Thornthwaite como guía para establecer analogías
1966   climáticas: I. Ejemplos en *Pinus radiata* D. Don. IDIA (Inf. Invest. Agric.)
Supl. 3:43–48. Inst. Nac. Technol. Agropecu., Buenos Aires.

————.   El balance hídrico de Thornthwaite como guía para establecer analogías
1967   climáticas. Algunos ejemplos en *Pinus radiata* D. Don. Doc. FAO World
Symposium on Man-Made Forests and their Industrial Importance, Canberra, Aust. 14–24 April 1967. Vol. 2:981–992.

GUEST, E.   Notes on trees and shrubs for lower Iraq. Iraq Dep. Agric. Bull. 26.
1932   Baghdad. 18 p.

HADEN-GUEST, S., J. K. WRIGHT, and E. M. TETCLAFF (editors).   A world geography
1956   of forest resources. Am. Geographical Soc. Ronald Press, New York. 736 p.

HALL, N., et al.   The use of trees and shrubs in the dry country of Australia. Aust.
1972   Gov. Publ. Serv., Canberra. xxx + 558 p.

HATHEWAY, W. H.   Composition of certain native dry forest: Mokuleia, Oahu, T. H.
1952   Ecol. Monogr. 22:153–168.

HAUMAN, L., A. BURKHART, L. R. PARODI, and A. L. CABRERA.   La vegetación de la
1947   Argentina. Geografia de la Republica Argentina. Edited by the Sociedad
Argentina de Esudios Geográficos 8:5–349.

HICKEL, R.   Les cèdres méditerranéens. Silva Medit. 4:3–7. Firenze.
1927

HUGUET, L. R., and N. SANCHEZ MEJORADA.   Las coniferas de México. FAO Publ.
1958   Div. Rome. 7 p.

ISRAEL DEPARTMENT OF FORESTS.   The Ilanoth National Arboretum. Israel Dep. For.,
1959   Ilanoth. 19 p.

JAHANDIEZ, E., et al.   Catalogue des plantes du Maroc. 4 vols. Imprimerie Minerva,
1931–   Algiers.
1941

JONES, D. K.   Carob (*Ceratonia siliqua*) culture in Cyprus. FAO/53/2/1225. Food
1953   Agric. Organ. U.N., Rome. 24 p.

JONES, L.   Effect of storage at various moisture contents and temperatures on seed
1967   germination of silk oak, Australian pine, and *Eucalyptus* spp. U. S. For.
Serv. Res. Note SE-83. Southeastern For. Exp. Stn. Asheville, N. C. 4 p.

KAUL, R. N. ed.   Afforestation in arid zones. Monogr. Biol. 20. W. Junk N. V. Publ.,
1970   The Hague. 435 p.

KAUL, R. N., and B. N. GANGULI.   Kherji (*Prosopis spicigera*). Cent. Arid Zone Res.
1962   Inst., Jodhpur, India.

KEMP, R. H.   Trials of exotic tree species in the savanna region of Nigeria. Part I.
1969   Aims, procedure and summary of results. Savanna For. Res. Stn. Res. Pap.
4. Samaru, Zaria, Nigeria. 15 p.

————.   Trials of exotic tree species in the savanna region of Nigeria. Part II. Short
1970   notes on selected species. Savanna For. Res. Stn. Res. Pap 6. Samaru,
Zaria, Nigeria. 62 p.

LACAZE, J.   Essences résineuses californiennes susceptibles de s'acclimater au Maroc.
1952   Ann. Rech. For. Maroc. 1951:91–136.

LAURIE, M. V.   Tree planting practices in African savannas. FAO For. Dev. Pap. 19.
1974   185 p.

LEONARDIS, R. F. J.   Arboles de la Argentina y aplicaciones de su madera. Editorial
1949   "Suelo Argentino," Buenos Aires. 277+[6] p. (Biblioteca "Suelo Argentin").

LETOURNEUX, C. Tree planting practices in tropical Asia. FAO For. Dev. Pap. 11.
    1957   Rome. 172 p.
LITTLE, E. L., JR. Southwestern trees: a guide to the native species of New Mexico
    1950   and Arizona. U. S. Dep. Agric., Agric. Handb. 9. Washington, D.C. 109 p.
LITTLE, E. L., JR., and F. H. WADSWORTH. Common trees of Puerto Rico and the
    1964   Virgin Islands. U. S. Dep. Agric., Agric. Handb. 249. Washington, D. C.
           548 p. (Spanish edition also available.)
LITTLE, E. L., JR., R. O. WOODBURY, and F. H. WADSWORTH. Trees of Puerto Rico
    1974   and the Virgin Islands: second volume. U. S. Dep. Agric., Agric. Handb.
           449. Washington, D. C. 1024 p.
LOOCK, E. E. M. The pines of Mexico and British Honduras. S. Afr. Dep. For. Bull.
    1950   35. Pretoria. 244 p.
LÓPEZ, E. D. Los montes artificiales en el país. Bol. Inform. Uruguay Minist.
    1945   Ganad. Agric. 2. Montevideo. [457] p.
LÓPEZ, E. D., and C. M. CUSSAC. Arboles forestales en el Uruguay y problemas afines.
    1943   Imprenta J. Mercant, Montevideo. [204] p.
McCANN, C. 100 beautiful trees of India, a description and pictorial handbook. 2nd
    [1959] ed. rev. enlarged. D. B. Taraporevala Sons, Bombay. 168 p.
MAGINI, E., and N. P. TULSTRUP. Tree seed notes. FAO For. Dev. Pap. 5. Rome.
    1955   354 p.
MANGIERI, H. R., and M. J. DIMITRI. Los eucaliptos en la silvicultura; estudio
    1961   botánico y forestal de las especies más comúnmente cultivadas en Sudamér-
           ica. Editorial Acme, Buenos Aires. 226 p.
MARTÍN BLAÑOS, M. M. Eucaliptos de mayor interés para España. Bol. Inst. For.
    1955   Invest. Exp. 26(74). Madrid. 95 p.
MARTINEZ, M. Las pináceas mexicanas. 3rd ed. Univ. Nac. Autónoma Mexico.
    1963   400 p.
McCOMB, A. L., and J. K. JACKSON. The role of tree plantations in savanna develop-
    1969   ment: technical and economic aspects, with special reference to Nigeria.
           Unasylva 23(3):8–18.
METRO, A. Eucalypts for planting. FAO For. For. Prod. Stud. 11. Rome. 403 p.
    1954
MOULDS, F. R. Exotics can succeed in forestry as in agriculture. J. For. 55:563–566.
    1957
OUDEN, P. DEN, and B. K. BOOM. Manual of cultivated conifers hardy in the cold-
    1965   and warm-temperature zone. Nijhoff, The Hague. 526 p.
PARODI, L. R. Enciclopedia Argentina de agricultura y jardineria. Vol. 1. Editorial
    1959   Acme S.A.C.I., Buenos Aires. 931 p.
PARRY, M. S. Tree planting practices in tropical Africa. FAO For. Dev. Pap. 8.
    1956   Rome. 302 p.
PAVARI, A., and A. DE PHILIPPIS. La sperimentazione di specie forestali esotiche in
    1941   Italia: resultati del primo ventennio. Ann. Sper. Agric. 38. Rome. 647 p.
PENFOLD, A. R., and J. L. WILLIS. The eucalypts: botany, cultivation, chemistry,
    1961   and utilization. Leonard Hill [Books] Ltd., London. Interscience, New
           York. 551 p.
POST, G. E. Flora of Syria, Palestine and Sinai. 2nd ed. rev. by J. E. Dinsmore.
    1934   2 vols. American Press, Beirut. 630 and 928 p.
POVEDA Y FUENTES, G. A. *La Acacia mollissima* Willd. en el norte de Marruecoas.
    1963   Montes 19:201–216, 305–322.
POYNTON, R. J. Notes on exotic forest trees in South Africa. 2nd. ed. rev. S. Afr.
    1960   Dep. For. Bull. 38. S. Afr. Gov. Printer, Pretoria. 105 p.
PUDDEN, H. H. C. Exotic forest trees in the Kenya Highlands. Kenya Gov. Printer,
    1957   Nairobi. 34 p.
REHDER, A. Manual of cultivated trees and shrubs hardy in North America, exclusive
    1940   of the subtropical and warm temperate regions. 2nd ed. rev. enlarged.
           Macmillan Co., New York. 906 p.
ROBERTSON, C. C. The trees of extra-tropical Australia. A reconnaissance of the

1926   forest trees of Australia from the point of view of their cultivation in South
        Africa. Cape Times Ltd., Gov. Printer, Cape Town. 265 p.

SANCHEZ MEJORADA, N., and L. HUGUET. Conifers of Mexico. Unasylva 13:24–35.
1959

SCHUBERT, G. H. Silviculturist's point of view on use of nonlocal trees. USDA For.
1975   Serv. Gen. Tech. Rep. RM-11. Rocky Mount. For. Range Exp. Stn., Ft.
        Collins, Colo. 12 p.

SCOTT, C. W. Pinus radiata. FAO For. For. Prod. Stud. 14. Rome. 328 p.
1960

STREETS, R. J. Exotic forest trees in the British Commonwealth, edited by Harry
1962   Champion. Clarendon Press, Oxford. 765 p.

SUDWORTH, G. B. Forest trees of the Pacific slope. U. S. Dep. Agric., For. Serv.,
1908   Washington, D. C. 441 p.

SULIMAN, A. G. M., and J. K. JACKSON. The heglig tree (*Balanites aegyptiaca* (L.)
1959   Del.). Sudan Silva 9(1):63–70.

TROUP, R. S. The silviculture of Indian trees. 3 vols. Clarendon Press, Oxford.
1921   1195 p.

U. S. FOREST SERVICE. Seeds of woody plants in the United States. Prepared by the
1974   Forest Service, C. S. Schopmeyer, Technical Coordinator. U.S. Dep. Agric.,
        Agric. Handb. 450. 883 p.

VIEIRA NATIVIDADE, J. Subericultura. Minist. Econ. Dir. Geral Serv. Flor. Aqüic.
1950   Lisboa, Portugal. 387 p.

WAHEED KHAN, M. A. Seeding and planting on clay plains. Sudan For. Dep. For.
1966   Res. Inst. Pam 16. Soba, Khartoum, Sudan. 19 p.

WESTERN AUSTRALIA, FORESTS DEPARTMENT. Exotic conifers in Western Australia.
1957   [Pap. presented at 7th Br. Commonw. For. Conf.: Aust. and N. Z. 1957.]
        Wyatt, Perth. 21 p.

WOLF, C. B., and W. W. WAGENER. The New World cypresses. El Aliso I. Rancha
1948   Santa Ana Bot. Gard., Anaheim, Calif. xiii + 444 p.

WORLD EUCALYPTUS CONFERENCE. Second, São Paulo, Brazil, 1961. Rep. Doc.
1961   2 vols. xxvii + 485 p.

YOURCHENKO, N. Principios básicos para la elección de especies en el mejoramiento
[1962]   agroforestal de la Patagonia aride. Proc. World For. Congr. (Seattle 1960)
        5(1):381–384.

Appendixes

A   Conversion Factors   463

B   Summary of Seed Handling Practices by Species   464

C   Summary of Nursery Practices by Species   472

D   Site Requirements of Trees Suitable for Arid Zones 476

Appendixes

APPENDIX A

Conversion Factors

Length:	1 meter (m) = 100 centimeters (cm) = 1,000 millimeters (mm)
	1 meter = 3.28 ft = 1.094 yd
	1 kilometer (km) = 1000 m = 0.621 mile
	1 yard = 3 feet = 36 inches = 0.914 m
Area:	1 m² = 1.196 sq yds
	1 km² = 100 hectares = 1,000,000 m² = 0.386 sq miles
	1 hectare (ha) = 10,000 m² = 2.47 acres
Weight:	1 kilogram (kg) = 1000 grams (g) = 2.20 pounds (lb)
	1 metric ton = 1.102 short tons = 0.98 long tons
Volume:	1 cm³ = 0.06 cu in
	1 m³ = 35.3 cu feet
	1 liter (l) = 1000 cm³ = 61 cu in = 0.264 U.S. gallons
	0.220 Brit. gallons
Pressure:	1 kg/cm² = 14.2 lbs/sq in
Roundwood measure:	1 m³ = 177 board feet (bf or bd ft) = 35 cu feet
Growth:	1 m³/ha = 71.5 bd ft/acre based on 5 bd ft/ft³

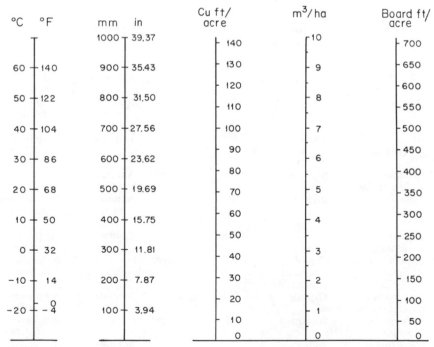

TEMPERATURE   RAINFALL   VOLUME STANDING TIMBER
(AFTER U.S.F.S.)

°C = 5/9 (°F − 32)   1" = approx. 25.4 mm   1m³/ha = 14.3 cu ft/acre   1m³/ha = 71.5 bf/acre
°F = 9/5 °C + 32   100mm = approx. 3.94 in

APPENDIX B

Summary of Seed Handling Practices by Species

Species	Fruit Type	Seeds per kg (000)	Collection		Method
			Time–Hemisphere		
			South Month	North	
Abies cilicica	Cone, falling apart at maturity	8		Late summer, before completely ripe	Hand-picking
Acacia cyano-phylla	Pod	60–70	Feb	Summer	Pick or strip onto canvas
Acacia tortilis	Pod	15		Summer	Pick or beat onto canvas
Acer negundo	Double samara	18–30	May	Late summer	Pick or strip onto canvas
Acer syriacum	Double samara			Late summer	Strip onto canvas
Ailanthus altissima	Samara	27	Apr, May	Late summer or autumn	Shake or strip onto canvas
Albizia lebbek	Pod	10		Autumn	Strip onto canvas
Alnus orientalis	Small un-winged nutlet	1,000		Late summer	Strip or shake onto canvas
Araucaria heterophylla	Massive cone	1.60	Apr, May	Autumn	Pick cones
Arbutus andrachne	Berry	500		Autumn or early winter	Pick or strip onto canvas
Argania sideroxylon	Nut	0.500		Summer	Strip onto canvas
Aspidosperma quebracho-blanco	Capsule; seed sa-mara-like	4–7	Sept		Strip onto canvas
Brachychiton populneum	Capsule	9.9		Summer	Strip from branches
Bulnesia retamo	Samara	45	Sept		Strip from branches
Caesalpinia spinosa	Pod			Summer	
Calligonum comosum	Achene	32		Late spring	Pick from ground or strip onto canvas

APPENDIX B *(Continued)*

| Extraction Method | Average Germina-tion % | Recommendations for | | Remarks |
		Storage	Pretreatment	
Dry, sieve, de-wing.	50	Dry, cold sealed	Cold stratification	Sow when fresh
Drying-trampling	85	Dry, cold sealed	Soak in hot water	
Drying-trampling	40	Dry, cold sealed	Soak in conc. H_2SO_4 1–2 hrs	
Dry enough to separate samaras and dewing	50	Cold strati-fication	Cold stratification	
Dry enough to separate samaras and dewing	80	Cold strati-fication	Cold stratification	
Drying	65	Dry, cold sealed	Cold stratification	
Threshing	70	Dry, cold sealed	Mechanical scari-fication or hot water	
Shaking		Dry, cold sealed	Cold stratification	Difficult to store
Drying; cones fall apart		Dry, cold unsealed	Cold stratification	Difficult to store
Maceration and flotation		Dry, cold sealed	5–6 days in warm water or cold stratify	Ripe fruit are red-violet
Drying	50	Dry, cold sealed		
Air dry		Dry, cold sealed		Viable only 6–9 months
Air dry	40–50	Dry, cold sealed		
		Dry, cold sealed		Lose viability quickly
		Dry, cold sealed		
Drying	80	Dry, cold sealed		Also propagated by cuttings

APPENDIX B (Continued)

Species	Fruit Type	Seeds per kg (000)	Collection		Method
			Time–Hemisphere		
			South Month	North	
Callitris glauca	Small, spherical cone	10		Autumn	Pick from tree onto canvas
Casuarina equisetifolia	Winged achene	700		Late summer	Pick, or cut twigs bearing fruit
Cedrus libani	Cone, falling apart at maturity	10		Late summer	Pick, or cut twigs bearing fruit
Celtis australis	Drupe	4.5		Autumn or early winter	Pick or strip onto canvas
Ceratonia siliqua	Pod	4–5		Autumn	Pick from tree
Cercis siliquastrum	Pod	30–60		Autumn	Pick or strip pods from tree
Crataegus azarolus	Pome	1.3		Autumn	Pick or strip fruit from tree
Cupressus arizonica	Globose cone, serotinous, persistent	60–100		1–several yrs. after ripe	Pick from tree
Cupressus macrocarpa	Globose cone	150	Feb–Mar	Late summer and autumn	Pick from tree
Cupressus sempervirens	Globose cone	100–160	Feb–Mar	Late summer and autumn	Pick from tree
Dalbergia sissoo	Wing-like pod with 1–3 seeds	45–55		Autumn	Pick or strip from tree
Elaeagnus angustifolia	Dry drupe	11		Late autumn or early winter	Pick from tree or ground
Eucalyptus camaldulensis	Capsule	200–1,000+		Spring to autumn	Pick from tree just before ripe
Fraxinus syriaca	Samara	25		Autumn	Pick from tree or ground

APPENDIX B *(Continued)*

Extraction Method	Average Germination %	Recommendations for		Remarks
		Storage	Pretreatment	
Drying	50	Dry, cold sealed		
Drying and sieving	70	Dry, cold sealed		
Soaking, drying dewinging	50	Dry, cold sealed or in cones at low temp.	Soak 2 hrs in water at room temp. or cold stratify	
Maceration and drying	60	Dry, cold sealed	Cold stratification	
Drying	80	Dry, cold sealed	Soak in conc. H_2SO_4 1–2 hrs then in water 48 hrs	
Drying	70	Dry, cold sealed	Soak in hot water or in conc. H_2SO_4 for 1 hr	
Maceration, flotation and screening		Dry, cold sealed	Warm plus cold stratification	
Drying and shaking	25	Dry, cold sealed	Cold stratification for some seed lots	
Drying and shaking	20	Dry, cold sealed	Cold stratification for some seed lots	
Drying and shaking	35	Dry, cold sealed	Cold stratification for some seed lots	
Drying, break pods in pieces with 1–2 seeds	80	Room cond. in tins or dry, cold sealed	Soak in water 24 hrs	
Maceration, flotation	55	Dry, cold sealed	Cold stratification	
Drying and sieving	90	Dry, cold sealed	None, needs light	Low purity. Must avoid loss before extraction
None	70	Dry, cold sealed	Sow promptly or cold stratification	Secondary dormancy induced by dry storage

APPENDIX B *(Continued)*

Species	Fruit Type	Seeds per kg (000)	Collection Time–Hemisphere South Month	North	Method
Genista raetam	Pod	12		Early summer	Pick from tree
Gleditsia triacanthos	Large pod	4–9	Apr, Jul	Autumn	Pick from tree or ground
Grevillea robusta	Boat-shaped follicle	80–100	Jan–Feb		
Haloxylon ammodendron	Utricle: 1–seeded winged	200–500		Autumn	Pick from tree or collect from ground
Jacaranda mimosaefolia	Pod	66	Je–Aug		Pick from tree
Juglans regia	Drupaceous, seed is a nut	0.060–0.110		Autumn	Pick, flail, or shake from tree and collect from ground
Juniperus excelsa	Berry-like cone	60–100		Late summer or autumn	Pick or strip onto canvas
Laurus nobilis	Small berry	70		Autumn	
Melia azedarach	Berry-like drupe	4–13 pits (1–5 seeds each)		Late autumn or early winter	Pick from tree after leaf-fall
Morus alba	Multiple of tiny drupes	250–700		Summer	Pick or strip onto canvas
Morus nigra	Multiple of tiny drupes	250–700		Summer	Pick or strip onto canvas
Parkinsonia aculeata	Pod	12		Autumn	Pick or strip onto canvas
Pinus halepensis	Cone serotinous and persistent	30–60	Mar–Apr	Collect last yr's cones mid- or late summer before fully ripe. Older cones any time	Pick cones from tree

APPENDIX B *(Continued)*

Extraction Method	Average Germination %	Recommendations for		Remarks
		Storage	Pretreatment	
Drying	90	Dry, cold sealed	Soak in hot water or 6–8 hrs conc. H_2SO_4	
Drying and breaking pods	75	Dry, cold sealed	Soak in hot water or 1 hr conc. H_2SO_4	
	Low	Dry, cold sealed?		Viable for only few mos
Drying	Low		Sow while fresh	Do not keep well in storage
Drying	80	Dry, cold sealed		Usually grown from cuttings
Remove husks	70	Cold stratification	Cold stratification	May be grown from cuttings
Soak in weak lye sol. then maceration and flotation		Dry, cold sealed	Cold + warm + cold stratification	Ripe (2- or 3-yr-old) "berries" are red, brown, or violet
Remove pulp	75		Soak in water 12–24 hours	Usually propagated by cuttings
Maceration and flotation	65	Dry, cold sealed, or room cond. for 1–yr.		Entire fruit may be planted
Mash fruit, macerate, float off pulp	70	Dry, cold sealed	Cold stratification	
Mash fruit, macerate, float off pulp	70	Dry, cold sealed	Cold stratification	
Drying, trampling or flailing	85–90	Dry, cold sealed	Scarify and soak in 38° C water 1 day	
Drying and shaking	70	Dry, cold sealed		Ripen in 2–3 yrs. Turn brown

APPENDIX B *(Continued)*

Species	Fruit Type	Seeds per kg (000)	Collection Time–Hemisphere South Month	Collection Time–Hemisphere North	Method
Pistacia atlantica	Drupe	8		Autumn or early winter	Pick from tree
Platanus orientalis	Globose, multiple of achenes	200		Autumn	Pick from tree or collect from ground
Prosopis alba	Pod	10.5	Dec–Feb		Pick from tree or collect from ground
Prosopis spicigera	Pod	13–28		Autumn	Pick from tree
Quercus suber	Acorn	0.110– 0.200		Early autumn or winter	Pick from tree
Quillaja saponaria	Follicle	140			Pick from tree
Rhus coriaria	Drupe	30		Autumn or winter	Pick fruit clusters from tree
Robinia pseudoacacia	Pod	32–70	Apr–Je	Autumn through winter	Flail or strip onto canvas
Schinopsis lorentzii	Samara	8	May–Jul		Pick from tree
Schinus molle	Drupe	35–65	Jan–Je	End of dry season	Pick from tree
Tamarindus indica	Pod	0.900	Nov–Mar	End of dry season	Pick from tree
Taxodium distichum	Globose cone breaking apart at maturity	20	Je	Early winter	Pick from tree
Tetraclinis articulata	Woody cone	100		Autumn	Flail or strip onto canvas
Ulmus pumila	Samara	100– 200		Spring	Flail or strip onto canvas
Zizyphus spina-christi	Drupe	1.5		Late summer	Flail or strip onto canvas

APPENDIX B (Continued)

Extraction Method	Average Germina-tion %	Recommendations for		Remarks
		Storage	Pretreatment	
Macerate in weak lye sol. rub on screen	Low	Dry, cold sealed? Do not keep well	Cold stratification?	Red seeds usually empty
None. Break dry fruit into separate achenes	<50	Dry, cold sealed	Cold stratification	Be sure only sound seeds are collected
Drying and threshing	60	Dry, cold sealed	Hot water?	Usually seeded directly in field
Drying and threshing	40–60	Dry, cold sealed	Soak in cold water	
Brisk stirring to remove cups	70	Cold strati-fication		Do not collect from ground. Ripe acorns brown
Drying		Dry, cold sealed		
Separate sound from empty seed by flota-tion	30–60	Dry, cold sealed	Soak in conc. H_2SO_4 1–2 hrs then cold stratify	
Thresh, run through fan-ning mill or separate by flotation	70	Dry, cold sealed	Hot water or conc. H_2SO_4 20–60 min.	
Drying	60	Dry, cold sealed		
Drying	50	Dry, cold sealed or room con-ditions		Retain viability for long period
Drying	60	Dry, cold sealed		
Air dry and trample or flail to break cones apart	40	Dry, cold sealed	Cold stratification	
	50	Dry, cold sealed		
	50+	Dry, cold sealed	None	
Maceration, flotation	60–80	Dry, cold sealed	Soak in conc. H_2SO_4 2–6 hrs then cold stratify	Entire fruit may also be planted

APPENDIX C

Summary of Nursery Practices by Species

| Species | Sowing | | Trans-planting–Season |
	Season	Recommendation	
Abies cilicica	Autumn	Containers	Winter
Acacia cyanophylla	Summer	Beds or containers	Summer
Acacia tortilis	Summer	Containers	Summer
Acer negundo	Spring	Beds	Spring
Ailanthus altissima	Spring	Beds	Spring
Alnus orientalis	Spring	Beds	Summer
Araucaria heterophylla	Autumn	Pots	Spring
Aspidosperma quebracho-blanco	Spring	Containers	
Azadirachta indica	Spring	Soil	Rainy season
Bulnesia retamo	Spring	Beds	Rainy season
Calligonum comosum	Summer	Containers	Summer
Casuarina equisetifolia	Spring	Containers	Summer
Casuarina glauca	Spring	Containers	Summer
Cedrus libani	Spring	Containers	Summer
Celtis australis	Autumn	Beds	Winter
Ceratonia siliqua	Autumn or spring	Containers	Spring
Crataegus azarolus	Autumn	Beds	Winter
Cupressus sempervirens	Autumn	Containers	Winter
Dalbergia sissoo	Spring	Beds or containers	Spring
Elaeagnus angustifolia	Spring	Beds or containers	Spring
Eucalyptus camaldulensis	Spring	Containers	Summer
Ficus sycomorus	Spring	Cuttings	
Fraxinus syriaca	Autumn	Beds	Spring
Gleditsia triacanthos	Spring	Containers	Spring
Grevillea robusta	Spring	Beds	Spring
Haloxylon ammodendron	Winter	Containers	
Juglans regia	Winter	Beds	Spring
Juniperus excelsa	Autumn	Containers	Winter
Melia azedarach	Spring	Beds	Spring
Morus alba	Spring	Containers	Summer
Parkinsonia aculeata	Spring	Beds	Spring
Pinus brutia	Autumn	Containers	Winter
Pinus canariensis	Autumn	Containers	Winter
Pinus halepensis	Autumn	Containers	Winter
Pinus nigra	Autumn	Containers	Winter

APPENDIX C *(Continued)*

Transplanting–Recommendation	Relative Growth Rate in Nursery	Remarks
Containers	Slow	Shading required. Keep more than 1 year in the nursery
Rows or containers	Fast	May not need to be transplanted
Containers	Medium	
Rows	Fast	
Rows	Fast	Vigorous grower
Rows	Medium	
Containers	Slow	
	Slow	Long taproot. Field planting
	Fast	
Beds	Medium	
Containers	Fast	Sown and eventually transplanted in pure sand
Rows	Fast	
Rows	Fast	
Rows	Slow	Long taproot
Rows	Fast	
Containers	Medium	Taprooted, transplanting not recommended
Rows	Medium	
Containers	Medium	
Rows or containers	Fast	Direct sowing in beds recommended
Rows	Medium	
Containers	Fast	If necessary, retard growth by cutting back the tops
Rows	Fast	
Rows	Fast	
Rows	Medium	
	Slow	Sown in pure sand, do not transplant
Rows	Medium	Taprooted, improve stock by root-pruning in midsummer
Containers	Slow	Keep 2 years in nursery
Rows	Fast	Direct sowing recommended; very vigorous growth
Rows	Fast	
Rows	Fast	
Containers	Medium	
Containers	Medium	Very liable to damping-off
Containers	Medium	
Containers	Slow	If necessary, keep more than 1 year in nursery; very liable to damping-off

APPENDIX C *(Continued)*

| Species | Sowing | | Trans-planting–Season |
	Season	Recom-mendation	
Pinus pinaster	Autumn	Containers	Winter
Pinus pinea	Autumn	Containers	Winter
Pistacia atlantica	Autumn	Containers	Winter
Platanus orientalis	Autumn or spring	Containers	Spring
× *Populus euramericana*	Spring	Cuttings	
Prosopis juliflora	Spring	Beds	Spring
Prosopis spicigera	Spring	Beds	Spring
Quercus suber	Spring	Beds	
Rhus coriaria	Spring	Beds	
Robinia pseudoacacia	Spring	Containers	Spring
Salix spp.	Spring	Cuttings	
Schinopsis lorentzii	Late summer to early autumn	Beds	Mid-winter
Schinus molle	Late summer to early autumn	Beds	Spring
Tamarix articulata	Spring	Cuttings	
Taxodium distichum	Autumn	Beds	Spring
Tetraclinis articulata	Autumn	Containers	Winter
Ulmus pumila	Spring	Containers	Spring
Zizyphus spina-christi	Spring	Beds	Spring

APPENDIX C *(Continued)*

Transplanting–Recommendation	Relative Growth Rate in Nursery	Remarks
Containers	Medium	
Containers	Medium	Do not transplant, taprooted, usually sown on planting site
Containers	Slow	
Rows	Fast	
	Very fast	
Rows	Fast	
Rows	Medium	Do not transplant, heavy taproot, usually direct sowing on planting site
	Slow	
	Medium	Vigorous grower; cut back top to retard growth
Rows	Fast	
	Fast	
Rows or containers	Slow	Shade until germination, then half-shade
Rows	Medium, fast	
Beds	Medium	
Containers	Medium	
Rows	Fast	
Rows	Medium	

APPENDIX D
Site Requirements of Trees Suitable for Arid Zones

Species	I	II	III	IV	V	VI	VII	VIII
Acacia arabica			x	x	x			
Acacia cyanophylla			x	x				
Acacia melanoxylon	x	x	x					
Acacia pycnantha			x	x				
Acacia salicina			x	x				
Acacia tortilis					x			
Acer negundo		x						
Ailanthus altissima	x	x	x					
Argania sideroxylon				x	x			
Aspidosperma quebracho-blanco				x	x			
Betula utilis							x	
Brachychiton populneum			x					
Bulnesia retamo				x			x	
Callitris glauca			x	x				x
Caragana arborescens							x	
Cassia siamea			x	x				
Casuarina equisetifolia		x	x	x		x		
Cedrus spp.	x	x						
Celtis australis		x	x					
Ceratonia siliqua		x	x					
Conocarpus lancifolius					x	x		x
Crataegus azarolus			x				x	
Cupressus arizonica	x	x	x					
Cupressus sempervirens		x	x			x		
Dalbergia sissoo			x			x		
Elaeagnus angustifolia			x	x			x	x
Eucalyptus brockwayi			x	x				x
Eucalyptus camaldulensis		x	x	x		x		
Eucalyptus dundasi			x	x				x
Eucalyptus gomphocephala		x	x		x			x
Eucalyptus gracilis				x				x
Eucalyptus microtheca			x	x		x		
Eucalyptus occidentalis		x	x	x		x		x
Eucalyptus oleosa					x			x
Eucalyptus salmonophloia			x	x				x
Eucalyptus salubris			x	x				x
Eucalyptus sargenti			x	x				x
Eucalyptus spathulata				x	x			x
Eucalyptus torquata					x	x		
Ficus sycomorus				x				
Fraxinus angustifolia	x	x						

I	Altitude about 1,000 m (3,300 ft), rainfall about 1,000 mm (40 in)
II	Altitude about 400–800 m (1,300–2,600 ft), rainfall 600–800 mm (24–32 in)
III	Rainfall 300–600 mm (12–24 in)
IV	Steppe, rainfall 200–400 mm (8–16 in)
V	Bordering deserts, rainfall less than 200 mm (8 in)
VI	On wet soil along rivers rainfall less than 200 mm (8 in)
VII	Cold arid zones
VIII	Alkaline soils

Cercis, 88, 91
  siliquastrum L., 299, **383–84**, 466–67
Chamaecyparis, 78
Chinaberry (*Melia azedarach* L.), 414,
  415
Christ thorn (*Zisyphus spina-christi* (L.)
  Willd.), **455–56**
Chrysothamnus, 329
Cirsium, 181
Cistus, 419, 425, 452
Citrus (*Citrus* spp.), 448
Cladosporum, 93
Clover (*Trifolium* spp.), 181, 329
Coffee (*Coffea* spp.), 409
Coniferae, 78
Conocarpus lancifolius Engl., 291, 331,
  384–85, 476
Cooba, (*Acacia salicina* Lindl.), **360**
Coolibah (*Eucalyptus microtheca* F.
  Muell.), **398–99**
Cordia, 417
Cottonwood (*Populus* spp.), 77, 279, 434
Crataegus, 67, 72, 385
  azarolus L., **385**, 466–67, 472–73, 476
Crotalaria juncea L., 312
Cupressus, 66, 78, 82, 112, 118, 121, 152,
  196, 228, 270, 419, 425
  arizonica Greene, 312, 340, 385, **386**,
    466–67, 476
  atlantica Gaussen = *C. sempervirens*
    L. var., 390
  glabra Sudw. = *C. arizonica* Greene
  lusitanica Mill., **386**, 387
    var. *benthamii* (Endl.) Carr., 386
  macrocarpa Hartw., 312, **387–88**, 431,
    466–67
  sempervirens L., 34, 303, 312, 340,
    388–90, 466–67, 472–73, 476
    var. *horizontalis* (Mill.) Loud., 303,
      318, 389, 390
    var. *pyramidalis* Nyman, 267, 303,
      389, 390
Cyclops (*Acacia cyclops* A. Cunn.), **356**
Cynodon dactylon (L.) Pers., 179
Cyperus, 179
Cypress, (*Cupressus* spp.), 34, 54, 64, 67,
  71, 75, 132, 138, 388
  Arizona (*C. arizonica* Greene), 385,
    386
  horizontal (*C. sempervirens* var. *hori-
    zontalis* (Mill.) Loud., 389
  Italian (*C. sempervirens* L.), **388–90**
  Mexican (*C. lusitanica* Mill.), **386**, 387
  Monterey (*C. macrocarpa* Hartw.),
    387–88
  pyramidal (*C. sempervirens* var. *pyra-
    midalis* Nyman), 389
Cypress pine, white (*Callitris glauca* R.
  Br.), **374**

Dalbergia, 291, 292
  sissoo Roxb., 118, 149, 283, 291, 294,
    318, 319, 330, 340, **390–92**, 415,
    466–67, 472–73, 476
Damas (*Conocarpus lancifolius* Engl.),
  384–85
Date, desert; *see* Desert date
Delonix regia (Bojer) Raf., 66, 335, 340,
  392
Desert date (*Balanites aegyptiaca* (L.)
  Del.), **370**
Diospyros, 134
Dodonaea viscosa Jacq., 112
Douglas-fir (*Pseudotsuga menziesii*
  (Mirb.) Franco), 88
Dundas mahogany (*Eucalyptus brock-
  wayi* C. A. Gardner), 393

Elaeagnus, 112, 298
  angustifolia L., 66, 147, 299, 312, 318,
    326, 331, 339, 340, **392–93**, 466–67,
    472–73, 476
Elm (*Ulmus* spp.), 152, 253
  American (*U. americana* L.), **453–54**
  Chinese (*U. parvifolia* Jacq.), **455**
  Siberian (*U. pumila* L.), **454–55**
Ephedra, 329
Erica, 419, 425
Espino (*Acacia caven* (Mol.) Molina),
  356
Eucalypt (*Eucalyptus* spp.), 41, 44, 53,
  54, 55, 64, 65, 70, 75, 79, 88, 92,
  95, 108, 115, 119, 120, 121, 123, 127,
  128, 130, 132, 133, 134, 136, 138,
  139, 140, 147, 151, 167, 185, 186,
  191, 199, 223, 228, 244, 249, 252,
  253, 270, 272, 273, 274–76, 281,
  282, 292, 309, 316, 318, 326, 330,
  335, 338, 348, 350, 351, 359, 393,
  395, 396, 398, 400, 402
Eucalyptus, 75, 82, 118, 138, 205, 270,
  273, 276, 287, 291, 310, 335, 339,
  393
  astringens Maiden, 275, 276, 399
  blakelyi Maiden, 398
  brockwayi C. A. Gardner, 275, 276,
    312, 331, 340, 393, 399, 476
  camaldulensis Dehnh., 63, 64, 88, 105,
    275, 276, 283, 287, 291, 298, 299,
    312, 318, 330, 340, 350, 393–95,
    396, 400, 404, 466–67, 472–73, 476
  citriodora Hook., 79
  coolabah Blakeley & Jacobs = *E. mi-
    crotheca* F. Muell.
  cornuta Labill., 330
  corynocalyx F. Muell., 275
  dumosa A. Cunn., 41
  dundasi Maiden, 312, 331, 340, 395,
    476

Eucalyptus (*Continued*)
  globulus Labill., 274, 283, 330
  gomphocephala A. DC, 224, 275, 276, 326, 330, 331, 340, 356, **395–96**, 397, 476
  gracilis F. Muell., 312, 331, 340, **396**, 476
  grandis (Mill.) Maiden, 350
  hemiphloia F. Muell., 318, 330, 398
  largiflorens F. Muell., 41
  leucoxylon F. Muell., 275, 276, **396**, 397, 398, 402
  maculata Hook., 275
  melliodora A. Cunn., 275, 276, 394, 396, **398**
  microcarpa Maiden, 394, 402
  microtheca F. Muell., 118, 288, 291, **398–99**, 476
  occidentalis Endl., 275, 276, 287, 319, 330, 331, 340, **399**, 476
  oleosa F. Muell., 41, 275, 331, 340, **399–400**, 476
    var. *glauca* Maiden, 41
  ovata Labill., 394
  paniculata Sm., 275
  robusta Sm., 330
  rudis Endl., 275, **400**, 401
  saligna Sm., 330, 350
  salmonophloia F. Muell., 275, 331, 340, **400–401**, 402, 476
  salubris F. Muell., 275, 312, 331, 340, **402**, 476
  sargenti Maiden, 312, 331, 340, **402**, 476
  sideroxylon A. Cunn., 275, 276, 330, 396, **402–3**
  spathulata Hook., 331, 340, **404**, 476
  tereticornis Sm., 275, **404**, 405
  torquata J. G. Luehm., 275, 340, **404–5**, 476
  uncinata Turcz., 41
Eugenia jambolana Lam., 296
Euphorbia (*Euphorbia* spp.), 37
Euphorbia, 337, 360
  tirucalli L., **405–6**

Fagus, 96
Ficus, 100, 146, 147, 319
  benjamina L., 340
  carica L., 406
  sycomorus L., 147, **406**, 472–73, 476
Fig (*Ficus carica* L.), **406**
Fir, Douglas; see Douglas-fir
Flamboyant (*Delonix regia* (Bojer) Raf.), **392**
Frankincense (*Boswellia serrata* Roxb.), **371**
Fraxinus, 74, 78, 90, 91, 115, 118, 196, 335, 339

  angustifolia Vahl, 476
  anomala Torr., 91
  excelsior L., 91
  lanceolata Borkh. = *F. pennsylvanica* Marsh.
  pennsylvanica Marsh., 311, 312
  syriaca Boiss., **406–7**, 466–67, 472–73
Fungi, 32, 92, 93, 106, 119, 125, 126, 143, 155, 156, 159, 163, 164, 182, 187, 230, 234, 254, 270, 274, 280, 311, 351
Fusarium, 93

Genista, 425
  raetam Forsk., 65, **468–69**, 477
Gimlet (*Euclalyptus salubris* F. Muell.), **402**
Ginkgo (*Ginkgo biloba* L.), 91, 92
Gleditsia, 88, 356
  triacanthos L., 283, 291, 297, 331, **407–8**, 468–69, 472–73, 477
Grevillea, 311, 335
  robusta 'A. Cunn., 66, 298, 299, 340, **408–9**, 468–69, 472–73, 477
Guamúchil (*Pithecellobium dulce* (Roxb.) Benth.), **432–33**
Gum (*Eucalyptus* spp.)
  coral-flowered (*E. torquata* Luehm.), **404–5**
  forest red (*E. tereticornis* Sm.), **404**, 405
  river red (*E. camaldulensis* Dehnh.), **393–95**
  salmon (*E. salmonophloia* F. Muell.), **400–401**
Gum arabic (*Acacia senegal* Willd.), 89, 230, **360–61**, 365
Gymnocladus, 88

Hackberry (*Celtis occidentalis* L.), **381–82**
  European (*C. australis* L.), **380**, 381
Haloxylon (*Haloxylon articulatum* (Cav.) Bunge), **409–10**
Haloxylon, 229, 230, 231, 297, 361
  ammodendron Bunge, 39, 40, 94, 146, 147, 241, 283, 321, 326, 331, **409**, 468–69, 472–73, 477
  aphyllum Minkw., 321, 326, 409
  articulatum (Cav.) Bunge, **409–10**
  persicum Bunge = *H. ammodendron* Bunge
Hawthorn, common (*Crataegus azarolus* L.), 67, 68, **385**
Heglig tree (*Balanites aegyptiaca* (L.) Del.), **370**
Honeylocust (*Gleditsia triacanthos* L.), 297, **407–8**

Horsebean (*Parkinsonia aculeata* L.),
417

Ilex, 88
Imperata, 322
Indian lilac (*Melia azedarach* L.), 415
Ironbark (*Eucalyptus* spp.)
  red flowering (*E. sideroxylon* A.
    Cunn.), 402–3
  white (*E. leucoxylon* F. Muell.), 396,
    397

Jacaranda (*Jacaranda mimosaefolia* D.
    Don), 410
Jacaranda, 335
  mimosaefolia D. Don, 340, 410, 468–69
Jhand (*Prosopis spicigera* L.), 437
Judas tree (*Cercis siliquastrum* L.), 383–
  84
Juglans, 83, 283, 292
  regia L., 291, 410, 468–69, 472–73,
    477
Jujube (*Zizyphus jujuba* Lam.), 455
Juniper (*Juniperus* spp.), 53, 72, 91, 329,
  422
  common (*J. communis* L.), 410–11
  Greek (*J. excelsa* Bieb.), 411
  Rocky Mountain (*J. scopulorum* Sarg.),
    411–12
Juniperus, 88, 91, 112, 115, 152, 196,
  234, 339, 379, 419, 425, 430
  communis L., 340, 410–11, 477
  excelsa Bieb., 411, 468–69, 472–73,
    477
  scopulorum Sarg., 66, 411–12, 418
  virginiana L., 312, 412

Khaya senegalensis (Desr.) A. Juss., 291,
  412–13
Kurrajong (*Brachychiton populneum*
  (Schott) R. Br.), 371, 372

Laretia, 22
  acaulis Gill. and Hook. = *L. compacta*
    Reiche
  compacta Reiche, 413–14
Larix, 79, 181, 430
Laurel, Greek (*Laurus nobilis* L.), 414
Laurus nobilis L., 414, 468–69, 477
Leguminosae, 78
Libocedrus, 79
Lichens, 45
Lilac, Indian (*Melia azedarach* L.), 415
Liquidambar, 78
Liriodendron, 78
Llareta (*Laretia compacta* Reiche), 413–
  14
Locust
  black (*Robinia pseudoacacia* L.), 152,
    254, 329, 381, 443–44

honey; *see* Honeylocust
  West African (*Parkia clappertoniana*
    Keay), 416

Mahogany, dry-zone (*Khaya senegalensis*
  (Desr.) A. Juss.), 412–13
Mahogany, Dundas; *see* Dundas mahog-
  any
Mallee (*Eucalyptus* spp.), 41, 326, 404
  giant (*E. oleosa* F. Muell.), 399–400
Mallet (Eucalyptus spp.)
  Salt River (*E. sargenti* Maiden), 402
  swamp (*E. spathulata* Hook.), 404
Mango (*Mangifera indica* L.), 296
Maple (*Acer* spp.), 54, 65, 363
  Syrian (*A. syriacum* Boiss. & Gaill.),
    363
Melia, 291, 335
  azadirachta L. = *Azadirachta indica*
    A. Juss.
  azedarach L., 66, 115, 196, 291, 340,
    414, 415, 468–69, 472–73, 477
Mesquite (*Prosopis juliflora* (Swartz)
  DC), 44, 435–36
Milk-bush (*Euphorbia tirucalli* L.),
  405–6
Mimosaceae, 37
Moitch (*Eucalyptus rudis* Endl.), 400,
  401
Morus, 150, 291, 391, 477
  alba L., 66, 283, 291, 297, 415–16,
    468–69, 472–73
  nigra L., 297, 416, 468–69
Mulberry (*Morus* spp.), 291, 391
  black (*M. nigra* L.), 416
  white (*M. alba* L.), 415–16
Myoporum, 309

Ñandubay (*Prosopis algarobilla* Griseb.),
  435
Neem (*Azadirachta indica* A. Juss.), 369
Nettle tree (*Celtis australis* L.), 380, 381
Norfolk Island pine (*Araucaria hetero-
  phylla* (Salisb.) Franco), 365–66

Oak (*Quercus* spp.), 53, 54, 79, 92, 94,
  122, 152, 215, 351, 379, 383, 422,
  431, 438, 439, 440, 442
  bur (*Q. macrocarpa* Michx.), 440–41,
    442
  California blue (*Q. douglasii* Hook. &
    Arn.), 440, 441
  cork (*Q. suber* L.), 441–42
  kermes (*Q. coccifera* L.), 439
  river; *see* River oak
  she; *see* She-oak
  silky; *see* Silky oak
  valonia (*Q. aegilops* L.), 439
  white (*Q.* spp.), 68, 86

Ochroma, 76
Olea europaea L., 15, 452
Olive, European (*Olea europaea* L.), 15, 91
Olive, Russian; *see* Russian-olive
Opuntia, 36, 337

Pagoda tree (*Sophora japonica* L.), 448
Palm, 37, 53
Parkia clappertoniana Keay, 416
Parkinsonia aculeata L., 66, 112, 340, 417, 468–69, 472–73, 477
Pea tree (*Caragana arborescens* Lam.), 329, 375
Penicillium, 93
Pennisetum purpureum Schumach., 112, 312
Pepper tree (*Schinus molle* L.), 447–48
Peumus boldus Molina, 418
Picea, 79, 96
　pungens Engelm., 418–19
Pine (*Pinus* spp.), 53, 54, 55, 58, 64, 65, 67, 70, 71, 72, 75, 76, 79, 80, 81, 88, 92, 93, 94, 96, 109, 118, 122, 127, 128, 130, 132, 138, 144, 147, 152, 163, 181, 214, 232, 234, 253, 270, 272, 273, 276, 282, 329, 348, 351, 356, 375, 388, 390, 419, 430
　Aleppo (*P. halepensis* Mill.), 15, 135, 227, 253, 272, 424, 425
　black (*P. nigra* Arnold), 426
　brutia (*P. brutia* Ten.), 253, 419, 420
　Canary Island (*P. canariensis* C. Sm.), 253, 419, 421
　Chihuahua (*P. leiophylla* var *chihuahuana* (Engelm.) Shaw), 425–26
　Corsican (*P. nigra* Arnold), 426
　Digger (*P. sabiniana* Dougl.), 441
　insignis (*P. radiata* D. Don), 431
　Italian stone (*P. pinea* L.), 230
　limber (*P. flexilis* James), 423, 425
　maritime (*P. pinaster* Ait.), 58, 60, 426–27
　Mexican nut (*P. cembroides* Zucc.), 422
　Monterey (*P. radiata* D. Don), 273, 346, 347, 350, 431
　Norfolk Island; *see* Norfolk Island pine
　pinyon (*P. edulis* L.), 422–23
　ponderosa (*P. ponderosa* Laws.), 429–30
　stone (*P. pinea* L.), 427–29
　stone (*P.* spp.), 122
　umbrella (*P. pinea* L.), 427–29
Pinus, 79, 96, 118, 196, 319, 419
　brutia Ten., 72, 80, 115, 121, 228, 276, 312, 326, 340, 350, 419, 420, 425, 472–73, 477

　canariensis C. Sm., 134, 312, 348, 419, 421, 472–73
　cembroides Zucc., 276, 422
　coulteri D. Don, 276
　echinata Mill., 79
　edulis Engelm., 422–23
　eldarica Medw., 276
　elliottii Engelm., 79
　flexilis James, 423, 425
　halepensis Mill., 15, 63, 66, 72, 73, 80, 115, 121, 135, 163, 228, 267, 276, 312, 316, 340, 348, 419, 424, 425, 452, 468–69, 472–73, 477
　insignis Dougl. = P. radiata D. Don
　jeffreyi Grev. & Balf., 276
　laricio Poir. = *P. nigra* Arnold
　leiophylla var. *chihuahuana* (Engelm.) Shaw, 425–26
　maritima Poir. = *P. pinaster* Ait.
　nigra Arnold, 63, 88, 121, 419, 426, 472–73, 477
　palustris Mill., 79
　pinaster Ait., 58, 59, 61, 62, 63, 66, 72, 276, 351, 425, 426–27, 474–75, 477
　pinea L., 66, 80, 81, 115, 118, 122, 230, 326, 425, 427–29, 474–75
　ponderosa Laws., 60, 81, 96, 276, 312, 412, 418, 429–30, 477
　radiata D. Don, 63, 96, 136, 139, 147, 276, 281, 282, 346, 347, 350, 387, 431, 477
　rigida Mill., 79
　sabiniana Dougl., 80, 440, 441
　taeda L., 79
Pinyon (*Pinus edulis* Engelm.), 422–23
Pistachio (*Pistacia* spp.), 53, 80, 93, 432
　desert (*P. atlantica* Desf.), 431–32
Pistacia, 80, 425, 440
　atlantica Desf., 81, 431–32, 470–71, 474–75, 477
　lentiscus L., 274, 340, 452
　vera L., 432
Pithecellobium dulce (Roxb.) Benth., 432–33
Pittosporum, 309
Plane (*Platanus* spp.), 335
　oriental (*P. orientalis* L.), 433
Platanus, 74, 78, 80, 283
　occidentalis L., 339
　orientalis L., 100, 147, 291, 433, 470–71, 474–75, 477
Poinciana (*Denonix regia* (Bojer) Raf.), 392
Poinciana regia Bojer = *Delonix regia* (Bojer) Raf.
Polylepis, 22
Poplar (*Populus* spp.), 22, 44, 54, 147, 148, 253, 272, 276–81, 282, 286, 292, 294, 296, 330, 335, 434

balsam (*P. balsamifera* L.), 296
black (*P. nigra* L.), 279, 434
Chile (*P. nigra* L. var.), 279
Euphrates (*P. euphratica* Oliv.), 434
Euramerican (× *P. euramericana* (Dode) Guinier), 279, 296, 325
hybrid, 279, 325, 329, 434
Lombardy (*P. nigra* var. *italica* (Muenchh.) Koehne), 445
white (*P. alba* L.), 434
Populus, 65, 77, 84, 100, 112, 146, 147, 149, 278, 291, 312, 319, 393, 418, **434, 445**
alba L., 253, 276, 296, 311, 434, 477
bolleana Lauche = *P. alba* L. var., 311, 312
deltoides Bartr., 253, 279
euphratica Oliv., 253, 434, 437, 477
× *euramericana* (Dode) Guinier, 279, 325, 434, 474–75
nigra L., 253, 276, 434
var. *italica* (Muenchh.) Koehne, 296
tremula L., 477
Portulaca, 181
Prosopis, 40, 54, 128, 132, 205, 291, 297, 320, 327, 330, 335, 354, 368, 434, 437
alba Griseb., 150, 297, 356, **434–35**, 446, 447, 470–71, 477
algarobilla Griseb., 434, **435**
chilensis (Molina) Stuntz = *P. tamarugo* F. Phil.
juliflora (Swartz) DC, 40, 73, 112, 149, 291, 299, 319, 340, **435–36**, 437, 445, 447, 474–75, 477
nigra Hieron., 40, 150, 297, 356, 434, 446, 447
spicigera L., 291, 297, 327, 436, **437**, 470–71, 474–75, 477
tamarugo F. Phil., 44, 297, 330, 331, **437–38**, 477
Prunus, 88, 91
virginiana L., 312
Pseudotsuga, 79
douglasii Carr. = *P. menziesii* (Mirb.) Franco
menziesii (Mirb.) Franco, 412, 418, 429
taxifolia (Poir.) Britt. = *P. menziesii* (Mirb.) Franco
Purshia tridentata (Pursh) DC, 88, 430
Purslane (*Portulaca* spp.), 181
Pyrus communis L., 477

Quackgrass (*Agropyron junceum* (L.) Beauv.), 181
Quebracho (*Aspidosperma* spp.), 94
Quebracho, red (*Schinopsis lorentzii* Engelm.), **446–47**

Quebracho, white (*Aspidosperma quebracho-blanco* Schlecht.), 64, **368–69**
Quebracho colorado; *see* Quebracho colorado santiagueño
Quebracho colorado santiagueño (*Schinopsis lorentzii* Engelm.), 368, **446–47**
Quercus, 47, 74, 83, 88, 118, 122, 419, 425, 438
aegilops L., **439**
calliprinos Webb = *Q. coccifera* L., 452
coccifera L., **439**, 440
douglasii Hook & Arn., **440**, 441
ilex L., 378
macrocarpa Michx., 68, 312, **440–41**, 442
pubescens Willd., 378
robur L., 312
suber L., **441–42**, 470–71, 474–75, 477
Quillaja saponaria Molina, **442**, 470–71

Redbud (*Cercis siliquastrum* L.), **383–84**
Redcedar, eastern (*Juniperus virginiana* L.), **412**
Retama raetam Webb = *Genista raetam* Forsk.
Retamo (*Bulnesia retamo* Griseb.), **371–72**, 373
Rhizopus, 93
Rhus, 66, 425, 443
coriaria L., 312, **442–43**, 470–71, 474–75, 477
Ricinus communis L., 312, 323
River oak (*Casuarina cunninghamiana* Miquel), **375–76**
Robinia, 88, 292, 335
pseudoacacia L., 115, 118, 283, 291, 296, 312, 319, 339, 340, **443–44**, 470–71, 474–75, 477
Russian-olive (*Elaeagnus angustifolia* L.), 177, 329, **392–93**

Saccharum, 320
aegyptiacum Will., 318, 323
munja Roxb., 318, 323
Salix, 65, 100, 146, 147, 291, 319, 360, 393, **445**, 474–75, 477
alba L., 312, 477
arbuscula L., 311, 312
caspica Pall., 327
humboldtiana Willd., 312, **445–46**, 447
incana Schronk. = *S. viminalis* L.
matsudana Koidz., 327
viminalis L., **446**
Salvadora (*Salvadora persica* L.), **446**
Salvadora, 297
persica L., 331, **446**, 477

Sarcobatus, 329
Saxaul (Haloxylon ammodendron Bunge), 94, 230, **409**
Schinopsis, 356, 447
  lorentzii Engelm., 299, 368, **446–47**, 470–71, 474–75
Schinus, 311
  molle L., 299, 340, 356, 434, 435, 445, **447–48**, 470–71, 474–75, 477
  terebenthifolius Raddi, 340
She-oak (Casuarina equisetifolia Forst.), **376–77**
Shisham (Dalbergia sissoo Roxb.), 291, **390–92**
Silky oak (Grevillea robusta A. Cunn.), **408–9**
Siris (Albizia lebbek (L.) Benth.), **364–65**
Sissoo (Dalbergia sissoo Roxb.), **390–92**
Smilex, 425
Soapbark (Quillaja saponaria Molina), **442**
Sophora japonica L., 66, **448**, 477
Spicigera (Prosopis spicigera L.), **437**
Spruce (Picea spp.), 92, 109, 144
  blue (P. pungens Engelm.), **418–19**
Strawberry tree (Arbutus andrachne L.), 67, 68, **366–67**
Styphnolobium japonicum (L.) Schott = Sophora japonica L.
Sumach, elm-leaved (Rhus coriaria L.), **442–43**
Sunflower (Helianthus spp.), 135
Sycamore (Ficus sycomorus L.), **406**

Tamarindus indica L., 291, 296, 470–71
Tamarisk (Tamarix spp.), 44, 147, 148, 309, 327, 330
  athel (T. aphylla (L.) Karst.), **449–50**
  French (T. gallica L.), **450**, 451
Tamarix, 42, 100, 105, 112, 146, 147, 149, 287, 291, 309, 310, 319, 320, 335, 354, 393, 437, 450
  aphylla (L.) Karst., 283, 291, 326, 340, **449–50**
  articulata Vahl = T. aphylla (L.) Karst., 312, 474–75, 477
  gallica L., 312, 331, 340, **450**, 451, 477
  laxa Willd., 327
  leptostachis Bunge, 327
  ramosissima Ledeb., 327
  szovitsiana Bunge, 327
Tamarugo (Prosopis tamarugo F. Phil.), 297, **437–38**
Taxodium distichum (L.) Rich., 66, 330, **450–52**, 470–71, 474–75, 477

Taxus, 88
Tea (Thea, spp.), 409
Teak (Tectona grandis L.f.), 134, 296
Tecoma (Tecoma undulata G. Don), **452**
Tecoma, 335
  undulata G. Don, 34, 437, **452**
Terebinto (Schinus molle L.), **447–48**
Tetraclinis articulata (Vahl) Mast., **452–53**, 470–71, 474–75, 477
Thistle (Cirsium spp.), 181
Thuja, 78
Tortilis tree (Acacia tortilis Hayne), **361–63**
Tree of heaven (Ailanthus altissima (Mill.) Swingle), **363–64**
Trifolium, 181
Tsuga, 79, 96
Tuart (Eucalyptus gomphocephala A. DC), **395–96**, 397

Ulmus, 65, 74, 78, 81, 112, 283, 339
  americana L., 312, **453–54**
  parvifolia Jacq., 65, 312, **455**, 477
  pinnato-ramosa Dieck, 312, 313
  pumila L., 66, 291, 312, 340, **454–55**, 470–71, 474–75, 477

Vitex, 319

Walnut (Juglans spp.), 94
  Persian (J. regia L.), **410**
Wattle (Acacia spp.), 42
  blue-leafed (A. cyanophylla Lindl.), 265, **356**, 357
  golden (A. pycnantha Benth.), **359–60**
Willow (Salix spp.), 22, 44, 54, 148, 253, 276, 296, 330, 360, **445**
  basket (S. viminalis L.), **446**
  Humboldt's (S. humboldtiana Willd.), **445–46**

Yareta (Laretia compacta Reiche), **413–14**
Yate, swamp (Eucalyptus occidentalis Endl.), **399**
Yellow box (Eucalyptus gracilis F. Muell.), **398**
Yorrell (Eucalyptus gracilis F. Muell.), **396**

Zizyphus, 360, 368, 384, 417, 456
  jujuba Lam., 331, **455**, 456, 477
  mistol Griseb., 40
  spina-christi (L.) Willd., 340, **455–56**, 470–71, 474–75

Subject Index

Acorns, storage of, 72, 97, 438, 471
Adaptability of trees and shrubs, 31, 38, 41, 58, 345
Afforestation, 24, 58, 202–63
  choice of species, 345–60; *see also* Special plantations
  costs, 55, 100, 203, 209, 225, 247, 257–58, 294–95, 309, 348–49
After-ripening of seed, 87, 91, 412, 438
Air drying of cones and fruits, 71–74, 375, 377
Air pollutants, effect on trees, 339
Air pollution and selection of species, 338–40
Air-pruning, 145, 146
Alkali, 107
  black, 31
  white, 30
Alkalinity, soil; *see* Soil, alkalinity
Alkalinity, water (including saline), 28, 102, 105, 287
Altitude
  effect on climate, 23–24
  effect on vegetation, 23–24, 33
  requirements of trees, 476–77; *see also* Silvics of arid-zone tree species
Altitudinal climates, 23–24
Amenity plantings, 202, 265, 331–38
Animals
  large, protection from, 150, 248–50, 280–81, 300, 309, 313, 319, 322, 337
  small; *see* Birds; Insects; Mammals, small; Nematodes
Antitranspirants, 234–35
Aprons, polythene, 242–43, 329
Arbor days, 331
Arid climates
  effects on soils, 26–27
  definitions, 15
Arid zone
  definition, 31
  forestry programs and policies, 48–49
  forests, 45–49
  silvicultural criterion, 46

soils, criterion, 25
Arid zones, 3–52, 275; *see also* Zones
  cold, 12, 22, 191, 274, 277, 283, 291, 476–77
  ecological features of, 12
  hot, 291, 292, 296, 339
  human environment in, 3–6
  importance of tree planting in, 6–9
Aridity, resistance of species to, 275–76
Auxin, 147

Balled plants, 102, 104, 105, 106, 110, 125–32, 164, 169, 173, 174, 178, 235, 240, 241, 269, 292, 367
  root pruning of, 186
Barbatells, 149
Belts, temperature, 15–22
  continental, 22
  equitorial, 20–21
  subtropical, 22
  tropical, 21–22
Birds, 32, 72, 112, 150–51, 154, 231, 232, 252
Board, marking, 116–17
Brush disposal; *see* Site preparation for planting, debris disposal
Buildings
  nursery, 101, 102, 113
  planting site, 256–57
Burning, controlled, 216

Campo de carracas, 268
Campos cerrados, 46, 47
Canal bank plantations, 295
Carbon dioxide fertilization of air, 192
Care of nursery stock, 150–98
Care of plantations, 244–48
Casehardening, 74–75
Catinga, 47
Chaco, 46, 47
Chapariole, 47
Chaparral, 3, 13, 46, 47, 206, 333, 349
Chemicals, seed staining, 82; *see also* Seed, germinability tests

Choice of species, 24, 54–63, 476–77; see also Products; and specific type of planting or plantation
for amenity planting, 335, 339–40
for canal plantations, 276, 296, 358, 365, 375, 433, 434, 445
for cold arid zones, 363, 375, 381, 393, 407, 410, 412, 415, 418, 422, 423, 426, 429, 431, 441, 444, 446, 448, 452, 453, 455, 476–77
for dune fixation, 70, 312, 325–27, 356, 374, 377, 409, 410, 417, 425, 426, 427, 428, 429, 433, 436, 450, 455
for erosion control, 70, 296, 313, 318–19, 355, 356, 360, 364, 372, 375, 377, 386, 408, 411, 412, 417, 419, 425, 426, 428, 434, 440, 443, 444, 445, 450, 452
exotics, 345–53; see also Exotics
fast growing, 115, 273, 275, 371
for fodder, 296–97; see also Products, primary or extracted, fodder
forest-tree orchards, 273–80
for fuelwood, 283; see also Products, primary or extracted, fuelwood
for general afforestation, 359, 361, 365, 377, 379, 388, 390, 391, 394, 396, 403, 404, 419, 421, 425, 426, 427, 428, 429, 435, 437, 438, 444, 447, 452, 455
for groves, 339–40
for hedges, 112, 319, 357, 358, 375, 385, 406, 408, 414
for honey production, 298–99; see also Products, primary or extracted, honey
for industrial areas, 339
for irrigated plantations, 274, 275, 276, 291–92, 311, 355, 359, 375, 384, 390, 395, 415
for mine waste stabilization, 329, 444
for ornamentals, 335, 358, 360, 363, 364, 365, 369, 371, 375, 377, 379, 380, 382, 384, 385, 386, 388, 390, 392, 393, 395, 396, 401, 402, 403, 404, 405, 408, 409, 410, 411, 412, 414, 415, 416, 417, 418, 419, 421, 422, 423, 425, 429, 433, 436, 441, 444, 446, 448, 450, 452, 454, 455; see also Choice of species, for roadside planting
for parks, 334, 339–40
for refractory sites, 356
for roadside planting, 335–38, 356, 363, 365, 369, 371, 375, 377, 384, 385, 392, 395, 398, 401, 402, 404, 405, 406, 407, 409, 413, 414, 415, 416, 434, 435, 444, 448, 450, 452, 455

for saline soils, 312–13, 329, 331, 396, 402, 407, 437, 449, 450; see also Soils, saline
for shade and shelter, 334, 354
for cattle, 298, 409, 415, 446, 448
for coffee and tea plantations, 409
for shelterbelts, 277, 300, 303, 309–13, 314, 356, 359, 360, 363, 374, 375, 376, 377, 382, 385, 386, 388, 390, 393, 395, 396, 398, 399, 401, 402, 404, 406, 408, 412, 419, 425, 426, 429, 430, 434, 435, 441, 446, 448, 450, 454, 455
for stabilization of mining waste, 329
for streambank plantings, 276, 319, 445, 446
for swamp reclamation, 330, 377, 400
for watershed protection, 440
for wildlife food and cover, 393, 408, 412
for windbreak planting; see Choice of species, for shelterbelts
Classification of arid climates, 12–15
Classification of arid zone vegetation, 35–38; see also Vegetation
Climate, 9–25, 227, 272, 276
altitudinal, 23–24
arid, 10, 16–19, 58
classification of, 12–15
definition of, 12, 15
effect on soils, 26–27
continental, 14–15, 22, 24, 29, 37, 58, 292, 381, 407, 440, 455
desert, 12, 20, 359, 384
equitorial, 20–21
extremely arid, 16–19
homoclimates, 16–19, 346
humid, 386
light, 24–25
macroclimate, 346
major types, 14
Mediterranean, 12, 14, 58, 283, 348, 379, 418, 419, 425, 431, 440, 441, 452
Meig's classification, 12–14
microclimate, 5, 45, 266, 346
monsoon, 14, 390
mountainous, 23–24
plateau, 24
semiarid, 16–19, 58
subdesert, 12
subhumid, 386, 445
subtropical, 22, 359, 370, 447
temperate, 58, 359, 447
tropical, 14, 21–22, 375
Climatic belts, 15–22
continental, 22
equitorial, 20–21

subtropical, 22
tropical, 21–22
Climatic change, 34, 35
Climatic zones, 353; *see also* Zones
Climax (ecological), 33, 34, 318
  disturbance, 34
  false, 34
Clones, 55, 276, 279, 280, 330
  insect resistant, 278
Cloudbursts, 314–15
Cold arid zones, 12, 22, 476–77
Collecting and handling tree seed, 53–99,
  464–71; *see also* Silvics of arid-zone
  tree species
Community, climax, 33
Community, plant, 33, 35, 36, 37
Competition, 24, 33, 117, 191, 205, 206,
  222, 227, 240, 242, 247, 269, 270,
  271, 283, 294, 313, 319
Compost, 157
Condensation, surface; *see* Dew
Cones, 53
  air drying, 71–74
  collection of; *see* Seed, collection of
  extraction of seed from; *see* Extraction
    of seed
  kiln drying, 74
  refractory, 74, 75, 366, 431
Container planting stock, 164, 169; *see
  also* Containerized seedlings; Containers
Containerized seedlings, 125–46, 319,
  324; *see also* Balled plants
  advantages, 119
  greenhouse culture, 144
  irrigation, 165, 173, 193; *see also* Irri-
    gation
  mulching, 163; *see also* Mulching
  number per container, 119
  planting gun for, 144–45
  root pruning, 183, 185, 186
  transplanting of, 120
  weed control, 132, 141, 163, 178, 179
Containers, 106, 108, 109, 110, 111, 113,
  118–19, 123, 125–46, 150, 151, 156,
  163, 164, 165, 167, 169, 173, 177,
  178, 179, 183, 185, 186, 187, 188,
  190, 192, 193, 194, 196, 197, 198,
  199
  chemicals in, 105
  color of, 128, 141
  preservatives, 135, 136
  root spiraling in, 126
  soil, 109
  sowing depth, 118
  sowing technique, 118–19, 122, 127
  types of
    bamboo tubes, 134

baskets, 134
biodegradable, 128
book planter, 128, 145, 146
brikas, 132
bullet, Walters', 128, 140, 144, 145
cane, 134
cardboard, 128, 137–38
concrete pots, 128, 133–34
donas, 134
earthenware pots, 128, 132–33, 140,
  165
Japanese paper pot, 137–38, 139
leaf cups, 134
local plant material, 134–35
metal, 128, 138–40
minicontainers, 128, 143–46, 192
multipots, 145, 146
Ontario tubes, 128, 140, 143
paper, 128, 137–38, 139
peat, 132
plastic, 128, 140–46
  bags, 103, 140
  polypots, 140, 147
  tubes, 118, 140
plug units, 128, 145–46
root balls, 128–29
single cell, 128, 145, 146
soil balls, 128, 129–32
soil blocks, 128, 130
styroblock, 128, 145–46
sunflower stems, 135
wall-less, 128–32
wood pulp, 138
wood residue, 135–36
wood trays, 137–38
wood veneer, 128, 135–36
Contour strips, 222, 223
Conversion factors, metric to U. S., 463
Coppice, regeneration, 275, 354, 356,
  361, 369, 370, 374, 375, 390, 394,
  396, 399, 403, 404, 407, 415, 418,
  421, 425, 435, 437, 442, 445, 446,
  449, 452, 455; *see also* Silviculture
  and management
Costs, afforestation; *see* Afforestation,
  costs
Costs, nursery; *see* Nurseries, costs
Crop rotation, 157
Cultivation; *see also* Silviculture and
  management; Weeding
  of containers, 178
  dry farming techniques, 247
  mole hills, 214
  nusery, 113, 150, 177–83
    hand, 117, 178, 223
    machine, 117, 178
  pits, 213–14, 221, 222

Cultivation (*Continued*)
  of plantations, 203, 210–15, 227, 240,
      247–48, 266, 269, 270, 272, 274,
      277, 278, 279, 283, 286, 294, 296
  plowing, 205–6, 211, 213, 221, 222,
      254, 269, 275
  of roadside trees, 336
  rooters, 211–13
  scalping, 214–15
  screefing, 214–15
  of seed spots, 233
  of shelterbelts, 309, 313
  strip, 211, 221, 232, 243, 247
  subsoiling, 211–13, 221, 269
  of trial plots, 353
Cuttings
  auxin treatment of, 147
  barbatells, 149
  root cuttings, 363, 375, 443
  root-shoot cuttings, 149–50, 292, 365,
      390, 391, 415
  storage of, 148
  stumps, 292, 293, 390
  twig cuttings, 55, 100, 146–50, 172,
      202, 277, 351, 354, 365, 371, 390,
      406, 410, 414, 416, 445, 446, 449,
      450, 452, 465, 469

Damping-off, 105, 107, 115, 118, 119,
      151, 157, 473
  control of, 151, 153–54, 159, 187, 232,
      384
Debris disposal; *see* Site preparation for
      planting, debris disposal
Desert, 33, 34, 326, 449
  climate, 12, 20, 359, 384
      definition of, 12
  pavement, 28, 29
  soils, 25, 27–28
  vegetation, 28, 35, 37
Deserts, principal world, 3, 16–19, 27
Dew, 11–12, 323, 326
Direct seeding (sowing); *see* Seeding,
      direct
Disease, human; *see also* Products, pri-
      mary or extracted, medicines
  caused by *Bilharzia*, 370
  Guinea worm, 370
  malaria, 331
  skin rash, 447
Disease, plant, 32, 119, 150, 152–54, 270,
      271, 279, 311, 314, 345, 351, 353
  by air pollution, 339
  chemical (nutrient) imbalance, 107,
      154–55, 156, 161, 254, 272, 273
  chlorosis, 105, 107, 134, 155, 156, 159,
      272, 395
  damping-off; *see* Damping-off

decay, 314, 399
die back, 276
Dutch elm disease, 454
nutrient deficiency; *see* Disease, plant,
      chemical (nutrient) imbalance
phloem necrosis, 454
of poplars, 279–80
protection of plantations from, 250, 254
root rot, 105
stunting, 155, 156
symptoms, 272
Divider, seed sampling, 77
Dormancy, seed, 83, 86–91; *see also* Sil-
      vics of arid-zone tree species
  definition of, 86
  double, 86, 91
  embryo, 86, 87–88, 91, 365, 381, 423,
      452
  immature embryo, 86, 91
  induced, 86, 90, 425, 428, 467
  mechanical resistance of seed coat, 86,
      91
  pretreatments to overcome; *see* Pre-
      treatment of seed to break dormancy
  secondary, 86, 90, 467
  seed coat, 86, 88–90, 91, 355, 423, 444,
      448
Drainage, 166, 272, 329–30
Drip irrigation, 245–46, 329
Drought resistance, 156, 233, 311, 395,
      403; *see also* Plants, drought-resist-
      ing
Drought year, 10
Drum, see extraction, 74, 75
Dry month, definition of, 12
Dune fixation, 55, 70, 195, 265, 312, 319–
      27, 328
  planting methods, 324–25
  pre-fixation by
      bitumen mulch, 323
      crust-forming chemicals, 323
      mechanical barriers, 321–22
      sand-binding grasses, 322–24
  species; *see* Choice of species, for dune
      fixation
  technique, 321–25
Dunes, 26, 27, 37, 228, 319
  coastal, 319, 320, 356

Ecological factors, 31
Ecological features of arid zones, 12
Ecological requirements, 352, 353–56,
      476–77; *see also* Silvics of arid-zone
      tree species
Ecology, 31
Ecology of arid-zone vegetation, 31–45
Ecosystem, 32, 273
Ecotype, 58, 63, 289

Edaphic factors; *see* Soil; Soils
Effect of arid climate on soils, 26–27
Elimination trials, 352–53
Elite stands, 55, 56
Elite trees, 55, 56
Environmental conservation, 264
Eradication of vegetation, 204–10, 249,
    349; *see also* Weeding
Erosion, 26, 39, 45, 171, 204, 216, 218,
    220, 222, 265, 279, 301, 314–19,
    328, 329, 363
  control, mechanical, 315–17
  control, vegetative, 315, 317, 318–19;
    see also Choice of species, for erosion
    control
  damage, 45, 314–15
  streambank, 319
  water, 26, 28, 45, 48, 166, 174, 210,
    217, 224, 327
  wind, 26, 28, 48, 301, 304
Etiolation, 191
Evaporation, 11, 13, 22, 24, 26, 44, 48,
    105, 141, 152, 161, 162, 166, 170,
    187, 227, 228, 243, 247, 295, 301,
    304, 305, 327, 331
Evapotranspiration, 10, 13, 14, 23, 165,
    297, 346, 347
Evapotranspirometer, 14
Evergreen scrub, 37
Evetria, 152
Exotics, 47, 57, 152, 230, 248, 273, 274,
    275, 276, 291, 298, 311, 318, 335,
    339, 345, 346, 348, 349, 350, 352–
    53, 425, 452
  introduction trials, 352–53
  wood properties of, 351
Explosives, use in planting, 242
Extraction of seed, 71–77, 465, 467, 469,
    471
  air drying, 71–74, 375, 377
  by breaking cones, 366
  from *Cedrus* cones, 75
  chemicals, use of, 72
  kiln drying, 74
  by maceration, 72, 380, 381, 415
    in lye solution, 412, 431
  from non-pulpy fruits, 72
  from pulpy fruits, 72–73, 369, 380, 381
  from serotinous cones, 431

Fertility, soil, 154–56, 157
Fertilization, 56, 102, 154, 156, 192, 254,
    268, 269, 271–73, 314, 319, 328,
    351, 353
  environmental effects, 273
Fertilizers, 56, 106, 135, 154, 155, 156–
    60, 240, 269, 271, 273, 353

chemical, 157, 158–60, 163, 271
cycling of, 272
liquid, 159–60, 271
organic, 271
  animal origin, 157, 158, 271
  vegetable origin, 157, 271
pelleted, 154, 271, 328–29
requirements, 156–60
time of application, 271
Field planting, 233–44
Fire, ecological effects, 46–47
Fire, protection from, 249–50, 270
Firebreaks, 249, 257, 270, 332
Flood control; *see* Erosion
Flowering of honey trees, 299
Fodder trees, 296–97; *see also* Products,
    primary or extracted, fodder
Fog, 44
Fog drip, 44
Forest aesthetics, 44, 45, 48
Forest influences, 9–10
Forest planting in low rainful zones,
    202–4
Forest recreation, 44, 300, 332–34
Forest-tree orchards, 266–82
  choice of species, 273–81
  environmental effects, 273
  fertilization, 271–73
  financial aspects of, 281–82
  ground preparation, 269
  mycorrhizae in, 270
  planting, 269
  protection of, 270
  site selection, 268–69
  soil fertility, 271–73
  spacing, 269
  tending, 269
  thinning, 269
Forest tree planting
  costs and benefits, 9
  importance in arid zones, 6–8
Forestry programs and policies, 48–49,
    281–82
Forests
  in arid zones, 45–49, 202
  destruction by man and livestock, 45
  gallery, 375
  high, 38, 45–46
  open, 3, 45, 46–48
  programs and policies, 48–49, 281–82
  scrub, 3, 363, 385, 419
  wildlife in arid zones, 44
Frost, 292, 311, 326, 345, 346
  damage, 15, 177, 228
  hardiness, 288; *see also* Choice of spe-
    cies, for cold arid zones
  heaving, 228
  protection, 177

Fruit
  collection of; *see* Seed, collection of
  definition of, 53
  extraction of seed from; *see* Extraction
    of seed
  types of, 464, 466, 468, 470
Fuelwood plantations, 282–83; *see also*
  Products, primary or extracted, fuelwood
Fumigants, 93, 152, 182–83
Fumigation of seed, 93, 361
Fumigation of soil, 152, 254
Fungicides, 93, 97, 153–54, 232, 366
  care in handling, 154

Garigue, 3, 46, 47, 60, 202, 206
Genetic
  characteristics, 54–57, 70
  clones, 55, 276, 278, 279, 280, 330
  considerations in forest planting, 54–63
  ecotype, 58, 63, 289
  genotype, 54, 55, 56, 272, 277
  hybrids, 279, 395, 434, 445
  phenotype, 54, 55, 60
  race (strain), 42, 56, 58, 63, 78, 345,
    395, 403, 443
    of maritime pine, 58–63
  research, 55
Genotype, 54, 55, 56, 272, 277
Geology, effect on plants, 33, 204
Germinability, seed, 80–84; *see also* Seed,
  germinability tests
Germinability tests; *see* Seed, germinability tests
Germination, seed, 115, 117
  epigeous, 92
  hypogeous, 83, 92
  inhibiting chemicals, 87
  inhibition by light, 374
  physiology, 91–92, 374
  processes, 91–92
  tests; *see* Seed, germinability tests
Gradoni, 217, 316
Grafting, 55
Graphs, pluviothermic, 15–16, 20–21, 60,
  346, 347
Grassland, 30, 349
  open, 36, 37, 47
  wooded, 30, 36, 37, 46
Grazing damage, 35, 301, 320
Grazing management, 48–49
Greenbelts, 291
Greenhouses, 191–92
Greening of areas, 332
Groves, 264, 300, 336
Growing season, 11
Growth trials, 352, 353
Grubs, white, 151–52

Gypsum
  addition to reduce salinity, 288
  layer, 26, 28

Habitat, definition of, 32
Halophytes, 31, 37, 43–44, 409
Hardening-off, 119, 155, 165, 166, 168,
  184, 185, 186, 187, 190, 191, 193,
  289
Heat damage, 186, 187
Heat lesions, 186
Hedges, 112, 319, 357, 358, 375, 385,
  406, 408, 414
Heeling-in, 196–97, 198, 235
Herbicides, 180–83, 205, 206, 207–10,
  249, 251, 256, 279, 283; *see also*
  Pesticides
  fumigants, 93, 152, 182–83
  non-selective, 180–82, 208–9, 210, 256
  pollution by, 209–10
  selective, 180–82, 208–9, 210
  sterilant, 182, 256
Homoclimates, 16–19, 346
Humus, 157; *see also* Soil, humus
Hybrids
  eucalypt, 395
  poplar, 279, 434
  willow, 445
Hydrologic cycle, 13
Hydrophytes, 38, 43–44

Identification of parent trees, 65
Indigo-carmine stain, 82
Indole-3-acetic acid, 147
Inoculation of soil; *see* Soil, inoculation
Insect control
  biological, 251, 252
  chemical; *see* Insecticides
  phytosanitation, 251
  sanitation, 57, 151, 280
  silvicultural, 280
Insecticides, 93, 151, 152, 251, 252, 253,
  280, 432
  care in handling, 154
  pollution by, 209–10
Insects, 32, 93, 150, 157, 182, 229, 270,
  279, 311, 314, 345, 351, 353, 363,
  395
  ants, 150, 151, 280
  beetle
    ambrosia, 253–54
    May or June, 151
  borer
    eucalyptus, 252–53
    locust, 444
    shoot, 413
  Capnodes, 253
  Capnodis miliaris Klug., 253, 279

cone, 51
cutworms, 152
grubs, white, 151
Hypsispila sp., 413
important of arid zone plantations, 252–54
kermes, 439
Mediterranean fruit fly, 368
Megacyllene robiniae (Forst.), 444
mosquitoes, 331
moth, tip, 152
Noctuidae, 152
Phalaenidae, 152
Phoracantha semipunctata Fabr., 252–53
Phyllophaga, 151–52
pine processionary caterpillar, 253, 421
Platypus sulcatus Chapuis, 253
in poplars, 279–80
protection of plantations from; *see* Insect control; Insecticides; *name of insect*
scale, 448, 449
seed, 51, 354, 355, 358, 361, 408, 435, 438
termites, 161, 280, 374, 375, 392, 393, 396, 399, 401, 402
Thaumentopoea wilkinsonii Tams, 253, 421
Iodide-potassium-iodide stain, 82
Irrigated plantations, 245–47, 276, 280, 283–95
choice of species; *see* Choice of species, for irrigated plantations
culture, 293–94
establishment and planting, 292–93
financial aspects, 294–95
watering regimes, 288–89
Irrigation, 25, 31, 153, 154, 161, 162, 164–77, 185, 187, 272, 275, 277, 278, 286–90, 292, 296, 305, 311, 313, 314, 327, 331, 338
cycle, 293
nursery, 164–77
border-strip, 169–70
of containerized seedlings, 165, 167
corrugated method, 171
distribution system, 111, 169–77
flooding, 166, 169–70, 173
furrow, 106, 117, 166, 169, 170–71, 173
hose, 120, 169, 172, 173
porous hose, 166, 169, 173
pumps, 104–5, 168–69
quantity of water needed, 165–68
sprinkler, 117, 159, 166, 167, 168, 169, 170, 173–77, 186, 189
occilating, 174–76

perforated pipe, 174
rotary, 176–77
subsurface, 166, 169, 171–72
supply, 102, 104–5
water quality, 102, 105–6
watering can, 120, 123, 172, 173
plantation, 286–90
bamboo tubes, use of, 246
border-strip, 289
drip method, 245–46, 329
flooding, contour, 290
flooding, surface, 286, 289
furrow, 290
herringbone, 290
hose, 338
infiltration method, 290
inundation method, 290
water quality, 287
Isohyetal maps, 226

Kiln drying of cones, 74

Labels
seed container, 97
seedbeds, 116
Land smoothing, 225
Lath house, 189, 191
Light, 24–25, 374
requirements, 25
saturated, 25
Lignotuber, 41
Liming, 327
Lomas, 44–45

Mallee, 32, 38, 41
Mammals, small, 32, 150–51, 157, 182, 229, 391, 406
control, 112, 231, 248, 252, 280–81
Manure; *see* Fertilizers
Maquis, 13, 41, 45, 46, 47, 202, 206, 349, 366, 383
Marking board, 116–17
Marking roller, 116, 117
Mediterranean climate, definition of, 12; *see also* Climate, Mediterranean
Meig's classification of dry climates, 12–14
Mesophytes, 38, 40, 41
Méthode Steppique, 222–25, 275
Microclimate, 5, 45, 266, 297
Mining waste, stabilization of, 265, 327–29
Mist, 11–12, 44, 45
Moisture, atmospheric, 13, 40
Moisture conservation, 242–44; *see also* Dune fixation
by gravel mulch, 244
by kraft paper mulch, 242
by polythene aprons, 242–43

Moisture conservation (*Continued*)
  by shingle shading, 244
  by stone mulch, 243
  by twig shading, 244
Moisture harvesting; *see* Moisture conservation; Terraces
Moisture index, Thornthwaite's, 13, 14
Mole hills, 214
Monoculture, 273
Monte type, 37
Mulches; *see* Mulching
Mulching, 15, 151, 160–63, 225, 242, 243, 244, 293, 318, 374; *see also* Dune fixation
Mycorrhizae, 106, 125, 143, 155, 156, 163–64, 254, 270, 274, 351, 430
  temperature tolerance of, 143, 164, 187, 206, 234
Mycorrhizal inoculation; *see* Soil, inoculation

Natural regeneration, 202
Nematodes, 182, 252
Nitrogen deficiency; *see* Disease, plant, chemical (nutrient) imbalance
Nitrogen fixing bacteria, 377, 444
  inoculation of soil with, 377
Noise abating screens, 338
Noise pollution, 338
Nurse crops, 45
Nurseries, forest tree, 100–201, 230
  accessibility, 104, 108
  advantages and disadvantages, 102
  area required, 109
  beds, 101
  buildings, 101, 102, 113
  climate, 101
  container sowing techniques, 118–19
  containers; *see* Containerized seedlings
  costs, 103–4, 198, 199
  cover crops, 110
  cultivation, 113, 177–83
  damage
    by flooding, 107, 111
    by frost, 107
    by sedimentation, 111
    by wind, 107
  development of area, 108–13
  diseases, 105, 152–54
  drainage, 108, 109, 113, 154
  fences, 111
  fertilization, 102; *see also* Fertilization; Fertilizers
  gardens in, 113
  grading of stock, 192–94
  ground plan, 108–9
  hedges, 112
  inventory, 192

irrigation; *see* Irrigation, nursery
labor, 108
leveling, 107, 109–10, 169, 176
lifting stock, 118, 123, 149, 192–95, 233, 235
location, 104
machinery, 100, 110
mulching, 160–63; *see also* Mulching
packing stock for shipment, 192–95
paths, 111, 123
permanent, 101, 102–8, 169
pests, 117, 157
plant production, 113–50
potted stock, 111, 125–46; *see also* Containerized seedlings
practices, 472–75
protection, 111–12, 150–54, 168
records, 116, 198–99
roads, 102, 110
seedbeds, 110–11; *see also* Seedbeds
shading, 168, 186–91, 473, 475
site preparation, 109–10
site selection, 101
soil management, 110–11
soil preparation, 113
soils, 106–7
sowing, 114–19, 189, 472, 474
  of containers, 118–19
  of seedbeds, 116–18
    labelling, 116
    time of, 114–15
storage areas, 113
temporary, 101–2, 103, 169
terracing, 109
topography, 107–8
transplanting, 109, 118, 120–25, 472–75; *see also* Transplanting
vegetative propagation, 146–50; *see also* Vegetative propagation, nursery
water supply, 104–5
weeding, 177–83
windbreaks in, 111, 147
Nutrient cycling, 272

Open and wooded grassland, 37
Ornamental species; *see* Choice of species, for ornamentals

Parks, 265
Parks for recreation, 331, 332–34, 339–40
Pavement, desert, 28, 29
Pesticides, 207–10; *see also* Herbicides; Insecticides
  pollution by, 209–10
pH; *see* Soil, pH
Phenotype, 54, 55, 60
Photoperiod, 277, 348
Phreatophytes, 44

Phyllodes, 122
Physiographic factors, 346; *see also* Geology; Soils; Topography
Physiological condition of seedlings, 113–14
Physiological shock, 126
Phytogeography, 349–50
Pioneer crop, 45
Pits, 213–14, 220, 221, 222, 228, 274
Plant community, 33, 35, 36
Plant production, nursery, 113–50
Plantamón, 236–37
Plantation trials, 352, 353
Plantations
    amenity, 245, 265, 331–38, 436
    buildings, 256–57
    canal bank, 294, 295–96, 297, 330
    care of, 244–48
    cultivation, 257; *see also* Cultivation, of plantations
    for environmental improvement, 264–65, 299–314
    fuelwood, 282–83
    irrigated; *see* Irrigated plantations
    major types of, 264–66
    for minor products, 296–99
    mixed, 266, 267, 291
    multiple use, 265–66, 296, 299, 352
    noise abating, 338
    pathways in, 256, 257
    prerequisites for success, 259
    for production of goods, 264, 265, 266–69
    for protection, 258, 265; *see also* Shelterbelts and windbreaks
    protection from
        disease; *see* Disease, plant
        fire, 249–50
        insects; *see* Insect control; Insecticides; *name of insect*
        large animals; *see* Animals, large, protection from
    recreational parks, 265, 299, 332–34
    recruiting in, 244, 257
    replacement in, 244
    roads in, 256
    roadside, 245, 265, 331, 334–38
    on saline soils, 331–32
    single use, 265–66
    site selection, 268–69
    for soil stabilization, 265, 314–31
    spacing in, 203, 225–27, 230, 269, 270, 283, 353
    special, 264–344
    swampland, 329–31
    types of, 8, 202, 264–66
    watering, 245–47
    weeding; *see* Weeding

Planting
    costs and benefits, 9
    dibble, 145, 146, 148, 240–41
    field, 100, 127, 132, 202, 229, 230, 231, 233–44, 257, 292, 319
    balled stock, 240, 319
    containerized stock; *see* Containerized seedlings; Containers
    dibble, 145, 146, 148, 240–41
    gun, 144–45
    mattock, 146
    methods, 236–42
        dibble, 240–41
        explosives, 242
        hole, 238–40
        machine, 241–42; *see also* Planting, machines
        slit, 236–38
    naked-rooted stock, 235–36
    pits, 220, 228, 274
    season, 227–29
    trenches, 220
    machines, 238–39, 241–42, 254–55
    site, 202–4
        preparation, 203, 204–25, 286; *see also* Site preparation for planting
        protection of, 204
        selection, 204
        topographic factors, 202–3, 204
    stock, 102, 104; *see also* Containerized seedlings; Nurseries; Seedlings
        bare-rooted; *see* Planting, stock, naked-rooted
        grading, 183, 192–94
        naked-rooted, 101, 104, 106, 110, 114, 115, 125, 126, 127, 164, 166, 168, 169, 170, 173, 174, 183, 184, 193, 233
        preconditioning of, 104
        seedling, 109, 110
        storage of, 196–97, 235
        transplants, 109, 110, 114, 115; *see also* Transplant, stock; Transplanting
        transport of, 149, 197–98, 230
    tools, 236–37, 238, 240, 254–56, 293
        auger, 238–39
Plantings
    aesthetic, 202, 266, 299, 302, 332, 335, 336, 338; *see also* Choice of species, for ornamentals
    noise abating, 299
    temporary, 336
Plants
    climbing, 36–37
    drought-escaping, 42
    drought-enduring, 42
    drought-evading, 42

Plants (*Continued*)
  drought-resisting, 42–43
  ephemeral, 35, 36, 38, 42
  halophytes, 31, 37, 43–44, 409
  hardened, 185, 186
  hardiness of, 15
  hydrophytes, 38, 43–44
  mesic, 33
  mesophytes, 38, 40, 41
  microphyllous, 36, 37, 41
  non-succulent, 38, 41, 42, 43
  phreatophytes, 44
  salt tolerant, 320; *see also* Choice of
    species, for saline soils
  sclerophylls, 37, 41, 47
  succulent, 35, 36, 38, 42, 43
  table-topped, 191
  temperature requirements, 15, 476–77;
    see also Silvics of arid-zone tree
    species
  xerophilous, 45
  xerophytic, 291, 313, 345
  xerophytes, 37, 38–43, 326
Plowing; *see* Cultivation, plowing
Plus stands, 54, 57
Plus trees, 54, 57
Pluviothermic
  diagrams, 20–21, 59
  equation, 12
  graphs, 15–16, 20–21, 60, 346, 347
Pollarding; *see* Silviculture and manage-
    ment, pollarding
Pollution, environmental
  air, 338–40
  chemical, 209–10, 273
  noise, 338
Potted stock, 125–46, 191; *see also* Con-
    tainerized seedlings; Containers
Prairie, 440
Precipitation, 3, 9, 10–11, 12, 14, 24, 34,
    44, 58, 269, 316, 326, 327, 347; *see
    also* Rain
  minimum required, 11
  seasonal distribution, 14, 16–19, 228,
    348
Prerequisites for successful plantations,
    259
Preservatives
  for burlap, 161, 188
  copper-8-quinolinolate, 188
  copper naphthenate, 136, 161
  copper oleate, 188
  copper resinate, 188
  copper tallate, 188
  creosote, 135
  for wood, 135, 136, 189
Pretreatment of seed to break dormancy,
    83, 87, 228, 465, 467, 469, 471; *see*

  also Silvics of arid-zone tree species
embryo dormancy
  animal digestive processes, 88
  cold stratification; *see* Stratification
  ethylene chlorhydrin, 88
  light, 374, 399
  low temperature, 87
  naked stratification, 87
  potassium nitrate, 88
  radiation, far red and infra red, 84
  thiourea, 88
immature embryo, warm plus cold
    stratification, 91
mechanical resistance of seed coat by
    cracking, 91
seed coat
  animal digestive processes, 89
  boiling or hot water, 89–90, 355,
    356, 358, 359, 360, 365, 366, 375,
    408, 436, 448, 465, 467, 469, 471
  cold water soaking, 354, 361, 367,
    375, 383, 391, 415, 417, 428, 437,
    465, 467, 469, 471
  by microorganisms, 89, 90
  scarification, 354, 417
    acid, 89, 90, 375, 382, 383, 392,
      408, 412, 417, 423, 436, 443,
      444, 455, 465, 467, 469, 471
    mechanical, 89, 396, 465, 469, 471
  warm stratification, 90
Pretreatment of seed with fungicides, 88,
    153–54, 366; *see also* Fungicides
Principles of wind shelter, 301–6
Products
  primary or extracted
    beads, 415
    Christmas trees, 366
    cork, 264, 441
    dyes, 418, 429, 439, 448
    fat, 446
    fertilizer from leaves, 416
    fodder, 48, 202, 264, 266, 284, 296–
      97, 298, 311, 327, 330, 334, 352,
      354, 355, 358, 359, 361, 365, 368,
      370, 371, 375, 376, 380, 383, 385,
      386, 398, 408, 409, 410, 413, 415,
      435, 436, 437, 438, 441, 444, 445,
      446, 452, 455
    food, human, 416, 435, 436
    food, wildlife, 441
    frankincense, 371
    fruit, 48, 291, 334, 370, 380, 385,
      393, 406, 416, 455
    fuelwood, 45, 46, 48, 202, 206, 226,
      258, 264, 266, 274, 281, 282–83,
      284, 285, 291, 294, 295, 296, 297,
      301, 313, 325, 327, 329, 352, 354,
      355, 356, 358, 359, 360, 361, 363,

369, 370, 375, 376, 377, 384, 392,
   395, 396, 398, 399, 402, 406, 408,
   409, 410, 411, 412, 414, 415, 416,
   426, 431, 436, 437, 438, 439, 440,
   441, 442, 444, 448, 450, 452, 455
gum arabic, 266, 359, 361
gums, 48, 264, 365
honey, 48, 264, 276, 298–99, 325,
   352, 367, 395, 396, 398, 403, 405,
   409, 436
incense, 371
insecticide, 370
leaves for silkworms, 416
medicines, 359, 371, 411, 448
minor, 202, 264
mucilage, 358
nuts, 291, 368, 410, 422
oil, castor, 323
oil, cooking, 368
oil, eucalyptus, 399
oil, juniper, 411
oils, 48, 202, 264, 352
pepper, 448
perfume, 358, 371, 411
piling, 395, 435
poles, 48, 202, 206, 226, 258, 264,
   266, 276, 277, 281, 283, 313, 325,
   352, 359, 369, 370, 372, 374, 375,
   377, 385, 386, 390, 395, 402, 419,
   427, 429, 435
posts, 48, 206, 226, 258, 264, 266,
   281, 283, 301, 313, 325, 352, 356,
   358, 369, 374, 375, 377, 386, 390,
   395, 398, 399, 402, 403, 404, 408,
   412, 425, 429, 430, 435, 436, 438,
   444, 446, 452
resins, 48, 371, 419, 421, 425, 426,
   427, 429, 448
salt from leaves, 446
sawlogs, 226, 268, 359
seeds, edible, 422, 429, 431
snail poison, 370
soap, 370, 442
soil additive to reduce alkalinity, 446
sugar, 363
supports, plant, 281, 372
tannin, 48, 264, 276, 296, 325, 355,
   356, 358, 360, 396, 399, 403, 418,
   439, 443, 446
tea, 418
toothbrushes, 446
vegetable lard, 372, 373
secondary or manufactured
   agricultural implements, 48, 355,
      361, 380, 437, 438, 450, 452, 455
   baskets, 445, 446
   boxes and cases, 281, 354, 409, 415,
      419, 425, 433, 434, 445, 446

building material; *see* Products, secondary or manufactured, construction material
cabinet work, 409, 413, 416
canoes, 354
carriages, railway, 359, 396
carts, 355
carvings, 452
casks (cooperage), 435, 441, 454
cellulose, 276
charcoal, 46, 48, 264, 266, 325, 352,
   359, 368, 385, 399, 409, 410, 416,
   418, 435, 438, 439, 442, 455
chests, 390, 412
construction material, 48, 355, 368,
   369, 374, 385, 386, 399, 401, 419,
   421, 425, 426, 430, 431, 446, 452
crates, 281, 282, 431, 454
excelsior, 434
flooring, 365, 435
furniture, 354, 359, 365, 367, 369,
   390, 409, 412, 413, 415, 433, 441,
   450, 452, 454
handles, tool, 380, 418
knees, ship, 385
lasts, 435
lumber (carpentry), 266, 366, 386,
   390, 392, 407, 408, 410, 412, 426,
   427, 430, 441, 445, 446, 447, 448
matchsticks, 434
musical instruments, 416
oars, 380
paneling, 365, 412
paving blocks, 435
pencil wood, 412
pulp, paper, 202, 226, 258, 264, 268,
   282, 371, 395, 427, 429, 431, 434
pulp, textile, 395
rope, 418
shuttles, 361
sleepers (ties), railway, 359, 369,
   395, 396, 403, 408, 411, 426, 427,
   441, 446, 452
tanks, 452
ties, railway; *see* Products, secondary or manufactured, sleepers
timber, 264, 266, 268, 282, 295, 311,
   325, 327, 330
timbers
   bridge, 452
   construction, 276
   hewn, 396
   mine, 274, 276, 281, 395, 401,
      402, 404, 429, 430, 438
toys, 446
turnery products, 370, 384, 409, 411,
   444, 445, 446
veneer, 392, 433, 434

Products (*Continued*)
  secondary or manufactured (*Continued*)
    wheels, 365, 450
    wood wool, 434
    woodwork, 359, 390
Programs and policies; *see* Forestry programs and policies
Propagation, plant; *see* Reproduction, artificial
Provenance, 57–63, 116, 203, 229, 275, 348, 352, 394, 403, 426, 435
  altitudinal limits, 60
  trials, 63
  zones, 60
Pruning
  air, 145, 146, 150
  root; *see* Root, pruning
  top, 149, 185, 193, 234, 475

Quality of seed, 77–86, 117
  genuineness, 77, 78
  purity, 77
  sampling, 77
  viability, 77
  weight, 77

Race, genetic; *see* Genetic, race
Rain (rainfall, rainwater), 13, 14, 28, 29, 30, 31, 32, 33, 35, 36, 40, 42, 44, 115, 210, 222, 224, 225, 226, 235, 238, 242, 245, 249, 256, 270, 272, 274, 275, 283, 289, 293, 314, 315, 316, 321, 323, 326, 346, 350; *see also* Precipitation
  distribution
    areal, 226
    seasonal, 10–11, 14, 226, 269, 283, 286, 292, 346, 350
  maximum and minimum annual, 10
  species requirements, 476–77; *see also* Silvics of arid-zone tree species
Recreational use, 44, 264, 265, 329, 332; *see also* Groves; Parks for recreation
Recruiting, 230, 244, 257, 279
Reference collection of fruit, cones, and seeds, 65
Regeneration; *see* Reproduction
Relics (ecological), 34, 35
Repellents, 151, 154, 231, 232, 248; *see also* Animals, large; Mammals, small care in handling, 154
Replanting; *see* Recruiting
Reproduction
  artificial, 49, 55, 309; *see also* Cuttings; Planting; Seeding, direct
  natural, 38, 202, 203; *see also* Coppice, regeneration; Silviculture and management

Research and education, 49
Retrogression (ecological), 34
Roadside plantations, 334–38
  choice of species; *see* Choice of species, for roadside planting
  protection of, 337–38
  spacing in, 335, 336, 338
Rodents; *see* Mammals, small
Roller, marking, 116, 117
Root
  aeration, 289; *see also* Soil, waterlogged
  closure, 40
  competition, 40, 294; *see also* Competition
  growth, 92, 114, 134, 155–56, 165, 183, 228, 384
  pruning, 123, 128, 129, 132, 145, 146, 183–86
  to protect agricultural crops, 313
  spiraling, 126, 141, 145, 229, 234
  suckers, 279, 296, 300, 311, 335, 354, 356, 363, 364, 369, 375, 390, 413, 415, 435, 437, 443, 444, 449
  systems, 25, 40, 44, 120, 121, 122, 125, 126, 128, 129, 136, 150, 156, 183–86, 195, 229, 233, 296, 311, 325, 335, 338, 370, 388, 409, 410, 428, 432
Root-shoot cuttings; *see* Cuttings, root-shoot
Rooter, 211, 213, 222, 225
Roots, 32, 38, 39, 40, 42, 43, 44, 101, 114, 123, 124, 126, 128, 129, 130, 132, 136, 138, 144, 145, 151, 163, 164, 165, 166, 171, 172, 183–86, 193, 214, 222, 223, 228, 229, 230, 231, 233, 234, 235, 236, 238, 240, 241, 242, 245, 246, 269, 272, 274, 279, 280, 289, 295, 313, 323, 351, 359, 368, 372, 376, 399, 419
Rotavator, 215
Runoff, 10, 11, 32, 33, 166, 174, 210, 273, 316
  collection of, 217, 225

Saline soils, plantations on, 331; *see also* Choice of species, for saline soils; Soils, saline
Savanna, 3, 13, 29, 33, 38, 46–47, 202, 206, 225, 268, 349, 353, 354, 360, 361, 370, 412, 416
  derived, 416
Scalping, 214–15
Screefing, 214–15
Screens, seed spot, 232
Scrubs, 301, 333, 363, 385

Season, planting, 227–29
Seed, 53–54, 180, 227, 230, 231, 232, 311, 351; *see also* Silvics of arid-zone tree species
  after-ripening, 87, 91, 228
  anatomy, 53–54
  bearing age of trees, 64
  blind, 84
  calculation of amount needed, 85–86
  chemicals for germinability tests, 81–82
  cleaning, 75–77; *see also* Extraction of seed
    depulping, 72–73
    dewinging, 75, 76
    by fire, 76–77
    by flotation, 76, 93, 443
    by maceration, 72
    by sieving, 75
    by winnowing, 76
  collecting and handling, 53–99
  collection of, 55, 63–70
    age of parent trees, 64
    equipment, 69–70
    genetic considerations, 70
    methods, 68–70
    season, 64–65, 464, 466, 468, 470
    records, 65
    zones, 60, 345
  color, 80–81
  counter, vacuum, 83
  dewinging machine, 75, 76
  distribution to nurseries, 97
  dormancy; *see* Dormancy, seed
  embryo, 53
  extraction; *see* Extraction of seed; Seed, cleaning
  fumigation of, 93, 355, 361, 408, 435, 438
  fungicides, 153–54, 232, 366
  genuineness, 77, 78
  germinability tests, 80–84
    chemical stains, 81–82
    color, 80–81
    conditions, prescribed, 82–83
    cutting, 80, 84, 85
    flotation, 80
    oil spot, 80
    results, calculations of, 84–86
    rules, international, 83, 96
    transparency, 81
    X-ray, 81
  germination, 91–92, 119, 160, 161, 172, 182, 187, 228, 229, 230, 231, 232, 233, 292, 321, 465, 467, 469, 471; *see also* Silvics of arid-zone tree species
    capacity, 84–85
    effective, 85

inhibition
  chemical, 87
  light, 374
  percentage, 79, 84
  tests; *see* Seed, germinability tests
germinative energy, 84, 85, 118, 229, 232
germinators, 82
handling practices, 464–71; *see also* Silvics of arid-zone tree species
hard, 84
harvest forecast, 65–66
harvesting
  from ground, 68
  from standing trees, 68–69
  tools and equipment, 69–70
identification of parent trees, 65
impurities in, 78–79
labeling, 97
laws, export and import, 97, 351
longevity, 94
maturity, 64–65, 67–68
moisture content, 72
  calculation by toluene distillation, 96
  calculation by weight, 96
number and weight, 79–80, 464, 466, 468, 470; *see also* Silvics of arid-zone tree species
number per kilogram, formula, 80
orchards, 55, 56, 57
origin; *see* Provenance
pelleting of, 154
pretreatment; *see* Pretreatment of seed to break dormancy
pretreatment with aluminum powder, 232
pretreatment with fungicides; *see* Pretreatment of seed with fungicides
production, 56, 57, 229
  fertilization to increase, 56
protection from biotic agents; *see* Birds; Disease, plant; Fungicides; Insects; Mammals, small; Repellents
provenance (provienance); *see* Provenance
pure, definition of, 78
purity, 76, 78–79, 85, 118
  percentage, 79, 85
quality; *see* Quality of seed
reference collection, 65, 78
ripeness, criteria of, 67–68
samples
  bulk, 77
  size of, 83
  working, 77
sanitation, 92–93
scarification; *see* Pretreatment of seed to break dormancy

Seed (*Continued*)
  season of maturity, 64–65, 68
  separation from fruit and cones; *see*
    Extraction of seed
  size, 79, 118
  sorting into size classes, 116
  sowing; *see* Nurseries, sowing; Seed-
    ing, direct
  statement of origin, 65
  storage, 72, 93–97, 465, 467, 469, 471;
    see also Silvics of arid-zone tree
    species
    cold sealed, 96
    cold stratification, 96–97; *see also*
      Pretreatment of seed to break
      dormancy; Stratification
    conditions, 94–95
    containers for, 94
    moisture content, 72, 96
  stratification; *see* Stratification
  testing; *see* Seed, germinability tests
  transport of, 70
  types, illustration, 66
  utilization value, 85
  viability tests; *see* Seed, germinability
    tests
  weight; *see* Seed, number and weight
  weight required, 85–86
  year, definition of, 67
Seedbeds, 110–11, 120
  care during germination, 119–20
  density in, 117–18
  labeling, 116
  shading of; *see* Shading, of seedbeds
  sowing, 114–19, 127
    broadcast, 116, 117
    covering of seeds, 117
    depth, 118
    in drills, 116, 117
    in lines, 116
    by machines, 118
    time of, 114–15
  thinning, 119
  ventilation of, 119
  watering, 120; *see also* Irrigation,
    nursery
Seeding, direct, 100, 122, 202, 229–33,
    292, 321, 329, 355, 359, 360, 365,
    370, 383, 391, 437
  from aircraft, 231
  broadcast, 229, 230, 231, 361, 409
  cross-sowing, 231
  depth, 232
  dibbling, 410
  partial, 231–32
    furrow, 361
    pit, 361

  spot, 231, 232
  strip, 231, 232
  tools, 232
  versus field planting, 229–30
Seeding trough, 117
Seedlings, 229–30
  abnormal, 84
  age-class designation, 120
  albino, 84
  balled; *see* Balled plants
  bare-rooted; *see* Planting, stock, naked-
    rooted
  care during germination, 119–20
  container; *see* Containerized seedlings
  definition of, 120
  development, 121
  lifting of; *see* Nurseries, lifting stock
  physiological condition of, 113–14
  physiological shock, 126
  potted; *see* Containerized seedlings;
    Containers
  storage of, 196–97, 235
  water stress in, 233
Semiarid zone, 3, 24, 275–76
  definition of, 3
  silvicultural criterion, 3
Semidesert, 28
Shade trees; *see* Choice of species, for
    ornamentals, for roadside planting,
    for shade and shelter
Shading, 186–91, 244
  effects, 191
  lath house, 189, 191
  natural, 190–91
  permanent, 189–90
  of seedbeds, 119, 187–89
  temporary, 189, 190
  of transplant beds, 189–91
Shelterbelts and windbreaks, 44, 48, 112,
    174, 191, 245, 264, 277, 278, 279,
    281, 291, 294, 297, 300, 301–14,
    327, 328, 330, 334, 352
  arrangement of species in, 313
  care of, 313
  choice of species; *see* Choice of species,
    for shelterbelts
  design, 306–9
  effect on crop yield, 305–6
  effect on wind, 302–4, 306–7
  principles of wind shelter, 301–6
  protection of, 309, 313, 314
  renovation of, 314
Shifting cultivation, 7, 47
Silvics of arid-zone tree species, 353–456,
    476–77
Silviculture and management, 46, 47, 202,
    216, 248, 254, 264, 266, 267, 268,
    273, 276, 280, 282, 332, 334, 349,

353; *see also* Silvics of arid-zone tree species
clearcutting, 275, 292
coppice, 275, 292, 309, 314
monoculture, 273
pollarding, 380, 437, 446, 455
pruning, 254
thinning, 203, 227, 230, 254, 268, 269
Site (ecological), 32
Site preparation for planting, 204–25, 257, 286, 309, 328–29, 330, 333
chemical treatment of soil, 288
cultivation, 204, 210–15, 278
debris disposal, 215–16
drainage, 288, 330–31
eradication of vegetation, 204–10, 288
by burning, effect of, 206
leaching, 288, 289, 331
leveling, 204, 278, 288, 292, 293
terracing, 204, 217–22
Site requirements for tree species, 476–77; *see also* Silvics of arid-zone tree species
range of tolerance, 348
Small mammals; *see* Mammals, small
Sodium selinite stain, 82
Sodium tellurate stain, 82
Soil, 25–31, 33
acidification, 153
acidity, 155
aeration, 113, 154, 162, 177, 210, 213, 294
alkali, 30, 31, 107
alkalinity, 30, 152, 156, 161, 272
control of, 107
artificial, 110
clay minerals, 156
chemicals, 156, 269, 331
calcium, exchangeable, 31
calcium carbonate, 26, 27, 28, 29, 30, 31, 155
calcium phosphate, 155
calcium sulphate, 26, 29
carbonates, 107
gypsum, 26, 28, 29
lime, 106
phosphates, 155
potassium carbonate, 31
salt, 43, 44, 107
sodium, exchangeable, 31
sodium carbonate, 31
sodium chloride, 26, 30
sodium salts, 28, 29, 30, 31
sodium sulphate, 26, 30
colloids, 31
color, 187
compacting, 225
conservation, 70

depth, 106, 164, 205, 226, 283
erosion; *see* Erosion
fertility, 31, 102, 106, 117, 154–56, 157, 271, 278
fertilization; *see* Fertilization; Fertilizers
field capacity, 167
forming processes, 25, 26
groups, 27–31
gypsum layer, 26, 28, 29
hardpan, 106, 172, 213, 331
horizon, 25, 28, 29, 30, 332
humus, 30, 32, 135, 222
inoculation with mycorrhizal fungi, 106, 125, 143, 156, 163, 164, 254, 351
inoculation with nitrogen-fixing bacteria, 377
leaching, 25, 26, 28, 29, 30, 31, 182, 206, 331; *see also* Soil, chemicals
lime layer, 28, 29
loess, 27, 28, 29
microorganisms, 162, 294
minerals; *see* Soil, nutrients
moisture, 12, 25, 26, 32, 33, 40, 42, 114, 121, 125, 137, 141, 151, 178, 183, 186, 187, 205, 214, 218, 226, 231, 234, 240, 242, 247, 254, 269, 270, 293, 294, 296, 297, 301, 316, 321, 329, 346, 347
nutrients, 31, 121, 152, 205, 206, 268, 269, 271, 293, 320, 328, 330
orders, 25
organic matter, 28, 29, 30, 31, 152, 156, 320
parent material, 25, 26, 27, 29, 30, 31
pH, 105, 107, 152, 153, 155, 159, 161, 254, 269, 320, 327, 328, 412, 429, 453
profile, 25
quality, 205, 226, 269, 283, 296
salinity, 346; *see also* Soils, saline
slippage, 218, 315
stabilization, 314–31
sterilization, 153, 182
structure, 278
subsoil, 39, 40, 45, 106, 107, 164, 172, 214, 221, 318, 354, 413
temperature, 13, 114, 143, 187, 294, 303
texture, 106, 204, 205, 346
topsoil, 109, 210, 218, 222, 265, 315, 316, 319, 328
type, 353
virgin, 102
water holding capacity, 187, 327
waterlogged, 166, 167, 170, 245, 289, 330

Soil (*Continued*)
  weathering, 26, 27, 28, 319
  wilting point, 42, 234
Soils, 202
  acid, 431, 444
  alkali, 30, 31
  alkaline, 12, 28, 30–31, 107, 155, 163,
    272, 275, 276, 280, 289, 320, 393,
    396, 399, 400, 407, 412, 415, 426,
    453, 476–77
  alluvial, 25, 31, 107, 288, 315, 330,
    354, 359, 360, 361, 371, 384, 390,
    395, 396, 398, 399, 407, 415, 417,
    431, 450, 456
  arid zone, 25–31
  azonal, 25, 26, 27, 31
  black cotton, 30, 354, 360, 369, 390,
    399
  Brown, 27, 28, 399
  calcareous, 30, 60, 156, 356, 377, 382,
    395, 399, 400, 403, 404, 412, 426,
    428, 431, 440, 441, 452
  Calcisols, 28, 30
  Chernozem, 25, 27, 29–30, 31
  Chestnut, 27, 28–29, 30, 288
  clay, 10, 26, 238, 294, 327, 363, 369,
    370, 380
  Desert, 25, 27–28
  dolomitic, 60
  effect of arid climate on, 26–27
  Gray, 27, 28, 399
  hammada, 43
  intrazonal, 25, 26, 27, 30
  limestone, 361, 377, 381, 444
  Lithosols, 31
  loess, 27, 28, 29
  marl, 428
  peat, 330, 399
  podsol, 359
  Prairie, 25
  Red Desert, 27–28
  Reddish Brown, 28
  Reddish Chestnut, 28–29
  regur, 30
  Rendzina, 30, 433
  saline, 25, 28, 30–31, 43, 287, 289, 296,
    297, 312, 313, 320, 330, 332, 340,
    354, 359, 377, 385, 393, 395, 399,
    400, 402, 404, 432, 434, 435, 437,
    441, 445, 446, 450
    plantations on, 331; *see also* Choice
      of species, for saline soils
  salty; *see* Soils, saline
  sands, 106, 117, 132, 221, 228, 238,
    297, 319, 320, 321, 322, 323, 324,
    325, 326, 327, 354, 360, 363, 368,
    369, 370, 371, 372, 374, 375, 377,
    378, 382

  sandy, 25, 28, 164, 173, 187, 287
  sandy loam, 37, 106, 314, 356, 374
  Sierozems, 27–28
  silt loam, 28
  silts, 290, 319, 354, 375
  stony, 221
  swamp, 25
  Terra Rossa, 30, 382, 439
  Triassic sand, 50
  tropical Chernozem, 30
  volcanic, 419
  zonal, 25, 26, 30
Sowing of seeds; *see* Nurseries, sowing;
    Seedbeds, sowing; Seeding, direct
Spacing in plantations, 225–27, 230, 269,
    270, 308–9, 319
  by isohyetal zones, 226
Special plantations, 264–344
Species, alkali tolerant, 407
Species for arid zone afforestation, 345–
    460; *see also* Choice of species
Stabilization of mining waste, 327–29
Steppe, 3, 29, 30, 37, 47, 224, 363, 431,
    449, 456, 476–77
Steppe Method, 222–25
Storage of planting stock, 196–97, 235
Storage of seeds; *see* Seed, storage
Strain, genetic; *see* Genetic, race
Stratification
  cold, 87, 90, 91, 96–97, 148, 149, 363,
    365, 366, 367, 380, 381, 382, 384,
    385, 386, 388, 390, 393, 407, 410,
    412, 415, 418, 422, 423, 426, 427,
    430, 431, 433, 438, 443, 452, 454,
    455, 465, 467, 469, 471
  cold plus warm, 469
  dry, 72, 97, 366, 415, 438
  naked, 87
  warm, 90, 91
  warm plus cold, 91, 385, 412
Strips, contour, 222
  cultivation of, 211, 221
Stumps (cuttings), 292, 293
Subdesert, definition of, 12
Subdesert areas, 283
Subdesert grassless scrub, 36
Subdesert grassy scrub (shrub), 36
Subdesert shrub and grass, 35
Subdesert shrub and scattered trees, 35
Subsoiler, 211, 212
Succession, ecological, 33, 34, 45, 318
Succulence, 38, 191
Succulent shrub, 36
Succulents, 38
Suckers, root; *see* Root, suckers
Surface mining, 329–30
Swampland plantations, 329–31